readings in
physiological
psychology

readings in
physiological
psychology

Jack Roy Strange
Southern Methodist University

Ray Foster
Parsons State Hospital, Kansas

wadsworth publishing company, inc.
belmont, california

preface

The thirty-three articles in this book provide the undergraduate student direct contact with up-to-date, important research—research that is ordinarily accessible only in various contemporary journals and books in the fields of psychology, biology, physiology, pharmacology, and medicine. Each of these articles was selected for the importance of its contribution to physiological psychology. Recent research was given priority; most of the articles were published in the last ten years, and a large number of them are too recent to have been discussed fully in standard textbooks.

The selections are intended to compliment a standard textbook in an undergraduate course in physiological psychology. They can also be used to supplement the lectures of a teacher who prefers to dispense with a textbook, or they can provide up-to-date background material for a graduate seminar.

To help undergraduates comprehend these selections without becoming mired in the numerous technical details, an introductory section discusses the art of reading a scientific article.

A number of other special features have been included to increase the usefulness of this book. A second introductory section provides a historical frame of reference into which the reader can fit these specific articles and thereby appreciate more fully their nature and importance. Questions at the beginning of each reading are designed to guide the student, alerting him to the article's important findings and salient points. Original bibliographies have been retained so that a topic can be probed more deeply whenever the teacher or student wishes. The glossary at the end of the book defines selected technical terms to enable the student to build a basic vocabulary of physiological psychology. Finally, an index provides cross-references so that the reader may compare the treatment of a topic or a term in the different articles.

The organization of the book follows the usual sequence of topics in a course in physiological psychology. However, each chapter, even each individual article, can stand alone, so that an instructor is left free to plan and construct his course in the manner most meaningful to his students.

The editors wish to thank the authors for permitting the inclusion of their articles in this book; credit is given them in source notes for the articles. The excellence of a book of readings comes from the contributing authors; in the case of this book, they are the leading research scientists in the field of physiological psychology.

We particularly wish to thank Daniel P. Kimble, of the University of Oregon, who not only reviewed the manuscript but contributed greatly to the development of the glossary. And for their most valuable reviews of the manuscript, we are grateful to Robert W. Lansing, of the University of Arizona; Richard T. Louttit, of the Division of Research Grants, National Institutes of Health; Mark R. Rosenzweig, of the University of California, Berkeley; and Alice Van Krevelen, of Berea College. The editors also wish to thank Sunny Foster and their research assistant, Steve Davis, both of whom helped in innumerable ways.

Jack Roy Strange
Ray Foster

contents

introduction (part one)   1

introduction (part two)   5

chapter 1

the nervous system   13

1   Neuron Doctrine and Electrophysiology
—Theodore Holmes Bullock   14
2   The Reticular Formation—J. D.
French   25
3   The Limbic System—Paul D. Mac-
Lean   29

chapter 2

vision and hearing   40

4   An Opponent-Process Theory of Color
Vision—Leo M. Hurvich and Dorothea
Jameson   41
5   Electrical Activity in the Vertebrate Retina—Tsuneo Tomita   60
6   Discriminatory Capacity of the Auditory
System—William D. Neff   73
7   ''Attention'' in Unanesthetized Cats—
Raúl Hernández-Peón, Harald Scherrer, and Michel Jouvet   83

chapter 3

chemical and somesthetic senses   87

8   Touch and Taste in the Cat—M. J.
Cohen, S. Landgren, L. Ström, and
Y. Zotterman   88
9   Gustatory Nerve Impulses in Rat, Cat,
and Rabbit—Carl Pfaffmann   117
10   Cutaneous Impulses in the Cat—R. M.
Gaze and G. Gordon   128
11   The Corpus Callosum in Contralateral
Transfer in Cats—John S. Stamm and
R. W. Sperry   135

chapter 4

emotion   143

12   Prolegomena to a Theory of the Emotions—E. Gellhorn   144
13   The Physiology of Fear and Anger—
Daniel H. Funkenstein   168
14   Conditioned Fear by Electrical Stimulation of the Monkey Brain—José M. R.
Delgado, H. Enger Rosvold, and Edmund Looney   174

chapter 5

motivation 1   184

15   Physiological Theory of Drive—Clifford
T. Morgan   185

16   Non-Specific Brain Mechanisms—H. W. Magoun   206

17   Positive Reinforcement Induced by Intracerebral Stimulation in the Monkey—Ben Bursten and José M. R. Delgado   214

18   Rewarding and Punishing Effects from Stimulation of Posterior Hypothalamus of Cat—Warren W. Roberts   220

19   Satiation Effects in Self-Stimulation of the Brain—James Olds   231

chapter 6

motivation 2   237

20   Neural and Chemical Regulation of Behavior—Frank A. Beach   238

21   Neural Mediation of Mating in Male Cats—Frank A. Beach, Arthur Zitrin, and Julian Jaynes   255

22   Influence of Sex Hormones on Social Behavior in Monkeys—Allan F. Mirsky   264

23   Effect of Female Sex Hormones on Incubation Behavior in the Ring Dove—Daniel S. Lehrman   275

24   Hibernation in Mammals and Birds—Charles P. Lyman   281

chapter 7

learning   290

25   Neural Basis of the Conditioned Response—Roger W. Sperry   291

26   Thalamic Structures and Conditioned Response in Rats—Robert Thompson   296

27   Hippocampal Lesions and Delayed Alternation in the Rat—Ronald J. Racine and Daniel P. Kimble   303

28   Thyroid Hormone and Conditioning—W. J. Richards and J. C. Stockburger   306

29   Cerebral Cholinesterase Activity and "Hypothesis" Behavior—J. Trevor Peirce   309

chapter 8

brain lesions   315

30   Constructional Apraxia and Unilateral Cerebral Lesions—Malcolm Piercy, H. Hécaen, and J. de Ajuriaguerra   316

31   Visual-Constructive Disabilities and Lesions of Left Cerebral Hemisphere—J. McFie and O. L. Zangwill   331

32   Limbic System Lesions in the Cat—Robert A. McCleary   348

33   Effects of Bilateral Hippocampal Lesions in Rats—Daniel P. Kimble   359

glossary of selected terms   371

index   376

how to read a scientific article

Reading a scientific article requires the use of a group of learned skills. Some of these skills are needed in all college courses, whereas others are specific to the sciences. One of these skills—needed in almost all courses—is the art of critical reading. By the time a college student is a sophomore, his use of textbooks has taught him to pay attention to details—and yet to see these details as subservient to ideas and to see ideas in the form of a thesis or central concept. This ability to read critically is a skill essential to the understanding of scientific articles.

Besides this general reading ability, the physiological psychology student needs a basic knowledge of biology and psychology, with some understanding of technical terminology, laboratory equipment and techniques, and experimental methods and measurements. He must also learn to use his textbook and other sources to orient him in the general area into which a specific article fits.

On reading a scientific article, the perceptive student will be aware that it is not written in the style of a textbook. Research articles are generally written to relay information from one scientist to another; thus, a common background is implicit. The scientists share a knowledge of the established and tentative findings in the specific area and an under-

1

standing of theoretical frames of reference and correct experimental designs. A student is a third party allowed to listen in on a conversation between two experts. To comprehend their conversation fully, he must be willing at times to refer to his textbook and secondary sources. Aware of the students' plight, the editors have chosen articles that are outstanding in their findings but that require comparatively little sophistication in the specific area covered. Even so, a student should welcome the challenge of occasionally checking back to general references.

The first step in studying a scientific article is to read the title and then skim through the entire article very quickly to get a general idea of the author's purpose and findings. Then the student should read the summary and conclusions very carefully. Next, he should stop and ask questions. In this readings book the editors provide a few questions, but even here a student is wise to ask additional questions of his own: What hypotheses (if any) are tested by the author? What theoretical framework is used? What positive and what negative findings are presented? How do these findings fit into what was already known in this area? How wide (or narrow) an application can be made of these findings? What are the limitations of the study? The questions should also include details of techniques and methods of execution of the research. These minute points may be crucial in establishing or destroying the whole hypothesis.

With these questions in mind, the student should carefully reread the article. If his questions are not satisfactorily answered, he should reread the pertinent passages and then outline or underline important points. At this point he has completed an adequate reading of the article.

The selection by Roger Sperry, "On the Neural Basis of the Conditioned Response"

(pp. 291–296), well illustrates these steps in studying a scientific article. The title gives the author's purpose: to discuss the role of the nervous system in learning. A skimming of the article shows that it is not the report of an experiment; it is a theoretical discussion that uses established experimental findings to build a set of postulates about the neural basis of learning. These postulates are presented in such a way that they might later be tested by a series of experiments. At this step the student might ask the following questions: What facts are available to disprove the hypothesis that static brain traces (engrams) are the only neural changes that account for the retention of a learned act? What does Sperry mean by "anticipatory set" or "expectancy"? What theoretical importance is given to "central facilitory (or inhibitory) set"? In long-term retention of a learned act, what is the relation between "dynamic facilitory set" and relatively static engrams? What types of experiments can be designed to test Sperry's conclusions?

In a careful rereading of Sperry's article, the student would discover which of his questions were pertinent—that is, when answered, these questions would give him full comprehension of the selection. Some of the questions would very likely send him back to a textbook to obtain information both about learning and about the nervous system. After underlining and/or outlining the article, the student would complete his study of the reading by Sperry.

In the study of articles that report an experiment, certain pitfalls and stumbling blocks—of a kind not encountered in the selection by Sperry—occur. One type of pitfall involves the "fine print" used by journals to save space.[1] The experimental details concerning subjects, apparatus, design, and proce-

---

[1] In this book the "fine print" of the journal articles has been changed to regular-size type.

dures are placed in small type and in a very concise form; for example, *E* stands for experimenter and *S*s for subjects.

It is important to know precisely what subjects have been used in an experiment so that the findings will be understood as applying to that specific group and to the population from which they were drawn (but then only if they are an adequate sample of the population). It can be hazardous to extrapolate from the subjects used in an experiment to other individuals coming from a different population. Since many different species of animal subjects are used in physiological psychology experiments, a reader should keep in mind that the results were obtained with a particular species (rats, for example) and may be, but are not necessarily, applicable to other species (such as cats or dogs).

Attention must also be paid to the description of apparatus—usually presented very cryptically, since the author assumes that the reader is familiar with general laboratory equipment. Only innovations in apparatus are described in detail. Similarly, the section on experimental design and procedure is given in a kind of shorthand because the reader is supposed to be familiar with general types of designs and methods. A beginning student needs to familiarize himself with such general aspects of experimentation. Again, only innovations will be given in detail.

In the presentation and discussion of results, a difficulty arises because an understanding of statistical treatment is assumed. Fortunately, a student does not need to be a statistician to comprehend the results and conclusions of an experiment. However, he does need to know that statistical techniques are available to test the significance of research findings. He must realize that numerical differences may be meaningless or misleading unless shown to be statistically significant. Until the student has the opportunity to master statistics, he must assume that the experimenter has used the correct statistical treatment of the data. He must realize, of course, that research scientists do challenge each other's experimental designs and statistical treatments. Until the student is more expert in these areas, he must rely on his instructor and textbook to point out weaknesses in these aspects of reported research.

A good example of an experimental report is Robert Thompson's article, "Thalamic Structures Critical for Retention of an Avoidance Conditioned Response in Rats" (pp. 296–303). The title gives the author's purpose: to find the areas in the thalamus essential for a rat's retention of an avoidance conditioned response. After skimming the article and noting the author's conclusions, the student would ask such questions as the following: What previous experiments led up to this one? How was conditioning obtained? What surgical techniques are used in studying the thalamus? What is the necessity for a post-mortem histological examination of the brain? What are the three "functionally and anatomically distinct" thalamic areas that serve in maintaining the CR in this experiment? What are the "exceptional cases" described by Thompson? How should these cases be studied? After asking these and similar questions, the student should reread the article carefully. He should note that the subjects are "75 adult albino rats of the Harlan strain." In the section describing apparatus, he should note that a complete description of the equipment was given in an earlier publication by Thompson. However, enough information about the apparatus is given to allow full comprehension of the experiment. The general procedure of the surgery and histology can be accepted by the student who simply wants to understand the experiment. A student who wishes to learn the details of the surgical, anesthetic, and histological techniques would do some library research at this point.

The section on experimental procedure is straightforward, but a student would want to be certain that he grasps both the experimental and control aspects of the procedure before reading on. In the section headed "Results," Thompson presents amounts of retention of learning in terms of percent of "savings" in trials at the time of relearning. These savings scores for the operated and the control groups are compared, and differences are tested for statistical significance. The student who does not know statistics is spared the mathematics involved, because Thompson does not describe the statistical test used. He simply says that "a nonparametric test" was used and gives a reference to a source, which will be of interest to a reader sophisticated in statistics.

With the help of the foregoing steps, the beginning student of physiological psychology should have no difficulty with the mechanics of studying scientific articles, and thus can use his intellect in the fascinating pursuit of the facts and theories of physiological psychology.

historical perspective

Physiological psychology is the field that established psychology as a science. The stage was set for the emergence of this field by the publication of two books: Charles Darwin's *The Origin of Species* (1859) and Gustav Fechner's *Elemente der Psychophysik* (1860). In 1875 physiological psychology was officially included as a part of biological science by the institution of college courses in the subject at two major universities. Acting independently, William James at Harvard and Wilhelm Wundt at Leipzig in Germany each offered a graduate course in biology titled "Physiological Psychology." Four years later, in 1879, Wundt further established the field by founding a research laboratory at Leipzig for the training and granting of Ph.D.s in psychology.

Along with metaphysics, axiology (ethics and esthetics), and logic, psychology had been one of the traditional branches of philosophy (as had physics and chemistry before it). Philosophical psychology included discussion and speculation about the "mind," breaking it into "cognition" (intellect), "conation" (will), and "affection" (emotion). After psychology became a science, these same topics continued to be explored, but experimentally. In addition, the field broadened to include all aspects of physical and mental behavior.

At the beginning of the nineteenth century, research in biology and medicine resulted in the establishment of physiology and neuro-anatomy as important experimental areas. As the century progressed, workers in these fields became more and more interested in the relationship between neural structure and neural function. Whenever their interest turned to the correlation of neural structure and function with overt behavior, they were *de facto* physiological psychologists, even though the field had not yet emerged as a separate discipline.

Of great importance to the development of physiological psychology was the early research concerning the nervous system. An excellent starting place for the history of this subject is with Sir Charles Bell in England at the opening of the nineteenth century. Bell's research in neuroanatomy laid the foundation for the understanding of the functioning of the nervous system. Bell was one of the first to demonstrate that the dorsal roots of the spinal cord are exclusively sensory and the ventral roots exclusively motor. This discovery led Bell to the realization that the peripheral parts of the sensory and motor systems of the body are separate and distinct—a finding that was necessary before reflex action could be understood. Bell also noted that each sense organ has a response to specific stimuli; however, rather than interpret sensations in terms of specific nerve energies, he guessed correctly that the brain sorted out and interpreted sensory impulses.

Contemporaneously with Bell, Pierre Flourens in France performed experiments that determined the functions of the main parts of the brain. Flourens, a highly skilled neurosurgeon, demonstrated that the cerebellum supplies motor coordination and that the cerebrum has a general integrative function. It was Flourens, among others, who used his knowl-

edge of brain anatomy to refute the pseudo-science of phrenology (feeling the bumps on the head to reveal personality) that was in vogue early in the nineteenth century.

By the middle of the nineteenth century, a Scottish surgeon, Marshall Hall, drew together previous findings about reflex action through a series of brilliant experiments, including the sectioning of the spinal cord of a snake. Although reflexes and the sensory and motor nerves serving them were then understood, precise knowledge of the anatomy and functioning of the nerve cells (neurons) had to await advancements in histology. In 1886–87 Auguste Forel introduced the concept of discrete nerve cells, and in 1889 S. Ramon y Cajal discovered the synapse between neurons, thus exploding the prevalent view that a solid, continuous nerve net served the tissues of the body. Cajal's discovery led to W. Waldeyer's proposal of the term "neuron theory" in 1891.

The first reading in this book (by Theodore Bullock) is an up-to-date statement of "neuron doctrine." Bullock follows directly from the original theories of Cajal and Waldeyer and shows how an important breakthrough in science needs many years of experimental research to supply the details of the theory. Bullock, having collected these details, draws conclusions that are correct but surprising to a student who is familiar only with the account given in a typical introductory psychology textbook.

It was also in the nineteenth century that the anatomy and functions of the "old" cortex (paleocortex) were described. At that time the conclusion was that only olfaction and related functions (such as chewing) were served by this part of the brain. In Reading 3, Paul MacLean gives a modern evaluation of the paleocortex and the other parts of the brain included in the limbic system, which serves emotion and motivation as well as the lower functions previously attributed to it. In his article, MacLean describes the limbic system in full and shows the dramatic revival of interest in it.

The nineteenth century was also the time of basic research into all aspects of the senses. Because of the impact of Sir Isaac Newton's book *Opticks* (1704), vision became the most thoroughly studied of the sense modalities. In the early 1800s, Bell delved into all aspects of vision, treating the eye as an optical system. Early in the century the laws of color mixing were known, the luminosity curve had been drawn, and light and dark adaptation were understood.

In 1801 Thomas Young proposed a three-color theory of color vision; by the middle of the century, Hermann von Helmholtz expanded Young's theory into the Young-Helmholtz trichromatic theory. Helmholtz assumed that there are three kinds of color receptors in the retina: one for blue, one for green, and one for red. White and all other colors (hues) are supposed to be produced by a simple process of addition of these three types of color receptors.

In 1878 Helmholtz's color theory was opposed by Ewald Hering, who proposed a three-pair, six-color theory. According to Hering, the three pairs are white-black, yellow-blue, and red-green. Hering postulated that there are three different photochemical substances in the retina of the eye, each substance accounting for the sensations of two hues. One of the hues results from the photochemical breakdown of the substance (catabolism), and the other hue is the result of the photochemical build-up (anabolism).

For half a century Hering's theory opposed Helmholtz's. Then gradually the trichromatic view won more and more favor, until Hering's theory seemed to be of historical interest only. In science, however, theories stand or fall on the data and the facts for which they can account. In their article in Chapter 2 of this book, Leo Hurvich and Dorothea Jameson revive the Hering theory and bring it up to date. It is now called an "opponent-process theory of color vision," and is again a respectable alternative to the trichromatic type of color-vision theory. Hurvich and Jameson demonstrate that many color-vision phenomena can best be explained in terms of the "opponent process" Further evidence for this type of theory is presented in Reading 5, by Tsuneo Tomita.

Both historically and at the present time, the sense of hearing is second to that of vision in research interest. Sir Charles Bell covered hearing in his writings, but not nearly so thoroughly as he covered vision. Like Bell. Helmholtz spent more time on vision than on hearing, but the work he did on hearing was outstanding. In 1863 Helmholtz published *Tonemphfindungen*; which covers the physics of sound (acoustics), the anatomy and physiology of the ear, and the psychology of hearing (sensation and perception). Helmholtz viewed the cochlea of the ear (including the basilar membrane) as analogous to the strings of a piano. His piano theory (also called the resonance theory) laid the foundation for a number of modern theories—for example, the Galambos and Davis place theory. In recent years, place (resonance) theories have been combined with periodicity (telephone-type) theories to explain the perception of pitch.

Because of crude sound-producing apparatus (tuning forks), Helmholtz was greatly handicapped in supplying exact stimuli for his experiments in hearing. The great advance in hearing research began in the 1920s with the development of electronic amplifying and other acoustical equipment, and has allowed research in hearing to gain on the lead held by vision research. Reading 6, by William Neff, illustrates the use of modern equipment and newly developed surgical techniques in the study of hearing. The work of Raúl Hernández-Peón and his collaborators emphasizes the psychological aspects of hearing, but their article (Reading 7) includes another good illustration of the use of modern techniques in the study of hearing.

Chapter 3 of this book is titled "Chemical and Somesthetic Senses" and includes articles on taste and touch. These so-called "minor" senses were also studied during the nineteenth century, but not so intensively as were vision and hearing. The receptors for taste were studied by Bell, and the sense of smell had been investigated by the great botanical classifier Linnaeus a century earlier. However, compared with vision and hearing, relatively little was known about the chemical senses until recently. Reading 8, by M. J. Cohen et al., presents an excellent review of the recent research in both taste and touch, covering the detailed development of surgical and other techniques for the study of these senses.

Reading 9, by Carl Pfaffmann, is a very good illustration of a present-day experiment in gustation. This experiment is but one of the recent ones in a long line of research by Pfaffman on the sense of taste. His research has led to the better understanding of all the senses because of his demonstration that taste impulses are complex patterns of neural firings. It is the brain that must sort out the pattern to reveal the sense information present.

Interestingly enough, the nineteenth-century work on touch was more advanced than that on the chemical senses. During that era, E. H. Weber explored the cutaneous senses thoroughly. He subdivided the sense of touch into pressure, temperature sense, and the sense of locality. It was Weber who first noted that the relation between a stimulus and a sensation is a constant ratio. He discovered that a "just noticeable difference" (j.n.d.) in sensation follows a set ratio as stimuli increase in magnitude and that the constant ratio is different for each sense modality. His formula,

$$\frac{\text{Increment in Stimulus}}{\text{Stimulus}}\, K = \text{j. n. d.}$$

led to Gustav Fechner's development of the Weber-Fechner logarithmic "law" (actually a hypothesis) concerning the relation between stimulus and sensation. Their formulation was used for over one hundred years and has just recently been replaced by a power-function hypothesis derived by S. S. Stevens at Harvard.

From Weber's day to the present, a scientific lag has existed in research into receptors, the neural pathways, and the centers in the central nervous system that serve the cutaneous senses. Reading 10, by R. M. Gaze and G. Gordon, is a report of a recent attempt to close this gap in knowledge. This article shows the student the difficulty that exists in searching for brain centers and pathways.

Reading 11, by John Stamm and Roger Sperry, establishes that the corpus callosum is essential for the contralateral transfer of a learned somesthetic discrimination in cats. ("Somesthesis" is a synonym for "somatic senses.") This type of experiment also cuts the time lag in research and facilitates comprehension of these important senses.

Chapter 4 covers the important topic of emotion. It was late in the nineteenth century before complex states like emotion were studied scientifically. In 1884 William James published a theory of emotion. He emphasized that the neural feedback from visceral and skeletal muscles is important in the feeling of an emotion. According to James, it is merely common sense that says "I see a bear, then I feel afraid, and, because of my fear, I run away." According to his theory, the statement should be "I see a bear, then I run away, and, because I run, I feel afraid." One year later (1885), completely independent of James, Carl Lange in Copenhagen formulated the same theory; however, Lange emphasized feedback from the vasomotor system of the body rather than from visceral and skeletal muscles.

By 1927 W. B. Cannon and Phillip Bard had discovered the importance of the hypothalamus in emotion. The Cannon-Bard theory postulated that there is a control center in the hypothalamus that receives sensory information and then directs all aspects of the emotion. The statement that would follow from their theory would be "I see a bear" (the hypothalamic center is alerted); and then simultaneously "I feel emotion and I run away." Through the years much controversy has revolved around the James-Lange and the Cannon-Bard theories. As it has turned out, neither of these theories was based on enough facts and details to be definitive.

By 1950 Donald Lindsley had accepted the role of the hypothalamus in emotion and proposed an "activation theory of emotion," emphasizing the importance of the reticular activating system (RAS) in alerting the organism when involved in emotion-producing situations (see Reading 2, by J. D. French, for general information about the RAS). For some time the importance of the RAS in emotion has tended to be overly stressed in psychology textbooks.

The most recent approach to the understanding of emotion goes back to J. W. Papez's emphasis (1937) on the limbic system (also called the "visceral brain"), which includes the hypothalamus and parts of both the neocortex and the paleocortex. At the present time, Paul MacLean (Reading 3) has extended and strengthened Papez's view, which is also used by E. Gellhorn (Reading 12) as the frame of reference for his excellent review of current research on emotion. Gellhorn also points out the implications of emotion theory for psychotherapy. Reading 14, by José Delgado and his collaborators, also demonstrates the importance of the limbic system in emotions.

Around the time of World War I, W. B. Cannon also studied the biochemical influences on emotion. He stressed the importance in strong emotion (rage and fear) of the adrenal hormone adrenalin (epinephrin). He was not able, however, to differentiate between fear and rage biochemically. It was not until the discovery of a second adrenal hormone, noradrenalin (norepinephrin), that such a differentiation could be attempted. Such an attempt is reported in Reading 13 by Daniel Funkenstein.

Because of the extensive amount of current research on motivation, two chapters (5 and 6) of this book are devoted to recent articles in this area. In contrast with this strong contemporary interest in motivation is the very small contribution to the understanding of the physiology of motivation made by nineteenth-century scientists. In Vienna at the end of the century, Sigmund Freud formulated his theory of psychoanalysis, which is basically a theory of motivation and emotion. (Freud's term "instinct" is best translated today as "drive.") Because the study of neurophysiology was new at the turn of the century, it furnished Freud little in the way of factual support for his biological hypotheses about "instincts."

In America, in 1917, R. S. Woodworth published *Dynamic Psychology*, in which he suggested that psychology itself is best thought of as a "motivology." Woodworth's contemporary W. B. Cannon, also convinced of the importance of motivation, pioneered in the study of the physiology of this area. In 1915 Cannon published *Bodily Changes in Pain, Hunger, Fear, and Rage*. In attempting to explain motivation, Cannon proposed local theories of hunger and thirst—local in the sense that emptiness of the stomach and dryness of the mouth and throat are supposed to be the basis of hunger and thirst, respectively.

By the 1940s Clifford Morgan, Frank Beach, and others had noted that research evidence went against the Cannon-type local theories. They proposed some concept of "central motive state." In Reading 15 Morgan reviews the history of this concept and brings it up to date as a "central theory of motivation."

Recent work has been in the area of locating the brain structures involved in motivation. An example of such research is H. W. Magoun's article on non-specific brain mechanisms involved in arousal and wakefulness (Reading 16). Once such structures are located, experimenters have found that much can be learned by implanting electrodes in these areas and allowing the experimental animal to stimulate itself. Readings 17, 18, and 19 present a cross section of these current self-stimulation studies.

As mentioned earlier, Cannon studied the biochemical as well as the neural aspects of motivation. The search for the biochemical factors in motivation continues today as an active and productive area of research. Frank Beach, in Reading 20, gives a comprehensive review of this literature. This review is especially strong in the area of the influence of hormones on behavior—Beach's own area—which has been a very active field of research, generally. In Reading 21, Beach and his collaborators demonstrate the importance of the correlation of cortical centers and hormonal

factors in overt behavior. In Reading 23, Daniel Lehrman illustrates the intricate interrelationship between neural and chemical factors in the nesting behavior of ring doves.

Chapter 7 covers the topic of learning. As with motivation, the serious study of the physiology of learning began in the twentieth century. At the turn of the century, the great Russian physiologist I. P. Pavlov was engrossed in his work on conditioning. Pavlov attempted to explain conditioning in terms of excitatory and inhibitory currents and gradients set up in the brain. Although his theory has been disproved, it started the search for the neural correlates of learning—for the "engram" that logically should be established in the brain by the process of learning.

Through the years the pendulum has swung back and forth between the view that specific points in the brain contain a specific engram to the view at the other extreme—that the whole cerebrum is important in even the simplest learning. In the early part of the nineteenth century, Pierre Flourens speculated from his experiments that the cerebral hemispheres act as a unit in complex behavior such as learning. As various specific brain centers were discovered (for example, Paul Broca's discovery in 1860 of the location of the speech center), the pendulum swung back, and the search was on for specific centers for everything, including learning. In the 1920s, the American psychologist K. S. Lashley reversed the trend and proposed that in learning the whole cerebrum is involved in what he termed "mass action." He also spoke of the "equipotentiality" of all parts of the cerebrum to take over the functions of damaged areas. In Reading 25, Roger Sperry discusses the research that has followed Lashley's. After reviewing the literature, Sperry postulates a dual role of the brain in learning.

The learned act is "stored" temporarily by a general "central set" mechanism and then is made permanent in an engram. This theoretical speculation combines the concepts of "mass action" and specificity in the neurophysiology of learning. However, much experimental evidence is needed before Sperry's hypotheses can be either substantiated or disproved.

Not only is the cerebrum involved in learning, but lower brain centers are also involved. In Reading 26, Robert Thompson presents experimental results that pinpoint the thalamic nuclei and adjacent midbrain structures involved in maintaining an avoidance conditioned response. Similarly, Ronald Racine and Daniel Kimble in Reading 27 show that hippocampal lesions in the rat affect performance on a delayed alternation task.

In learning, as in the other areas of physiological psychology, the search for biochemical factors and their interrelationship with neural factors is most important. The study of the biochemistry of learning is a relatively new area of research, but important contributions often come from the sciences of biochemistry and biophysics.

Reading 28, by W. J. Richards and J. C. Stockburger, is the report of a basic experiment on the influence of hormones on learning. Their results establish the effects of the thyroid hormone on learning and extinction. Reading 29, by J. Trevor Peirce, brings together the chemical and neural factors in learning by studying the differences in cortical cholinesterase that occur when animals are placed in various learning situations. Since cholinesterase is important in the functioning of nerve cells, this study shows how closely related are the biochemical and the neurophysiological factors in learning.

Perhaps the oldest area that can be sub-sumed under physiological psychology is the study of brain injuries. The history of this study goes back to antiquity and before. Even prehistoric peoples noticed the changes in behavior that occur after brain damage. The Inca Indians in Peru even perfected trepanation (cutting a hole in the skull) in order to operate on the brain and produce lesions. In the early nineteenth century, the work of men like Flourens was centered on producing brain lesions in experimental animals and in extirpating whole sections of the brain and observing changes in behavior.

Reading 32, by Robert A. McCleary, and Reading 33, by Daniel Kimble, follow in the tradition of the producing of brain lesions to discover the functions of brain areas. A very important aspect of their work is that they are exploring the limbic system, the study of which promises to solve many of the mysteries about the brain control of motivation and emotion.

Another approach to the study of the effects of brain lesions on behavior is to study brain-damaged patients in hospitals. This approach is a difficult one because the lesions in the brain occur by chance (resulting from tumors, gunshot wounds, automobile accidents, and toxic conditions) and are seldom in the precise location needed for study. The history of this approach includes Broca's discovery (in 1860) of the speech center through his study of a brain-damaged patient. This approach is illustrated in Reading 30 (Malcolm Piercy et al.) and in Reading 31 (J. McFie and O. L. Zangwill). Both of these studies are concerned with the effects on behavior of certain unilateral injuries to the cerebrum. The patients studied were affected with spatial agnosia, constructional apraxia, or with both conditions. With the aid of this type of study, physiological psychologists are able to extrapolate more accurately from the many animal studies that must be made in lieu of experiments with human beings.

The history of physiological psychology, like all histories, is a fascinating study of man's ideas and the "hard" facts reacting one against the other. The development and modifications of these ideas are our only claims to knowledge. The process leads us into the future and promises as exciting a search in the time to come as in the times past.

the nervous system

In the first reading in this chapter, Theodore Bullock makes a modern statement of "neuron doctrine" that was first proposed in the late nineteenth century. Before the discovery that the neuron is the structural unit of the nervous system, neuroanatomy was only a gross anatomy that permitted little access to an understanding of the functioning of the nervous system. In recent years Huxley, Hodgkin, and Eccles have performed experiments that have laid the foundation for explaining nerve cell activity. For their great contribution to cellular neurophysiology, they received the Nobel Prize in 1964.

Bullock points out that we now have enough experimental evidence to revise the four main "classical" conceptions of neuron functioning. First, the "all-or-none impulse" is characteristic only of the axon, not the dendrites and cell body. Second, excitation of cell body and dendrites does not lead to an "impulse" but builds up to help determine the firing of an impulse in the axon. Third, dendrites do not send impulses to the cell body but influence the axon and perhaps other dendrites by means of "local, graded," low-amplitude activity. Fourth, the synapse is not the only place for activities such as selection and evaluation; several other such places exist

within the neuron. Bullock's article is a re-
minder that science is dynamic and requires a
constant updating of all "doctrines" and theories as new experimental results come in.

The article by J. D. French (Reading 2)
represents an approach somewhat different
from that of Bullock's. This approach is to
study the anatomy and functioning of a part
of the nervous system, discovering its relation
to behavior. In this case the part studied is that
area of the brain stem called the "reticular
formation," also referred to as the recticular
activating system (RAS). As French points
out, the RAS is an "integrating machine" that
helps awaken the brain and keep it alert and,
in addition, monitors stimuli, directs traffic in
the nervous system, smooths out muscle activity, and even contributes "to the highest
mental processes—the focusing of attention,
introspection, and doubtless all forms of reasoning."

For the final reading in this chapter, it is
necessary to sketch in the over-all structure of
the forebrain (diencephalon and telencephalon). The telencephalon is the most recently
evolved part of the brain. It is made up of the
basal ganglia (including the *corpus striatum*)
and the *cerebral hemispheres* (*cerebrum*).
Important centers are located in the *cortex* of
the cerebrum. Some of these centers are in the
neocortex (newly evolved cortex), and others
are in the *paleocortex* ("old" cortex). Fish
possess only a small paleocortex whereas mammals, especially man, have a very large neocortex as well as a small paleocortex. In this
article (Reading 3), Paul MacLean describes
the limbic system and discusses its importance.
The limbic system is a border system, involving mainly the paleocortex but also part of the
neocortex (the *cingulate gyrus*) and the
amygdala in the basal ganglia. The old-cortex
parts of the limbic system include the *septal
area* (beneath the anterior portion of the

corpus callosum) and the *hippocampus*, which
lies in the ventral surface of the cerebrum.
The limbic system, in conjunction with the
hypothalamus (in the *diencephalon*), is important in emotion and is the area most
explored in self-stimulation experiments. In
the later chapters on motivation and emotion,
reference will again be made to the limbic
system.

Each of the articles in this chapter changes
or supplements our knowledge and understanding of the nervous system. Bullock asks
us to refine our thinking about the electrochemical events in the neuron and synapse by
using recent findings in research to supplant
speculation with facts. French shows how a
knowledge of the functioning of the reticular
formation clears up some of the mystery of
cortical activity, ranging from sleep to attention. MacLean makes us aware of the necessity
of re-examining brain areas relegated by classical neuroanatomy to a few simple functions.
The limbic system is important not only in
alimentary activities but also in such complex
and important behavior as emotion, motivation, and possibly memory.

1   neuron doctrine
and
electrophysiology *

Theodore Holmes Bullock

1. What does Bullock mean by "temporally patterned impulse sequences"?
2. What contribution to neuron study was made
   by the invention of the capillary ultramicroelectrode?

* T. H. Bullock, "Neuron Doctrine and Electro-
Physiology," *Science*, 129 (April 17, 1959), 997–1002.
Reprinted with permission.

3. Which regions of the neuron membrane support electrochemical activity? What are the several forms of this activity?

4. Logically, what future discoveries about the structure and functioning of the neuron should follow these findings presented by Bullock?

The neuron doctrine, which we chiefly owe to Cajal (1), was unquestionably a giant stride forward in the understanding of the substratum of nervous function. It forms the basis of all modern work on the nervous system. It asserts that the nerve cell and its processes, together called the neuron, form the cellular units of the nervous system which are directly involved in nervous function; that all nerve fibers are neuronal processes; that the neuron and all its extensions develop embryologically from a single neuroblast; and that the neuron is a trophic unit, all its processes being dependent upon the nucleated cell body for their maintenance and regeneration. Although this is not inherent in the original anatomical concept, the neuron has classically come to be regarded as a functional unit, and it is here that newer information forces a reappraisal.

We can appreciate the significance of the neuron doctrine more fully by visualizing the alternative concepts historically available (2). In various forms, these alternatives, as formulated by Gerlach in the '70's and by Golgi, Meynert, Weigert, Held, Apathy, Bethe, and Nissl, among others, during several subsequent decades, assumed a diffuse reticulum of anastomosing dendritic and axonal processes. The "reticularists," as this heterogeneous group came to be called, were united mainly in their conviction that anatomical continuity of fibers and branches was the prevalent condition in the nervous system. But without assuming some kind of discontinuity and a useful, noncapricious lability it was extremely difficult, to say the least, to analyze, in a functionally meaningful way, pathways, connections, and the processing of discrete responses through complex centers, and this difficulty became more acute after the discovery of propagating all-or-none nerve impulses.

early evidence of independent neurons

Actually, the idea that nerve fibers are the greatly elongated extensions of nerve cells, though by no means generally accepted until after the time Harrison observed the outgrowth of processes in tissue culture (1907), had been clearly stated by workers in the first half of the last century (Kölliker, Wagner, and Remak). The individuality of the nerve cell in degenerative as well as in embryological processes was strongly indicated by the works of Forel and His in the '80's. But a convincing illustration of these principles and of the fact that *axons generally terminate among dendritic ramifications*—but freely and without forming a reticulum—awaited that scientific stellar nova, Santiago Ramon y Cajal. It is one of the ironies of history that his start and all his early work were based on the exploitation of a remarkable silver impregnation method discovered by the Italian Camillio Golgi in 1873 but virtually unknown until 14 years later when Cajal, among others (including the Norwegian Fridtjof Nansen, the future polar explorer), began to use it. Golgi shared with Cajal the Nobel Prize of 1906 because of the crucial role his method had played in the 20 formative years of the neuron doctrine. But even at that date he had not given up his reticularism and regarded Cajal as an adversary. Flurries of controversy continued for years, but of all the contributions of neurohistologists none has stood the test of time as well as those of Cajal, as amazing for their quality as for their quantity (3).

As a subsidiary doctrine, Cajal made the brilliant inference from the anatomical arrangement of sensory, motor, and internuncial neurons that they are all *dynamically polarized*, usually in such a way that excitation can be transmitted only from the axon of one neuron to dendrites or soma of the next and, within a neuron, must normally spread from dendritic to axonal poles (Fig. 1).

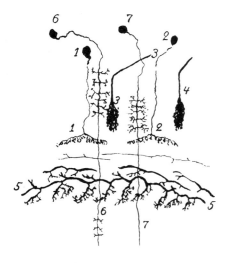

Fig. 1. Neurons of the optic ganglia (medulla externa) of a crab stained by the Golgi silver impregnation method. Since the eye is above and the brain is below, it is reasonable to assume that most transmission is downward—therefore, from terminals like 3 and 4 to upper (dendritic) processes of 6 and 7. But it is not so easy to say what direction transmission takes in the purely local neurons (1 and 2) or the coarse horizontal fibers (5). [From Hanström (11).]

convergence of physiology and anatomy

The parallel strides made in electrophysiology during much of the same period, from the time of Helmholtz in the middle of the last century to the period just before and after

World War I, and the work especially of Keith Lucas, E. D. Adrian, Herbert Gasser, and Joseph Erlanger led to the discovery of the change in electrical potential with action which, in the single nerve fiber, came to be called the nerve impulse. This was found to be an all-or-none event of the order of 1 millisecond in duration and capable of following a preceding impulse only after a short interval. Thus, the concept of a quantum of activity or a *unit of function* came to be emphasized, and the nervous system came to be regarded as a kind of digital computer with a binary—that is, yes-or-no—response. Some would prefer to call it a pulse-coded device, since the intervals between pulses are graded and can introduce noise. We can now recognize four basic tenets which grew out of the impact of electrophysiology on the neuron doctrine during this classical period of the '20's and '30's (classical from the standpoint of present-day textbooks) and which still dominate much of the thinking in the field.

1. We came to think that the all-or-none impulse was synonymous with the neuron in action—that is, that the impulse together with its afterpotentials was the only form of truly nervous activity.

2. We thought that when any part of the neuron was excited this excitation spread to all parts of the neuron as a propagated nerve impulse.

3. We thought that Cajal's doctrine of the dynamic polarity of neurons meant that dendrites propagate impulses toward the cell body.

4. We have thought for many years that the secret of all labile functions must lie in the properties of a junction between neurons. This locus, called the synapse, was supposed to be the only seat of selection, evaluation, fatigue, and facilitation and perhaps of long-persistent changes as well.

four main revisions

The evidence of the last few years has significantly altered all four of these tenets.

1. We now believe that the neuron is a functional unit somewhat in the same sense that a person is in society, in that it speaks with one voice at a time. At least so long as the neuron has but one output path (in terms of the textbook vertebrate neuron, one axon), it will speak with one voice at a time in the all-or-none pulsed code output essential for long-distance propagation. But we know that some neurons have two axons and can deliver two nonidentical pulse-coded outputs at the same time in different directions (4). More important, we believe that this pulsed form of activity—the nerve impulse or *spike*—is only characteristic of a specialized portion of the neuron, the axon, as is explained further below.

2. We now believe that the responses of many or most parts of the neuron to imping-ing excitation do not spread to become im-pulses directly but help determine the firing of impulses at some critical region such as the base of the axon—somewhat in the same man-ner as the impinging sights and sounds act upon the trigger finger of a man with a pistol. These responses we will call *prepotentials* or subthreshold processes, and some of them are enumerated below.

3. We now believe that many parts of the neuron cannot respond in an all-or-none man-ner and therefore cannot propagate without decrement. The establishment of the conduc-tion of the nerve impulse without decrement was one of the achievements of the '20's and early '30's but apparently applies only to a special portion of the neuron—the axon. *Dec-remental conduction* is probably characteristic of the great bulk of neuronal surface mem-brane—that is to say, the cell membrane of the

extensive ramifications of dendrites making up much of the gray matter of higher animals and the neuropiles of lower. Decremental conduc-tion requires that all such membranes be within shouting distance of the locus of spike initiation—in other words, within the distance of electrotonic spread—in order to be able to exert a physiological influence on the genera-tion of all-or-none events by the neuron. Many dendrites are so short that we can easily believe this condition is met, but some are so long and fine that it remains seriously open to question whether they can directly influence to any significant degree the initiation of spikes by the cell or whether their main role is quite another one (Fig. 2). In this paragraph we have been traversing a no man's land from areas of more general agreement to areas of less and less agreement, and here we pass definitely into the area of personal specula-tion. But it has been suggested that much of the activity of dendrites has its significance in an influence upon other neurons, even though the activity is local, graded, and small in amplitude. It seems likely that brain waves are the synchronized subthreshold dendritic po-tentials of many neurons summed and, further, are perhaps more than a mere by-product like the noise of a car, but are a physiologically significant causal agent (5).

4. We now believe that labile and integra-tive processes, insofar as they are localizable to the single unit level, are not confined to the synapse but occur as well at other places in the sequence of events preceding the initiation of the propagated spike (6). There may be as many as four or five *different kinds of cir-cumscribed loci* in various parts of the neuron, each of which is integrative in the sense that it does not pass on whatever comes to it in a one-to-one relation but exercises some labile evaluative action (Fig. 3).

These changes in viewpoint add up to a

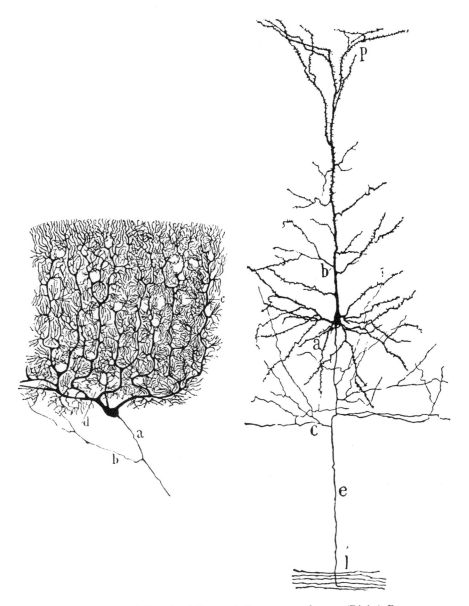

Fig. 2. (Above) Purkinje cell of the cerebellar cortex of man. (Right) Pyramidal cell of the cerebral cortex of man. Both are shown incompletely; the axon
actually extends a long distance downward. (Golgi stain.) The great arboriza-
tion of dendrites probably does not conduct impulses, and even electrotonic
influence from the farthest ones must be very weak in the spike-initiating
region, be that soma, or base of the larger dendrites, or axon. [From Cajal,
Histologie du Système Nerveux de l'Homme et des Vertébrés (12).]

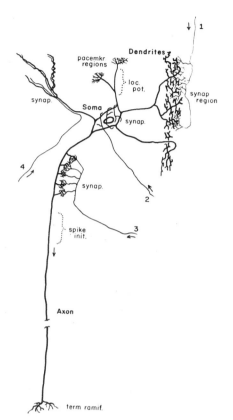

Fig. 3. Schematic representation of a neuron from the cardiac ganglion of a crab. There are several pre-synaptic pathways converging from diverse sources—inhibiting, exciting (other followers and pacemakers), accelerating (1, 2, 3, 4). These produce synaptic potentials in their several special loci. Restricted regions also initiate spontaneous activity ("pace-maker" regions, shown purely diagrammatically); local potentials (labeled only in one place but perhaps repeated elsewhere); and propagated impulses ("spike init.," also located arbitrarily). Only the axon supports all-or-none activity. Terminal ramifications are presumed to act by graded, local potentials. Integration occurs at each of the sites of confluence or transition from one event to the next. [Modified from Alexandrowicz (13).].

quiet but sweeping revolution. They renew the old hope that we may one day be able to explain complex behavior in terms of neurons—of their patterns and properties. In my

opinion that day is still far away. But now, in contrast to a decade ago, our models do not lack degrees of freedom at the level of the physiology of the single neuron. On the contrary, the permutations of the half dozen integrative processes now known within the neuron permit so much complexity that we need rather to know what restrictions to place upon the models. However, I think we are getting closer to an explanation of one of the most basic features of the neuronal basis of behavior—namely, the mechanism of origin of *temporally patterned impulse sequences.* Such patterns are the coded commands or output of every neuron, high or low, and the problem of how the characteristic sequences within and among neurons of a group are formulated has hardly been investigated heretofore. "Characteristic" means recurrent, and if we state the problem in terms of the mechanism of formulating a meaningful pattern and then retaining or stabilizing that mechanism, we have essentially stated in one form the basic problem of the neuronal basis of instinct as well as of learning.

capillary ultramicroelectrode

These drastic changes in viewpoint are almost entirely due to the technical advances made possible by the intracellular electrode, a device introduced by Ling and Gerard in 1949 (7) and perfected by a number of other workers, which makes it possible to record from inside the larger neurons many of the events that occur prior to the initiation of the all-or-none impulse, with but very slight damage. The electrode is a glass capillary tube drawn out to submicroscopic dimensions, of the order of a few tenths of a micron in outside diameter, filled with an appropriate salt solution as conductor and inserted into the cell to measure the electrical potential difference between the inside and a second electrode outside the cell.

The technique is not extraordinarily difficult, but under the best of conditions, it presents problems. The electrodes are of high resistance—from several to many tens of megohms—and require special circuits for reasonable fidelity of recording of rapid events. They introduce many microvolts of noise. The capillary pipettes have to be drawn again and again to the same shape, carefully filled, and frequently replaced, for they break not only under the stress of a little connective tissue but of their own accord, presumably from internal stresses. While the tips are quite visible in air, they are beyond the limits of ordinary microscopy under water, and in most experiments the penetration is made blindly. A rather satisfactory sign that the tip has penetrated into a cell is provided by the sudden appearance of a negative potential of several score millivolts. The main limitation, however, aside from uncertainty about exactly where the tip is located, is the intolerance of small cells and processes—below about 10 microns—of even the finest electrodes thus far produced. Our knowledge is based on sampling from a rather small number of types of large neurons, and even here only from the axon, the cell body, and perhaps the bases of the larger dendrites.

Let us now look a little more closely at the major evidence for the main conclusions stated above.

subthreshold activity

Every neuron so far penetrated gives at least one output of all-or-none spikes, and a few have been encountered which can give two different rhythms of spikes and which have two axons or major processes going in differ-

ent directions (4). But it would probably occasion less surprise today than ever before were someone to find a neuron which gave no all-or-none impulses but whose axon carried only graded and decrementally spreading activity. This may well be the primitive property, and it may well be retained in the many very short axoned neurons in the highest centers of both invertebrates and vertebrates. This is to say that the possibility remains with us that in the most complex and finely textured higher centers, made up largely of very small neurons, perhaps much of the normal functioning is carried out *without nerve impulses*—that is without all-or-none, propagated spikes but by means of graded and decrementally spreading activity. Perhaps the first direct demonstration that subthreshold events in one neuron can increase the activity in another neuron has recently been supplied by experiments of Watanabe and myself on the nine-celled ganglion of the lobster heart (8). Here, relatively long-lasting pulses of current repeatedly applied through the intracellular electrode into one of the five large anterior cells increased the pace of firing of small posterior cells many millimeters away, even when the applied currents were below threshold or were in the wrong polarity for spike production. (The internally anodal stimuli caused the distant small cells to tend to fire during the long pulse, while the internally cathodal currents caused the small cells to tend to fire their impulses just after termination of the current.) These effects, obtained without the intervention of nerve impulses, are not due to escape of current but occur only if the stimulated cell is penetrated.

the several forms of activity

Like the multiplication of the fundamental particles of physics, the known forms of

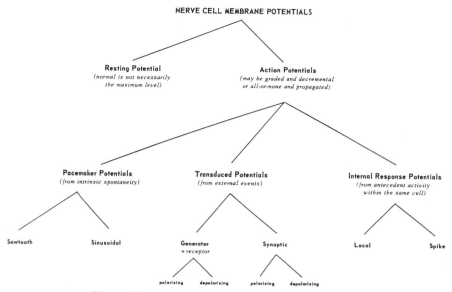

Fig. 4. The types of nerve cell membrane potentials.

activity of nerve cells have multiplied from a single one—the all-or-none impulse or spike—which was all that was known up to 1938. In that year Hodgkin, using the giant fiber of the squid, and very soon thereafter Katz, using the sciatic nerve of the frog, discovered the local potential, which can be graded and which spreads essentially passively—"electrotonically"—declining to half amplitude about every millimeter. Later work has shown several more kinds, the exact number depending on the distinctions one wishes to make.

The scheme proposed in Fig. 4 indicates the relations between most of these. The first two, the *spike* potential and the *local* potential, are regarded as responses to antecedent activity within the same cell (when physiologically activated, not artificially stimulated); both are mediated by the local electric currents across the membrane as the result of the change in resistance of the already active regions and the standing "batteries" or electromotive forces between the two sides of the membrane. The

one is regenerative, all-or-none, and propagated; the other is graded and decremental. In contrast, *generator* potentials of receptor neurons and *synaptic* potentials are responses of cells to impinging external events of specific kinds—sensory stimuli and junctional transmitters. These are two subdivisions of each of these categories based on the polarity of the response. On the basis of other differences, further subdivisions can be defined. There are also prepotentials resulting from no impinging environmental change but occurring under normal steady-state conditions and therefore properly called *spontaneous*. These can be manifested in more than one form: one is more or less sinusoidal (the time course is relatively independent of the occurrence of spikes); another is more or less saw-tooth-like (the time course is dependent on the intervention of a spike or local potential to reset the starting condition; a relaxation oscillation).

It is highly probable that some if not all of these different kinds of activity represent specialized kinds of cell surface membranes (9). This is suggested by the striking differences in properties and by the localization of each of these processes to restricted regions of the neuron. The circumscribed loci may recur at more than one site on the surface of a given neuron. Any one of the prepotentials is probably capable of causing spike initiation, at the restricted locus where this occurs, but commonly two or more prepotentials will act in sequence to this end. Perhaps any of the potentials can interact with any of the others to alter its rate of development or amplitude. But besides these sources of complexity a still more important source may prove to be the anatomical distribution of these different kinds of cell membrane over the neuron, their spatial separation, and the possibilities of interaction, of attenuation, and of invasion by the explosive all-or-none spike process. Only some regions of the cell are capable of supporting such a process, and perhaps it is just those which cannot support it that are most integrative.

changes of state not visible in potential

But this does not exhaust the list of separate processes within the neuron which contribute to the determination of firing. Besides the

processes reflected in the membrane potential, there are others whose occurrence may give no sign in the membrane potential.

For example, many junctions manifest the property known as *facilitation*. This means that successively arriving impulses in the presynaptic pathway cause larger and larger synaptic potentials in the postsynaptic neuron. The excitability of the postsynaptic membrane may be said to have increased—although there may be no change whatever in the level of membrane potential after one synaptic potential has passed off and before the next has begun—from the corresponding level at an earlier stage, when the excitability was lower. Another junction upon the same neuron may under the same conditions manifest the opposite property, which may be called *diminution;* that is to say, successive responses are smaller (Fig. 5).

Aftereffects provide still other indications of differences in excitability not predictable from the membrane potential. Some cells under certain conditions continue to fire for a considerable time after the input has ceased; others show the opposite response—namely, a prompt rebound or overshooting return after input has ceased. Thus, if the response to the input is an increase in the level of activity, then there may occur after the cessation of this input a continued afterdischarge—a maintained high level of activity for some time; or

Fig. 5. Facilitation and diminution. An ultramicroelectrode inside a nerve cell (of the cardiac ganglion of a lobster) recorded first the synaptic potentials resulting from a burst of five arriving impulses from one presynaptic pathway (from posterior small cells) and then those responding to a series of impulses arriving in another pathway (from the central nervous system). The former responses show diminution—the amplitude declines; the latter show facilitation —the amplitude grows. (Calibration, 100 msec, 21 mv.) [Courtesy of Dr. Carlo Terzuolo.]

there may occur a rebound, which would mean in this case a period of decreased activity even below the previous background level. If on the other hand, the given input has for its effect an inhibition of ongoing activity, upon its cessation there may continue for a period an afterinhibition, or there may occur a rebound increase in activity above the previous ongoing level.

Whereas the classical concept of the neuron has recognized the importance of excitability, this has been measured or thought of in terms of the spike threshold. The spike threshold is certainly important, although only at one point in the neuron—namely, the point where spikes are initiated. After this initiation has occurred, the spike excitability elsewhere is relatively unimportant, because the margin of safety is usually quite large for the activation of each successive point along the axon. What the newer knowledge has added is understanding that prior to initiation of the spike there are critical forms of excitability not measured by thresholds, because they determine the responses of subthreshold, graded and local events as a function of what came before them.

spontaneity

Still further increasing the complexity of the combination of processes possible is the tendency to spontaneous activity in some neurons. By means of penetrating microelectrodes, spontaneity has now been examined from within in a number of cells—central neurons, receptors, and pacemakers of the heart. The observed voltages are enormously greater than in the usual arrangement of two electrodes outside the cell shunted by extracellular fluids, and this has permitted new insight into the intimate events that occur prior to each spontaneous discharge.

As a consequence, we can see the *continual change of state* at the subthreshold level, at least insofar as it is reflected in the potential of the cell body and nearby cell membrane (Fig. 6). We can infer also from the observations that the tendency to spontaneous change of state inheres in certain restricted regions of the neuron (the pacemaker loci), which influence the rest in turn indirectly. Furthermore, there is evidence that, at least in some neurons, more than one locus of spontaneity can exist at the same time in different parts of

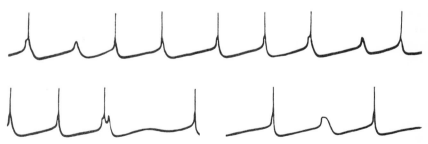

Fig. 6. Spontaneous activity in a ganglion cell as revealed by an electrode inside the soma (nerve cell body). The spikes are about 10 mv here (electrotonically spread from the axon) and are followed by a repolarization, then a gradual depolarization—the pacemaker potential, which at a critical level sets off a local potential. This, in turn, usually rises high enough to trigger a spike but is seen here several times by itself. Once (in the first half of the bottom row) the local potential fails to be set off. (Time, 0.5 second.) [Courtesy of Dr. Carlo Terzuolo.]

the cell, each with a different rate of change of state. The continual change of state of parts of the neuron under steady conditions of its environment may have significance not only in generating spontaneous activity but also in altering the responsiveness of the cell to any input impinging upon it. In addition, the spontaneous subthreshold potential changes of one neuron may influence other neurons, perhaps by electrotonic spread over short processes and perhaps by less specific mass field effects—for example, when many cells "beat" in unison, as in brain waves (10).

conclusion

In sum, anatomically the neuron doctrine has never been more firm. The classical controversy gradually focused upon the issue of protoplasmic or neurofibrillar continuity between neurons. Today, while a number of exceptional cases of nerve cell syncytia are commonly accepted (for example, giant fibers of earthworm and squid), the weight of evidence from silver impregnation and, especially in recent years, from electron microscopy is against any such continuity. Physiologically, however, we have a new appreciation of the complexity-within-unity of the neuron. Like a person, it is truly a functional unit, but it is composed of parts of very different function not only with respect to metabolism and maintenance but also in the realms of processing diverse input and determining output— that is, of integration. The impulse is not the only form of nerve cell activity; excitation of one part of the neuron does not necessarily involve the whole neuron; many dendrites may not propagate impulses at all; and the synapse is not the only locus of selection, evaluation, fatigue, and persistent change. Several forms of graded activity—for example, pace-maker, synaptic, and local potentials—

each confined to a circumscribed region or repeating regions of the neuron, can separately or sequentially integrate arriving events, with the history and milieu, to determine output in the restricted region where spikes are initiated. The size, number, and distribution over the neuron of these functionally differentiated regions and the labile coupling functions between the successive processes that eventually determine what information is transferred to the next neuron provide an enormous range of possible complexity within this single cellular unit.

In the face of this gradual but sweeping change in functional concepts, any statement but the most diffuse about expectations for the future must be very dangerous. Nevertheless I will venture to suggest that in the near future we will gain significant new insight at this unitary level of neurophysiology with respect to the functions and differentiations among dendrites, the chemical and perhaps ultramicroscopic specification of different kinds of surface membrane, additional labile processes, sites of possible persistent change, and the normal functional significance of intercellular reactions mediated by graded activity without the intervention of all-or-none impulses.

references

1. S. Ramon y Cajal, *Neuron Theory or Reticular Theory?* (Consejo Superior de Investigaciones Científicas, Madrid, 1954), English translation.
2. A. T. Rasmussen, *Some Trends in Neuroanatomy* (Brown, Dubuque, Iowa, 1947).
3. For a complete bibliography, see S. Ramon y Cajal, *Recollections of My Life;* English translation by E. H. Craigie, *Mem. Am. Phil. Soc.* 8 (1937).
4. T. H. Bullock and C. A. Terzuolo, *J. Physiol. (London)* 138, 341 (1957).

5. F. Bremer, *Physiol. Revs.* 38, 357 (1958).

6. T. H. Bullock, *Revs. Modern Phys.*, in press; *Exptl. Cell Research* 5, suppl. 323 (1958).

7. G. Ling and R. W. Gerard, *J. Cellular Comp. Physiol.* 34, 383 (1949).

8. The study by Watanabe and Bullock was aided by a grant from the National Institute of Neurological Diseases and Blindness, National Institutes of Health, and by a contract (NR 101–454) between the Office of Naval Research, Department of the Navy, and the University of California.

9. H. Grundfest, *Physiol. Revs.* 37, 337 (1957).

10. See further: *Ciba Foundation Symposium, Neurological Basis of Behavior* (Churchill, London, 1958); J. C. Eccles, *The Physiology of Nerve Cells* (Johns Hopkins Press, Baltimore, Md., 1957); H. Fernandez-Moran and R. Brown, *Exptl. Cell Research* 5, suppl. (1958); A. Fessard, *Proc. Intern. Physiol. Congr. 20th Congr. Brussels* (1956).

11. B. Hanström, *Arkiv. Zool.* 16, 10 (1924).

12. S. Ramon y Cajal, *Histologie du Système Nerveux de l'Homme et des Vertébrés* (Maloine, Paris, 1909–11).

13. J. S. Alexandrowicz, *Quart J. Microscop. Sci.* 75, 182 (1932).

2   the reticular formation*

J. D. French

1. What is the importance of the connections between the sensory nerve trunks of the body and the reticular formation?

*J. D. French, "The Reticular Formation," *Scientific American*. Copyright © 1957 in the U.S. and Berne Convention countries by Scientific American, Inc. Reprinted with permission. All rights reserved. Available separately @ 20¢ as offprint No. 66 from

2. In what manner is the reticular formation "a general alarm"?

3. How does the RAS help control motor activities?

4. Exactly how does the RAS contribute to the "highest mental processes" (such as reasoning)?

The title "reticular formation" might suggest various things—a football line-up, a chess gambit, a geological structure or whatnot—

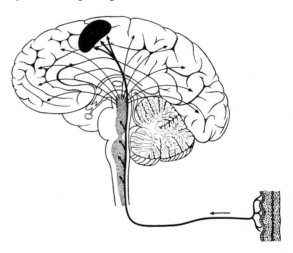

The reticular formation is the stippled area in this cross section of the brain. A sense organ (*lower right*) is connected to a sensory area in the brain (*upper left*) by a pathway extending up the spinal cord. This pathway branches into the reticular formation. When a stimulus travels along the pathway, the reticular formation may "awaken" the entire brain (*black arrows*).

but as readers of *Scientific American* well know, it is actually a part of the brain, a once mysterious part which has recently come in for a great deal of attention from biologists. The reticular formation is a tiny nerve network in the central part of the brain stem. Investigators have discovered that this bit of

W. H. Freeman and Company, 660 Market Street, San Francisco, California.

nerve tissue, no bigger than your little finger, is a far more important structure than anyone had dreamed. It underlies our awareness of the world and our ability to think, to learn and to act. Without it, an individual is reduced to a helpless, senseless, paralyzed blob of protoplasm.

The actual seat of the power to think, to perceive, indeed to respond to a stimulus with anything more than a reflex reaction, lies in the cortex of the brain. But the cortex cannot perceive or think unless it is "awake." Consider the alarm ring that awakens you in the morning: several seconds pass before you recognize the disturbance and can respond to stop the painful jangle. A sensory signal arriving at the cortex while it is asleep goes unrecognized. Experiments on anesthetized individuals have shown further that stimulation of the cortex alone is not sufficient to awaken the brain. Something else must arouse the cortex: that something is the reticular formation.

It was only about eight years ago that two eminent physiologists, H. W. Magoun of the U.S. and Giuseppe Moruzzi of Italy, working together at Northwestern University, discovered this fact. They were exploring the mystery of the reticular formation's functions by means of an electrode planted in this area in the brain of a cat. They found that stimulation of the area with a small electric current would awaken a drowsing cat as peacefully as a scratch on the head. The animal's behavior, and recordings of changes in its brain waves with the electroencephalograph, showed all the signs of a normal arousal from sleep. Magoun and Moruzzi decided that the reticular formation acted as a kind of sentinel which aroused the cortex, and they named it the RAS (reticular activating system).

Now mysteries began to clear—not only with regard to the function of the reticular

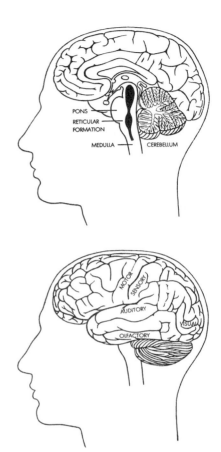

Relationship of the reticular formation (*black area*) to various parts of the brain is indicated at the top. The functional areas of the brain are outlined at bottom.

formation but also as to some previously puzzling features of the nervous system's anatomy. All the great sensory nerve trunks in the body have brush-like branches which stream into the reticular formation. Sensory signals from all parts of the body go to the cortex by direct pathways, but on the way through the brain stem they also feed into the reticular formation. Evidently the reticular formation, when so stimulated, sends arousing signals to the cortex. The awakened cortex can then interpret the sensory signals it is receiving directly.

The RAS is a kind of general alarm: that is to say, it responds in the same way to any sensory stimulus, whether from the organs of hearing, seeing, touch or whatever. Its response is simply to arouse the brain, not to relay any specific message. Its signals spray the entire cortex rather than any one center of sensation. A noise, a flash of light, a pinch on the hand, the smell of burning wood, a pain in the stomach—any of these excites the reticular formation to alert the cortex to a state of wakefulness, so that when the specific stimulus arrives at the appropriate center in the cortex, the brain can identify it.

Apparently the RAS learns to be selective in its sensitivity to particular stimuli. A mother may be instantly awakened by the faintest whimper of her baby. Father, on the other hand, may sleep through baby's fiercest bellowings but be aroused by a faint smell of smoke. A city dweller may sleep peacefully in the midst of the riotous din of traffic while his visitor from the country spends a sleepless night wishing he were elsewhere. It is as if the RAS becomes endowed by experience with the ability to discriminate among stimuli, disregarding those it has found unimportant and responding to those that are helpful. Happily so. Imagine how unbearable life would be if you could not shut out most of the environment from consciousness and were at the mercy of the thousands of sights and sounds simultaneously clamoring for attention.

The RAS, like the starter in an automobile, starts the brain engine running, but this is by no means the end of its job. It goes on functioning to keep the individual in a conscious state. ("Consciousness" is a controversial word among psychologists, but for our purposes its meaning is clear enough.) If the RAS cannot function normally, consciousness is impossible. A person whose reticular formation has been permanently injured or destroyed falls into a coma from which he can never recover. He may live on for a year or more, but he remains as helpless and shut off from communication as a vegetable.

If uninjured, the RAS can maintain a wakeful state (but not consciousness) even in the absence of the cortex. In a newborn baby the cortex has not yet begun to function, but the infant nevertheless has short periods of wakefulness throughout the day. The same is true of the tragic creatures born without any cortex at all (called anencephalic monsters). Such a child (sometimes kept alive for three or four years) never achieves any understanding or real contact with its surroundings, but it has periods of wakefulness during which it swallows and digests food, smiles and coos when fondled and cries when treated roughly. We must conclude, therefore, that wakefulness of a very crude sort is possible without the cortex, so long as the RAS can function.

For sustained wakefulness, however, the cortex certainly is essential. The alert state seems to depend upon an interplay between the cortex and the RAS. The reticular formation is stimulated not only by the sensory nerves but also by impulses from some parts of the cortex. This has been demonstrated by electrical stimulation of certain areas of the cortex in monkeys: such stimulation will awaken a sleeping monkey. When the experiment is tried on a monkey that is awake, it evokes a dramatic response. The monkey instantly stops whatever it is doing and looks about intently and slightly puzzled, as if to say: "What was that?" It does not seem distressed or agitated—only warily alert. So it would seem that in the waking state the RAS plays a part, in combination with the cortex, in focusing attention and probably in many other mental processes.

All this raises the possibility that the RAS may be importantly involved in mental disorders. Investigations of this possibility have already begun by means of experiments with drugs. It is natural to start with anesthetic and sleep-inducing drugs, to see how they affect the RAS. The results of these experiments are illuminating but not surprising. They show that the drug blocks the flow of nerve impulses in the reticular formation but has little effect on the flow along the direct pathways from sense organs to the cortex. As the anesthesia wears off, the flow in the RAS returns to normal. A stimulating drug, on the other hand, has the opposite effect: it enhances the conduction of impulses in the RAS. It will be interesting to extend these experiments to the new tranquilizing drugs and the substances that produce experimental psychoses. Already there is evidence that these drugs do affect the functioning of the RAS.

Still another domain is under the control of this amazingly cogent bit of tissue in the brain. The RAS apparently has a hand in regulating all the motor activities of the body. It can modify muscle movements of both the voluntary type (controlled by the brain) and the reflex type (controlled in the spinal cord).

Just as the brain cortex has specific centers of sensation, it also has specific motor centers which generate muscle contractions. If one stimulates a motor center with an electric current, the appropriate muscles will respond, but the resulting body movements are jerky and uncontrolled. These powerful movements are normally controlled and polished by other motor centers of the cortex, acting through the reticular formation. If the RAS is not stimulated or does not function properly, the movements will be jerky.

More surprising is the fact that the RAS can also act on the reflexes, centered in the spinal cord. The reflex apparatus has two functions. First, it generates automatic muscle movements. When signals from a sudden and alarming sensory stimulus (*e.g.*, touching something hot) arrive at the spinal cord, they are passed on immediately to an adjacent motor nerve and travel right back to the affected part of the body to jerk it away. In general, the automatic, reflex activities are protective—responses to danger or sudden challenges in the surroundings. But some of them can be tricked into action by suddenly stretching a muscle: for example, a tap on the knee elicits the well-known knee jerk.

The second function of the reflex system is to keep the muscles ready for action by maintaining "tone"—that is, a state of partial contraction. Just as a violin string must be stretched to a certain tension before it can emit music, so a muscle must be maintained at a certain tension to respond efficiently to a stimulus. The mechanism that regulates its resting tension, or "tone," is a small structure within the muscle called a "spindle." When a muscle contracts, it squeezes the spindle; when it relaxes, the pressure on the spindle loosens. Either departure from normal tone causes the spindle to send signals by way of a sensory nerve to the spinal cord; there they excite a motor nerve to correct the contraction or relaxation of the muscle. This feedback system automatically keeps each muscle at precisely the right tone. And the appropriate tone itself is adjusted to suit the needs of the moment by nerve impulses which regulate the sensitivity of the spindle.

Now experiments have clearly demonstrated that the RAS exerts some control over voluntary and reflex motor reactions. Let us take for illustration an experiment on the reflex knee jerk, which is easy and convenient to perform. A monkey is anesthetized and a pen is tied to its toe to record the size of its knee kicks on a rotating drum. We keep tapping its knee and we get a uniform response, recorded as a nice series of regular curves on the drum. Then we suddenly stimulate the reticular formation electrically. The knee jerks immediately become larger: the RAS has enhanced them. When we stop stimulating it, the kicks return to normal size. Now in the course of exploratory experiments along the reticular formation a new fact emerges. If we stimulate the formation at a point toward its lower end in the brain stem, the kicks are not enhanced but instead are inhibited!

Following up this finding, we discover that these centers can enhance or inhibit sensory as well as motor impulses. In short, the RAS acts as a kind of traffic control center, facilitating or inhibiting the flow of signals in the nervous system.

The astonishing generality of the RAS gives us a new outlook on the nervous system. Neurologists have tended to think of the nervous system as a collection of more or less separate circuits, each doing a particular job. It now appears that the system is much more closely integrated than had been thought. This should hardly surprise us. A simple organism such as the amoeba reacts with totality toward stimuli: the whole cell is occupied in the act of finding, engulfing and digesting food. Man, even with his 10 billion nerve cells, is not radically different. He must focus his sensory and motor systems on the problem in hand, and for this he obviously must be equipped with some integrating machine.

The RAS seems to be such a machine. It awakens the brain to consciousness and keeps it alert; it directs the traffic of messages in the nervous system; it monitors the myriads of stimuli that beat upon our senses, accepting what we need to perceive and rejecting what is irrelevant; it tempers and refines our muscular activity and bodily movements. We can go even further and say that it contributes in an important way to the highest mental processes —the focusing of attention, introspection, and doubtless all forms of reasoning.

3 the limbic system *

Paul D. MacLean

1. Why did MacLean choose the quotation from Freud as his opening paragraph?

2. What are the functions traditionally attributed to the "old cortex"?

3. In what sense is the "limbic" system an integrated unit?

4. Which of the experiments cited best support MacLean's thesis?

5. What lines of research are likely to be stimulated by this article?

However jealously we may . . . have defended the independence of psychology from all other sciences, . . . we are here overshadowed by the immutable biological fact that the living individual serves two purposes, self-preservation and the preservation of the species, which seem to be independent of each other, which we have not been able to trace back to a common source, and whose interests often conflict in animal life. Here we are really discussing biological psychology, we are studying the psychological concomitants of biological processes. (Sigmund Freud: *New Introductory Lectures on Psycho-Analysis*, pp. 124–125, 1949.)

*P. D. MacLean, "The Limbic System with Respect to Self-Preservation and the Preservation of the Species," *Journal of Nervous and Mental Disease*, 127 (July 1958), 1–11. © Williams & Wilkins Co., 1958.

Experimentation during the past two decades has provided evidence in support of a postulated dichotomy in the function of the phylogenetically old and new cortex (25, 13). This dichotomy—or schizophysiology as it has been called (15, 17)—has important implications for neurology and psychiatry because of its relevance to distinctive attributes of emotional and intellectual behavior.

The structural basis for this dichotomy was implicit in the anatomical findings of Broca that were published in 1878 (1). He demonstrated that a large cerebral convolution, which he called the great limbic lobe, is found as a common denominator in the brains of all mammals. He chose the word "limbic" to indicate that this lobe surrounds—literally, forms a border around—the brain stem. The greater part of the "old" cortex is found in the limbic lobe. Experimentation has shown that this primitive lobe is also, physiologically speaking, a common denominator of a variety of emotional and viscerosomatic functions in the mammal.

The relative constancy in the development of the limbic cortex throughout the phylogeny of the mammal stands in contrast to the rapid evolution of the neocortex which mushrooms around it. In contradistinction to the limbic cortex, the neocortex might be likened to an expanding numerator representing in phylogeny the growth of intellectual functions.

The phylogenetically old cortex may be broadly subdivided into two types, (i) the archicortex, so called because it is the first type of cortex to differentiate, and (ii) the mesocortex which derives its name from the fact that it is intermediate in position and structure between the archicortex and surrounding neocortex. The archicortex and mesocortex envelop the ring-like limbic lobe in two concentric bands. The mesocortex which forms the outer band makes up most of the superficial cortex of the limbic lobe and extends somewhat beyond its boundaries as perilimbic cortex. In evolution, the inner band of archicortex becomes largely buried through a process of folding, and in higher forms it undergoes so much displacement by the corpus callosum that the bulk of it comes to lie in the hippocampus in the inferomedial part of the temporal lobe.

It is to be emphasized that the limbic cortex is structurally primitive compared with the neocortex and is essentially similar in all mammals. This would suggest that it functions at an animalistic level in both animal and man. Furthermore, the limbic cortex, in contrast to the neocortex, has a wealth of large connecting pathways with the hypothalamus. These include the medial forebrain bundle, stria terminalis, fornix and mammillo-thalamic tract. Recently Nauta (23) has confirmed Cajal's findings (29) of a sizeable bundle of fibers in the fornix that project to the tuberal nuclei which sit astride the portal circulation of the pituitary. As suggested by physiological studies (17), it has also been learned through the work of Nauta that the limbic cortex has strong reciprocating connections with the central grey and paramedian reticulum of the midbrain (24). These nervous structures together with the hypothalamus play a fundamental role in integrating the performance of mechanisms involved in self-preservation and procreation.

Other structures associated with the limbic cortex include the septum, amygdala, anterior and midline thalamic nuclei, the habenula, and parts of the basal ganglia. It has become evident that the limbic cortex and its subcortical cell stations comprise a functionally integrated system. In keeping with Broca's terminology, this system may be appropriately referred to as the limbic system (14). Unlike the term rhinencephalon,[1] which has commonly been used to apply to this system, the word limbic, as Broca pointed out (1), implies no theory in regard to function. It also has the advantage of being a short as well as a descriptive term.

With continued investigation it is beginning to appear that respective portions of the limbic system are predominantly concerned

with emotionally determined functions pertaining to the *preservation of the self* or to the *preservation of the species*. This paper will single out for emphasis recent findings that have suggested such a functional localization with respect to these two basic life principles.

findings pertinent to self-preservation

As illustrated in Figure 1, one can identify by means of strychnine neuronography five regions of interrelated limbic and extralimbic cortex. The region shown in stipple will be referred to as the frontotemporal region. It embraces the interrelated cortex of the orbital, insular, temporal polar, and pyriform areas, all of which "fire" into the amygdala and the archicortex contained in the segment of the

---

[1] According to Elliot Smith (31), "The term 'rhinencephale' was originally applied by St. Hilaire to a type of uniocular monsters without any direct reference to a region of the brain. . . . Richard Owen [an English biologist who lived from 1804–1892] subsequently introduced the term . . . to distinguish those parts of the brain . . . known as the olfactory bulb and the olfactory peduncle." In 1890, the English anatomist Turner reintroduced the term to refer not only to these structures, but also to the lateral olfactory tract and pyriform lobe. Since then, His and others have variously applied the term to these and other parts of the brain, with the result that one finds general confusion in the literature as to what it signifies.

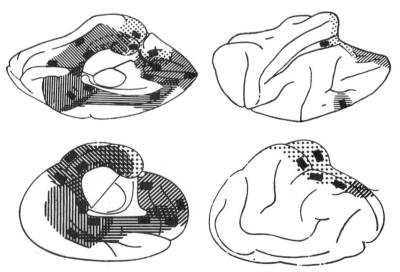

Fig. 1. Various shadings represent five regions comprising limbic and extralimbic cortex that can be differentiated by physiological neuronography (21, 27). The frontotemporal region is shown in stipple. Top two figures show lateral and medial surfaces of cat's brain; bottom two figures are corresponding representations of monkey's brain. (From MacLean, EEG Clin. Neurophysiol., 4: 407–418, 1952.)

hippocampus proximal to the amygdala. This region receives a confluence of afferents from the lateral olfactory tract and ascending pathways from the brainstem (cf. Fig. 2).

The frontotemporal region has been subject to much investigation because it is so often the site of injury and disease resulting in psycho-

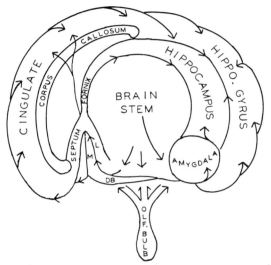

Fig. 2. Schematic drawing, indicating divergence of pathways from the brain stem and olfactory bulb into respective portions of the limbic lobe. See text in regard to functional implications. DB, diagonal band; L, lateral septal nuclei; M, medial septal nuclei; OLF, olfactory.

motor epilepsy. The complemental findings of ablation and stimulation studies indicate that this region is primarily concerned with functions that insure *self-preservation.*

An analysis of stimulation studies in unrestrained and waking animals reveals that responses obtained from intermixed points within the frontotemporal region fall principally into two categories (10, 5, 14, 20). One category includes responses of an alimentary nature such as licking, chewing, eating, retching, etc. In the other category are responses that one associates with the animal's search for food and its struggle for survival. These include sniffing, searching, and angry attack or defense with appropriate vocalization.

Patients who suffer from psychomotor epilepsy as a consequence of epileptogenic foci in this region show comparable manifestations during their seizures (26). At the same time, they have symptoms that lend insight into the subjective functions of this region. In keeping with the automatisms that appear, they commonly experience during the aura alimentary symptoms and vivid emotions. There may be alimentary feelings of thirst, hunger, or nausea, whereas the emotional feelings are characteristically fearsome or unpleasant in nature. Feelings of fear, terror, dread and sadness may be associated with a sense of epigastric distress, suffocation, choking, or a racing heart. Sometimes the patient will experience an alternation of opposite feelings, a manifestation which suggests that there may be a reciprocal innervation of feeling states comparable to the reciprocal innervation of muscles (17).

Bilateral ablations of the frontotemporal region in animals appear to abolish a number of self-preservative functions related to eating and self-protection. In an extension of Klüver and Bucy's classical studies (11), Pribram and Bagshaw showed that the removal of this region in wild animals results in tameness and docility (28). There is an apparent loss of fear, and the animals will expose themselves again and again to the same harmful situation. Ordinarily frugivorous, the monkey post-operatively will eat raw meat or fish. It will put feces or nuts and bolts in the mouth and sometimes swallow them. In short, such an animal loses the ability to look after its self-protection and to eat properly.

From the foregoing findings, one is led to infer that the frontotemporal portion of the limbic system is largely concerned with survival mechanisms involved in obtaining and assimilating food. The role of this primitive part of the brain in regard to self-preservation has a number of significant implications for psychiatry and psychosomatic medicine that have been discussed elsewhere (14, 16).

findings pertinent to preservation of species

Curiously enough, in addition to tameness, animals with bilateral ablations of the fronto-temporal region reveal exaggerated sexuality that is often bizarre in nature. This was well illustrated by the experiments of Schreiner and Kling in which they removed part of this region in cats (30). Male cats would indiscriminately mount other male cats, a female dog, a female monkey or even a chicken. These findings suggest the occurrence of a release, in a Jacksonian sense, of other parts of the brain involved in procreative functions.

This leads to the consideration of another group of related limbic structures that seem to be involved in forms of behavior which taken together, might be interpreted as being conducive to the preservation of the species, rather than the self. As will be indicated, continuing investigation is beginning to suggest that a neural system involving parts of the hippocampus, cingulate gyrus, and septum is implicated in pleasure and grooming reactions and sexual manifestations. Long ago Cajal (29) emphasized the close anatomical relationship of these structures which are schematically represented in Figure 2. The figure illustrates that the septal region is a place of confluence for sensory data coming by way of the medial olfactory tract and ascending from the brainstem. From what is known of functional localization, the structures associated with the septum are in a position which might possibly allow the association of the somato-genital sense with the visual and olfactory senses.

In the course of investigating the structures under consideration, we have employed a method that allows one to perform chemical or electrical stimulation of the brain and at the same time to record the EEG and behavioral changes in unrestrained and waking animals.[2] It is basically a stereotaxic method which involves the implantation of needle guides in the skull of an animal through which insulated needles with lead-off wires can be subsequently introduced into desired points of the brain without the use of anesthesia. Chemical stimulation has usually been carried out by depositing micro-amounts of cholinergic drugs in crystalline form. Among the reasons for resorting to this type of stimulation was the belief that the prolonged action of the drug might bring to the fore behavioral changes that would not become apparent during short-lasting electrical stimulation.

One series of experiments on cats has focused attention on an intermediate segment of the hippocampus lying between frontal planes A1.5–A4.5 of Horsley-Clarke coordinates (18, 19). Figure 3 shows the track of a needle that was used to deposit crystalline carbachol in this portion of the hippocampus. For the present discussion, only the behavioral changes occurring during the stage of subsidence need be considered. During the second and third hour when the seizure activity is abating, the cat characteristically manifests enhanced pleasure and grooming reactions (15,19) and is unusually receptive to genital stimulation (19). By enhanced pleasure reactions is meant the appearance in a conspicuous form of those manifestations that are interpreted as signs of contentment and passivity in the cat. These

[2] See Ref. 18 for detailed description of method.

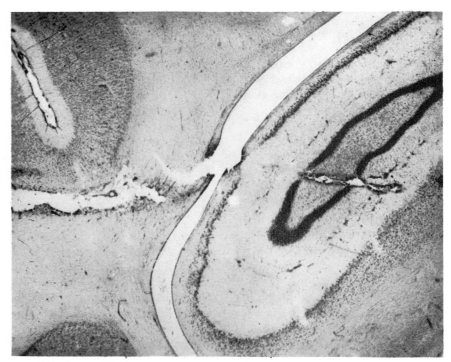

Fig. 3. Microscopic section showing needle track in the intermediate portion of hippocampus that was investigated in the group of experiments described in text. In this instance a micro-amount of crystalline carbachol was deposited at the site where the track ended. (From MacLean, Arch. Neurol. Psychiat., **78**: 113–127, 1957.)

include spontaneous loud purring, kneading and fanning of the forepaws; turning over on the back, rolling, twisting, stretching, and fanning of forepaws; rubbing head and body vigorously against inanimate objects or the examiner. Enhanced grooming refers to the appearance in a conspicuous and enduring form of grooming activity. Receptivity to genital stimulation, over and above its manifest meaning, implies the susceptibility of the male cat to the inducement of an erection. In our experience, and in the experience of others, it is only a rare male cat that will not resist and avoid genital stimulation.

If insufficient carbachol is deposited in the hippocampus to induce the high voltage seizure activity associated with Stage 2, the only

noteworthy behavioral changes that become manifest are enhanced pleasure and grooming reactions and receptivity to genital stimulation. The same applies in regard to the application of methacholine or acetylcholine with physostigmine, which fail to induce the intense seizure discharges seen with carbachol.

It is to be emphasized that the foregoing changes in disposition are in marked contrast to the manifestations that occur if these cholinergic drugs escape from the hippocampus into the overlying ventrical. In this event, there results a syndrome characterized by contralateral circling and angry behavior (15, 17, 19).

Enhanced pleasure and grooming reactions

were observed following 14 of 26 stimulations of the hippocampus. This compared with two such positive reactions following 28 stimulations in neighboring structures and elsewhere. They were not seen when empty needles or relatively inert substances were placed in the hippocampus. If the results of this exploratory study were subjected to chi square analysis, they would be highly significant (P < 0.001).

During electrical stimulation of the part of the hippocampus in question, one observes few, if any, noteworthy changes. If, however, an afterdischarge is produced, there occurs during and following it a number of pronounced alterations in behavior. The changes following the afterdischarge are pertinent here. The following account is broadly descriptive of the enhanced pleasure and grooming reactions observed in 21 of 34 cats following hippocampal afterdischarges (19). Shortly after the vocalization that signals the end of the afterdischarge, the animal commonly begins to scratch its head or body. Sometimes it will immediately bite near the stump of its tail or in the genital region. Afterwards there may follow a period of protracted intensive grooming. The grooming may from the start be largely confined to the genital region or may involve an orderly progression from head and forepaws, to body and hind limbs, to stump of tail and region of anus and genitalia. In the male cat a partial erection may appear in the course of protracted grooming of the genitalia.

Intensive grooming activity may continue for several minutes, after which the animal may stretch out, purr, fan its forepaws and show other manifestations of contentment. If approached by the experimenter during the period of grooming, it characteristically manifests enhanced pleasure reactions. Cadilhac has made similar observations (2). Penile erection may easily be induced (19). It is striking to

see the effect of hippocampal seizures on animals that have been trained in a shuttle box to avoid a shock following the sound of a buzzer. Ordinarily, a well-trained cat appears quiet, vigilant and somewhat apprehensive during such testing. Following a hippocampal afterdischarge, it is surprising to see such an animal become preoccupied with grooming and then stretch out in a relaxed attitude on the floor of the shuttle box fanning the forepaws while going off to sleep.

It is significant that rats also show intensive self-grooming following hippocampal afterdischarges (17, 19). As in the cat, the grooming may last for several minutes, and here, too,

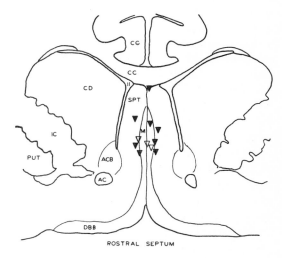

Fig. 4. Trembly has found that chemical stimulation in or near the medial septal nuclei of cats is followed by enhanced pleasure reactions (32). Triangles in above diagram indicate points of stimulation. Black triangle, positive response; open triangle, negative response. In a comparable number of stimulations at more rostral or caudal levels of the septum, enhanced pleasure reactions did not appear. AC, anterior commissure; ACB, nucleus accumbens; CD, caudate nucleus; DBB, diagonal band of Broca; M, medial septal nuclei; SPT, septum.

one may see a partially erected penis when grooming focuses on the genital region.

In a series of related, but as yet unpublished, studies, Drs. Walter Lockhart, Bruce Trembly, and Chul Kim have stimulated the septal nuclei and cingulate gyrus. The medial septal nuclei are a source of afferents to the hippocampus. Trembly observed enhanced pleasure reactions in cats following eight of eleven cholinergic stimulations in or near these nuclei (32). Such responses were not seen following an equal number of stimulations elsewhere in the septal region. Figure 4 shows the localization of the positive points of stimulation. Kim has observed pleasure and grooming reactions following afterdischarges induced by electrical stimulation of the septum and in one instance noted a spontaneous penile erection. He has also seen spontaneous erections following electrical or chemical stimulation of the anterior supracallosal cingulate gyrus. Spontaneous or easily induced erections have been observed in a few instances by Lockhart during seizure activity induced by application of cholinergic drugs to the cortex just above the posterior cingulate gyrus (EEG illustration in Ref. 15).

This last observation calls to mind Erickson's case of hypersexuality in a 55-year-old woman who had a tumor in the paracentral lobule which lies just above the cingulate gyrus (3). There are other relevant observations. In 1939 Harterius reported that electrical stimulation in the region of the septum induced ovulation in rabbits (6). In 1909 Von Bechterew stated that his collaborator, Pussep, elicited penile erection in the dog upon stimulation in the region of the anterior thalamus (33). These stimulations might have involved the anterior thalamic nuclei which are closely related to the cingulate gyrus. In an analysis of the extensive material of the Hess collection, Hess and Meyer have recently reported that the points of stimulation which most com-

monly led to grooming (Fellreinigung) were in the septal region (8). Other positive points were in the cingulate gyrus. The hippocampus was not explored.

Changes of an opposite nature that are seen following variously placed lesions in the structures under consideration would appear to offer further correlations. For example, following bilateral ablations of the anterior cingulate gyrus and *probably part of the underlying bundle of the cingulum*, Ward noted that monkeys showed "a loss of mimetic activity, grooming and signs of affection" (34). In 1936 Fulton and Ingraham reported that interruption of pathways in the region of the septum resulted in angry behavior (4), a change, it should be emphasized, that contrasts with the effects of frontotemporal lesions.

From the foregoing observations it might be inferred that a portion of the limbic system involving related parts of the septum, hippocampus, and cingulate gyrus is concerned with expressive and feeling states that are conductive to sociability and other preliminaries of copulation and reproduction. In other words, this portion of the limbic system, in contrast to the frontotemporal region, appears to bear on activities that are directed for the purpose of preserving the species rather than the self.

comment

The pleasure, grooming, and sexual manifestations that have been described raise a number of provocative questions about cerebral organization and behavior: How do they possibly relate to the recent striking observations of Olds and Milner, who found that rats with electrodes implanted in the septum and other limbic structures would repeatedly press a bar to obtain electrical stimulation of the brain (22)?[3] How are they to be regarded in the light of the relief of tension, sometimes compared to the feeling state after orgasm, that some patients experience following psychomotor seizures? How are they to be considered with respect to the localization of morbid function in certain forms of psychotic behavior? What possible relevance do they have to the beneficial effects of electroshock treatment in which, as noted by Jung (9) and recently emphasized by Liberson and Cadilhac (12), the hippocampus is especially prone to seizure discharge?

Here it will be enough to deal with the first question and to consider it in the light of what has already been said about the possibility of reciprocal innervation with respect to emotional feeling states. The recognized emotions can be classified from the standpoint of self-preservation and the preservation of the species. Emotional feelings that are informative in regard to threats to self-preservation or to the preservation of the species, or to the eradication of these threats, are characteristically "unpleasant" in nature. In this category are fear, anger, and sorrow. On the other side are pleasurable feelings that are informative of the removal of threats, the active gratification of needs, and the temporary achievement of a state of internal and/or external homeostasis. The emotions of joy and love come conspicuously to mind.

In psychoanalytic theory the pleasure principle is *in part* the principle that pleasure results from the *reduction of instinctual tension* (7). But if, as already suggested, reciprocal innervation applies to feeling states, it would make it possible to look upon pleasure

in a less negative sense. In other words, pleasure might be thought to have its own specific machinery which ordinarily does not go into play until there is inhibition of mechanisms responsible for the subjective and objective manifestations related to threats to self-preservation and preservation of the species. This, incidentally, suggests how vicarious forms of oral and sexual activities would tend to check "instinctual tensions" and to give release to pleasurable feelings. It also makes it possible to visualize how under some situations the mechanisms for pleasure and displeasure might be brought into play simultaneously, seeming to allow, as it were, joy through suffering or providing the functional substrate for the psychological states of masochism and sadism.

In the experiments of Olds and Milner, it is possible that by self-stimulation of the brain the animal is taking advantage of reciprocal innervation within the limbic system whereby so-called instinctual tensions associated with self-preservation and preservation of the species are inhibited and replaced by pleasurable feelings of gratification of oral or sexual appetite. Or again, from what has been said about the organization of the frontotemporal region, it is easy to imagine how the interweaving of neural structures responsible for opposed effects would make it possible for the stimulating electrodes to activate simultaneously mechanisms responsible for pleasure and displeasure. This would amount to an experimental approximation of situations—some of which were mentioned in the previous paragraph—that are commonly referred to as perversities of Nature.

The nature of the mechanisms of the limbic system that have been dealt with in this paper has been conducive to focusing attention on the preservation and procreation of the animal being. If one were to proceed to a higher level

[3] These findings have since been extended and essentially confirmed by J. V. Brady and J. C. Lilly, using cats and monkeys. The results of this work will be found in a forthcoming publication of the Henry Ford Symposium on the Reticular Formation, Boston, Little, Brown and Co.

and to speak of the preservation and procreation of ideas, it would be necessary to consider neocortical systems.

summary

The greater part of the phylogenetically old cortex is contained in the great limbic lobe of Broca. This lobe is found as a common denominator in the brains of all mammals. Together with its subcortical cell stations it comprises a functionally integrated system, which, in keeping with Broca's terminology, may be referred to as the *limbic system*. Evidence is cited which indicates that the frontotemporal portion of the limbic system is largely concerned with mechanisms that are involved in obtaining and assimilating food and are thereby essential to *self-preservation*. Attention is then turned to recent findings that are beginning to suggest that another portion of the limbic system, involving parts of the septum, hippocampus and cingulate gyrus, is concerned with expressive and feeling states that are conducive to the *preservation of the species*. Some of the implications of these new findings in regard to a number of provocative neurological questions are discussed.

references

1. Broca, P. Anatomie comparée des circonvolutions cérébrales. Le grand lobe limbique et la scissure limbique dans la serie des mammifères. Rev. anthrop., 1: 385–498. 1878.

2. Cadilhac, J. *Hippocampe et épilepsie.* A propos d'une série d'expériences sur le cobaye et le chat et de l'exploration électrique de la corne d'Ammon chez l'homme. Paul Déhan, Montpellier, 1955.

3. Erickson, T. C. Erotomania (nymphomania) as an expression of cortical epileptiform discharge. Arch. Neurol. Psychiat., 53: 226–231, 1945.

4. Fulton, J. F. and Ingraham, F. D. Emotional disturbances following experimental lesions of the base of the brain (prechiasmal). Am. J. Physiol., 90: 353, 1929.

5. Gastaut, H. Correlations entre le système nerveux végétatif et le système de la vie de relation dans le rhinencéphale. J. Physiol. Path. gén. 44: 431–470, 1952.

6. Harterius, H. O. Studies on a neurohypophysical mechanism influencing gonadotropic activity. Cold Spr. Harb. Symp. quant. Biol., 5: 280–288, 1937.

7. Hendrick, I. *Facts and Theories of Psychoanalysis.* Alfred A. Knopf, New York. 1939.

8. Hess, W. R. and Meyer, A. E. Triebafte Fellreinigung der Katze als Symptom diencephaler Reizung. Helv. Physiol. Acta., 14: 397–410, 1956.

9. Jung, R. Hirnelektrische Untersuchungen über den Elektrokrampf: die Erregungsabläufe in corticalen und subcorticalen Hirnregionen bei Katze und Hund. Arch. f. Psychiat. und Ztschr. f. Neurol., 183: 206–244, 1949.

10. Kaada, B. R. Somato-motor, autonomic and electrocorticographic responses to electrical stimulation of 'rhinencephalic' and other structures in primates, cat and dog. Acta physiol. scand., 24: 1951 (Suppl. 83).

11. Klüver, H. and Bucy, P. C. Preliminary analysis of functions of the temporal lobes in monkeys. Arch. Neurol. Psychiat., 42: 979–1000, 1939.

12. Liberson, W. T. and Cadilhac, J. G. Electroshock and rhinencephalic seizure states. Confin. neurol., Basel. 13: 278–286, 1953.

13. MacLean, P. D. Psychosomatic disease and the "visceral brain." Recent developments bearing on the Papez theory of

emotion. Psychosom. Med., **11**: 338–353, 1949.

14. MacLean, P. D. Some psychiatric implications of physiological studies on frontotemporal portion of limbic system (visceral brain). Neurosurg., **11**: 29–44, 1954.

15. MacLean, P. D. The limbic system and its hippocampal formation. Studies in animals and their possible application to man. J. Neurosurg., **11**: 29–44, 1954.

16. MacLean, P. D. Studies on limbic system ("visceral brain") and their bearing on psychosomatic problems. Wittkower, E., and Cleghorn, R. (Eds): *Recent Developments in Psychosomatic Medicine.* Pitman, London, 1954.

17. MacLean, P. D. The limbic system ("visceral brain") in relation to central gray and reticulum of the brain stem. Evidence of interdependence in emotional processes. Psychosom. Med., **17**: 355–366, 1955.

18. MacLean, P. D. Chemical and electrical stimulation of hippocampus in unrestrained animals. Part I. Methods and EEG findings. Arch. Neurol. Psychiat., **78**: 113–127, 1957.

19. MacLean, P. D. Chemical and electrical stimulation of hippocampus in unrestrained animals. Part II. Behavioral findings. Arch. Neurol. Psychiat., **78**: 128–142, 1957.

20. MacLean, P. D. and Delgado, J. M. R. Electrical and chemical stimulation of frontotemporal portion of limbic system in the waking animal. Electroenceph. Clin. Neurophysiol. **5**: 91–100, 1953.

21. MacLean, P. D. and Pribram, K. H. Neuronographic analysis of medial and basal cerebral cortex. I. Cat. J. Neurophysiol., **16**: 312–323, 1953.

22. Olds, J. and Milner, P. Positive reinforcement produced by electrical stimulation of septal areas and other regions of the rat brain. J. comp. physiol. Psychol., **47**: 419–427, 1954.

23. Nauta, W. J. H. An experimental study of the fornix in the rat. J. comp. Neurol., **104**: 247–270. 1956.

24. Nauta, W. J. H. and Kuypers, H. G. J. M. Some ascending pathways in the brain stem reticular formation of the cat. International Symposium on the Reticular Formation (Henry Ford Foundation), 1958. In press.

25. Papez, J. W. A proposed mechanism of emotion. Arch. Neurol. Psychiat., **38**: 725–743, 1937.

26. Penfield, W. and Jasper, H. *Epilepsy and Functional Anatomy of the Human Brain.* Little, Brown and Co., Boston, 1954.

27. Pribram, K. H. and MacLean, P. D. Neuronographic analysis of medial and basal cerebral cortex. II. Monkey. J. Neurophysiol., **16**: 324–340, 1953.

28. Pribram, K. H. and Bagshaw, M. Further analysis of the temporal lobe syndrome utilizing frontotemporal ablations. J. comp. Neurol., **99**: 347–375, 1953.

29. Ramón y Cajal, S. *Studies on the cerebral cortex [Limbic Structures].* Tr. by Lisbeth Kraft. Lloyd-Luke, Ltd., London, 1955.

30. Schreiner, L. and Kling, A. Behavioral changes following rhinencephalic injury in cat. J. Neurophysiol., **16**: 643–659, 1953.

31. Smith, G. E. Notes upon the natural subdivision of the cerebral hemisphere. J. Anat. Physiol., **35**: 431–454, 1901.

32. Trembly, B. A study of the functions of the septal nuclei. A thesis submitted to the faculty of the Yale University School of Medicine in candidacy for the degree of Doctor of Medicine, 1956, 127 pp.

33. Von Bechterew, W. *Die functionen der nervencentra.* Jena, 1909, vol. 2.

34. Ward, A. A., Jr. The cingular gyrus: Area 24. J. Neurophysiol., **11**: 13–23, 1948.

vision and hearing

In 1878 Ewald Hering formulated an alternative to the Young-Helmholtz trichromatic theory. Hering postulated three chemical substances in the retina that respond to three pairs of colors (white-black, yellow-blue, and red-green). In recent years it appeared that the Young-Helmholtz view had prevailed over Hering's; yet the trichromatic theory could not explain all the known facts of color vision. In 1957 Leo Hurvich and Dorothea Jameson revived and reworked Hering's theory. Their view is presented in the first reading in this section (Reading 4) and is called an "opponent-process theory of color vision." This theory assumes that three color receptors (cones) lead to two pairs of neural responses in the second- or third-order neurons in the retina. The assumption of only three types of cones is an attempt to compromise with the trichromatic theory. Hurvich and Jameson present the opponent-colors theory as a working hypothesis that explains both normal color vision and color-blindness better than does the trichromatic hypothesis. They also show that their theory is compatible with the latest neurophysiological findings.

In keeping with the Hurvich and Jameson hypothesis, work with microelectrodes placed in the retinal nerve fibers demonstrates red-green and yellow-blue responses. In addition, a luminosity response has been found, also in keeping with the opponent-colors hypothesis. In the second reading in this section (Reading 5), Tsuneo Tomita presents evidence that these three responses occur in all vertebrate eyes. His article gives adequate review of the microelectrode research that preceded his experiment. (It is important to note that techniques developed in one area of research can be utilized in another area. Research workers in physiological psychology cannot pursue a narrow course of research successfully without keeping in touch with advancements in the whole field.)

Next to vision, the sense of hearing has been of the greatest interest to psychologists. For several decades, important contributions to the physiological psychology of audition have been made by William D. Neff. In the first reading on hearing in this chapter (Reading 6), Neff warns that only tentative inferences about behavior can be made from purely physiological studies of limited areas of the nervous system: "Sooner or later it is necessary to study behavior itself." His article on auditory discriminatory behavior is an excellent example of a complete series of experiments in physiological psychology with changes in behavior used as the dependent variable. In his experiments, Neff discovered that no subarea of the auditory cortex is critical for any discriminatory capacity tested in the cat. However, he did find that unilateral lesions in the auditory cortex and bilateral lesions in the inferior colliculus produce a disturbance of the cat's ability to localize sound in space.

Another important area of auditory research concerns electrode implantation in the cochlear nucleus of the auditory nerve. In the final article in this chapter (Reading 7), Raúl Hernández-Peón and his collaborators demonstrate that when cats give attention to a visual object of interest (such as a mouse) they do not give as marked an electrical response in the cochlear nucleus as they give when not paying attention to such an object. Further research is needed, however, to verify this interesting phenomenon. These authors also point out that the cat's ability to inhibit responses to an auditory stimulus is selective. Such selectivity helps explain an animal's habituation to a continued, persistent sound or tone. (In the reading by H. W. Magoun on non-specific brain mechanisms in Chapter 5, reference is made to this finding by Hernández-Peón et al.)

Although the senses of vision and hearing have been studied longer and more intensively than the other senses, complete theories of their functioning are still unavailable. The articles in this chapter show the range and depth of effort necessary to fit known facts into a theoretical framework. History is utilized (Hurvich and Jameson) as well as intricate techniques (Tomita and Hernández-Peón et al.) and an understanding of over-all behavior (Neff).

4   an opponent-process theory of color vision *

Leo M. Hurvich and Dorothea Jameson

1. Is the fact that the Young-Helmholtz theory of color vision is derived from the physics of color mixing pertinent to the difficulties it has explaining many of the phenomena of color vision?

* L. M. Hurvich and D. Jameson, "An Opponent-Process Theory of Color Vision," *Psychol. Rev.*, 64 (1957), 384–404. Reprinted with permission.

2. Why was the Hering theory of color vision considered completely outmoded until very recently?

3. What is the basic "opponent-colors mechanism"? How does it function?

4. What photochemical postulates are necessary in an opponent-process theory of color vision?

5. Which visual phenomena are explained better by a Hering-type theory and which by a Young-Helmholtz type?

The two major theoretical accounts of color vision are those classified as the Young-Helmholtz and the Hering types of theories. For many years the former has been judged by most workers in the field to provide the simplest explanation of the way in which light stimuli give rise to color sensations. The advantages that appear to favor the Young-Helmholtz three-component hypothesis are two: it is parsimonious, and its postulates are easily quantifiable and hence subject to precise experimental test. In its parsimonious and easily quantifiable form, the theory is simple: in addition to the rods which subserve twilight vision, the eye contains three kinds of cone photoreceptors; each type of cone contains a differently selective photochemical substance; each is associated with its own specific nerve fiber; and each cone-photochemical-nerve fiber system is correlated with one of the three specific "fundamental" color sensations, namely, red, green, and blue (or violet). All sensations are considered as compounded of varying amounts of these three excitatory systems, with white arising from equal and simultaneous excitation of all three, and yellow from equal red and green excitations.

The Young-Helmholtz three-cone, three-nerve, three-sensation theory derives directly from the basic fact of color mixture, namely, that all visible hues can be matched by the mixture, in proper proportions, of only three physical light stimuli. Based squarely on this fact, the theory is readily quantified in terms of the three measurable variables of color mixture experiments. But the three measured variables, it must be emphasized, are the three physical light stimuli used in the color mixture experiments; they are not the postulated three "fundamental" color sensations, for with each different stimulus triad used for color matching a different and equally valid triad of color mixture functions is obtained. Consequently, throughout some hundred years since the original formulation of the idea, a continued series of attempts has been made to find the proper transformation of the three measured color-mixture curves that will bridge the gap and yield the unique spectral distribution curves of the desired physiological correlates of the three postulated "fundamental" color sensations. An infinity of such transformations is available for trial, and almost every serious adherent of the theory has proposed at least one new set of "fundamental sensation curves" (48, pp. 368–372). The search, however, continues, because serious defects have been found in every proposal made thus far. When the explanatory or predictive power of the theory in any given quantified form is tested it cannot handle more than a limited number of facts satisfactorily (11, p. 805).

Moreover, some facts of color experience seem unassimilable into the framework of the simple Young-Helmholtz theory with its three independent, fundamental, process-sensation systems. How can this system of three independent processes be made to account, for example, for the apparent linkages that seem to occur between specific pairs of colors as either the stimulus conditions or the conditions of the human observer are varied? Why should the red and green hues in the spectrum predominate at low stimulus levels, and the yellow and blue hue components increase concomitantly as the spectrum is increased in luminance (43)? Why, as stimulus size is greatly decreased, should discrimination between yellow and blue hues become progressively worse than that between red and green (4, 10)? Why should the hues drop out in pairs in instances of congenital color defect, or when the visual system is impaired by disease (29, 31)? On the other hand, since the sensation of white is granted no special physiological process in this parsimonious theory, but occurs as the fusion product of three equally large fundamental hue sensations, how account for the large degree of independence of white and chromatic qualities when the adaptation of the visual system is varied (37, 41)?

As more and more *ad hoc* hypotheses are added to the original Young-Helmholtz formulation in order to answer these and other problems forced by the increasing accumulation of experimental data, we naturally find the formulation becoming less and less precise and quantifiable, and obviously less parsimonious. We also find, however, that exactly those phenomena that require modification and extension of the simple "three-color theory" remind us more and more of its chief theoretical rival, the Hering theory of three paired, opponent color processes.

In view of this situation, it seems highly desirable that we take a close second look at Hering's alternative approach to an understanding of color phenomena. The vast accumulation of psychophysical data for which any adequate theoretical proposal must account requires that the basic postulates of the theory, as outlined qualitatively by Hering (13, 14), be restated in quantitative terms for such a critical scrutiny to be most meaningful. This paper will review our attempt to provide such a quantitative restatement, and will summarize briefly some of the critical comparisons between the theoretical deductions and relevant psychophysical data. (Detailed quantitative accounts are given in 21, 22, 23, 25, 26, 27.)

basic schema for the hering theory

the three variables

The Hering theory is like the Young-Helmholtz theory in that it, too, postulates three independent variables as the basis for color vision, but the Hering variables are three pairs of visual processes directly associated with three pairs of unique sensory qualities. The two members of each pair are opponent, both in terms of the opposite nature of the assumed physiological processes and in terms of the mutually exclusive sensory qualities. These paired and opponent visual qualities are yellow-blue, red-green, and white-black.

The basic schema for the opponent-colors mechanism is shown diagrammatically in Fig. 1. The three paired opponent response systems are labeled *y-b*, *r-g*, and *w-bk*. The

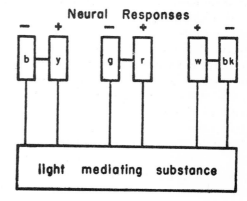

Fig. 1. Basic schema for Hering opponent-colors mechanism.

convention of positive and negative signs is used to indicate that each neural system is capable of two modes of response that are physiologically opponent in nature, and that the paired sensory qualities correlated with these opposed modes of response are also mutually opponent or exclusive. That is, we may experience red-blues or green-blues but never yellow-blues, and we see yellow-greens or blue-greens, but never red-greens, and so on. In the absence of any external visual stimulus, the state of the visual system is assumed to be a condition of active equilibrium, and this equilibrium condition is associated with the neutral, homogeneous "gray" sensation perceived after a long stay in complete darkness. This sensation is quite different from the black experience of the white-black opponent pair. Blackness arises neither by direct light stimulation nor in the simple absence of light, but rather by way of either simultaneous or successive contrast during, or following, light stimulation of some part of the retina.

properties of paired systems

The three pairs of visual response processes are independent of each other; that is, they have different response thresholds, they follow different laws of increase with increase in strength of stimulation, and probably have different time constants. The achromatic system is the most sensitive; that is, the amount of photochemical absorption necessary to excite the achromatic white response is less than the amount of photochemical activity required to stimulate either the y-b or r-g chromatic pairs. This characteristic accounts for the existence of the so-called achromatic interval, i.e., the fact that spectral lines appear achromatic at the absolute threshold for visibility (42, p. 167). Similarly, the red-green system has a lower threshold than the yellow-blue one.

The failure of the yellow-blue system to respond at near-threshold levels that are sufficient to activate the red-green system exhibits itself in the facts of so-called "small field dichromasy," in which the eye behaves, with respect to stimuli that are very small in area as well as of low intensity, in a manner similar to the congenital tritanope, i.e., a specific type of "color blind" individual for whom yellow and blue discriminations are impossible and the only hues seen are reds and greens (4, 49).

With increase in level of stimulation the different paired systems also show differences in rate of response increase, such that the achromatic response increase is probably the most rapid of the three, with the result that at very high intensities all spectral stimuli show a strong whitening, or desaturation, relative to their appearance at some intermediate luminance level (42, p. 168). Of the two chromatic pairs, the yellow-blue system, although exhibiting a higher threshold, shows a more rapid rate of increase in response with increase in luminance than does the red-green system. Thus, the mixed hues of the spectrum—the violets, blue-greens, yellow-greens, and the oranges—all vary systematically with increase in spectral luminance, and all show a tendency to be more blue or yellow, respectively, at high luminances, and more red or green at the lower luminance levels (the Bezold-Brücke hue shift phenomenon).

The opponent systems show a tendency toward restoring the balanced equilibrium condition associated with the neutral "gray" sensation. Thus excitation, say, of the r process in the r-g system results in a decrease with time in r responsiveness, and in an increase in the responsiveness of the opponent g process. If we think of the r process as perhaps associated with the building up of an electrical potential in the neural system, and of the g process as associated with the collapse of the potential during impulse firing, then it is easy to see that as the neural potential is increased to higher values there will be a tendency to resist further build up, and also an increased disposition of the tissue toward impulse firing in order to restore the potential to its normal equilibrium value. Although we are not at all ready to ascribe a specific neural correlate of this sort to the postulated opponent processes at this time, the neurophysiological parallels are useful for conceptualizing the opponent-process notion as a real biological phenomenon.

To return to our example, if the responsiveness of the opponent g process tends to increase as r excitation is continued, then when the r stimulus is removed we can expect g activity to be released, strongly at first, then more slowly, and ultimately fading out as equilibrium is again approached. The sensory correlate of this reversal of opponent activities with removal of stimulation is, of course, the familiar phenomenon of the complementary after-image. If the stimulus (of constant magnitude) is not removed but continues to act for a considerable length of time, then the r process, whose responsiveness is being continuously decreased, will eventually cease to respond further, and a new equilibrium state will be reached. The disappearance of a sensory response with continued constant stimulation can be observed either by the *Ganzfeld* technique, in which the whole retina is uniformly illuminated by diffuse light (18), or by the "painted image" technique, in which optical means are used to fix a well-defined image on the retina in such a way that its retinal position remains constant and independent of eye movements (39). By either method the eventual result of continued steady stimulation is a disappearance of the visual experience: the light seems to have gone out in the *Ganzfeld* situation, or, in the fixed-image situation, the perceived object simply fades out of view.

Not only are the visual responses modified by changes in time in the excitabilities of the opponent processes, but they are also importantly affected by spatial interaction among the various elements of the visual field. Within certain limits there is evidence of summation of similar kinds of activity in adjacent elements, as in threshold responses for small stimulus areas (5, pp. 846–852). But perhaps more important for the over-all functioning of the visual system are the antagonistic interactions, such that r activity in one area induces g activity in adjacent areas, and similarly for the yellow-blue and white-black paired response systems. These opponent spatial induction effects are evident in all the familiar color and brightness contrast phenomena (35, pp. 138–142). They are probably also primarily responsible for the great visual-image clarity that characterizes vision in spite of the fact that the optical system of the eye is obviously imperfect, and that consequently the light image formed on the retinal surface lacks sharply defined boundaries (17, pp. 151–159). The spatial interaction causing intensification of opponent qualities at adjacent surfaces would seem an ideal crispening device to sharpen up the initially blurred retinal image.

photochemical postulates

In addition to the various temporal and spatial induction effects, which are assumed to be based in the neural visual-response tissue, visual adaptation probably also involves changes in the photochemical activities that initiate the neural responses, since a certain amount of photochemical bleaching is expected to occur with continued exposure of the photosensitive materials to a retinal light stimulus. In order for the three paired opponent-response systems to be selectively stimulated, there must,

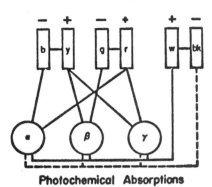

Neural Responses

Photochemical Absorptions

Neural Responses

Photochemical Absorptions

$$y-b = k_1(\beta+\gamma-2\alpha)$$

$$r-g = k_2(\alpha+\gamma-2\beta)$$

$$w-bk = k_3(\alpha+\gamma+\beta)-k_4(\alpha+\beta+\gamma)$$

Fig. 2. Schematic diagram showing relations between photosensitive materials α, β, and γ and neural opponent response processes y-b, r-g, and w-bk.

of course, be more than one substance available for photochemical mediation between the incident light and the neural excitation. Whatever the specific nature of the photosensitive materials, they must form a link in the system of three independent variables, and hence we

have postulated three independent photosensitive materials, which we may call α, β and γ.

Our schematic model now takes the form shown in Fig. 2A or 2B. The three independent photosensitive materials may be contained in discrete retinal units with complex interconnections to the neural response systems, as shown in Fig. 2A, or two or more of these materials may be combined in receptor units having simpler connections to the neural response systems, as diagrammed in Fig. 2B. There is no way of differentiating these models in terms of visual behavior; and however the three photochemicals may be segregated or combined in the retina, and whatever the number of different photoreceptor units, there remain only three independent photosensitive materials, and the theory remains a three-variable, opponent-colors schema.

quantification of opponents theory

Since our aim is to present this schema in quantitative terms, one of the first questions that has to be asked is this: Is it possible to obtain by psychophysical experiment direct measurements of the spectral distributions of the three basic response variables of the Hering theory?

measures of achromatic and chromatic responses

It can fairly be assumed that the achromatic, white response is closely connected with the distribution of the brightness quality throughout the visible spectrum (20). The induced rather than directly stimulated black component of the achromatic white-black response pair has this same distribution, but of opposite sign, since the strength of the black contrast response is directly related to the magnitude of either the surrounding or the preceding whiteness or brightness.

A method for determining the spectral distributions of the paired chromatic responses is implicit in the opponents theory itself. Since the two members of each hue pair are mutually opponent or exclusive, then a yellow response of given strength should be exactly canceled by a stimulus that, taken alone, elicits the same magnitude of blue response, and a similar relation should hold between red and green responses. Thus a null method, based on the antagonism of the two members of each hue pair, can be used to measure the spectral distributions of the chromatic responses. In brief, a wave length is first selected that evokes, say, a blue hue response. The observer then views, in turn, a series of spectral wave lengths that appear yellowish in hue (yellow-greens, yellow, and yellow-reds). To each of these yellow stimuli just enough of the previously selected blue stimulus is then added exactly to cancel the yellow hue without introducing any blueness. The observer simply reports when the test field appears neither yellow nor blue; the hue remainder that he sees may be green, neutral, or red, depending on the test wave length. Knowing the energies of the series of spectral yellow stimuli, and having determined experimentally the energy of the blue stimulus of fixed wave length that is required for the hue cancellation in each case, we can now plot the distribution of the relative magnitudes of yellow hue response evoked by the various test wave lengths. The procedure is simply reversed to obtain the distribution of the blue component of the yellow-blue pair; that is, varying amounts of a fixed wave length of yellow hue are used to cancel the blue hue quality of a series of "blue" test wave lengths. By using a red stimulus of fixed wave length and variable energy to cancel the greens, and a green stimulus to cancel the reds, the spectral distribution of the red-green pair of chromatic responses is similarly determined.

brightness, hue, and saturation

All wave lengths evoke some whiteness as well as hue; the whiteness and brightness of an equal energy spectrum is relatively small at the two spectral extremes and relatively high at the intermediate wave lengths.

The short wave lengths appear as red-blue hues (violets); there is a narrow band of pure or unique blue where the red-green function is equal to zero; then come the blue-greens, followed by a narrow band of unique green at the wave length where the yellow-blue function is equal to zero; this is followed by the yellow-greens, and then pure yellow occurs at the second intersection of the red-green function with the zero ordinate value; and finally the yellow-red hues appear in the long wave length region (19). A quantitative expression for hue, a "hue coefficient," can be obtained by taking the value of one of the chromatic responses, say, the yellow value at 550 mμ, relative to the total of all chromatic responses at that wave length, in this case, yellow plus green.

The saturation of the color depends on the relative amounts of chromatic and achromatic responses. At the two spectral extremes where the chromatic responses are large relative to the white response, the spectral saturation is high. Where the reverse is true, spectral saturation is low. This can be expressed quantitatively in the form of a "saturation coefficient." To use the same example, the total of the yellow-plus-green values relative to the white plus yellow plus green is relatively low at 550 mμ, and this wave length appears much less saturated than does, say, either 440 mμ or 670 mμ.

color mixture

Since color-mixture experiments simply involve matching the three perceived qualities evoked by one stimulus by the proper mixture of three other stimuli, it is possible to determine the color-mixture relations that are inherent in response curves for any three arbitrarily selected mixture primaries. That is, the red-green value, the yellow-blue value and the white value of the total visual response to any wave length of unit energy are matched by the totals of the three corresponding values for the three mixture primaries when the latter stimuli are combined in the proper ratios. On paper, the color equations for most spectral matches require the admission of negative values for one of the mixture primaries. In actual color-mixture experiments, these negative values are realized by removing one of the mixture primaries from the matching field and adding it to the test stimulus.

To calculate, for example, the amounts of energy required for a color match to a given wave length λ by the mixture of the spectral primaries 460 mμ, 530 mμ and 650 mμ, let $a =$ the energy at 460 mμ, $b =$ the energy at 530 mμ, and $c =$ the energy at 650 mμ. The three equations to be solved for these three unknowns a, b, and c are then:

$$a(r_{460}) + b(r_{530}) + c(r_{650}) = r\lambda$$
$$a(y_{460}) + b(y_{530}) + c(y_{650}) = y\lambda$$
$$a(w_{460}) + b(w_{530}) + c(w_{650}) = w\lambda$$

The values for r (or for $-r$ when the response function is negative, indicating that the hue is green rather than red), for y (or for $-y$ when the response is blue rather than yellow), and for w are then read from the response functions for unit energy for each wave length in

question. The values $r\lambda$, $y\lambda$ and $w\lambda$ represent the unit energy response values for any spectral wave length for which a color-mixture equation is to be calculated. Solving this set of three equations for the three unknowns a, b, and c, we then have a color-mixture equation of the form

$$a_{460} + b_{530} + c_{650} = 1\lambda$$

This equation, which is expressed in energy units, may be converted to photometric units in the usual way by multiplying each energy value by the relative luminosity (given by the achromatic response function) at the given wave length.

Since the relations between the measured response functions and the color-mixture data are, as we have just seen, known for two individual observers, it is now also possible (by assuming specific spectral loci for the unique hues) to reverse the procedure and derive opponent-response functions from the color-mixture data for Wright and Thomson,

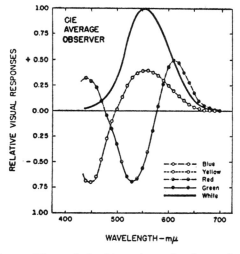

Fig. 3. Theoretical chromatic and achromatic response functions for equal energy spectrum for CIE average observer.

or for any other observer whose color-mixture data are available. Since it seems preferable to develop a general theoretical model on the basis of a representative average, rather than a small number of individual observers, we have used for the model chromatic and achromatic response functions derived from the average color-mixture data for the CIE international standard observer (30). These derived functions are shown in Fig. 3. (The details of the derivation are given in 22.) They are, of course, smoother and more regular than the individual, measured functions, but in other respects they are quite similar.

photochemical distributions

The specific set of a, β, and γ photosensitive absorption functions that have been assumed for the theoretical model are shown in Fig. 4. These curves have not been measured, and

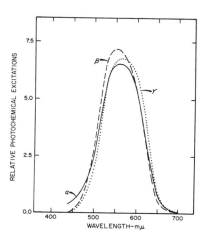

Fig. 4. Spectral distribution curves for assumed photosensitive materials.

they have the particular forms shown and the high degree of overlap exhibited because of the specific interrelations that we have postulated a priori between the photochemical events and the neural response activities of the visual opponent mechanisms. Once the photopigments actually present in the human retina have been identified by the biochemists, the visual theorist will have no need to make such a priori postulates, and the specific interrelations required between the identified photosensitive materials and the neural processes underlying the color responses can easily be deduced. As matters now stand, however, the functions shown in Fig. 4 meet the basic demands of the known facts, and any changes in these theoretical absorption functions that will no doubt be required by results of photochemical researches will not importantly affect any of the basic postulates of the theoretical model. The broadness and similarity of shape of all three selective functions that we have assumed are characteristic of all visual pigments so far identified in a variety of animal species (2).

These assumed photopigment distributions do not enter into the consideration of color phenomena, in normal vision, until we come to an examination of some of the phenomena of chromatic adaptation in which selective photochemical bleaching seems to act as one of the important determinants. The other determinants are, of course, the spatial and temporal induction effects in the neural opponent response processes that have been mentioned earlier.

dependence of hue and saturation on both wave length and luminance

What are the visual phenomena for which the model can account? As we have already indicated, the measured chromatic and achromatic response functions provide a direct and quantifiable description of the color sensations evoked by any stimulus of specified wave-length composition (23). The achromatic, white function is taken as a direct expression of spectral brightness. Spectral hue, which is determined by the chromatic responses evoked by each wave length, can also be expressed quantitatively as a coefficient value relating the magnitude of response of one chromatic system to the total of all chromatic responses at that wave length. It is clear, from the varying rate of change in the hue coefficient function from one region of the spectrum to the next, that an observer's ability to discriminate among neighboring wave lengths on the basis of hue changes alone will also differ for the different regions of the spectrum. This discriminative capacity is obviously also quantifiable in terms of the amount of wave-length change required to elicit a threshold change of fixed amount in the value of the hue coefficient. With change in the luminance at which the spectrum is presented, these coefficient functions will be altered, in the sense that the yellow-blue values will increase at the higher luminances, and will be diminished at the lower luminances. This is so because, in accordance with the different energy-vs.-response function postulated for the yellow-blue system as compared with the red-green one, as the excitation level is increased, the yellow and blue spectral responses will be uniformly magnified relative to the red and green ones at the higher levels, and uniformly diminished at the lower levels. Although the exact differential between the two paired systems is not known, under certain circumstances an over-all difference in response magnitudes of approximately 20 per cent seems to occur for a log unit change in luminance. Thus, at some wave length for which, say, the red and yellow responses are equal at a luminance of 10 mL, the yellow will be about 20% greater than the red at 100 mL, and about

20% less at a luminance of only 1 mL. If we assume this 20% differential between y-b and r-g response magnitudes per log unit of luminance change as a reasonable value, and compute the spectral hue coefficients for a range of approximately three log units of luminance variation, then we can specify the amount of hue shift associated with a change in intensity of any wave length. Conversely, we can also specify the wave length changes necessary to maintain a constant hue sensation (constant hue coefficient value) as the luminance is increased or decreased (38).

These hue phenomena do not involve the achromatic response pair at all, and depend only on the two paired chromatic response systems. Whatever the chromatic response to a given stimulus, the perceived color saturation clearly will also depend on the extent to which the white system is simultaneously responding. For any given amount of chromatic response, the color will obviously appear less saturated if there is a large magnitude of white response to dilute the color, and more saturated if the white component of the total response is relatively small. The perceived saturation of the spectrum is also expressed as a quantitative coefficient function. Here the value taken as the saturation coefficient is the ratio of the total chromatic to the chromatic-plus-white responses at each wave length. The relatively high values at the spectral extremes and the minimal value in the pure yellow region are perfectly consistent both with qualitative reports and with the experimental data on this problem (e.g., 28). Again, as in the hue functions, the rate of change of the saturation coefficient from one spectral region to the next is indicative of a varying discriminative capacity with respect to wave length; and, again, the form of the function as shown applies to a moderate luminance level and varies in a determinable manner with change in the level of excitation in accordance with the different energy-vs.-response rates of the three independent response systems.

In view of the variations in the hue and saturation functions with change in luminance, we should expect that discrimination functions that depend on changes in these two color attributes, such as discrimination of one wave length from the next in an equal brightness spectrum, would also reflect such a dependence on luminance (45). The higher values of difference threshold obtained at the low luminance level may be explained by a general reduction of discriminative capacity in dim light. The shift of the midspectral maximum toward lower wave lengths, and the relatively greater heightening of the minimum in the yellow region, cannot, however, be attributed to such a generalized reduction in discriminatory capacity. The selectively greater loss in yellow and blue responses at the low-luminance level that is one of the postulates of our model does, however, account for changes of exactly this sort in the form of the function. This is shown by the two theoretical functions computed from pairs of spectral hue and saturation functions that are associated with the two specified luminance levels. Since brightness is kept constant in such experiments, only the hue and saturation variables need be considered in our analysis of these functions (22).

chromatic adaptation

The phenomena that we have treated thus far all refer to the individual with normal color vision in a neutral state of adaptation. What of his color perception after the visual system has been exposed for some time to a strongly colored illuminant? For analytical purposes, the simplest situation of this sort is the one in which the eye has been exposed to a large surround field of given color and luminance, and the test stimuli are viewed at the same level of luminance as the surround. Under these circumstances, the three photochemical receptor substances will probably have undergone some selective bleaching, and because of the similar brightness of the surround and test fields, spatial induction effects in the neural response processes will probably be fairly constant. To simplify the treatment for these particular conditions, therefore, we may ignore the constant neural inductions and consider the photosensitive changes as exercising a controlling influence on the response systems.

We know that under these circumstances the color-mixture data do not change. That is, with uniform chromatic adaptation, any change in the perceived color of one side of a bipartite color-mixture field will also occur on the other side, and to exactly the same extent. Thus a color equation that has been made with the eye adapted to a neutral white light will also be a valid equation when the eye is adapted to a colored illuminant (15). These important constancies of color equations mean that whatever photochemical changes occur with adaptation must occur in a very specific way. That is, the spectral distribution functions representing the three selective photochemicals may be selectively multiplied or reduced by a constant factor, but no one of them can change its form (44, pp. 211–212). In other words, any single substance cannot lose a greater percentage of its absorption at one wave length than it loses at another wave length. Thus, exposure to a colored light can cause any one of the postulated photochemical functions shown in Fig. 4 to be multiplied or divided by a constant amount, but this is the only alteration in the photosensitive functions that is consistent with the fact that color equations are invariant with chromatic adaptation.

The extent to which the three substances are selectively attenuated as a result of exposure to colored light is clearly controlled by the light stimulus itself. That substance which initially absorbs most of the adapting light will suffer the greatest relative bleaching, and the substance which absorbs relatively little of the adapting light will be relatively little affected by it. Thus, by determining their relative absorptions of the adapting light, we can compute the relative changes in the heights of the photosensitive distribution functions for the three photopigments that we have postulated. Since the excitations of the opponent response systems depend on these photochemical light absorptions (see Fig. 2), we can now also determine the forms and magnitudes of the chromatic and achromatic response functions for the new condition of adaptation. In spite of the close overlap of the photosensitive functions that we have postulated, the "adapted" chromatic response functions determined in this way change in striking fashion relative to the functions for the neutral adaptation condition. The achromatic function changes too, but relatively very little. These theoretically computed adaptation changes are consistent with the kinds of change known to occur in situations of this sort. If the eye that has been adapted to white light is exposed for some time to a saturated red equal in brightness to the white, the normally red end of the spectrum does not become excessively dark, but the amount of redness seen is strongly reduced, and the greens become greatly supersaturated (3, pp. 133–137). Also, the wave length that formerly appeared pure yellow is now strongly greenish, and this is also true for the wave length that formerly appeared pure blue. These changes can be determined from the functions shown in Fig. 5 that have been computed for a given red adaptation, in comparison with

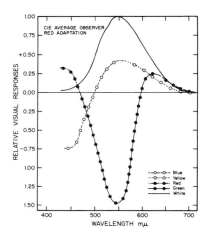

Fig. 5. Chromatic and achromatic visual response functions for red adaptation as predicted by theory.

the functions for the neutral state that were given in Fig. 3.

From this new set of "adapted" opponent response functions the hue and saturation coefficients and the discrimination data for this new state can also now be determined (26).

These "adapted" response functions are specified, as we said above, for a circumscribed set of conditions for which the photochemical adaptation changes could be taken as primary. As soon as the relative luminance conditions are altered, however, then the neural inductions enter importantly into the complex picture. For example, if a test stimulus seen within a strongly colored (say, red) surround looks neutral when its luminance is the same as that of the surround, then it will probably appear somewhat reddish at a higher luminance, and the complementary green at a lower luminance (12). (The test stimulus is assumed also to be of predominantly long wave-length composition.) In terms of opponent inductions this phenomenon is readily understood. If the red process excited by the red surround induces an opponent green process in the test area, then at an intermediate luminance this green induction is just strong enough to cancel the red-process activity aroused by the test stimulus itself. When the test stimulus is made brighter and the red response to it increases, the unchanged green induction from the surround becomes inadequate to cancel completely the increased red response to the stronger test stimulus, and the red test hue is now seen. At a much lower luminance of test stimulus, the red process is activated to a much lesser extent, and the green induction from the surround, which is still unchanged in strength, is now sufficient to impart a green hue to the perceived test area. These phenomena are not only consistent with the opponent induction postulate, but they also make it clear why attempts to treat the problem of chromatic adaptation exclusively as a matter of photochemical bleaching are foredoomed to failure (e.g., 1, 33).

color anomalies and color blindness

When we come to consider individuals who do not have normal color vision we find that their color vision can depart from the normal in two general ways. Their color perceptions may be distorted relative to the normal, or they may exhibit specific color weaknesses or losses. Also, they may show both types of these deviant characteristics at the same time. By distorted color perceptions we mean, for example, the perceptions of the particular type of anomalous individual who has the following characteristics: he sees a distinct orange in the spectral region described normally as pure yellow or nearly so; he needs three stimuli for color mixture; he makes color matches with high precision but uses quite different proportions of the mixture stimuli than does the normal observer. An individual of this type does not seem to have lost any of the efficiency of his neural visual response processes, and it seems reasonable to assume that his color distortions have their basis in the photochemical complex responsible for selective light absorption.

The particular assumptions that we have made concerning the kinds of deviation that the photosensitive materials may exhibit stem from a generalization made by Dartnall (2), on the basis of his researches concerned with the identification of visual photopigments in a variety of lower organisms. Dartnall has found that when the absorption curves of the various visual pigments are plotted as a function of the vibration frequency of the incident light (the reciprocal of the more usual wave-length specification), all the absorption curves have very nearly the same shape, and they can be made to coincide simply by shifting the curves so that they all reach an absorption maximum at the same frequency. In other words, a single template representing amount of absorption as ordinate, against frequency of radiant energy as abscissa, can be used to fit the absorption function of any visual pigment, whatever the locus of its absorption maximum. It seems reasonable to expect that this same generalization will apply to the photosensitive distributions of anomalous individuals with respect to the population of observers with normal color responses. We have consequently assumed that, in congenital abnormalities of the visual system, the normal photopigments can undergo changes that result in a uniform shift of the entire set of photosensitive distribution functions as a group along the frequency scale. These shifts are assumed to occur in either of two directions: toward higher frequencies (shorter wave lengths) resulting in the type of anomalous color vision identified as *protanomaly*, or toward lower frequencies (longer wave lengths) relative to the normal absorption loci, resulting in the

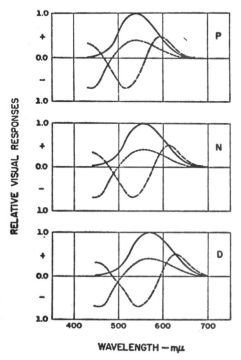

Fig. 6. Theoretical chromatic and achromatic response functions for equal energy spectrum. For observers with protanomalous, normal, and deuteranomalous photoreceptor systems and with normal strength visual response processes.

second major type of anomalous color vision known as *deuteranomaly*. The amount of these displacements may also vary in different degrees of congenital anomaly.

Since the absorption of light by the photosensitive materials provides the stimulus for the neural chromatic and achromatic response systems, the visual response functions thus controlled by the deviant photosensitive materials will necessarily be altered, too, and in a

systematic manner. Examples of theoretically derived anomalous response functions based on these assumptions are given in Fig. 6. The set of functions in the center block are those for the observer with normal photosensitive materials; those in the upper block are for a protanomalous type whose visual pigment absorptions are assumed to be shifted toward the shorter wave lengths by an amount equal to about 15 mμ from the normal peak of about 550 mμ. This type of individual will have a luminosity function (described by the achromatic, white response function) that peaks at a shorter wave length than the normal and will show considerable loss of luminosity at the red end of the spectrum (48, Ch. 25). The spectral hues will also be altered, with a distinctly reddish yellow occurring where the normal individual sees a unique or pure yellow, whereas the protanomalous observer's pure yellow occurs at a wave length described by the normal as quite greenish. In making color matches, such as a match between 589 mμ on one side of a bipartite field and a mixture of 530 mμ and 670 mμ on the other, this observer will require a much greater proportion of 670 mμ in the mixture than will the average observer with normal color vision (27, 46). This particular match, the Rayleigh equation, is the earliest and best-known diagnostic test for anomalous color vision. In this same test, the anomalous individual whose response functions are shown in the lower block in Fig. 6 will deviate from the normal in the opposite way; that is, he will require a much greater proportion of 530 mμ in the mixture for the Rayleigh equation (46). This type of anomalous individual (deuteranomalous) is assumed to have photopigment absorptions that are shifted toward the longer wave lengths, and he will see greenish-yellows where the normal sees yellow, yellows where the normal sees orange, etc. Since the neural response processes of both types of anomalies of this sort are assumed to be operating at the normal efficiency, these individuals will show high precision in making their distorted color matches, and their discriminatory capacities will also be good. As a matter of fact, anoma-

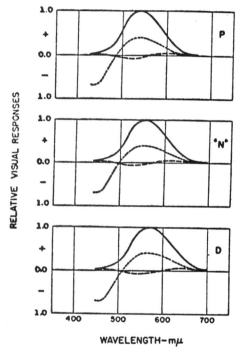

Fig. 7. Theoretical chromatic and achromatic response functions for equal energy spectrum. For observers with protanomalous, normal, and deuteranomalous photoreceptor systems and with impaired red-green response processes.

lous individuals of this sort have understandably high confidence in their own color capability, and they are extremely resistant toward accepting the results of diagnostic tests which indicate that their visual capacities are deviant from (with the implication of "inferior to") those of the normal population (36, pp. 235–238).

Not all anomalous individuals are as fortu-

nate as the types shown in Fig. 6, however. Many give evidence of real color weakness, in addition to distortions of the kinds already discussed (40). These color-weak individuals seem to have been deprived of some of the efficiency of the neural response processes, particularly of the red-green opponent pair, and their systems may be represented in terms of the theory by the kinds of response functions given as examples in Fig. 7. The visual pigments of these three types of individuals are taken to be the same as those shown in the preceding figure, respectively, but the red-green paired system is reduced to one-tenth of the normal strength. Such observers have real losses in color discrimination in addition to possible color distortions, and their color matches are imprecise as well as deviant. Individuals with congenitally abnormal color systems are frequently of this general type, and cases of acquired color blindness caused by degenerative disease invariably show this kind of color weakness at some stage in the development of the neural disorder (31).

When the weaknesses become extreme, whether in congenital or acquired disorders, the red-green system seems to be entirely lost to normal function, and a condition of dichromasy, or so-called "color blindness," results. That is, the visual system becomes a two-variable one, as shown in Fig. 8. Here the yellow-blue and the white-black neural systems remain intact and functioning, but there is no red-green response function. If the red-green loss occurs without changes in the visual pigments, the remaining yellow-blue and white-black response functions are like those of the normal individual; but, since there is no red-green system, the spectrum is divided into only two hue sections for these individuals. The short wave lengths which normally vary from violet through blue and blue-green to pure green all appear as blue, but of varying saturations, with a neutral region where the normal pure green occurs. Beyond this wave length the remainder of the spectrum appears yellow, in varying saturations, out to the extreme long-wave limit of visibility. The luminosity function is the same as for the observer with normal color vision. Individuals who fit this response pattern would be classi-

These two theoretically assumed kinds of deviation from the normal system—i.e., photo-pigment changes and neural losses or weak-nesses of the paired red-green response system—permit us to assemble a systematic picture of the many various manifestations of abnormal red-green vision that defy understanding in terms of any model of the visual system that

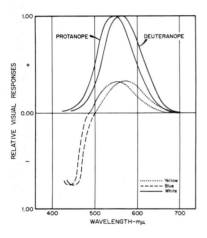

Fig. 8. Theoretical chromatic and achromatic response functions for equal energy spectrum. For observers with nonfunctioning red-green response processes.

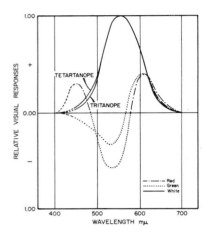

Fig. 9. Theoretical chromatic and achromatic response functions for equal energy spectrum. For observers with nonfunctioning yellow-blue response processes.

fied as *deuteranopes* (29). If the visual pig-ments are altered, so as to produce an absorp-tion shift toward the short wave lengths in addition to the complete red-green neural loss, then the spectrum is again divided into a short-wave blue and a long-wave yellow sec-tion, but the neutral region that divides the spectrum into the two major hues occurs at a shorter wave length than for the deuteran-opes. The luminosity function is also displaced in this type of dichromasy, as it is for the anomalous individuals with similar photopig-ment changes, and the type of "color-blind" vision associated with this pattern is called *protanopia* (29).

assumes a one-to-one correspondence between light absorption in the retinal receptors and the resulting color sensations (22, 27).

Defects or losses may also occur in the yellow-blue neural response system, although such defects seem to be much more rare than the red-green defects. Again, these yellow-blue neural losses may take place either with or without changes in the photosensitive ma-terials in the retina. Examples of the remaining red-green and white-black response functions in two types of yellow-blue blindness are given in Fig. 9. In each type of this disorder, the yellow-blue neural response function is missing, and the total gamut of colors for these individuals includes only neutral and reds and greens of various saturations. If there is no simultaneous photopigment disorder, there are two neutral points in the spectrum, one in the region where the normal sees a pure yellow, and another in the region where the normal sees a pure blue. Yellow-blue blindness of this sort is called *tetartanopia*, and only a few cases of it have been reported in the literature (e.g., 34, pp. 68–92). Slightly more common is the second type of yellow-blue blindness, known as *tritanopia* (49), in which not only the neural yellow-blue system is lost, but also the short-wave photopigment seems to be missing. Observers of this type have a neutral point in the normally yellow-green region of the spectrum, but there is no second neutral point, and the green hues extend into the short-wave region that appears violet to the person with normal color vision.

For all these types of deviant color vision, calculation from the theoretical spectral response functions of discrimination curves, color mixture equations, and other psychophysical relations are in good agreement with the experimental data that are available for the various kinds of defective color systems (22, 27).

opponents theory and neurophysiology

The conceptual model for the opponent-colors theory as originally presented by Hering drew its sharpest criticism on the grounds of being bad physiology. Some of this criticism was based on an erroneous interpretation of Hering's views, an interpretation that incorrectly assigned the opponent processes to the photochemical activities in the retinal cells. Hering's own concept of mutually opponent neural processes, each capable of being activated by external stimulation, was also, however, far ahead of the knowledge of neurophysiology at the time it was proposed (16). But this concept now turns out to be perfectly consistent with the picture of neural function that is only just recently beginning to build up from electrophysiological studies of the visual neural apparatus.

It has become clear that nerves do not simply respond or fail to respond when a stimulus is presented to the appropriate end-organ. Rather, they may respond according to any of a number of quite specific patterns. For example, a nerve fiber may (a) discharge at the onset of stimulation and subsequently gradually become quiet; (b) discharge at both onset and cessation of stimulation with a quiet period in between; or (c) cease any spontaneous activity when first stimulated and during continued stimulation, but respond with a burst of electrical impulses when the stimulus ceases to act (7). The on- and off-phases of discharge are mutually inhibitory processes, they are associated with slow electrical potentials of opposite sign, and they cancel each other when the experimental conditions are so manipulated as to cause both on- and off-discharges to impinge simultaneously on the same ganglion cell (6). In Granit's opinion (6), the evidence from electrophysiology provides a "belated vindication of Hering's view" that the visual system is characterized by mutually opponent neural processes.

The concept of mutual interaction among the various elements of the physiological field is also basic to the theory and is critical to an understanding of both areal effects and simultaneous contrast phenomena. Here again, we find the researches in electrophysiology indicating that individual nerve elements never act independently, and that visual function must be thought of in terms of the integrated action of all the units of the neural visual system (8). Hartline (9) has found that, even in the very simple Limulus eye, the discharge of impulses in any one optic nerve fiber depends not only upon the stimulus to the specific receptor unit from which that fiber arises but also upon the stimulation over the entire population of mutually interacting elements. Both excitatory and inhibitory interactions of the sort to be expected by theory have actually been demonstrated in the neural responses of the vertebrate visual system by Hartline (8), Kuffler (32), and Granit (6).

The way in which the postulated three independent systems of paired opponent processes (y-b, r-g, w-bk) are differentiated neurally is still a matter for conjecture. Hering thought it was a matter of process specificity, but was willing to use the concept of material, or structural, specificity, which he guessed would be more readily comprehended by most interested readers of his views at the time. Our own theoretical preference at this time is the conjecture that a particular color quality is more probably determined by a particular state of the nervous tissue than by activity of a particular structural element in the nervous network. Thus, we would be inclined to look for a difference between yellow-blue vs. red-green processes, rather than toward isolation of yellow-blue or red-green fibers or nerve cells.

summary

This paper has presented a summary of our progress to date in providing a quantitative formulation for the Hering opponent-colors theory, and in relating the postulated visual mechanism to specific problems of color sensation, color mixture and color discrimination; to the dependence of these functions on the physical variables of both stimulus wave length and energy level; to their further dependence on adapting and surround stimulation; and to the changes in these functions that occur in various kinds of abnormal color vision. It is our conclusion that the opponent-colors theory serves as a fruitful working hypothesis by bringing a systematic coherence to the mass of isolated color phenomena that have been reported and subjected to quantitative experiment throughout the years. The physiological concepts basic to the theory are also shown to be consistent with recent findings in neurophysiology.

references

1. Brewer, W. L. Fundamental response functions and binocular color matching. *J. Opt. Soc. Amer.*, 1954, **44**, 207–212.
2. Dartnall, H. J. A. The interpretation of spectral sensitivity curves. *Brit. med. Bull.*, 1953, **9**, 24–30.
3. Evans, R. M. *An introduction to color.* New York: Wiley, 1948.
4. Farnsworth, D. Tritanomalous vision as a threshold function. *Die Farbe*, 1955, **4**, 185–196.
5. Graham, C. H. Vision: III. Some neural correlations. In C. Murchison (Ed.), *A handbook of general experimental psychology.* Worcester: Clark Univer. Press, 1934, Pp. 829–879.
6. Granit, R. *Receptors and sensory perception.* New Haven: Yale Univer. Press, 1955.
7. Hartline, H. K. The response of single optic nerve fibers of the vertebrate eye to illumination of the retina. *Amer. J. Physiol.*, 1938, **121**, 400–415.
8. Hartline, H. K. The neural mechanisms of vision. *Harvey Lectures*, 1941–42, **37**, 39–68.
9. Hartline, H. K., Wagner, H. G., & Ratliff, F. Inhibition in the eye of limulus. *J. gen. Physiol.*, 1956, **39**, 651–673.
10. Hartridge, H. The polychromatic theory. *Documenta Ophthal.*, 1949, **3**, 166–193.

11. Hecht, S. Vision: II. The nature of the photoreceptor process. In C. Murchison (Ed.), *A handbook of general experimental psychology*. Worcester: Clark Univer. Press, 1934. Pp. 704–828.

12. Hedson, H. Fundamental problems in color vision. I. The principle governing changes in hue, saturation, and lightness of non-selective samples in chromatic illumination. *J. exp. Psychol.*, 1938, **23**, 439–476.

13. Hering, E. *Zur Lehre vom Lichtsinne.* Berlin, 1878.

14. Hering, E. Zur Erklärung der Farbenblindheit aus der Theorie der Gegenfarben. *Lotos, Jb. f. Naturwiss.*, 1880, **1**, 76–107.

15. Hering, E. Ueber Newton's Gesetz der Farbenmischung. *Lotos, Jb. f. Naturwiss.*, 1887, **7**, 177–268.

16. Hering, E. *Zur Theorie der Vorgänge in der lebendigen Substanz.* Prague: 1888. (English translation by F. Welby, in *Brain*, 1897, **20**, 232–258.)

17. Hering, E. *Grundzüge der Lehre vom Lichtsinn.* Berlin: Springer, 1920.

18. Hochberg, J. E., Triebel, W., & Seaman, G. Color adaptation under conditions of homogeneous visual stimulation (Ganzfeld). *J. exp. Psychol.*, 1951, **41**, 153–159.

19. Hurvich, L. M., & Jameson, Dorothea. The binocular fusion of yellow in relation to color theories. *Science*, 1951, **114**, 199–202.

20. Hurvich, L. M., & Jameson, Dorothea. Spectral sensitivity of the fovea. I. Neutral adaptation. *J. Opt. Soc. Amer.*, 1953, **43**, 485–494.

21. Hurvich, L. M., & Jameson, Dorothea. A quantitative theoretical account of color vision. *Trans. N.Y. Acad. Sci.*, 1955, **18**, 33–38.

22. Hurvich, L. M., & Jameson, Dorothea. Some quantitative aspects of an opponent-colors theory. II. Brightness, saturation, and hue in normal and dichromatic vision. *J. Opt. Soc. Amer.*, 1955, **45**, 602–616.

23. Hurvich, L. M., & Jameson, Dorothea. Some quantitative aspects of an opponent-colors theory. IV. A psychological color specification system. *J. Opt. Soc. Amer.*, 1956, **46**, 416–421.

24. Ishak, I. G. H. Determination of the tristimulus values of the spectrum for eight Egyptian observers and one British observer. *J. Opt. Soc. Amer.*, 1952, **42**, 844–849.

25. Jameson, Dorothea, & Hurvich, L. M. Some quantitative aspects of an opponent-colors theory. I. Chromatic responses and spectral saturation. *J. Opt. Soc. Amer.*, 1955, **45**, 546–552.

26. Jameson, Dorothea, & Hurvich, L. M. Some quantitative aspects of an opponent-colors theory. III. Changes in brightness, saturation, and hue with chromatic adaptation. *J. Opt. Soc. Amer.*, 1956, **46**, 405–415.

27. Jameson, Dorothea, & Hurvich, L. M. Theoretical analysis of anomalous color vision. *J. Opt. Soc. Amer.*, 1956, **46**, 1075–1089.

28. Jones, L. A., & Lowry, E. M. Retinal sensibility to saturation differences. *J. Opt. Soc. Amer.*, 1926, **13**, 25–34.

29. Judd, D. B. Current views on colour blindness. *Documenta Ophthal.*, 1949, **3**, 251–288.

30. Judd, D. B. Basic correlates of the visual stimulus. In S. S. Stevens (Ed.), *Handbook of experimental psychology*. New York: Wiley, 1951. Pp. 811–867.

31. Köllner, H. *Die Störungen des Farbensinnes.* Berlin: S. Karger, 1912.

32. Kuffler, S. W. Discharge patterns and functional organization of mammalian retina. *J. Neurophysiol.*, 1953, **16**, 37–68.

33. MacAdam, D. L. Chromatic adaptation. *J. Opt. Soc. Amer.*, 1956, **46**, 500–513.

34. Müller, G. E. *Darstellung und Erklärung der verschiedenen Typen der Farbenblindheit.* Göttingen: Vandenhoeck and Ruprecht, 1924.

35. Parsons, J. H. *An introduction to the*

study of colour vision. (2nd ed.) Cambridge: Cambridge Univer. Press, 1924.

36. Pickford, R. W. *Individual differences in colour vision.* London: Routledge and Kegan Paul, 1951.

37. Piéron, H. La dissociation de l'adaptation lumineuse et de l'adaptation chromatique et ses conséquences théoriques. *Année psychol.*, 1939, **40**, 1–14.

38. Purdy, D. M. The Bezold-Brücke phenomenon and contours for constant hue. *Amer. J. Psychol.*, 1937, **49**, 313–315.

39. Riggs, L. A., Ratliff, F., Cornsweet, Janet C., & Cornsweet, T. N. The disappearance of steadily fixated visual test objects. *J. Opt. Soc. Amer.*, 1953, **43**, 495–501.

40. Rosmanit, J. *Anleitung zur Feststellung der Farbentüchtigkeit.* Leipzig: Deuticke, 1914.

41. Troland, L. T. Apparent brightness: its conditions and properties. *Trans. Illum. Engr. Soc.*, 1916, **11**, 957–966.

42. Troland, L. T. *The principles of psychophysiology.* Vol. 2. *Sensation.* New York: D. Van Nostrand, 1930.

43. von Bezold, W. Ueber das Gesetz der Farbenmischung und die physiologischen Grundfarben. *Ann. Phys. u. Chem.*, 1873, **150**, 221–247.

44. von Kries, J. Die Gesichtsempfindungen. In W. Nagel (Ed.), *Handbuch der Physiologie des Menschen.* Brunswick: Vieweg, 1905. Pp. 109–282.

45. Weale, R. A. Hue-discrimination in paracentral parts of the human retina measured at different luminance levels. *J. Physiol.*, 1951, **113**, 115–122.

46. Willis, Marion P., & Farnsworth, D. Comparative evaluation of anomaloscopes. *Med. Res. Lab. Rep.* No. 190, 1952, **11**, No. 7, 1–89.

47. Wright, W. D., & Pitt, F. H. G. The colour-vision characteristics of two trichromats. *Proc. Phys. Soc.* (London), 1935, **47**, 205–217.

48. Wright, W. D. *Researches on normal and defective colour vision.* St. Louis: Mosby, 1947.

49. Wright, W. D. The characteristics of tritanopia. *J. Opt. Soc. Amer.*, 1952, **42**, 509–521.

5 electrical activity in the vertebrate retina *

Tsuneo Tomita

1. What is the difference between the ERG and the S potential?

2. In recording electrical activity of the retina, what differences in technique and finding are there for frog, fish, and turtle? Is the S potential found in all three?

3. What is the source of the S potential?

4. What are the different approaches to the recording of retinal potentials?

5. How is the frog retina different from most other vertebrate retinae?

We have learned a great deal about the initial active process in vision, absorption of light and breakdown of visual pigments. Also in electrophysiology, owing to the microdissection technique applied to cold-blooded vertebrate retinas by Hartline (14) and the microelectrode technique introduced in this field by Granit and Svaetichin (12), our knowledge concerning the relation between the photic stimulation as the input and the nervous activity as the encoded output of the retina has shown remarkable progress. A recent extension of the microelectrode technique by Mac-Nichol, Wolbarsht, and Wagner (20) in the goldfish retina is of particular interest because

* T. Tomita, "Electrical Activity in the Vertebrate Retina," *J. Opt. Soc. Amer.*, 53 (1963), 49–57. Reprinted with permission.

of observations concerning color-reception mechanisms.

Unfortunately, however, for the mechanisms which are intermediate between the initial photochemical processes and the encoded nervous activity, we must admit that our knowledge is far from satisfactory. Since the discovery nearly 100 years ago by Holmgren (1865) of electrical signs of activity on illumination of the eye, which are now known by the name of electroretinogram or ERG, it has been the goal of physiologists to explain this activity in terms of visual function. The ERG obviously consists of the sum of the activity of all of the cells which are closely packed together in the retina. Because of the complexity in structure of the retina, however, it has been difficult to analyze the ERG in terms of components that may easily be associated with special anatomical structures. While the analysis by Granit (9) of the ERG into three components, PI, PII, and PIII, is most generally accepted, attempts at localizing these three components in the retina have resulted in very diverse conclusions.

We have attempted since 1950 to solve this problem by means of recordings from penetrating microelectrodes within the frog's retina (35). The results of our experiments since then have been consistent in showing that the origin of most if not all of the fast components of the ERG, or PII and PIII, are not in the receptors themselves but proximal to them, probably in the bipolar cell layer (39, 43, 40, 15). Only the slow component, or PI, was localized more distally (35).

In the meantime, the intraretinal-microelectrode technique brought about Svaetichin's important discovery in the fish retina of a different type of response, now called the S potential. As I believe it is the general sentiment of investigators that the two potentials, the ERG and the S potential, will eventually provide the keys to the solution of intraretinal events, these two potentials are discussed as the topics in this paper. Before going into details, however, let us see for a moment what kinds of responses are obtained in the frog retina by means of very minute pipets with tip diameters of less than 0.1μ. An attempt at recording with such pipets was first made by Naka *et al.* (28), and this was followed by our work (41), in the hope that such minute pipets might be capable of recording intracellularly some of the ERG components.

The excised eye of the bullfrog, *Rana catesbeiana*, is cut along its equator and the vitreous humor is drained off by means of small pieces of Kleenex tissue arranged radially with one end in the vitreous humor a short distance across the cut edge of the eye, and the other end in contact with a piece of filter paper on which the eye is mounted. The eye together with the filter paper underneath is then mounted on a chlorided silver plate which serves as the indifferent electrode. Most experiments were carried out at room temperatures between $10°$ and $15°C$. These two precautions, draining off the vitreous humor and keeping the room temperature low, were found to be very useful for keeping the preparation in good condition.

When a pipet is inserted into the retina from its anterior surface, three types of impulse discharges—on, off and on/off—are obtained from the most superficial retinal layer. The spike height often exceeds 50 mV. A feature common to these responses, termed the Group-I responses for convenience's sake, is that they comprise impulse spikes accompanied by no discernible slow potential change. In addition, their receptive field is usually found at some distance peripheral to the site of recording, and antidromic impulses elicited by stimulation of the optic nerve invade the site of recording, indicating clearly that they are responses of single optic-nerve fibers. Wiesel (48) has earlier obtained similar recordings in the cat.

During further advancement of the pipet, spontaneous discharges are often observed which are probably due to injury of some small cells by the pipet. However, at a depth some 70 to 80 μ beyond the depth at which the Group-I responses are obtained, fairly stable responses are found intracellularly. They are characterized by impulse spikes superimposed on conspicuous slow potential changes resembling the ERG or some components of it. Recordings at this depth also show the usual three types of responses. In the on/off-type, the cell shows, when light is on, an initial hyperpolarization which is followed by depolarization with impulse spikes superimposed on it, and another depolarization, when light is off, with an off discharge. The initial hyperpolarization and the following two depolarizations at on and off resemble very much the a, b, and d wave of the ERG except that their amplitude is often more than 10 times larger than that in the ERG. (In spite of the resemblance of these potential changes to the three waves in the ERG, we will see later that it is unlikely that they contribute to the ERG.) In the off-type response, the cell is hyperpolarized during illumination and no impulse discharge occurs during that period; and, at the termination of light, depolarization occurs with impulse spikes superimposed on it. It is noteworthy that the hyperpolarization in the off-type response tends to start with a latency comparable to that of the a wave in the ERG and also of the a-wave-like hyperpolarization in the on/off-type response. In the on-type response, on the other hand, there is no discernible initial hyperpolarization. Depolarization starts with a latency comparable to that of the b wave in the ERG and of the b-wave-like depolarization in the on/off-type response. In

this respect, the on/off-type response appears to be the result of the combination of two processes—those of the off-type response and on-type response. These three types of responses that are characterized by slow potential changes with impulse spikes superimposed on their depolarization phases are termed the Group-II responses.

No impulse spikes are detectable beyond the layer at which the Group-II responses are found. Occasionally during further advancement of pipets, however, we have heard from the loudspeaker a buzzing noise in the dark which was disrupted during illumination. From a depth very close but slightly distal to the layer from which the buzzing noise arises, sustained negative potentials during illumination, termed by us the Group-III responses, are obtained. They are typical of the S potential first observed by Svaetichin (31) in the fish. The only differences are that the area effect is not so large as in the fish, and the range of depths within which the responses are found is somewhat narrower in the frog. The spectral-response curve of the frog's S potential, obtained by scanning with monochromatic light, was always of luminosity type, showing the peak around 570 mμ. Beyond this S-potential layer which is now known to be definitely proximal to the receptor layer, we have not yet succeeded in obtaining an intracellular response that could reasonably be attributed to receptor activity.

These were the observations on the frog, but by applying the same technique to the fish and turtle we obtained similar results, though the frequency with which these response groups were found was different according to the animal forms. In the carp, *Cyprinus carpio*, Group I and Group III were easily obtained, but with only occasional chances of obtaining Group II. In the turtle, *Geoclemys reevesii*, Group III or S potentials were easily found, but the chance of obtaining Group I and Group II was small. Incidentally, in the turtle both luminosity and chromaticity responses are found (Fig. 1), as in the fish, while in the frog only the luminosity type of response has been found so far.

We will now discuss more about the S potential and the ERG with reference from

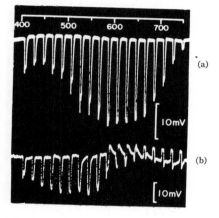

Fig. 1. A luminosity type (a) and a chromaticity type (b) of Group-III response or S potential (turtle).

time to time to the above observations with minute pipets.

S potential. As we have just seen, the S potential is found in all the cold-blooded vertebrates we studied. Since the same response was also observed in the cat (23, 13, 5), the S potential appears to be a phenomenon common to all the vertebrates. When this potential was first observed in the fish by Svaetichin (1953), it was believed to be the response of single cones and was termed the cone action potential. It is now agreed, however, that its origin is proximal to the receptors. Figure 2 illustrates the result of an experiment (37) in the fish, *Cyprinus auratus*, involving a coaxial microelectrode (43, 36, 38) with its inner pipet protruding a fixed distance of 50 μ beyond the tip of the outer pipet. Both

pipets with this fixed tip distance were inserted into the retina from its receptor side. The uppermost tracing in Fig. 2(a) gives a reference potential level obtained from the distal surface of the retina. Two lower tracings in the same record were obtained after

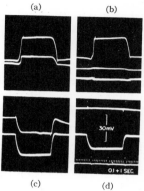

Fig. 2. Simultaneous depth recording of S potential (fish, *Cyprinus auralus*), from the inner and outer pipets of a coaxial microelectrode, with the tip distance kept fixed at 50μ and inserted from the receptor side. Readings of the micrometer gauge for the outer pipet: 140μ (a), 175μ (b), 210μ (c), 245μ (d). The inner pipet is always 50μ deeper. Tracings from the inner pipet carry pips at on and off of light to allow discrimination from tracings from the outer pipet which carries no pip. The top tracing in (a) is from the distal retinal surface to show a reference potential level (37).

the electrode was inserted 140 μ for the outer pipet and therefore 190 μ for the inner pipet. The tracing from the inner pipet carries pips at both on and off of the light in order to allow the discrimination of its tracing from that of the outer pipet which carries no pip. Subsequent recordings [2(a)–2(d)] were obtained by advancing the electrode in 35-μ steps. As can be seen in these recordings, large S potentials are recorded not only from the superfine inner pipet, but also from the outer pipet which was 5 μ at the tip in this case and thus too large to impale single cones.

Another feature of the S potential is that, so

far as the luminosity-type response is concerned, it shows a large area effect, the response amplitude being increased as the light spot on the retina is increased up to 3 mm in diameter or even more (44, 8). Later, marking experiments using staining at the pipet tip made by several investigators including Svaetichin himself were consistent in excluding the receptors as the origin of the S potential (19, 21, 29, 42, 8, 3).

It may then be suspected that the S potential might represent the activity of the bipolar cells onto which a number of receptors converge. However, several peculiar properties of the S potential also make this suspicion unlikely. First, the S potential does not seem to show any sign of polarity reversal regardless of the position of the recording pipet in the retina. This makes it difficult to assume the existence of an excitable membrane across which the S potential is produced. Second, no correlation is found statistically between the resting potential level and the response amplitude (34). Third, changes of the resting potential level by extrinsic current applied through the recording pipet or through one barrel of a double-barreled pipet have little effect on the response amplitude (19, 47, 34, 8). Only a shift of the resting potential level by adapting light has been shown by Mac-Nichol and Svaetichin (19) to influence the response amplitude to the test light. In the R–G type of S potential, for instance, in which the response to light of longer wavelengths is positive (R component) and the response to light of shorter wavelengths is negative (G component), the effect of blue adapting light on this unit is to make the baseline level more negative, the G component smaller, and the R component larger. The effect of red-adapting light on this same unit is just the opposite, making the baseline level more positive, the G component larger,

and the R component smaller. This kind of behavior of the S potential may not be inconsistent with what one expects from the membrane theory. However, we have an example which is difficult to understand on this same basis.

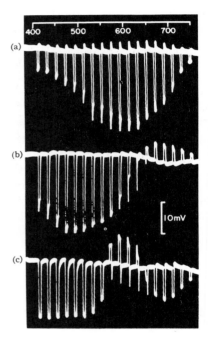

Fig. 3. Three types Group-III responses. S potentials (carp) luminosity type (a), biphasic chromaticity type (b), and triphasic chromaticity type (c).

The three types of responses obtained in the carp are illustrated in Fig. 3: the luminosity type in (a) which is found in about 60% of S potentials, the biphasic chromaticity type in (b) which is found in 25%, and the triphasic chromaticity type in (c) in 15%. Working on the biphasic chromaticity type with adapting light, we obtained the same result as Mac-Nichol and Svaetichin. In the triphasic chromaticity type, however, the situation was not so simple. This type of S potential in response to a test light of 710 mμ was compared with responses of the same unit to the same test light but adapted to light at the following three different wavelengths: 700 mμ (a), 580 mμ (b), and 400 mμ (c). The result is quite acceptable on the basis of the membrane theory: The response to the test light which is negative-going is made smaller by making the resting potential level more negative by adapting light of 700 mμ, and is augmented by making the resting potential level more positive by adapting light of 580 mμ. However, the effect of the adapting light of 400 mμ is to make the resting potential level more negative and the response to the test light larger, despite the fact that the response to the test light has the same polarity as the shift of resting potential level by this adapting light. This appears to be indicating something concerning the color-reception mechanism, but at this point I just wish to point out that the amplitude of the S potential does not necessarily depend on the resting potential level.

All the above-mentioned properties of the S potential are difficult to reconcile on the basis of conventional neurophysiology. Nevertheless, we had to postulate the concept of "compartments" as the structures responsible for the S potential (44), since it was quite a common observation that, after an S potential from one site had deteriorated, another large S potential could be found when the pipet was displaced a small distance. It is noteworthy that some similarities are recognized between the S potential and the response of gland cells. Lundberg (18) working on the salivary gland cells with intracellular microelectrodes, observed that a sustained negative potential is produced in response to stimulation of the innervating nerve, and that the response amplitude remains unchanged after the resting potential level has been shifted by extrinsic current. According to recent works of Svaetichin and his co-workers (33, 17, 22), S potentials originate in the horizontal cells and in the Müller cells, both of which are glial in nature (45). The former produce the luminosity type of response and the latter the chromaticity type of response. They conclude that the S potential is a phenomenon associated with some metabolic interaction between these glia cells and the neurons such as bipolars and ganglion cells. However, since Svaetichin himself admits, "we are perfectly aware of the difficulties arising when presenting the concept of neuron—glia interaction as a working hypothesis for electrophysiological studies of the nervous activity" (31), it is felt that their conclusion will have to survive many crucial tests before becoming generally accepted. It is to be noted, however, that my earlier impression that the S potential is probably "extracellular" (37) may not contradict the new idea of Svaetichin and his co-workers in the sense that in the retina almost all the "extraneuronal" space is occupied by glia cells, sharing the architecture common to the nervous system, and that the glia cells are proposed by Sjöstrand (30) to represent what is referred to as the extracellular space in the nervous system. In any case, our experience about the degree of ease of obtaining S potentials in the fish, turtle, and frog agrees with the order of the size of horizontal cells in these animal forms (Sjöstrand, personal communication), or with the coarseness in arrangement of neuronal cells, particularly the bipolars.

In connection with all the above peculiar properties of the S potential, I must refer to another observation of Watanabe and Tosaka (46) that the response type of the S potential from one recording site remains the same regardless of which retinal regions are illuminated. In order to account for this, one has to consider some specific connection, direct or indirect, between each compartment of the S potential and the receptors. As another feature of the S potential, a response produced by simultaneous illumination with two spots of light of the same quality on separate retinal regions is always larger than that produced by either one of these light spots alone. In other words, the effect of spatial interaction on the S potential is always summative. In this respect, the S potential appears to represent some earlier process that takes place before the entry of inhibitory process. The observation of Grüsser (13) that the S potential in the cat persists after the retinal circulation is clamped may support this view. We will see later that this summative property of the S potential makes a strong contrast with what is found for the ERG in the fish.

ERG. Turning now to the subject of ERG, let us first discuss the slow potential changes that are distinct in the Group-II responses and S potentials obtained in the frog with minute pipets. It was suspected that some of these slow potentials might be constituents of the ERG, and that, if this is true, any agent that is known to influence the ERG should also influence the slow potentials in question in a similar manner. We tried to test this point with some chemicals first, but knowing that the responses in Group-II neurons were immediately lost by dislocation of recording pipets due to mechanical disturbance caused by applying chemicals, we compared the effect of polarizing current across the retina on the ERG with its effects on the slow potentials in Group-II responses as well as on the S potentials (41). The test revealed little relation between the S potential and the ERG. While the ERG was regularly augmented by polarizing current applied with the vitreous as cathode and suppressed by current in the opposite direction, confirming the result of Granit and Helme (11), the effect of such current on the S potential was various, showing no constant result. Current in one direction augmented some of the S potentials, but suppressed some others, while having little effect on the rest. Tests with chemicals applied in gaseous form (Murakami and Sasaki, unpublished) also failed to show any definite relation between the S potential and the ERG. The effect of polarizing current on Group-II

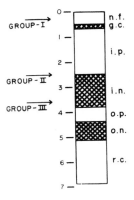

Fig. 4. Schematic diagram showing the retina thickness (frog) and approximate depths at which Group I, II and III responses are found. Numerals show distances in 35μ steps. n.f. nerve fiber layer; g.c. ganglion cell layer; i.p. inner plexiform layer; i.n. inner nuclear layer; o.p. outer plexiform layer; o.n. outer nuclear layer; r.c. rod and cone layer (41).

responses was somewhat constant, but still it proved difficult to relate them directly to the ERG.

As another approach to this problem, an attempt was made to localize the responses in the retina by readings of the micrometer gauge. As depicted in Fig. 4, the Group-II responses are localized around the border of the inner plexiform and inner nuclear layers. From about the same depth, Brown and Wiesel (5), and also Byzov (7), have observed spike discharges. Their extracellular recordings did not show up slow potentials, but inferring from the depth, it is probable that the impulse discharges they obtained are from the same cell type as our Group-II neurons. Inferring also from the depth, the cell type in question is more like a bipolar than a ganglion, but from the result of physiological tests, the Group-II neurons look more like ganglion cells. For instance, impulse spikes are provoked in these neurons by stimulation of the optic nerve (41). Byzov (7), who earlier observed this fact, considers that the cells in question are Dogiel's cells or ganglion cells displaced into the bipolar cell layer. My opinion is, however, that the Group-II neurons are ganglion cells impaled at their soma or more likely at their dendrites after they have been pressed down a certain distance by the pipet. This may account for failure to record from the depth corresponding to the ganglion-cell layer. There are also several other pieces of evidence. First, the slow potential changes in Group-II neurons are what one can predict in the ganglion cells from their three types of responses which have been known since Hartline (14). The results of intracellular recording by Wiesel (48) from ganglion cells in the cat also show that the pattern of impulse discharge depends entirely on the slow potential changes recorded simultaneously. Second, Brown and Wiesel (5) report that the units responding with impulse discharges, found in the cat from a depth corresponding to the inner nuclear layer, change their response type in the same manner as observed in the ganglion cells by Kuffler (16). Third, although this observation of Brown and Wiesel was not confirmed in our experiment on the frog, since the response type of each ganglion cell in the frog is far more fixed than in the cat, comparison of the receptive fields of Group-I and Group-II responses disclosed no substantial differences. It is probable, therefore, that the Group-I responses, which have been identified as responses in the axons of ganglion cells, and the Group-II responses in

question, are obtained from different regions of the same cell type, the ganglion cell. Going on this assumption, it is no longer possible to assign the ERG to Group-II neurons, because the ganglion cells are known not to take part in any significant way in the generation of the ERG. Since, according to us, the main part of fast ERG components arises from the bipolar layer, this main part of the ERG appears, as was suggested by Granit (10), to be a manifestation of processes that subserve and underlie the ganglion-cell activity.

In connection with this assertion, however, it is necessary to refer to the recent works on mammals of Brown and Wiesel (5) and Brown and Watanabe (4). While many of their conclusions on the localization of ERG components in the cat and monkey are similar to our work in cold-blooded retinas, there is one big difference in the point that all the *a* wave, or PIII is located in mammals in the receptor layer. In both cat and monkey, the *a* wave remains normal after the retinal circulation is clamped, while other fast components are abolished, and in the foveal region of the monkey retina where the inner layers are absent, the *a* wave is larger than in other retinal areas. I had an opportunity to observe these experiments throughout the past summer and became quite convinced of the correctness of their conclusion. Later, however, our old experiment on the frog was repeated carefully by us with the result that our earlier conclusion was confirmed. As may be easily seen, one advantage of using the cold-blooded retina is that easy and direct access to the receptors is possible by having the retina detached from the pigment epithelium and mounted with the receptor side up. Such a preparation responds to light with a perfect ERG (except for the *c* wave) even with much larger *a*, *b*, and *d* wave than in the opened eye. This has proved to be due to removal of the R membrane, a high-resistance membrane which normally exists immediately behind the receptor layer and which acts to limit the size of ERG (40). If in such a preparation the receptors were the main source of the *a* wave, a pair of pipets, one at the distal margin of the receptors and the other inserted into the retina down to their proximal margin, should record the largest *a* wave. However, this never happened. The *a* wave was almost absent at this positioning of the pipets, appearing clearly only after the intraretinal pipet was advanced further. The discrepancy concerning the origin of the *a* wave between the results on mammals and the frog is difficult to account for, but the problem may be settled by assuming that the *a* wave is made up of more than one component from different retinal layers and that in different species the component that dominates differs. We have obtained some results in support of this assumption from cold-blooded retinas. One such experiment will be mentioned below.

The arrangement is shown in Fig. 5. A coaxial microelectrode is applied to the frog's opened eye with its outer pipet in contact with the inner retinal surface to record the

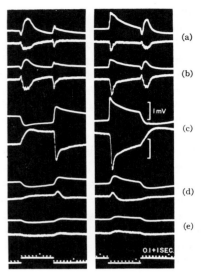

Fig. 6. Effect of sodium azide on both surface and intraretinal ERG's in the frog, obtained simultaneously by arrangement in Fig. 5. The inner pipet is kept located at a depth of 140μ from the vitreal retinal surface. (a) control record before azide, from preparation with the vitreous humor drained off; and (b) another control record but after filling the eye cup with Ringer solution. Subsequent records: 2 min (c), 4 min (d), and 6 min (e), after replacement of Ringer solution in the eye cup with 0.1% azide-Ringer. With on/off of light for the records in left column, and with off/on for those in right column.

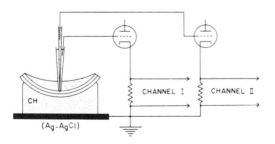

Fig. 5. Arrangement for simultaneous recording of surface and intraretinal ERG's. The outer pipet of a coaxial microelectrode is in contact with the retinal surface to record the surface ERG. The inner pipet protrudes out of the tip of the outer pipet into the retina to record the intraretinal ERG. CH is Ringer-soaked chalk which is concave at the top to fit the eye cup.

surface ERG through one channel of a two-channel amplifier. The inner, superfine pipet, which is connected to the other channel of the amplifier, protrudes out of the tip of the outer pipet into the retina to a minimal depth at which the intraretinally obtained ERG is just reversed in polarity [lower tracing in Fig. 6(a)]. It is indicated by this depth that the inner pipet has just penetrated through layers producing the major portion of ERG to the opposite side (40). At this positioning of the pipets, 0.1% azide–Ringer, a PII depressant (27, 26), is applied in the eye cup. Component PIII soon becomes dominant in both surface and intraretinal ERG's (c). Since the intraretinal ERG is kept reversed in polarity up to this stage of azide action, the emf for the ERG in which PIII is now dominant is undoubtedly intervening between the two pipets in some layers. In the course of time, both surface and intraretinal ERG's become small again (d), and eventually the intraretinal ERG takes the same polarity and amplitude as the surface ERG (e), indicating clearly that the emf responsible for this remaining response no longer exists in layers between the two pipets but somewhere else. Since, by further advancement of the inner pipet towards the R membrane, the response from the inner pipet reverses its polarity again to show a mirror image of that from the outer pipet (not illustrated), it is concluded that this portion of PIII which survives azide originates more distally than all the rest of the ERG in which a large portion of PIII is involved. It is probable that this fraction of PIII having a more distal origin arises from receptors, although it may remain to be solved why the polarity of PIII is just the opposite of what one expects from other types of receptors, as earlier discussed by Granit (10). While it is general that the distal tip of the receptor becomes negative when excited, the component PIII is in the direction that makes the distal tip positive instead of negative.

Whatever the localization of ERG components is, it was very discouraging that all the responses recorded in good isolation from minute pipets seemed to be disqualified as candidates of ERG constituents. This suggests that the ERG might eventually remain a tool of study of only a mass response instead of individual cell activities in the retina, and might leave us with a situation concerning the ERG studies not much different from that before the advent of the microelectrode technique.

Keeping the notion of the ERG as a mass response in mind, we will discuss Granit's concept that the PII and PIII are associated

with excitatory and inhibitory processes, in the light of some new observations. It is reported by Motokawa, Oikawa, Tasaki, and Ogawa (24) that the carp retina, detached from the pigment epithelium and mounted on the indifferent electrode with the receptor side up, gives a characteristic pattern of slow response (Fig. 7) to a pipet placed on the distal retinal surface when the retina is scanned with a spot of light across the site of recording. When the light spot is on the re-

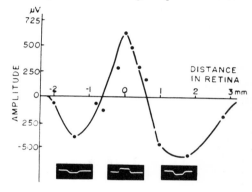

Fig. 7. Spatial distribution of the slow response in the carp, obtained from a pipet electrode on the distal retinal surface at point 0 and by scanning with a light spot across the site of recording (courtesy of Motokawa et al. (24).)

cording site, a positive response, which may be called focal slow response is obtained, but as the spot is moved away from the recording site, the response becomes negative (nonfocal slow response). More recently, Motokawa, Yamashita, and Ogawa (25) noticed that this kind of spatial distribution of the slow response in the fish is closely related to the discharge pattern of on/off-type ganglion cells. In the meantime, effects of chemicals on these focal and nonfocal slow responses were examined by Murakami and Sasaki (unpublished) with the result that both of these slow responses are believed to be the results of competition between two major ERG components, PII and PIII. By the action of ethanol, which is known to suppress PIII more or less selectively (1), the focal slow response which is normally positive is made negative, while the nonfocal slow response remains negative. The effect of a PII-depressant like sodium azide is just the opposite, making both focal and nonfocal slow responses positive. Taking into consideration that the polarity we are referring to is opposite to that of the ordinary ERG because of recordings from the receptor side, it is concluded that PIII is dominant in the focal slow response and PII is dominant in the nonfocal slow response.

One may then expect from Granit's concept that in the focal region where the component PIII is dominant, inhibition predominates over excitation, and that excitation predominates in the nonfocal region where the component PII is dominant. Exactly that which is expected is found in the carp retina in which the on/off-type elements outnumber the other types. The ratio of "off-center" to "on-center" responses of the on/off-type elements counts roughly 10 to 1, showing an overwhelming dominance in inhibition in the region where a light spot is applied, while excitation predominates in its neighboring region. It is apparent that the dominance in PIII (or PII) and the dominance in inhibition (or excitation) are in a parallel relation. Another parallel relation is found in the fish between the effect of spatial interaction on the nervous activity and the effect on the ERG. It has been known since Kuffler's studies on the cat (16) that if two small spots of light are both applied either near the center or in the periphery of the receptive field of an on/off-type ganglion cell, the effect of the two light spots on the nervous activity is summative in the sense that the effect of one spot of light, whether it is inhibitory or excitatory, is reinforced by the other. However, if one is near the center and the other is in the periphery, the effect is mutually counteractive. This is also true for the on/off-type ganglion cells in the fish. With regard to the ERG, as the area illuminated is increased, starting with a small focal light spot, the ERG shows an initial increase in amplitude (summative interaction). A further increase in area illuminated causes a decrease in amplitude again as the result of counteractive interaction between ERG's in the central and peripheral regions.

The observation on the frog is somewhat different from that on the fish. In the frog "additivity of the ERG" holds (2), that is, an ERG produced by simultaneous illumination of several spots on the retina equals the algebraic sum of ERG's produced separately by each light spot. In other words, in the frog the area effect on the ERG is only summative. This may appear to contradict observations on other species. However, this is fully accounted for by the special organization of the frog retina, in which an excitatory and an inhibitory influence have the same size and overlap each other, while in other species they usually do not. This is evidenced by the fact that in the frog the response type of each on/off-element is almost fixed, showing little change according to the site of illumination within the receptive field.

acknowledgment

The author wishes to express his appreciation to Dr. W. H. Miller, The Rockefeller Institute, New York, and to Dr. M. L. Wolbarsht, U.S. Naval Medical Research Institute, Bethesda, for their criticisms and assistance in preparing this paper.

Some works described in this paper were

accomplished with the Support of Research Grants No. MG1–60–1 and No. DA–CRD–AG–S92–544–62–C (Tsuneo Tomita, Responsible Investigator) from U.S. Army Research and Development Group, Far East.

references

1. C. G. Bernhard and C. R. Skoglund, "Selective Suppression with Ethylalcohol of Inhibition in the Optic Nerve and of the Negative Component PIII of the Electroretinogram," Acta Physiol. Scand. **2**, 10–21 (1941).
2. G. S. Brindley, "The Effect on the Frog's Electroretinogram of Varying the Amount of Retina Illuminated," J. Physiol. (London) **134**, 353–359 (1956).
3. K. T. Brown and K. Tasaki, "Localization of Electrical Activity in the Cat Retina by an Electrode Marking Method," J. Physiol. (London) **158**, 281–295 (1961).
4. K. T. Brown and K. Watanabe, "Isolation and Identification of a Receptor Potential from the Pure Cone Fovea of the Monkey Retina," Nature **193**, 958–960 (1962).
5. K. T. Brown and T. N. Wiesel, "Intraretinal Recording with Micropipette Electrodes in the Intact Cat Eye," J. Physiol. (London) **149**, 537–562 (1959).
6. ———, "Localization of Origins of Electroretinogram Components by Intraretinal Recording in the Intact Cat Eye," J. Physiol. (London) **158**, 257–280 (1961).
7. A. L. Byzov, "Sources of the Impulses Recorded from the Inner Layers of the Frog Retina" (in Russian), Biofizika **4**, 414–421 (1959).
8. P. Gouras, "Graded Potentials of Bream Retina," J. Physiol. (London) **152**, 487–505 (1960).
9. R. Granit, "The Components of the Retinal Action Potential and their Relation to the Discharge in the Optic Nerve," J. Physiol. (London) **77**, 207–240 (1933).
10. ———, Sensory Mechanisms of the Retina (Oxford University Press, London, 1947).
11. R. Granit and T. Helme, "Changes in Retinal Excitability due to Polarization and some Observations on the Relation between the Processes in Retina and Nerve," J. Neurophysiol. **2**, 556–565 (1939).
12. R. Granit and G. Svaetichin, "Principles and Technique of the Electrophysiological Analysis of Colour Reception with the Aid of Micro-Electrodes," Upsala Läkarefören. Förh. **65**, 161–177 (1939).
13. O. J. Grüsser, "Receptorpotentiale einzelner retinaler Zapfen der Katze," Naturwissenschaften **44**, 522–524 (1957).
14. H. K. Hartline, "The Response of Single Optic Nerve Fibres of the Vertebrate Retina," Am. J. Physiol. **121**, 400–415 (1938).
15. Y. Hashimoto, M. Murakami, and T. Tomita, "Localization of the ERG by Aid of Histological Method," Japan. J. Physiol. **11**, 62–70 (1961).
16. S. W. Kuffler, "Discharge Patterns and Functional Organization of Mammalian Retina," J. Neurophysiol. **16**, 37–68 (1953).
17. M. Laufer, G. Svaetichin, G. Mitarai, R. Fatechand, E. Vallecalle and J. Villegas, "The Effect of Temperature, Carbon Dioxide and Ammonia on the Neuron–Glia Unit," The Visual System; Neurophysiology and Psychophysics, edited by R. Jung and H. Kornhuber (Springer-Verlag, Berlin, 1961), pp. 457–463.
18. A. Lundberg, "Secretory Potentials and Secretion in the Sublingual Gland of the Cat," Nature **177**, 1080–1081 (1956).
19. E. F. MacNichol and G. Svaetichin, "Electric Responses from the Isolated Retinas of Fishes," Am. J. Ophthalmol. **46** [3], Part 2, 26–46 (1958).
20. E. F. MacNichol, M. L. Wolbarsht, and H. G. Wagner, "Electrophysiological Evidence for a Mechanism of Color Vi-

sion in the Goldfish," *Light and Life*, edited by W. D. McElroy and B. Glass (Johns Hopkins Press, Baltimore, Maryland, 1961), pp. 795–816.

21. G. Mitarai, "The Origin of the So-called Cone Action Potential," Proc. Japan Acad. **34**, 299–304 (1958).

22. G. Mitarai, G. Svaetichin, E. Vallecalle, R. Fatechand, J. Villegas, and M. Laufer, "Glia-Neuron Interactions and Adaptational Mechanisms of the Retina," *The Visual System: Neurophysiology and Psychophysics*, edited by R. Jung and H. Kornhuber (Springer-Verlag, Berlin, 1961), pp. 463–481.

23. K. Motokawa, T. Oikawa, and K. Tasaki, "Receptor Potential of the Vertebrate Retina," J. Neurophysiol. **20**, 186–199 (1957).

24. K. Motokawa, T. Oikawa, K. Tasaki, and T. Ogawa, "The Spatial Distribution of Electric Responses to Focal Illumination of the Carp's Retina," Tôhoku J. Exp. Med. **70**, 151–164 (1959).

25. K. Motokawa, E. Yamashita, and T. Ogawa, "The Physiological Basis of Simultaneous Contrast in the Retina," *The Visual System: Neurophysiology and Psychophysics*, edited by R. Jung and H. Kornhuber (Springer-Verlag, Berlin, 1961), pp. 32–45.

26. W. Müller-Limmroth and H. Blümer, "Ueber den Einfluss von Monojodessigsäure, Natriumazid und Natriumjodat auf das Ruhepotential und das Elektroretinogramm des Froschauges," Z. Biol. **109**, 420–439 (1957).

27. W. Noell, "Studies on the Electrophysiology and the Metabolism of the Retina," Project Report 21-1201-0004, No. 1, U.S. Air Force School of Aviation Medicine, Randolph Field, Texas (1953).

28. K. Naka, S. Inoma, Y. Kosugi, and C. Tong, "Recording of Action Potentials from Single Cells in the Frog Retina," Japan. J. Physiol. **10**, 436–442 (1960).

29. T. Oikawa, T. Ogawa, and K. Motokawa, "Origin of So-called Cone Action Potential," J. Neurophysiol. **22**, 102–111 (1959).

30. F. S. Sjöstrand, "Topographic Relationship between Neurons, Synapses and Glia Cells," *The Visual System: Neurophysiology and Psychophysics*, edited by R. Jung and H. Kornhuber (Springer-Verlag, Berlin, 1961), pp. 13–22.

31. G. Svaetichin, "The Cone Action Potential," Acta Physiol. Scand. **29**, Suppl. 106, 565–600 (1953).

32. ———, "Origin of the R-Potential in the Mammalian Retina," *The Visual System: Neurophysiology and Psychophysics*, edited by R. Jung and H. Kornhuber (Springer-Verlag, Berlin, 1961), pp. 61–62.

33. G. Svaetichin, M. Laufer, G. Mitarai, R. Fatechand, E. Vallecalle, and J. Villegas, "Glial Control of Neuronal Networks and Receptors," *The Visual System: Neurophysiology and Psychophysics*, edited by R. Jung and H. Kornhuber (Springer-Verlag, Berlin, 1961), pp. 445–456.

34. K. Tasaki, "Some Observations on the Retinal Potentials of the Fish," Arch, ital. biol. **98**, 81–91 (1960).

35. T. Tomita, "Studies on the Intraretinal Action Potential. Part I. Relation between the Localization of Micropipette in the Retina and the Shape of the Intraretinal Action Potential," Japan. J. Physiol. **1**, 110–117 (1950).

36. ———, "The Nature of Action Potentials in the Lateral Eye of the Horseshoe Crab as Revealed by Simultaneous Intra- and Extracellular Recording," Japan. J. Physiol. **6**, 327–340 (1956).

37. ———, "A Study on the Origin of Intraretinal Action Potential of Cyprinid Fish by Means of Pencil-Type Microelectrode," Japan. J. Physiol. **7**, 80–85 (1957).

38. ———, "A Compensation Circuit for

Coaxial and Double-Barreled Microelectrodes," IRE, Trans. Bio-Med. Electron. **9**, 138–141 (1962).

39. T. Tomita and A. Funaishi, "Studies on Intraretinal Action Potential with Low-Resistance Microelectrode," J. Neurophysiol. **15**, 75–84 (1952).

40. T. Tomita, M. Murakami, and Y. Hashimoto, "On the R Membrane in the Frog's Eye. Its Localization, and Relation to the Retinal Action Potential," J. Gen. Physiol. **43**, (6) Part 2, 81–94 (1960).

41. T. Tomita, M. Murakami, Y. Hashimoto, and Y. Sasaki, "Electrical Activity of Single Neurons in the Frog's Retina," *The Visual System: Neurophysiology and Psychophysics*, edited by R. Jung and H. Kornhuber (Springer-Verlag, Berlin, 1961), pp. 24–30.

42. T. Tomita, M. Murakami, Y. Sato, and Y. Hashimoto, "Further Study on the Origin of the So-called Cone Action Potential (S-Potential). Its Histological Determination," Japan. J. Physiol. **9**, 63–68 (1959).

43. T. Tomita and Y. Torihama, "Further Study on the Intraretinal Action Potential and on the Site of ERG Generation," Japan. J. Physiol. **6**, 118–136 (1956).

44. T. Tomita, T. Tosaka, K. Watanabe, and Y. Sato, "The Fish EIRG in Response to Different Types of Illumination," Japan. J. Physiol. **8**, 41–50 (1958).

45. G. M. Villegas, "Comparative Ultrastructure of the Retina in Fish, Monkey, and Man," *The Visual System: Neurophysiology and Psychophysics*, edited by R. Jung and H. Kornhuber (Springer-Verlag, Berlin, 1961), pp. 3–13.

46. K. Watanabe and T. Tosaka, "Functional Organization of the Cyprinid Fish Retina as Revealed by Discriminative Responses to Spectral Illumination," Japan. J. Physiol. **9**, 84–93 (1959).

47. K. Watanabe, T. Tosaka, and T. Yokota, "Effects of Extrinsic Electric Current on the Cyprinid Fish EIRG (S-Potential)," Japan. J. Physiol. **10**, 132–141 (1960).

48. T. N. Wiesel, "Recording Inhibition and Excitation in the Cat's Retinal Ganglion Cells with Intracellular Electrodes," Nature **183**, 264–265 (1959).

6 discriminatory capacity of the auditory system*

William D. Neff

1. What is the general procedure followed by Neff in his experiment?

2. How is a map of the auditory areas of the cortex constructed?

3. In what ways have auditory experiments on monkeys paralleled Neff's studies on cats?

4. What are the effects of bilateral ablation of auditory areas as compared with unilateral ablation?

We have frequently been warned against making unqualified inferences about what happens in large groups of neurons or in large sections of the central nervous system from evidence based upon what is seen by a gross- or micro-electrode in a more or less small part of the system. I would like to extend this warning still further and caution against making rash inferences about discriminatory behavior from information obtained from stud-

*W. D. Neff, "Discriminatory Capacity of Different Divisions of the Auditory System." In M. B. B. Brazier (ed.), *Brain and Behavior*, 1 (Washington, D.C.: Amer. Inst. Biol. Sci., 1961), 205–216. Reprinted with permission. The research reported in this paper was supported in part by grants from the Air Force Office of Scientific Research, the Operational Applications Office of the Air Force Command and Control Development Division, and the Office of Naval Research.

ies of anatomy or electrophysiology of the nervous system. Sooner or later, it is necessary to study behavior itself. I think it is appropriate, then, that we spend a short time discussing experiments in which the dependent variable has been changes in behavior.

Historically, the methods which have been used in studying discriminatory behavior have been two: One has been the observation of changes in discrimination (verbal behavior included) of clinical patients after disease, injury, or surgery of the nervous system. A second has been the observation and measurement of discriminations of animals before and after experimental manipulation of the nervous system. In most instances, the manipulations have consisted of ablating neural centers or cutting neural pathways. I shall talk about experiments in which this latter method was used in the investigation of auditory discrimination in the cat and monkey.

As introduction, let me review briefly a number of studies which have been reported in detail elsewhere. Most of these involved testing the capacity of animals to make different kinds of auditory discriminations before and after large bilateral ablations of the auditory areas of the cerebral cortex. After this review, I shall describe more recent experiments from our laboratory, in which we examined the effects of (1) bilateral ablation of subareas of auditory cortex, (2) large unilateral cortical ablations, and (3) subcortical transections of auditory pathways.

The procedure followed in our experiments is outlined below: (1) The experimental animal is trained to make an auditory discrimination. In some cases, thresholds of discriminatory capacity are then determined. (2) The neural center is ablated or the pathway is transected. (3) After recovery from surgery, the animal is retested. Retraining is given when necessary. (4) After retraining and retesting have been completed, the animal is

anesthetized and the auditory nervous system is explored by electrophysiological techniques in order to evaluate damage done by surgery. For example, if auditory pathways have been cut subcortically, the cortex is explored in order to discover if any responses are evoked by sounds presented to the ear. (5) The animal is sacrificed, the brain is sectioned and stained, and surgical damage is assessed.

We have studied discriminatory responses to the following auditory stimuli: (a) onset of tone or noise, (b) change in intensity of tone, (c) change in frequency of tone, (d) change in duration of tone, (e) change in temporal pattern of a sequence of tones, (f) localization of sound in space.

In all discriminations except localization of sound in space, the experimental animal (cat or monkey) is trained to avoid shock by moving from one compartment to the other of the double-grill box when a change occurs in an auditory signal. For example, in a frequency discrimination test, the animal is trained to make the avoidance response when a pulsing standard tone, constituting the negative stimulus, is changed in frequency (positive stimulus). Similarly for intensity and duration discriminations, the positive signal is stronger in intensity or longer in duration than the negative background stimulus. In pattern discrimination, the temporal order of groups of tonal pulses is changed (line 3, Figure 1) so that, for example, the negative signal consists of low-high-low, and the positive signal of the same tones but in the sequence high-low-high.

Localization of sound in space is tested in the apparatus shown in Figure 2. The animal (tests have been made only with the cat) is trained to localize a sound (buzzer) by approaching the source of sound, which is placed behind one or the other of two food boxes. If it responds correctly, it receives a food reward. By moving the food boxes closer

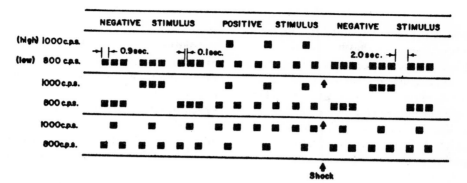

Fig. 1. Sequence of events in discriminations of frequency (line 1) and pattern (lines 2 and 3).

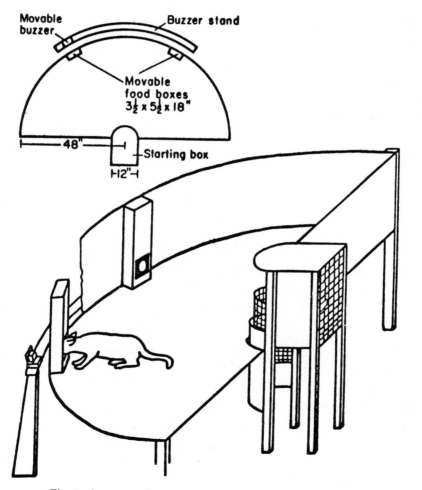

Fig. 2. Apparatus for testing localization of sound in space.

and closer together, a measure can be obtained of the smallest angle that the cat can discriminate. The cat is restrained in the starting box during the time when the buzzer is sounded. The animal is allowed to move about in the starting cage during presentation of the signal; the head is not fixed.

Areas of the cortex which have been classified as auditory in function are shown in Figure 3. Complete retrograde degeneration of the medial geniculate body, the thalamic center for the main auditory pathways, occurs after bilateral ablation of areas AI, AII, Ep, I and T. Evidence from electrophysiological studies indicates that not only these areas but also parts of the suprasylvian gyrus (SS), somatic area II (SII) and parts of the sensory-motor areas and lateral gyrus (not labeled in Figure 3) may also receive projection from subcortical auditory centers.

After bilateral ablations of auditory areas AI, AII, Ep and part of I-T, cats can make learned responses to the onset of tones, and the absolute intensity thresholds for tones throughout the frequency range are unchanged (43). Differential thresholds for intensity are not affected (60, 62). Discriminations of small changes in frequency can also be made if the testing procedure described above is followed (7, 20, 76).

Discriminations which are affected by bilateral ablation of AI, AII, and Ep include localization of sound in space, pattern discrimination, and duration discrimination (12, 57, 58). There is a severe decrement in ability to localize sound in space and to discriminate change in duration. Pattern discrimination is lost completely.

We have tested animals on localization of sound in space, intensity discrimination and frequency discrimination after bilateral ablations. There is complete loss of ability to

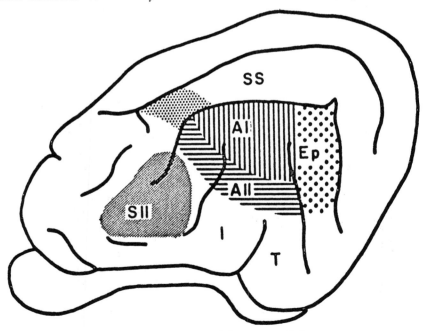

Fig. 3. Auditory areas of the cortex of the cat.

localize sound in space. Differential thresholds for intensity are not increased (60). Differential thresholds for frequency were not measured, but large changes (e.g. the change from a background of 800 cps to a positive signal of 1000 cps) can be discriminated (20).

Results for the monkey, paralleling those for the cat, have been obtained only for frequency and pattern discrimination; the former can be made after bilateral cortical ablations which include the primary projection area, the latter cannot (35).

For all discriminations, large bilateral ablations of auditory areas of the cortex, if done in one stage, produce a temporary loss in the learned habit. For onset of sound, intensity discrimination and frequency discrimination, relearning occurs: the time required for relearning may be as long as that required for initial learning.

For the discriminations which are affected by large bilateral ablations of auditory cortex, it may be asked, are any of the subareas critical? We have not studied all kinds of discriminations or all possible combinations of ablations, but we have considerable evidence for localization of sound in space and some for discriminations of duration and pattern.

Strominger (73) has found that, in the cat, no particular subarea of auditory cortex (AI, AII, Ep, I-T, or SS, Figure 3) is critical for localization of sound in space. A decrement in performance may occur after less than total ablation of these areas; the degree of decrement appears to be related roughly to the amount of retrograde degeneration produced in the medial geniculate body by the ablation.

The insular-temporal (I-T) region in the cat appears to be of particular importance for some kinds of learned auditory discriminations. Animals trained to make duration or pattern discrimination lose the learned habit after bilateral ablation of I-T and must relearn

post-operatively.[1] There may be permanent deficit in capacity to make discriminations involving change in temporal patterns.

In the monkey, a region anatomically homologous to insular-temporal cortex in the cat has been described (1). Bilateral ablation of this area in the monkey produces a loss in a learned auditory pattern discrimination; the discrimination can be relearned. A visual pattern discrimination is retained. In contrast, the visual pattern discrimination is disrupted by ablation of parietal-temporal-occipital cortex, but the auditory pattern discrimination is unaffected.[2]

On the basis of results obtained in experiments in which auditory discriminations have been studied after large bilateral ablations of cortex, it appears quite certain that large unilateral ablations will not affect absolute intensity thresholds and differential thresholds for intensity or frequency. In our experiments we have found no effects of unilateral ablations on duration or pattern discriminations.

Because there is some evidence for a difference between the contralateral and ipsilateral projection of each ear to higher centers of the auditory nervous system, a deficit in ability to localize sound in space might be expected after unilateral ablations of auditory cortex. Strominger (73) has found a deficiency in localizing ability in some animals after large unilateral cortical ablations. It is of interest to note that a partial loss in ability to localize sound in space has been reported in human patients with temporal lobe damage (66). Other investigators, however, have reported no change (77).

Unilateral transection of the auditory pathways of the cat at the level of the brachium of

[1] Neff, W. D., Goldberg, J. M., and Scharlock, D. P., unpublished observations.
[2] Neff, W. D., and Oder, H. E., unpublished observations.

the inferior colliculus (BIC) can produce a loss in ability to localize sound in space that is as great or greater than that produced by large unilateral ablation of auditory cortex. We have no evidence that any other changes in auditory discrimination occur after unilateral section of the BIC.

After bilateral transection of BIC there is complete loss of ability to localize sound in space (73). We have not tested pattern and duration discriminations but, judging from the effects of cortical ablations, a complete loss for both would be expected. Oesterreich (59) has found that discriminations of changes of intensity can be relearned after bilateral section of BIC, but that the differential threshold is raised by approximately 10 decibels. In one animal, for example, the differential threshold was 2.3 db before BIC section, and 12.0 db after section. This finding agrees with that reported by Raab and Ades (62).

Goldberg and Neff (21) have investigated the effects of bilateral BIC section on frequency discrimination in the cat. The animals which they tested may be divided into three groups, the division being made according to extent of surgical lesion:

1. Animals with incomplete section of BIC on one or both sides: Some intact brachium fibers were seen in sections made of the brain stem in the region of the experimental lesion. Evoked potentials in response to sound stimuli were recorded from the auditory areas of the cortex of the anesthetized animal.

2. Animals with complete bilateral section of BIC, as judged from brain stem sections: Evoked potentials in response to sound signals were, nevertheless, recorded from auditory cortex of one or both cerebral hemispheres.

3. Animals with bilateral transections which included all of BIC and extended somewhat beyond, especially in a medial direction: In animals of this group, no evoked potentials

were seen at the cortex in response to sound stimulation.

When tested postoperatively, animals of Group I (partial section of BIC) retained the learned frequency discrimination habit; animals of Group 2 (complete BIC section but evoked cortical R's present) showed a loss of the learned habit, but relearned; animals of Group 3 (complete BIC section and no evoked cortical R's) showed a loss of the learned habit and were unable to relearn frequency discrimination.

The electrophysiological results of the Goldberg experiment and similar results obtained by Oesterreich provide rather convincing evidence that nerve impulses initiated at the cochlea by acoustic stimuli reach the cortex by a pathway or pathways that lie, in part at least, outside of the main auditory pathway, which courses from inferior colliculus to medial geniculate body. We lack conclusive evidence as to the origin and exact location of this alternate auditory pathway. It may arise in medullary centers and follow a route outside of the lateral lemniscus to some thalamic center or centers other than the medial geniculate body, and from there to cortex. Or, it may be formed by collaterals leading from the lateral lemniscus into the reticular formation and via the latter to thalamus and eventually to cortex. If it follows the latter route, it is made up of long fibers with few synapses, since latencies of evoked responses recorded at the cortex are in the same range as those ordinarily measured with the main auditory pathway intact.

To summarize our findings: In the cat, after bilateral ablation of all cortical areas which receive projections from the medial geniculate body (AI, AII, Ep and I-T, Figure 3) or of all cortical areas from which evoked responses to acoustic stimuli may be recorded in the preparation anesthetized with pentobarbital (AI,

AII, Ep, I-T, SII and SS, Figure 3), (*a*) the ability to make learned responses to auditory signals is typically lost, if the ablation is made bilaterally in one-stage, but relearning of some discriminations is possible; (*b*) the capacity to detect onset of sounds at threshold intensities is unchanged; (*c*) the capacity to discriminate threshold changes in intensity is unchanged; (*d*) the capacity to respond to large changes in frequency remains; the effect upon threshold changes has not been measured carefully; (*e*) a deficit occurs in capacity to discriminate changes in duration; (*f*) a complete loss occurs in capacity to discriminate changes in temporal patterns of tones; (*g*) a complete loss occurs in capacity to localize sound in space.

Frequency and pattern discrimination have been studied in the monkey after large bilateral ablations of auditory cortex. The results are similar to those found for the cat. No subarea of auditory cortex appears to be critical for any discriminatory capacity tested in the cat. In some discriminations, postoperative deficit may be related to total amount of retrograde degeneration found in the medial geniculate body after cortical ablation. The insular-temporal region in the cat, and an anatomically homologous region in the monkey, plays a role in the retention of some learned auditory discriminations, e.g. duration and pattern discrimination.

In the cat, widespread ablation of auditory cortex of one cerebral hemisphere can produce a deficit in the capacity to localize sound in space. No effects of unilateral ablations have been noted in other auditory discriminations. Unilateral transection of the brachium of the inferior colliculus in the cat produces a deficit in ability to localize sound. Other discriminations are probably unaffected. Bilateral transection of the brachium of the inferior colliculus produces, in the cat, a complete loss in capability to localize sound in space, and would be expected to produce a complete loss of capability to discriminate changes in duration and in temporal patterns.

Bilateral transection of auditory pathways, at the level of the brachium of the inferior colliculus in the cat, produces a change of approximately ten decibels in the differential threshold for intensity. Discriminations of larger differences can be made after sections which not only cut the brachium completely but extend beyond its boundaries, and which eliminate evoked responses to acoustic signals at the cortex of the anesthetized preparation.

Bilateral transection of auditory pathways at the level of the brachium of the inferior colliculus in the cat does not produce a loss of capability to discriminate large changes in frequency if the lesion is confined to the BIC as anatomically defined. In such cases, although the BIC is completely transected, acoustic signals evoke responses at the cortex of the anesthetized animal. *When the bilateral transection extends beyond the BIC so as to eliminate evoked responses at the cortex, there is a complete loss in capability to discriminate changes in frequency.*

The geniculo-cortical division of the main auditory system is necessary for auditory discriminations which require the integration of incoming neural events over short periods of time, for example, localization of sound in space and discriminations of changes in duration of temporal patterns (55, 56). It appears that, in the absence of the geniculo-cortical division of the main auditory system, an alternate thalamo-cortical circuit is necessary for frequency discrimination. Information about frequency of sounds is probably coded in the auditory system in terms both of place and periodicity. Evidence, from experiments done to date, does not indicate whether or not the same neural centers or circuits are necessary for frequency discrimination coded in both ways. Discriminations involving response to onset of sound or to a change in intensity can apparently be made after elimination of all auditory input to the cerebral cortex. Intensity information is probably coded in one or more of three ways. (1) number of neural units activated; (2) frequency of nerve impulses in given neural units; (3) total flow of nerve impulses.

references

1. Akert, K., Woolsey, C. N., Diamond, I. T., and Neff, W. D., The cortical projection area of the posterior pole of the medial geniculate body in Macaca mulatta. *Anat. Record* (in press).
2. Barron, D. H., and Matthews, B. H. C., The interpretation of potential changes in the spinal cord. *J. Physiol.*, 1938, **92**: 276–321.
3. Benjamin, R. M., and Thompson, R. F., Differential effects of cortical lesions in infant and adult cats on roughness discrimination. *Exper. Neurol.*, 1959, **1**: 305–321.
4. Bennett, M. V. L., Electrical connections between supramedullary neurons. *Fed. Proc.*, 1960, **19**: 282.
5. Brookhart, J. M., and Blanchly, P. H., The influence of D.C. potential fields on cerebellar unit activity. In: *Proc. XIX International Physiological Congress*, Montreal, 1953: 236.
6. Bullock, T. H., and Hagiwara, S., Intracellular recording from the giant synapse of the squid. *J. Gen. Physiol.*, 1957, **40**: 565–577.
7. Butler, R. A., Diamond, I. T., and Neff, W. D., Role of auditory cortex in discrimination of changes in frequency. *J. Neurophysiol.*, 1957, **20**: 108–120.
8. Chang, H.-T., The repetitive discharges

9. of corticothalamic reverberating circuit. *J. Neurophysiol.*, 1950, **13**: 235–257.
9. Chorazyna, H., and Stepień, L., Impairment of recent memory of the auditory stimuli after bilateral ablations of sylvian gyri in dogs. *Bull. Acad. Polon. Sci., Ser. Sci. Biol.*, 1961, **9**: 117–120.
10. ———, Impairment of auditory recent memory produced by cortical lesions in dogs. *Acta Biol. Exper.*, 1961 (in press).
11. De Lorenzo, A. J. D., Electron microscopy of the cerebral cortex; I. The ultrastructure and histochemistry of synaptic junctions. *Bull. Johns Hopkins Hosp.*, 1961, **108**: 258–267.
12. Diamond, I. T., and Neff, W. D., Ablation of temporal cortex and discrimination of auditory patterns. *J. Neurophysiol.*, 1957, **20**: 300–315.
13. Eccles, J. C., and Krnjević, K., Potential changes recorded inside primary afferent fibres within the spinal cord. *J. Physiol.*, 1959, **149**: 250–273.
14. Estable, C., Considerations on the histological bases of neurophysiology. In: *Brain Mechanisms and Learning* (J. F. Delafresnaye, A. Fessard, R. Gerard, and J. Konorski, Eds.), Blackwell, Oxford, 1961: 309–334.
15. Furshpan, E. J., and Potter, D. D., Mechanism of nerve-impulse transmission at a crayfish synapse. *Nature*, 1957, **180**: 342–343.
16. Galambos, R., and Rupert, A., Action of the middle ear muscles in normal cats. *J. Acous. Soc. Am.*, 1959, **31**: 349–355.
17. Gerstein, G., Firing patterns of single cells in the auditory cortex. *Quarterly Progress Report*, Res. Lab. Electronics, MIT, April 15, 1960, No. 57: 150–159.
18. ———, Analysis of firing patterns in single neurons. *Science*, 1960, **131**: 1811–1812.
19. Gerstein, G., and Kiang, N. Y.-S., An approach to the quantitative analysis of electrophysiological data from single neurons. *Biophysical J.*, 1960, **1**: 15–28.
20. Goldberg, J. M., and Neff, W. D., Fre-

quency discrimination after bilateral ablation of cortical auditory areas. *J. Neurophysiol.*, 1961, **24**: 119–128.

21. ——, Frequency discrimination after bilateral section of the brachium of the inferior colliculus. *J. Comp. Neurol.*, 1961, **113**: 265–282.

22. Gray, E. G., Axo-somatic and axo-dendritic synapses of the cerebral cortex: An electron microscope study. *J. Anat.*, 1959, **93**: 420–433.

23. Green, J. D., and Naquet, R., Étude de la propagation locale et à distance des démarches épileptiques. IVe. Congres International d'Electro-encéphalographie et de Neurophysiologie Clinique. Editions 'Acta Medica Belgica', Brussels, 1957: 225–249.

24. Grundfest, H., Synaptic and ephaptic transmission. In: *Handbook of Physiology*—Neurophysiology I (J. Field, H. W. Magoun, and V. E. Hall, Eds.), *American Physiological Society*, Washington, D.C., 1959: 147–197.

25. Gumnit, R. J., D.C. potential changes from auditory cortex of cat. *J. Neurophysiol.*, 1960, **23**: 667–675.

26. Hagiwara, S., Watanabe, A., and Saito, N., Potential changes in syncytal neurons of lobster cardiac ganglion. *J. Neurophysiol.*, 1959, **22**: 554–572.

27. Henry, C., and Kruger, L., Extra and intra cerebral recording of seizure discharges in the experimental epileptic monkey. *EEG Clin. Neurophysiol.*, 1955, **7**: 145.

28. Hernández-Peón, R., Central mechanisms controlling conduction along central sensory pathways. *Acta Neurol. Latinoamer.*, 1955, **1**: 256–264.

29. Hernández-Peón, R., Guzmán-Flores, C., Alcaraz, M., and Fernández-Guardiola, A., Habituation in the visual pathway. *Acta Neurol. Latinoamer.*, 1958, **4**: 121–129.

30. Hernández-Peón, R., and Scherrer, H., "Habituation" to acoustic stimuli in cochlear nucleus. *Fed. Proc.*, 1955, **14**: 71.

31. Hernández-Peón, R., Scherrer, H., and Jouvet, M., Modification of electric activity in cochlear nucleus during "attention" in unanesthetized cats. *Science*, 1956, **123**: 331–332.

32. Hubel, D. H., and Wiesel, T. N., Receptive fields of single neurones in the cat's striate cortex. *J. Physiol.*, 1959, **148**: 574–591.

33. Hugelin, A., Dumont, S., and Paillas, N., Formation réticulaire et transmission des informations auditives au niveau de l'oreille moyenne et des voies acoustiques centrales. *EEG Clin. Neurophysiol.*, 1960, **12**: 797–818.

34. Hunt, C. C., and McIntyre, A. K., Characteristics of responses from receptors from the flexor longus digitorum muscle and the adjoining interosseous region of the cat. *J. Physiol.*, 1960, **153**: 74–87.

35. Jerison, H. J., and Neff, W. D., Effect of cortical ablation in the monkey on discrimination of auditory patterns. *Fed. Proc.*, 1953, **12**: 73–74.

36. Kerr, W. J., Althausen, T. L., Bassett, A. M., and Goldman, M. J., The symbalophone: A modified stethoscope for the lateralization and comparison of sounds. *Am. Heart J.* 1937, **14**: 594–597.

37. Kiang, N. Y.-S., Neame, J. H., and Clark, L. F., Evoked cortical activity from auditory cortex in anesthetized and unanesthetized cats. *Science*, 1961, **133**: 1927–1928.

38. Köhler, W., Relational determination in perception. In: *Cerebral Mechanisms in Behavior*, the Hixon Symposium (L. A. Jeffress, Ed.), John Wiley, New York, 1951: 200–243.

39. Köhler, W., and Wallach, H., Figural after-effects: An investigation of visual processes. *Proc. Am. Philosoph. Soc.*, 1944, **88**: 269–357.

40. Konorski, J., A new method of physiological investigation of recent memory in animals. *Bull. Acad. Polon. Sci., Ser. Sci. Biol.*, 1959, **7**: 115–117.

41. ——, The physiological approach to

the problem of recent memory. In: *Brain Mechanisms and Learning* (J. F. Delafresnaye, A. Fessard, R. W. Gerard and J. Konorski, Eds.), Blackwell, Oxford, 1961: 115–132.

42. Kraft, M. S., Obrist, W. D., and Pribram, K. H., The effect of irritative lesions of the striate cortex on learning of visual discriminations in monkeys. *J. Comp. Physiol. Psychol.*, 1960, **53**: 17–22.

43. Kryter, K. D., and Ades, H. W., Studies on the function of the higher acoustic nervous centers in the cat. *Am. J. Psychol.*, 1943, **56**: 501–536.

44. Landau, W. M., Goldstein, R., and Kleffner, F. R., Congenital aphasia: A clinicopathologic study. *Neurology*, 1960, **10**: 915–921.

45. Lashley, K. S., Chow, K. L., and Semmes, J., An examination of the electrical field theory of cerebral integration. *Psychol. Rev.*, 1951, **58**: 123–136.

46. Marsh, J. T., McCarthy, D. A., Sheatz, G., and Galambos, R., Amplitude changes in evoked auditory potentials during habituation and conditioning. *EEG Clin. Neurophysiol.*, 1961, **13**: 224–234.

47. McCulloch, W. S. (Ed.), Human decisions in complex systems. *Ann. New York Acad. Sci.*, 1961, **89**: 715–896.

48. Meyer, D. R., and Woolsey, C. N., Effects of localized cortical destruction on auditory discriminative conditioning in cat. *J. Neurophysiol.*, 1952, **15**: 149–162.

49. Mishkin, M., and Weiskrantz, L., Effects of delaying reward on visual-discrimination performance in monkeys with frontal lesions. *J. Comp. Physiol. Psychol.*, 1958, **51**: 276–281.

50. Morrell, F., Microelectrode and steady potential studies suggesting a dendritic locus of closure. In: The Moscow Colloquim on Electroencephalography of Higher Nervous Activity (H. H. Jasper and G. D. Smirnov, Eds.), *EEG Clin. Neurophysiol.*, 1960, *supp.* **13**: 65–79.

51. ———, Electrophysiological contribu-

tions to the neural basis of learning. *Physiol. Rev.*, 1961, **41**: 443–494.

52. ———, Effect of anodal polarization on the firing pattern of single cortical cells. *Ann. New York Acad. Sci.*, 1961, **92**: 860–876.

53. Mountcastle, V. B., Modality and topographic properties of single neurons of cat's somatic sensory cortex. *J. Neurophysiol.*, 1957, **20**: 408–434.

54. Moushegian, G., Rupert, A., Marsh, J. T., and Galambos, R., Evoked cortical potentials in absence of middle ear muscles. *Science*, 1961, **133**: 582–583.

55. Neff, W. D., Role of the auditory cortex in sound discrimination. In: *Neural Mechanisms of the Auditory and Vestibular Systems* (G. L. Rasmussen and W. F. Windle, Eds.), Thomas, Springfield, 1960: 211–216.

56. ———, Neural mechanisms of auditory discrimination. In: *Sensory Communication* (W. A. Rosenblith, Ed.), MIT Press, Cambridge, and John Wiley, New York, 1961: 259–278.

57. Neff, W. D., Arnott, G. P., and Fisher, J. D., Function of auditory cortex: Localization of sound in space. *Am. J. Physiol.*, 1950, **163**: 738.

58. Neff, W. D., Fisher, J. F., Diamond, I. T., and Yela, M., Role of auditory cortex in discrimination requiring localization of sound in space. *J. Neurophysiol.*, 1956, **19**: 500–512.

59. Oesterreich, R. E., The role of higher neural auditory centers in the discrimination of differential sound intensities. Doctoral dissertation, Univ. of Chicago, 1960.

60. Oesterreich, R. E., and Neff, W. D., Higher auditory centers and the DL for sound intensities. *Fed. Proc.*, 1960, **19**: 301.

61. Purpura, D. P., Nature of electrocortical potentials and synaptic organizations in cerebral and cerebellar cortex. *Intern. Rev. Neurobiol.*, 1959, **1**: 47–163.

62. Raab, D. H., and Ades, H. W., Cortical

and midbrain mediation of a conditioned discrimination of acoustic intensities. *Am. J. Physiol.*, 1946, **59**: 59–83.

63. Retzlaff, E., Neurohistological basis for the functioning of paired half-centers. *J. Comp. Neurol.*, 1954, **101**: 407–443.

64. Rose, J. E., Galambos, R., and Hughes, J. R., Microelectrode studies of the cochlear nuclei of the cat. *Bull. Johns Hopkins Hosp.*, 1959, **104**: 211–251.

65. Rusinov, V. S., General and localized alterations in the electroencephalogram during the formation of conditioned reflexes in man. In: The Moscow Colloquium on Electroencephalography of Higher Nervous Activity (H. H. Jasper and G. D. Smirnov, Eds.), *EEG Clin. Neurophysiol.*, 1960, *supp.* **13**: 309–319.

66. Sánchez-Longo, L. P., and Forster, F. M., Clinical significance of impairment of sound localization. *Neurology*, 1958, **8**: 119–125.

67. Simmons, F. B., Middle ear muscle activity at moderate sound levels. *Ann. Otol. Rhin. Laryngol.*, 1959, **68**: 1126–1143.

68. ———, Post-tetanic potentiation in the middle-ear-muscle acoustic reflex. *J. Acous. Soc. Am.*, 1960, **32**: 1589–1591.

69. Simmons, F. B., Galambos, R., and Rupert, A., Conditioned response of middle ear muscles. *Am. J. Physiol.*, 1959, **197**: 537–538.

70. Sperry, R. W., Miner, N., and Myers, R. E., Visual pattern perception following subpial slicing and tantalum wire implantations in the visual cortex. *J. Comp. Physiol. Psychol.*, 1955, **48**: 50–58.

71. Stamm, J. S., and Pribram, K. H., Effects of epileptogenic lesions in frontal cortex on learning and retention in monkeys. *J. Neurophysiol.*, 1960, **23**: 552–563.

72. ———, Effects of epileptogenic lesions in inferotemporal cortex on learning and retention in monkeys. *J. Comp. Physiol. Psychol.*, 1961 (in press).

73. Strominger, N. L., Localization of sound after central nervous system lesions. Doctoral dissertation, Univ. of Chicago, 1961.

74. Tasaki, I., Polley, E. H., and Orrego, F., Action potentials from individual elements in cat geniculate and striate cortex. *J. Neurophysiol.*, 1954, **17**: 454–474.

75. Terzuolo, C. A., and Bullock, T. H., Measurement of imposed voltage gradient adequate to modulate neuronal firing. *Proc. Nat. Acad. Sci.*, 1956, **42**: 687–694.

76. Thompson, R. F., Function of auditory cortex of cat in frequency discrimination. *J. Neurophysiol.*, 1960, **23**: 321–334.

77. Walsh, E. G., An investigation of sound localization in patients with neurological abnormalities. *Brain*, 1957, **80**: 222–250.

78. Watanabe, A., and Bullock, T. H., Modulation of activity of one neuron by subthreshold slow potentials in another in lobster cardiac ganglion. *J. Gen. Physiol.*, 1960, **43**: 1031–1045.

79. Woolsey, C. N., and Walzl, E. M., Topical projection of nerve fibers from local regions of the cochlea to the cerebral cortex of the cat. *Bull. Johns Hopkins Hosp.*, 1942, **71**: 315–344.

7   "attention" in unanesthetized cats*

Raúl Hernández-Peón, Harold Scherrer, and Michel Jouvet

1. How would an experimenter proceed in locating "a selective central inhibitory mechanism"?

2. Could these results obtained on cats be extrapolated to human beings? What problems are

*R. Hernández-Peón, H. Scherrer, M. Jouvet, "Modification of Electric Activity in Cochlear Nucleus during 'Attention' in Unanesthetized Cats," *Science*, 123 (24 February 1956), 331–332. Reprinted with permission.

involved? What experimental checking could be done?

Attention involves the selective awareness of certain sensory messages with the simultaneous suppression of others. Our sense organs are activated by a great variety of sensory stimuli, but relatively few evoke conscious sensation at any given moment. It is common experience that there is a pronounced reduction of extraneous sensory awareness when our attention is concentrated on some particular matter. During the attentive state, it seems as though the brain integrates for consciousness only a limited amount of sensory information, specifically, those impulses concerned with the object of attention.

An interference with impulses initiated by sensory stimuli other than those pertaining to the subject of attention seems to be an obvious possibility. It is clear that this afferent blockade might occur at any point along the classical sensory pathways from receptors to the cortical receiving areas, or else perhaps in the recently disclosed extraclassical sensory paths that traverse the brain-stem reticular system (1).

Recent evidence indicates the existence of central mechanisms that regulate sensory transmission. It has been shown that appropriate stimulation of the brain-stem reticular system will inhibit afferent conduction between the first- and second-order neurons in all three principal somatic paths (2–4). During central anesthesia, the afferent-evoked potentials in the first sensory relays are enhanced. This appears to be due to the release of a tonic descending inhibitory influence that operates during wakefulness and requires the functional integrity of the brain-stem reticular formation.

The possibility that a selective central inhibitory mechanism might operate during attention for filtering sensory impulses was tested by studying (5) afferent transmission in the second- or third-order neurons of the auditory pathway (cochlear nucleus) in unanesthetized, unrestrained cats during experimentally elicited attentive behavior. Bipolar stainless steel electrodes with a total diameter of 0.5 mm were implanted stereotaxically in the dorsal cochlear nucleus through a small hole bored in the skull. The electrode was fixed to the skull with dental cement. A minimum of 1 week elapsed between the operation and the first electroencephalographic recordings. Electric impulses in the form of short bursts of rectangular waves (0.01 to 0.02 sec) at a frequency of 1000 to 5000 cy/sec were delivered to a loudspeaker near the cats at an intensity comfortable to human observers in the same environment.

Three types of sensory modalities were used to attract the animal's attention: visual,

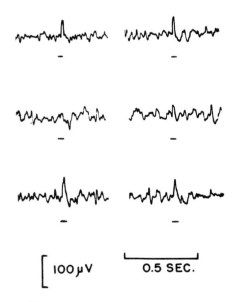

Fig. 1. Click responses recorded from the cochlear nucleus of the cat. (Top) cat is relaxed; (middle) cat is attentively sniffing an olfactory stimulus; (bottom) cat is relaxed again. Note the reduced amplitude of the click responses when the animal is sniffing.

olfactory, and somatic. During presentation of visual stimuli (two mice in a closed bottle), the auditory responses in the cochlear nucleus were greatly reduced in comparison with the control responses; they were practically abolished as long as the visual stimuli elicited behavioral evidence of attention. When the mice were removed, the auditory responses returned to the same order of magnitude as the initial controls. An olfactory stimulus that attracted the animal's attention produced a similar blocking effect. While the cat was attentively sniffing tubing through which fish odors were being delivered, the auditory potential in the cochlear nucleus was practically absent (Fig. 1). After the stimulus had been removed and when the cat appeared to be relaxed once more, the auditorily evoked responses in the cochlear nucleus were of the same magnitude as they had been prior to the olfactory stimulation. Similarly, a nociceptive shock delivered to the forepaw of the cat—a shock that apparently distracted the animal's attention—resulted in marked reduction of auditorily evoked responses in the cochlear nucleus.

If this sensory inhibition during attentive behavior, as demonstrated in the auditory pathway, occurs in all other sensory paths except the ones concerned with the object of attention, such an inhibitory mechanism might lead to favoring of the attended object by the selective exclusion of incoming signals. It is conceivable not only that such a selective sensory inhibition might operate simultaneously for various sensory modalities, leaving one or more unaffected but that the selectivity could extend to some discriminable aspects of any single modality—for example, to one tone and not to others. This suggestion finds support in the recent demonstration that sensory "habituation" may occur to a particular tone—that is, a slowly developing inhibitory effect

on auditorily evoked potentials observed in the cochlear nucleus on prolonged repetition of a given tone, an influence that does not affect other frequencies that are novel to the animal (6). The pathway by which this inhibitory influence acts on incoming auditory impulses remains to be determined, but experiments now in progress have shown that during electric stimulation of the midbrain reticular formation, the auditory potential in the cochlear nucleus is depressed (7).

The present observations suggest that the blocking of afferent impulses in the lower portions of a sensory path may be a mechanism whereby sensory stimuli out of the scope of attention can be markedly reduced while they are still in their trajectory toward higher levels of the central nervous system. This central inhibitory mechanism may, therefore, play an important role in selective exclusion of sensory messages along their passage toward mechanisms of perception and consciousness. In a recent symposium on brain mechanisms and consciousness, Adrian pointed out that "the signals from the sense organs must be treated differently when we attend to them and when we do not, and if we could decide where and how the divergence arises we should be nearer to understanding how the level of consciousness is reached" (8).

references

1. J. D. French, M. Verzeano, H. W. Magoun, *Arch. Neurol. Psychiat.* **69**, 505 (1953).
2. K.-E. Hagbarth and D. I. B. Kerr, *J. Neurophysiol.* **17**, 295 (1954).
3. R. Hernández-Peón and K.-E. Hagbarth, *ibid.* **18**, 44 (1955).
4. H. Scherrer and R. Hernández-Peón, *Federation Proc.* **14**, 132 (1955).
5. This work was aided by grants from the

Commonwealth Fund, the National Institute for Neurological Diseases and Blindness of the U.S. Public Health Service, and Eli Lilly and Company. This report is based on a paper presented before the American Physiological Society on 12 Apr. 1955.

6. R. Hernández-Peón and H. Scherrer, *Federation Proc.* **14,** 71 (1955); R. Hernández-Peón, M. Jouvet, H. Scherrer, in preparation.
7. M. Jouvet, E. Berkowitz, R. Hernandez-Peón, in preparation.
8. E. D. Adrian, in *Brain Mechanisms and Consciousness*, J. F. Delafresnaye, Ed. (Blackwell, Oxford, 1954), p. 238.

chemical and somesthetic senses

Although the senses of vision and hearing have been more widely and intensively studied, the research on chemical and somesthetic receptors has often contributed findings that generalize to all the sense modalities. From such research has come the view that neural impulses from groups of individual receptors form patterns that allow stimulus discrimination at the level of the cerebral cortex.

The first article (Reading 8, M. J. Cohen et al.) explores the "representation of sensory modalities on a cellular level in the mammalian cerebral cortex." This article is especially valuable to a student because a good history and references to the literature are included for each experiment and for each surgical and physiological technique as well. In keeping with the hypothesis of sensory patterning of neural impulses was the finding that some single cortical cells respond to stimulation of either the chorda tympani or the trigeminal nerve. Also lending support to the patterning hypothesis were five gustatory or cortical cells that responded to all types of gustatory stimulation. Of further importance to the patterning hypothesis is the demonstration that single, specific cortical cells serve independently each modality: taste, touch, and temperature. The same patterning effects were also noted for both electrical and physiological stimulation of pathways. Further research in this area is needed to follow up the indication that an inhibitory mechanism exists that is important in interaction between cortical and subcortical regions of the brain.

In the next article in this chapter (Reading 9), Carl Pfaffmann extends the patterning hypothesis—which he first discovered in cats—to rats and rabbits. For all three species he found that taste solutions to the tongue "elicit a maintained asynchronous discharge of impulses in the chorda tympani nerve." For all species, single nerve fibers respond to the different stimuli (HCl, KCl, NaCl, and sucrose), but with different thresholds of sensitivity. According to the patterning hypothesis, the discrimination of these responses is made in the cerebral cortex.

In the article by R. M. Gaze and G. Gordon (Reading 10), attention is turned to the cutaneous senses. This paper does not relate directly to the patterning hypothesis, but is a necessary preliminary to later cutaneous research on patterning. Until the cutaneous pathways to the brain are as well known as the gustatory pathways, patterns of neural impulses cannot be worked out. For the student, the main feature of this article is its presentation of the difficulty of locating central pathways and of the precision needed in approaching this task.

The final reading in this section (Reading 11, by John Stamm and Roger Sperry) turns attention to somesthetic sensitivity. Their article reports a straightforward experiment that establishes the fact that the corpus callosum in cats "is essential for the contralateral transfer of somesthetic discrimination from one to the other forepaw."

As research data on somesthesis and the other so-called "minor" senses accumulate, theoretical formulations approaching the level of sophistication of visual and auditory theory will be possible. These "minor" senses are an untapped source of research for future physiological psychologists.

8 touch and taste in the cat *

M. J. Cohen, S. Landgren, L. Strom, and Y. Zotterman

1. Why were two different surgical approaches to the cortical projection area used? What were the advantages and disadvantages of each approach?
2. What difficulties were encountered by the experimenters in the use of the traditional monophasic recording technique?
3. In general, how does the evoked cortical surface potential appear on the oscilloscope?
4. What experiments could be designed to locate the "possible inhibitory mechanism"?

Relatively little information is available concerning the representation of sensory modalities on a cellular level in the mammalian cerebral cortex. Questions arise as to whether a single cortical cell shares afferents from more than one modality; or whether different afferent paths serving the same modality converge on the same cortical cell. The cellular basis for the differentiation of qualities within a given modality such as vision or gustation still remains obscure and the fine cortical representation of the receptive fields within any modality is largely unknown. The importance of the patterning of impulses in cortical

* M. J. Cohen, S. Landgren, L. Ström, and Y. Zotterman, "Cortical Reception of Touch and Taste in the Cat," *Acta Physiol. Scandinav.*, 40 (1957), Suppl., pp. 1–50. Reprinted by courtesy of the authors.

cellular activity is also of interest. Does the discharge of impulses by a cortical cell reflect the frequency and temporal sequence seen in the peripheral neurone or is a more subtle type of coding employed?

It is the purpose of this study to attempt at least a partial solution of these questions with the hope that such information may aid in understanding the cortical elaboration of sensation.

The chorda tympani and the trigeminal component of the lingual nerve were selected as the afferent systems whose cortical representation was to be analyzed. These two nerves innervate the same general area of the tongue and share modalities such as touch and temperature in common. In addition, one modality, taste, is private to the chorda tympani. The peripheral aspect of taste has been worked out in some detail in the cat (43, 44, 38, 12), and it was hoped that this work on the peripheral aspect would provide a basis for the study of sensory qualities at the cortical level.

It has been shown by Patton and Amassian (37) that electrical stimulation of the chorda tympani in the cat evokes a potential which can be recorded within a localized area on the orbital surface of the cerebrum just rostral to the tip of the anterior ectosylvian gyrus. Bilateral destruction of this region in a variety of mammals is known to cause impairment of taste (24, 4, 3) and it is tempting to conclude that the area within which the evoked chorda tympani cortical potential is found corresponds to the cortical projection area of the gustatory path. However, as pointed out by Patton and Amassian, the chorda tympani contains afferent fibres from taste, thermal and tactile receptors from the tongue and it cannot be assumed *a priori* that the projection area of the chorda tympani is the cortical "taste" region. Thus a further analysis of the cortical representation of tongue afferents seemed necessary using a combination of electrical and physiological stimulation to clearly define the modalities involved. This has been carried out in the present study and has led to the conclusion that the most conspicuous component of the potential evoked by the chorda tympani is due to activity in fibres responding to tactile stimulation of the tongue. In addition to "touch cells," cortical cells responding to gustatory and thermal stimuli were also investigated and provided the basis for the type of cellular analysis of sensory modalities mentioned above.

materials and methods

anaesthesia

All experiments were done on cats. A total of 38 animals were used. Nembutal, given intraperitoneally at a dosage of 40 mg/kg body weight, was used for anaesthesia when studying cortical potentials evoked by electrical stimulation of afferent nerves. The desired level of anaesthesia was maintained during the course of the experiment by intravenous injections of the same drug. Several different types of anaesthesia were tried when recording from single cortical cells stimulated by electrical or physiological means. The narcosis was usually initiated by intraperitoneal injection of Intraval (Thiopentone sodium, May and Baker) at a dosage of 40 mg/kg body weight. As the effect of this anaesthetic rapidly wears off the animal could be maintained in a stage of anaesthesia during the experiment by intravenous injection of either Intraval or 1% chloralose. Of these two drugs, chloralose caused less depression of the cortical activity and yielded the best preparations.

In three control experiments of combination of aether during surgical preparation and curare (d—tubocurarine) during the recording was tried but was abandoned because the resulting cortical state was more depressed than with Intraval-chloralose. In a small number of experiments the spinal cord was cut at C 1, however, this also seemed to depress cortical activity. Whether cortical depression following cord section was due to circulatory or nervous effects is not known, but it appeared that the blood supply to the hemisphere under observation was unimpaired.

surgery

Two different approaches to the cortical projection area of the tongue were used, one direct and one indirect.

In the direct approach the hemisphere was exposed after removal of the eye, *m. temporalis*, *m. masseter* and the *os zygomaticus*. The ipsilateral mandible caudal to the molars was removed without opening the mouth cavity to expose the junction between the chorda tympani and the trigeminal component of the lingual nerve. This allowed these nerves to be cut or stimulated according to the demands of the experiment. The middle ear was opened with a dental drill and the chorda tympani exposed for recording or stimulation. In order to have the cortical hemisphere and the ipsilateral afferent nerves in the same paraffin pool, the skin was incised in a parasagittal plane just medial to the eye and ear and then ventrally towards the angulus mandibuli. The paraffin pool was kept at 37°C by a glass tube containing a heated wire coil.

The indirect approach demanded much less dissection. The skull was opened with a trephine close to the midline over the sinus frontalis to expose the cortex surrounding the sulcus cruciatus. In order to reach the tongue projection area on the orbital surface of the frontal lobe, the microelectrode was inserted at the lateral end of the sulcus cruciatus and driven ventrally through the cortex for 6 to 10 mm. This method had the advantage of a rapid dissection with little trauma to the animal and the possibility of using very light anaesthesia. The disadvantages were the inability of using electrical stimulation of the afferent nerves in combination with the physiological stimuli, and the difficulty of finding the appropriate cortical area without the aid of the evoked cortical surface potential. The indirect approach was used in one series of experiments to look for cortical cells stimulated via the tongue receptors.

fixation of the preparation

The animal was suspended in a frame designed by Mr. G. J. Winsbury of the department of Physiology, the Australian National University. Fixation of the skull was achieved by a technique similar to that used in the Horsley-Clarke apparatus. In experiments where ear plugs could not be used, they were replaced by a clamp fixed to the edge of the skull surrounding the exposed cortex or to the caudal process of the *os zygomaticus*. A fairly rigid fixation of the cranium was achieved this way. The greatest technical difficulty was encountered in immobilizing the cortex. The technique adopted consisted in minimizing the movement by exposing the whole hemisphere and draining the cerebrospinal fluid by opening the ventricles through the *cisterna magna* as described by Li and Jasper (33). In addition the thorax was opened and artificial respiration given with a minimum volume of 2% carbon dioxide in oxygen (23). Although effective, these arrangements were not enough to immobilize the cortex. Therefore a transparent plastic plate of the type described by Phillips (39) was lightly pressed against the cortical surface. The microelectrode was inserted through a hole in the plate or through the meshes of a nylon net which sometimes replaced the plate.

recording and stimulation techniques

The microelectrodes used consisted of the conventional micropipette drawn from pyrex glass and filled with 3 M KCl. Electrodes with a tip diameter of 1 to 3 μ and a resistance less than one megohm were used for recording mass effects from pools of neurones. When recording from single cells, electrodes were used with a tip diameter less than 1 μ and a resistance of 5 to 30 megohms. The microelectrodes were inserted with a micromanipulator designed by G. J. Winsbury and described by Eccles, Fatt, Landgren and Winsbury (18).

A positivity of the recording electrode is indicated as a downward deflection in all records. The spontaneous cortical activity always present in a lightly anaesthetised preparation made it necessary to use comparatively short amplifier time constants (50 msec) when recording the slow evoked cortical potentials with the superposed sweep technique. The slight distortion of the records was of no importance for the conclusions drawn in this paper. The time course of any slow, low amplitude potentials following large potentials were always checked with long time constant (0.5 sec) records.

The cortical potentials were recorded either between a platinum wire in contact with the surface of the cortex and a reference electrode, or between the tip of a microelectrode and the same reference electrode. The reference electrode was a chlorided silver plate wrapped in gauze cloth and sewn to the inside of the scalp skin flap which formed one side of the paraffin pool. The surface electrode was a small platinum bead at the end of a platinum wire spring.

Surface potentials from the cortex and action potentials from peripheral nerves were amplified in an RC-coupled amplifier, with a time constant which could be varied from 3 to 40 msec. For microelectrode recordings a DC-amplifier with a balanced cathode follower input stage was used. This amplifier could also be connected to perform as an RC-coupled one, with a time-constant which could be varied from 5 msec to 90 sec. The potentials were displayed on two double beam CRO-s with two cameras, one for running film recording on 35 mm paper, the other for single and multiple sweep recording on stationary 35 mm film.

Two Grass stimulators (S 4) and stimulus isolation units (SIU 4) were used for electrical stimulation. They were connected through a stimulus distribution unit which permitted connection of either or both stimulators to any one of five output receptacles. The stimulus electrodes were small flexible platinum hooks and they were also used to record from the nerves.

results

the length of the afferent nerve paths

The chorda tympani was stimulated electrically either in the middle ear or in the lingual nerve trunk 5 to 10 mm distal to the junction of the chorda and trigeminal part of the lingual nerve. The middle ear portion of the chorda was used both for stimulation and recording; the distance from this point to the root entry of the facial nerve was 20 to 25 mm. The distance from the middle ear to the stimulation point on the chorda-lingual trunk varied from 25 to 49 mm.

The trigeminal path was stimulated either central to the junction with the chorda or in the lingual nerve 5 to 10 mm distal to the junction. The length of the peripheral conduction path was 30 mm in the latter case.

In two cats, the nerves were dissected from the tongue to where the cranial roots join the medulla in order to determine the length of the conduction paths. The following measurements were obtained.

Chorda Tympani

Distance from the root entry of *n. facialis* to the borderline between the posterior and middle thirds of the tongue:

    Exp. 21/11. 55 (cat 3.2 kg) 85 mm.
    Exp. 16/2. 56 (cat 2.5 kg) 88 mm.

Distance from the root entry of *n. facialis* to the tip of the tongue:

    Exp. 21/11. 55 105 mm.
    Exp. 16/2. 56 118 mm.

The trigeminal component of n. lingualis

Distance from the root entry of *n. trigeminus* to the borderline between the caudal and middle thirds of the tongue:

    Exp. 21/11. 55 62 mm.
    Exp. 16/2. 56 70 mm.

Distance from the root entry of *n. trigeminus* to the tip of the tongue:

    Exp. 21/11. 55 82 mm.
    Exp. 16/2. 56 100 mm.

The length of the central pathways from the root entrances to the cerebral cortex can only be estimated roughly by measurements on dissected brains. The distance from the root entry of the facial nerve to the cortical projection area in the rostral extension of the ectosylvian gyrus is estimated as 60 mm. The corresponding distance from the root of the trigeminal nerve to the cortex is about 10 mm shorter. The total length of the chorda tympani path from the receptors of the tongue to the ipsilateral cerebral cortex is therefore approximately 140 to 180 mm and that of the trigeminal path about 110 to 150 mm.

the conduction velocity of the chorda fibres

In studying the diameters of chorda tympani fibres, Zotterman (43) found that a few were of large size (8 μ) but the great majority of the fibres had a diameter of 4 μ. On the basis of records from single touch, cold and pain fibres in the lingual nerve of the cat Zotterman (44) concluded that their respective relative conduction velocities were 5 : 2 : 1. The spike amplitude of the taste and warm fibres was about $\frac{1}{5}$ that of the largest touch fibres while the amplitude of the cold and pain spikes were $\frac{1}{9}$ that of the touch fibres. Thus in the chorda tympani or the lingual nerve, the spikes of largest amplitude were always associated with touch fibres and these fibres may be considered as the fastest of the tongue afferents.

In order to interpret the evoked cortical response, it was necessary to define the different fibre groups in the chorda tympani and to measure their thresholds and conduction velocities. The compound action potential of the chorda tympani was analyzed by differential recording from the intact chorda in the middle ear, when stimulating the lingual nerve. The potential obtained by this method is shown in Fig. 1 B. It has a rather complicated time course, but for the present purpose it is sufficient to note the small spike of shortest latency which is seen initiating the potential complex in Fig. 1 B. This spike appears with threshold stimulation of the nerve and was interpreted as due to the fastest of the chorda fibres, i.e. to fibres mediating touch from the tongue.

The experimental procedure generally required that the threshold of the fastest and second fastest group of chorda fibres be determined before cutting or crushing the chorda or the lingual nerve. The conventional monophasic recording technique could thus not be

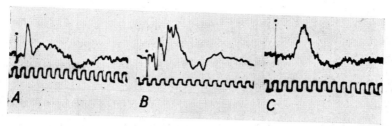

Fig. 1. (A) Monophasic spike potential recorded from the lingual nerve when stimulating the chorda tympani in the middle ear. Time: 1 msec. (B) Multiphasic action potential of chorda tympani recorded in the middle ear when stimulating the lingual nerve. Time: 1 msec. (C) Monophasic spike potential recorded from the nerve of the submaxillary gland when stimulating the chorda tympani in the middle ear. Time: 2 msec.

adopted. In a control experiment, however, the action potential of the chorda was recorded monophasically from the lingual nerve when stimulating the chorda tympani in the middle ear. The potential is shown in Fig. 1 A and consists of two components, a spike-like potential caused by a rather synchronous group of rapidly conducting fibres and a later wave of longer duration. The initial spike potential corresponds in time and threshold to the initial spike of the differentially recorded multiphasic potential, whereas the complex of later spikes seen in the multiphasic record appear simultaneously with the later wave in the monophasic potential. The relative thresholds and the conduction velocities of the fastest (I) and second fastest (II) group of chorda fibres are given in Table I.

As the efferent secretory fibres of the chorda tympani will contribute to the compound action potential of the nerve, it was considered of interest to determine the threshold and conduction velocity of this fibre group. This was done by recording from the branch of the chorda to the submaxillary gland while stimulating the chorda in the middle ear. The result is shown in Fig. 1 C. The potential was a rather uniform negative wave with a latency of 3.8 msec and a duration of 7 msec. The threshold of the potential was 1.5 times that of the lowest threshold chorda fibres recorded from the lingual nerve. The conduction velocity of the secretory fibres was 4 to 12 m/sec.

The records of the compound action potential of the chorda tympani thus demonstrate the existence of separable groups of afferent fibres which can be distinguished on the basis of differences in threshold and conduction velocity. The first group, with the lowest

Table 1

		Group I		Group II	
Exp.		Threshold	Cond. veloc. m/sec	Threshold (relative to Group I)	Cond. veloc. m/sec
16/2. 56.........		1	58	1.2	35
1/3. 56.........		1	61	1.4	30
19/3. 56.........		1	45	1.4	28	Differential recording
10/4. 56.........		1	46	1.2	38
10/4. 56.........		1	51	1.3	24	Monophasic recording

threshold and a conduction velocity of about 50 m/sec, can be assumed to correspond to the small number of large diameter touch fibres described by Zotterman. The second wave of the monophasic potential, corresponding to the second and all later components of the multiphasic potential, is apparently due to the activity of several different fibre types with conduction velocities varying from 6–30 m/sec. Using the relative figures of Zotterman quoted above the cold fibres from the tongue would be expected to have a conduction velocity of 20 m/sec and taste and warm fibres should have a slightly higher conduction rate. These fibres should thus contribute to the initial part of the later complex of the chorda action potential, whereas the secretory fibres should give rise to the tail of this potential.

evoked cortical potentials

the evoked cortical surface potential

The cortical surface potential evoked by electrical stimulation of the ipsilateral chorda

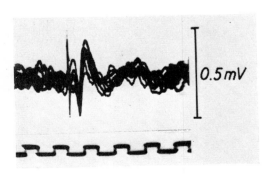

Fig. 2. Cortical surface response to single shock excitation of the ipsilateral chorda tympani. 25 superposed sweeps. Downward deflection indicates surface positivity. Time: 20 msec. Amplifier time constant TC = 40 msec.

tympani is shown in Fig. 2 and consists of an initial diphasic positive-negative wave with a very constant latency and duration followed immediately by a less regular positive-negative-positive complex of low amplitude and longer duration. An initial diphasic potential with a much lower amplitude was also obtained when the contralateral chorda was stimulated. The ipsilateral and contralateral trigeminal components of the lingual nerve also evoked similar potentials but generally of larger amplitude. These observations confirm the previous findings of Patton and Amassian (37) and were expected from earlier investigations on other parts of the somatosensory cortex (22, 2).

The latency of the initial positive phase of the evoked cortical potential (the primary response) is shown in the following table.

Table 2

Afferent nerve stimulated	Latency in msec Ipsilateral	Contralateral
Chorda tympani	4–6	5–10
Trigeminal comp. of the lingual nerve	3–4	5–6

The latencies were measured on records of 25 superposed sweeps or a series of 10 to 40 single sweeps. The ipsilateral potentials were studied in 15 and the contralateral in 6 animals.

The duration of the initial positive-negative potential was about 20 msec. The late negative wave was less regular and was sometimes difficult to separate from the spontaneous background activity. It had a latency of 20–30 msec and a duration of about 30 msec.

The peripheral conduction path of the ipsilateral chorda from the site of stimulation to the entry of the facial nerve into the medulla was about 60 mm. With a conduction velocity of 60 m/sec the fastest of the chorda fibres would have a peripheral conduction time of 1 msec. The time required for central conduction, including any synaptic delays, will then be 3–5 msec. In the case of the trigeminal component of the lingual nerve, the peripheral conduction path was 30 mm and the peripheral conduction time for the fastest of the ipsilateral fibres is therefore about 0.5 msec thus leaving 2.5 to 3.5 msec for central conduction and synaptic delay. As the contralateral paths were stimulated at corresponding levels their peripheral conduction times should be of the same magnitude as the ipsilateral paths. The latency of the contralateral responses was generally somewhat longer than the ipsilateral ones. In the case of the trigeminal path the difference in latency was 1–2 msec. The difference in latency between the contra- and ipsilateral chorda responses varied from 0 to 5 msec in different experiments. The responses from both sides were evoked by stimuli close to the threshold of the nerves and we therefore conclude that they are due to impulses in touch fibres, and that touch fibres of the chorda tympani and the trigeminal component of the lingual nerve have bilateral cortical projections.

The most conspicuous feature of the evoked surface response is the initial diphasic positive-negative potential. Experiments presented below provide further evidence that the initial positive phase of this potential when evoked by either chorda tympani or the trigeminal part of the lingual nerve is due to activity in the pathways normally responding to tactile stimulation of the tongue. As the borderlines of the cortical projection areas in this series were mapped on the basis of the initial positive potential, these maps indicate the cortical projection areas of touch from the tongue. The cortical projection areas of the ipsilateral chorda tympani and trigeminal

component of the lingual nerve were mapped in 15 experiments and those of the contralateral nerves in 5 experiments. Fig. 3 shows the result of one such experiment. It is of interest to note the great overlap in the cortical projection areas of the different tongue afferents. In many experiments the ipsilateral chorda response area extended somewhat more ventrally than the ipsilateral projection area of the trigeminal component of the lingual nerve. The projection area of the ipsilateral or contralateral trigeminal component was always larger than the response area of the ipsilateral chorda. The contralateral chorda tympani response was comparatively weak and was seen close to the point where the ipsilateral chorda evoked a potential of maximum amplitude. In some experiments no contralateral chorda response was obtained. The ipsilateral nerves of both pathways generally had their maximal response at the same point. The greatest amplitude of the contralateral trigeminal component response was found a few mm more rostrally. The extent of the response areas was greatly dependent on the state of the preparation. The largest response areas were obtained from lightly anaesthetized preparations in good circulatory condition with a normal body temperature and a temperature of 37°C in the paraffin bath covering the cortex.

Our observations agree with those of Patton and Amassian in regard to the localization of the responsive cortical zone. It is found dorsal to the rhinal fissure and the presylvian sulcus, caudal and ventral to the lateral tip of the coronal sulcus and cranial to a small dimple which is found rostral to the anterior sulcus and ventral to the rostral tip of the suprasylvian sulcus. It is thus within the area where the ectosylvian and suprasylvian gyri join the sigmoid gyrus.

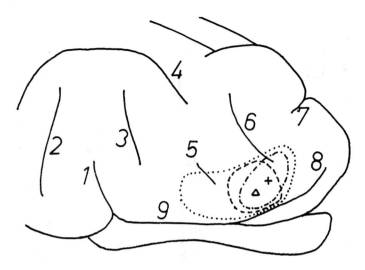

Fig. 3. Map of the cortical zones within which a cortical surface potential was evoked by electrical stimulation of the ipsilateral chorda tympani (dashed line), the ipsilateral trigeminal component of the lingual nerve (dotted line) and the contralateral trigeminal component of the lingual nerve (dash − dot line). △ maximal ipsilateral chorda and lingual-trigeminal response. + maximal contralateral lingual-trigeminal response. 1: Sulcus Sylvii; 2: S. posterior; 3: S. anterior; 4: S. suprasylvius; 5: small dimple often found anterior and ventral to the rostral ends of 3 and 4; 6: S. coronalis; 7: S. cruciatus; 8: S. praesylvius; 9: S. rhinalis. The map gives the results from one experiment.

The cortical potential evoked by stimulation of the glossopharyngeal nerve was investigated in one experiment only and the responsive zone of this nerve was found to overlap the dorsal part of the chorda-lingual area. The maximum amplitude of the glossopharyngeal response was found in the rostral part of the suprasylvian gyrus entirely outside the chorda lingual area, some 10–15 mm dorsal to the maximum response of the latter.

Bremer (4) has described an area "profonde à la base des circonvolutions présylviennes" as a sensorimotor area for the tongue and masticatory muscles in the cat. The motor effects of direct stimulation of the cortex within the area of the evoked chorda-lingual response was therefore tested in two experiments and in both instances movements of the jaw and pharynx muscles could be elicited from this area.

evoked potential recorded in volume at varying depths below the surface of the cortex (the focal potential)

Previous investigations (15, 40, 6, 2, 13) have shown that the initial portion of an evoked cortical potential changes from a positive wave to a negative wave of the same latency and duration when recording at increasing depths below the cortex surface. The same pattern was found irrespective of the function of the cortical area investigated and it should thus be expected to also appear in the cortical tongue area. This was found to be true. Fig. 4 shows a sequence of potentials recorded with a microelectrode at 0.35 to 2.25 mm below the surface of the cortex. The microelectrode penetrated the cortex in the area where the evoked surface potential showed a maximum amplitude. The afferent nerve stimulated in this case was the ipsilateral trigeminal component of the lingual nerve. The ipsilateral chorda potentials also showed a similar pattern. At a depth of 0.35 mm the response is still very similar to the evoked surface potential, with a diphasic positive-negative wave and a latency identical to that of the surface response. At 0.55 mm the initial positive wave is replaced by a negative spike-like potential of the same latency but of larger amplitude. The amplitude of this negative wave increases to a maximum at a depth of 1.10 mm (range in different experiments 0.8–1.5 mm) and then slowly declines with increasing depth and disappears at about 3 mm below the surface. The change from the positive-negative surface pattern to an initially negative potential was observed between 0.4 and 0.9 mm below the surface in different experiments. In one experiment the initial deep negative wave changed into a positive one at a depth of 2.4 mm. The positive potential showed a smaller amplitude than the surface positively. It was possibly caused by penetration of the microelectrode into superficial cortical layers in the depth of a sulcus.

The latency of the initial phase of the evoked potential was the same independent of its sign or its depth below the surface. When

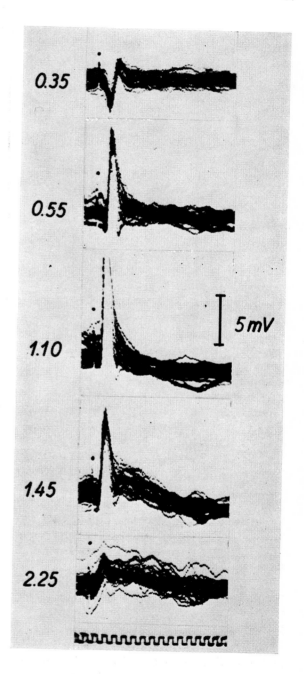

Fig. 4. The cortical focal response evoked by electrical stimulation of the ipsilateral trigeminal component of the lingual nerve and recorded with microelectrode at various depths below cortex surface. The figures indicate depth in mm below the surface. Downward deflection signals positivity in these and in all the subsequent records. Time: 5 msec. TC = 50 msec. 25 superposed sweeps.

the potential was produced by an afferent volley in the ipsilateral chorda tympani the latency was 4–6 msec. A volley in the ipsilateral trigeminal component of the lingual nerve, however, evoked a focal potential with a latency of 3–5 msec. The latencies thus agree with those of the potentials recorded with a surface wire lead and show a conduction time which is about 1 msec longer for the pathway through the chorda tympani than for that through the trigeminal nerve. Except for this difference in latency the cortical potentials evoked by electrical stimulation of the two afferent paths are very similar.

A close inspection of the records of Fig. 4 reveals a few other details of interest. At a depth of 1.10 mm the initial negative wave is of maximum amplitude and is followed by a shallow positivity of rather long duration. Viz.: 50–80 msec.

Further down below the surface of the cortex at 1.45 mm in Fig. 4 the initial negative spike-like potential is followed by another small negative wave. This is sometimes seen as a hump on the falling phase of the large negative wave and it has a latency of 10–20 msec. It is difficult to determine the duration of this late negative wave, because it is superimposed on the slow positive potential which follows the large initial negative spike at this depth. At a depth of 2.25 mm where the initial negativity is almost gone and the positivity has disappeared (Fig. 4), the small late negative wave has hardly been reduced in amplitude and has a duration of about 50 msec.

Microelectrode tracks were made in different parts of the cortical area within which the evoked surface response could be obtained. As the electrodes were moved farther from the point of maximum response, both the surface and deep focal potentials decreased in amplitude to the same extent until a point was reached where surface and deep responses were completely absent. There was no change in the sequence or shape of the evoked potentials as the electrode was moved away from the point of maximum response.

the afferent fibres responsible for the evoked potentials

The small difference in latency between the cortical surface potentials evoked by the ipsilateral chorda tympani and by the trigeminal component of the lingual nerve and also the similarity of their threshold to electrical stimulation raised the suspicion that they were both due primarily to impulses in fast afferents of low threshold, i.e. to touch fibres.

As described above it was possible to grade the strength of the electrical stimulus so as to stimulate discrete fibre groups of the chorda tympani. The surface response as well as the focal potentials evoked by the ipsilateral chorda at various depths below the surface of the cortex were tested using different stimulus strengths. It is clear that the primary response, whether positive or negative in sign, is maximal in amplitude below or just above the threshold of the second fastest fibre group. With further increase of the stimulus strength the amplitude as well as the time course of the primary response remained unchanged. The latency and low threshold for the primary cortical response indicated that it is evoked by the fast chorda fibres conducting at 30 to 60 m/sec.

The late negative wave also belongs to the effects of the fast, low threshold fibres. It is already fully developed with a stimulus strength of 0.27 V which only excites the fastest chorda fibres. In the experiment these fibres had a measured conduction velocity between 30 and 45 m/sec. The significance of this late negativity and also of the preceding positive potential will be discussed later. From our knowledge of the conduction rates in the different fibre types of the chorda, it now becomes clear that the initial and most conspicuous component of the evoked cortical potential is due to touch impulses from the tongue. The final proof will be given later in this paper, showing that chorda fibres belonging to the group with the lowest threshold end on cortical cells responding to tactile stimulation of the tongue.

the effect of strychnine on the evoked potentials

When a piece of filter paper soaked in 1% strychnine nitrate solution was placed on the surface of the cortex, typical changes well known from other cortical areas occurred in the evoked potential recorded with a surface wire lead. The initial surface positivity increased slightly in amplitude. The most conspicuous change, however, was the increase in amplitude of the surface negative phase following the initial positivity (see Fig. 5/A). This large negative wave was followed immediately by one or two positive-negative waves of lower amplitude. The effect of strychnine on the evoked potential recorded by the microelectrode down to a depth of about 0.4 mm below the surface of the cortex was essentially similar to the effect on the surface response. When recording at a depth of about 1 mm where the initial phase of the focal potential is negative, local application of strychnine caused a moderate increase of the initial negative phase and a very pronounced increase of the following positivity (Fig. 5 B). In the control records this positivity was a rather shallow wave with a duration of 50–80 msec. After strychnine its amplitude exceeded that of the initial negative phase. Its duration was about 50 msec. The negative-positive complex was sometimes fol-

lowed by a damped out series of negative-positive waves. When the evoked potential recorded from the surface was compared with that recorded about 1 mm below the surface it was seen that the large strychnine surface negative wave corresponded in time to the deep positive potential (Fig. 5 B and C).

As strychnine enhances the activity of certain neurones, the development of a large surface negative potential and a corresponding positivity below 0.8 mm may be interpreted as an increased activity in a superficial neuron pool which sends axons or dendrites down to the cortical layers about 1 mm below the surface.

interaction between consecutive afferent volleys

When the frequency of the shocks applied to the afferent nerve was increased above 5/sec the amplitude of the focal potential recorded at all depths below the surface of the cortex decreased. The focal potential failed almost completely at a stimulus frequency of 50/sec.

The ability of a test volley to evoke a cortical surface response at various intervals after a conditioning shock has been studied by many authors [for references see (16)]. It was found that the second response was not appreciably diminished until the stimulus interval was less than 150 msec and that at intervals less than 10 msec the test response was frequently completely abolished. In our experiments the superficial positive and the deep negative potentials were examined with conditioning and test volleys in the chorda tympani and also in the trigeminal component of the lingual nerve.

The cortical potential evoked by the test volley was reduced when the interval was

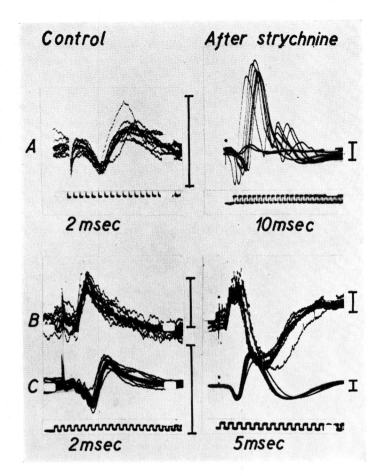

Fig. 5. Cortical response before (left) and after (right) local application of strychnine to cortex. (*A*) Surface response to stimulation of the ipsilateral chorda tympani. TC = 150 msec. (*B*) Response 1.3 mm below the surface. TC = 50 msec. (*C*) Surface response. TC = 40 msec. B. and C. are simultaneously recorded while stimulating the ipsilateral lingual nerve. Note the different time and voltage scales before and after strychnine application. All records formed by 10 superposed sweeps. 1 mV voltage scales to the right of each record.

shorter than 130 msec. At intervals of 20 msec the amplitude of the test response was reduced by approximately 50%.

The effect on the focal potentials evoked by a conditioning volley in the chorda and a test volley in the trigeminal component, or vice versa, was also investigated. Where the sequence consisted of trigeminal stimulation fol-lowed by chorda stimulation, the effect on the evoked potentials was very similar to that described when test and conditioning shocks were applied to the same nerve. With the reciprocal situation, however, it was never possible to completely abolish a trigeminal evoked response no matter how closely it followed the chorda conditioning volley. We take this to indicate that there are a significant number of cortical neurones that are stimulated only by the trigeminal volley, while most of the cortical cells fired by the chorda tympani are also stimulated by the trigeminal pathway. Further evidence for the convergence of chorda and trigeminal influence on the same cortical cells will be given below in the single unit studies.

experiments on single cortical cells

The microelectrode technique enabled us to record from single cortical cells. The type of action potential obtained when recording extracellularly close to a cell was generally a diphasic positive-negative spike with a duration of about 1 msec and an amplitude of 1 to 5 mV superimposed on a negative wave of 10 to 30 msec duration. The diphasic spike was interpreted as the propagated action potential of the neuron, and the slow negative wave as a summed effect of slow nonpropagated, postsynaptic potentials from the cell and of local as well as propagated potentials from the surrounding neurone pool. The slow negative wave is equivalent to the focal potential recorded with coarse electrodes at the corresponding depth.

When recording at a distance from a cell, monophasic negative spikes were seen and these changed to the diphasic type as the cell was approached. A microelectrode often slipped into a cell and a membrane potential of —20 to—70 mV was recorded together with a monophasic positive potential when the cell was fired. However, following penetration the membrane potential usually rapidly decreased and the cell fired at a high frequency and died. The observed intracellular potentials were similar to those described by Brock, Coombs and Eccles (5) for the motoneurone. A prepotential as well as a propagated spike were seen. As it was difficult to get a stable reasonably high membrane potential from these cells, very little information was gained from the intracellular records. Almost all effects described in the following part of the paper are based on extracellular records. When recording extracellularly the cells showed a constant response for 5 to more than 60 minutes and they offered an opportunity for analysis with physiological stimuli.

the convergence of chorda and trigeminal fibres on cortical cells

The first series of experiments on cortical cells made during this investigation was designed to determine if chorda and trigeminal fibres converged on single cortical cells. The ipsilateral afferent nerves were dissected free, cut and stimulated separately with electrical shocks strong enough to elicit the evoked cortical surface potential but subthreshold to the linguomandibular reflex (29). It was necessary to avoid this reflex in order to prevent the preparation from moving. As the reflex is elicited with rather weak stimulation of the trigeminal component of the lingual nerve the stimuli had to be chosen rather close to the threshold. Curare was not used in this series because it appeared to depress cortical activity. The linguomandibular reflex could be elicited through the ipsilateral chorda tympani but here a much stronger stimulus was required. In some experiments even a strong stimulus to the chorda did not give rise to the reflex. Unfortunately in this series of experiments the stimulus strength was not related to the group of afferent fibres stimulated, nor were the cells investigated with physiological stimuli to the tongue. Nothing is therefore known about the functions of the individual cells. However, our later experience with the difficulty of finding cells which could be excited by anything other than tactile stimulation of the tongue makes it likely that most of the cells which we found to be excited via the chorda and the trigeminal component of the lingual nerve are touch cells.

In this series a total of 80 single cortical cells were investigated. They were found between 0.2 and 3.4 mm below the surface of the cortex but more than 90% were recorded between 0.6 and 2.2 mm. Most of the cells (80%) were spontaneously active. Of the 80 cells observed 53 could not be stimulated either via the ipsilateral chorda tympani or via the trigeminal component of the lingual nerve; 17 cells were fired by both afferent paths; 9 cells were discharged only by an afferent volley in the trigeminal component of the lingual nerve and only one cell was private to the chorda tympani path.

A cell found at a depth of 1.25 mm below the surface of the cortex could be discharged by electrical stimulation of the ipsilateral chorda tympani as well as of the trigeminal component. The response was a diphasic positive-negative spike riding on the rising phase of a negative focal potential. The latencies from the stimulus artifact to the beginning of the negative potential was 4.6 to 5.0 msec and the latency of the spike potential of the cell was 5.2 to 6.4 msec. When stimulating the ipsilateral chorda tympani, on the other hand, the latency of the negative potential was 6.1 to 6.5 msec and that of the action potential of the cell was 6.4 to 7.6 msec. The response to the chorda volley thus occurred about 1 to 1.5 msec later than the trigeminal response. The difference in latency between the propagated spikes thus agrees very closely with the corresponding difference previously described between latencies of evoked focal potentials.

The important conclusion to be drawn from the above series of experiments is, however, that fibres from the chorda and the trigeminal path converge onto the same cortical cells.

One cell was only discharged via the trigeminal path. The chorda, however, evoked a large negative potential at this point indicating that cells in the neighbourhood are affected by the chorda volley. It can, of course, not be excluded that part of the negative chorda potential is due to a nonpropagated response in the cell which was discharged by the trigeminal volley. If this were true then it must be assumed that the convergence of chorda fibres on the cell was too small to elicit a propagated response. Evidence of such a difference in the convergence of chorda and trigeminal fibres on the same cortical cells was in fact seen in some of the cells which could be discharged via both afferent paths. In such cells a volley in the chorda gave rise to one spike while a weaker trigeminus shock elicited 2 or 3 spikes.

The cell which was discharged only via the chorda tympani was found at a depth of 2.2 mm and showed a latency of 7.3–10 msec. The long latency and the absence of a trigeminal evoked discharge suggests that this cell is not stimulated by touch fibres. In fact the depth corresponds to that of the small number of cortical cells which have been found responsive only to taste stimulation of the tongue.

It is interesting to note the large number of spontaneously active cells which could not be affected by the stimuli used. This may be due partially to the depressed state of the anaesthetized cortex. Two observations speak in favour of this suggestion. In some of these spontaneous cells in which no effect was noted when tested extracellularly with shocks to both afferent paths, a nonpropagated potential evoked by the afferent stimulation was observed when the microelectrode slipped intracellularly. The cell was thus affected by the stimulus although it was not observed in the extracellular record because the effect was too weak to elicit a propagated spike. It was also observed that the proportion of unaffected cells was smaller in very lightly anaesthetized preparations in good circulatory condition.

touch cells

A total of 43 single cortical cells were observed which responded to touch or light pressure of the tongue. They were found at all depths between 0.5 and 2.4 mm below the surface of the cortex. Of these cells 70% were found between 0.7 and 1.5 mm below the surface of the cortex, 20% were found deeper and 10% more superficially. All touch cells are thus found within the depths where the evoked potentials showed an initially negative phase and there was an obvious concentration of the observation at depths where this negative phase had its largest amplitude. When searching for cells, the microelectrode tracks were usually made within the area where the surface response had its maximal amplitude.

The stimulus used was light pressure on the surface of the tongue or a light stroke over the papillae with a glass rod. Generally a slight deformation of the tongue surface was enough to fire the cortex cell but in a few cases more pronounced pressure was necessary. Squirting a few drops of Ringer's solution on the tongue often elicited a response. In one case pricking the ipsilateral tip of the tongue with a needle was a more effective stimulus than touching this area with the glass rod. The majority of the touch cells were tested with taste solutions (bitter, salt, sweet and sour) and with warm and cold water. No touch cell did, however, respond to these stimuli. When possible, the cells were tested with electrical stimuli to the afferent nerves.

the receptive fields

The receptor areas of the touch cells investigated were all found within the anterior two-thirds of the tongue. Most of the cells (29) had an ipsilateral receptor area. Three cells showed a more diffuse receptor field located on both sides of the anterior half of the tongue. One of these cells also responded to touch within a restricted area of the *planum nasale* along both sides of the *philtrum*. Two cells showed a well-localized contralateral receptor area. The borderlines of the receptive field were not adequately investigated in the remaining 9 cells. That only a small number of the cells were stimulated from the contralateral side of the tongue may be due to the fact that most of the microelectrode tracks were made within the area where the ipsilateral surface potential showed a maximum amplitude. Although the cortical projection areas overlap, the maximum of the contralateral response is found somewhat more rostrally as described previously in this paper.

When the 29 ipsilateral receptor areas were compared, it was found that 6 were located on the papillae of the dorsal surface of the tongue. Twelve were found on the ipsilateral edge but did not reach the tip of the tongue. Some of these areas were rather small and well defined. One cell responded to stimulation of the ipsilateral edge and tip and three others only to the ipsilateral tip of the tongue. Only one cell was found responsive to tactile stimulation of the ventral side of the edge of the tongue. The remaining 6 cells showed less well-defined receptor fields comprising large regions of the anterior half of the ipsilateral side of the tongue.

the afferent fibres exciting the touch cells

A number of cortical cells which were shown responsive to tactile stimulation of the tongue were also fired by electrical stimulation of the ipsilateral chorda tympani or the ipsilateral trigeminal component of the lingual nerve. Their threshold to electrical stimulation was measured and compared with the threshold of action potentials recorded from the chorda tympani in the middle ear. It was found that the cortical touch cells responded to stimuli just above the threshold of the fast, low threshold chorda fibres and that this was also the threshold of the evoked cortical surface potential. These cortical cells are thus activated by the fastest of the chorda fibres with a conduction velocity of about 50 m/sec or in some cases by trigeminal fibres with approximately the same conduction velocity and threshold.

the latency of the physiologically stimulated touch cells

The latency from the moment of touching the tongue to the discharge of the cortical cell was measured in a number of experiments. The results are given in the following table.

Table 3

| | Number of | Latency, msec | |
Exp.	observations	Range	Mean
10/5. 55	2		8
24/5. 55	14	32–80	52
26/5. 55	9	11–15	12
27/6. 55	15	8–50	20
1/7. 55	48	9–34	14
23/2. 56	1		5
5/3. 56	15	11–87	32

A blunt platinum wire was used for tactile stimulation of the tongue and the contact artifact was passed through a RC amplifier and recorded on one beam of a dual beam oscilloscope to serve as a stimulus marker. In the last two experiments the impulse activity in a branch of the contralateral lingual nerve was used in order to obtain indication of the time course of the afferent volley. It is, of course, difficult to determine the exact moment of application of the touch stimulus to the receptor. The stimulating rod may have made contact with the tongue at an unknown distance from the receptor and then moved into the receptive field. If this has been the case, the latencies will be too long. As could be expected there is a great deal of variation in the measured values. Table 3 shows a range of latencies from 5 to 87 msec, i.e. from values comparable to the latencies found when the afferents were stimulated electrically up to values about 20 times as long as the latency for the electrically evoked response. The great variability is in agreement with the experiments of Lele, Sinclair and Wedell (30) in which they examined the reaction time to touch in human subjects. The reaction time to touch of a finger was, as could be expected, considerably longer and varied from 180 to 300 msec depending partially on the intensity of the stimulus.

the pattern of activity of the touch cells

When a short discrete touch stimulus was applied to the tongue using a blunt rod with a diameter of about 1 mm, the cortical touch cell responded with a typical pattern of activity. The activity of the cortical cell was recorded on one beam, and the afferent impulses in a cut branch of the contralateral lingual nerve on the other in order to monitor the form of the afferent volley. Although this index does not give an exact picture of the afferent inflow causing the cortical activity it does give an idea of the shape of the stimulus and the latency of the response. The moment of first contact with the tongue in this preparation is also marked by a small spike-like artifact visible in the lower trace of each record. With each touch of the tongue a negative wave is evoked with a duration of 20 to 30 msec and a latency of 20 msec. Two propagated action potentials are riding on top of this wave. A shallow positivity follows the negative wave and there is a pause in the impulse activity of the cell during the positive phase of the slow potential. The length of the pause was 50 to 100 msec with a mean value of 60 msec. A slow negative potential, with an irregular time course but generally of a longer duration and always with a lower amplitude than the initial negative wave, followed the positive phase and a series of propagated spikes occurred on top of the late slow negativity. The length of this late train of impulses varied greatly with the stimulus. The late response usually had a duration from 100 to 800 msec. The mean impulse frequency during the entire late series of response was 25 to 85 imp/sec. The frequency of firing during a burst may range from 500 to 800 imp/sec and the burst may be followed by pauses in activity generally lasting between 50 and 100 msec. During the pauses, a return of the baseline to zero or a slight positivity was usually seen. It is interesting to note that the afferent volley continues during the pause in activity of the cell following the initial response and that the late rhythmic bursts occur in the absence of any great activity in the tongue afferents.

When the touch cell was electrically stimulated via the low threshold fibres of the ipsilateral chorda tympani, the general pattern of activity is the same as that obtained with physiological stimulation. A slow negative wave is evoked and is seen carrying a cell action potential. This is followed by a shallow positive wave with a duration of 50 to 80 msec. No action potentials from the cell were observed during this slow positivity. The duration of the positive wave was measured in 36 records from 3 different touch cells and a mean time of 78 msec (SD ± 31 msec, 80% of the measurements between 57 and 78 msec) was obtained. The positivity was followed by a slow irregular negative wave carrying a series of action potentials of rather high frequency. The length of this late burst of impulses varied greatly in successive records although stimulus strength and duration were unchanged. A certain rhythmicity was seen also in the late activity induced by an electrical stimulus. It sometimes happened that cells, which usually followed the above-described pattern, did not fire a spike on top of the initial negative potential although a late series of spike discharges occurred as usual, following the positive potential.

The constant pattern of activity observed in the touch cells raised the question whether this behaviour was typical for all cortical touch cells and not merely peculiar to the few cells from which we happened to record. Great similarities are noted between the time course of the single unit activity pattern and that of the slow evoked focal potentials recorded with a coarse microelectrode at a depth of 1 to 1.5 mm below the cortex surface. The latency and duration of the initial negative and the following positive and negative potentials are the same as the latency and duration of the initial and the delayed touch cell discharge. The initial and late negative focal potentials also both appear with a stimulus strength close to the threshold of the afferent nerve. It may thus be concluded that a large group of cortical cells responds to a discrete tactile stimulation of the tongue with a pattern of activity consisting of one or two initial spikes followed by a silent period and then a burst of discharges at high frequency. The evoked activity of a single cortical cell long outlasts the duration of the afferent volley which initiated it.

The inhibition of the propagated action potential of the cell is very effective during the slow positivity following the initial response. This was recorded from a cell with a "spontaneous" activity of high frequency, presumably due to injury. When this cell was stimulated by an electric shock to the chorda, the impulse activity promptly ceased during the falling phase of the initial negative wave and did not reappear during the following positive potential. After a pause of 70 msec the cell started firing again at the previous high frequency and this activity was superposed on another slow negative wave.

The spontaneous high frequency discharge developed towards the end of the period during which the cell was observed. Such a discharge is probably due to a strong local stimulation of the cell resulting from an injury to the cell membrane caused by the microelectrode. *If this assumption is true, the pause in the spontaneous discharge following the afferent volley must be due to an inhibition of the cortical cell and not to a decrease of the excitatory inflow.* The ability of the cell to fire at a very high frequency before and after the inhibition associated with the positivity shows that this inhibition is not due to refractoriness of the cell.

the effect of consecutive stimuli on the excitability of the touch cell

Some interesting information concerning the excitability of the touch cells may be obtained from experiments in which two consecutive electric shocks were applied to the afferent path at varying intervals. The records were obtained from a cell which could be activated by touching the ipsilateral edge of the tongue. A conditioning and a test shock were applied to the ipsilateral lingual nerve. At an interval between the shocks of 2.5 to 5 msec the cell was fired by both volleys. When the interval was 7 msec the first volley fired the cell and the second only set up a small negative potential without a propagated spike. This occurred at all intervals between 7 and 50 msec. At an interval of 50 msec the cell was again fired by both shocks. The excitability of the cell is thus depressed between 7 and 50 msec after the first shock and this depression is not due to refractoriness of the cell as it is capable of firing at a much higher rate. Short bursts of activity with frequencies up to 800/sec were observed in physiologically activated touch cells and as mentioned above this particular cell could discharge at an interval of 2.5 msec. The cell is thus presumably inhibited during a length of time starting a few msec after the first propagated response and lasting for some 50 msec. Only 4 cells have so far been tested with two consecutive shocks. The length of the period of depression varied between 43 and 96 msec. It is of interest to compare these results with those obtained when studying the interaction between the evoked focal potentials recorded from a depth of about 1 mm below the surface of the cortex. As mentioned above, the test responses were depressed with intervals between the afferent volleys up to 130 msec. When the cell was fired repetitively with increasing stimulus frequency it failed to follow frequencies above 8/sec. Thus at this rate of stimulation the depression lasted longer than 125 msec.

The ability of repetitive stimulation to build up a prolonged state of depression in a cortical cell was observed in two other experiments. A spontaneously active cell responded to electrical stimulation of the ipsilateral lingual nerve at a frequency of 1/sec with a typical pattern of activity: an initial negative potential, which in this case did not carry a spike, a silent period and then a sequence of short bursts of impulses with the cell firing at high frequency during the bursts. When the stimulus frequency was increased to 5/sec the late series of discharges disappeared or diminished in frequency. During a series of stimuli at 25/sec each stimulus artifact was followed by a slow negative potential of reduced amplitude but only a few, randomly discharged single spikes were seen. Immediately after the cessation of the train of stimuli, there was a complete silence for 0.7 seconds and then the cell regained its irregular spontaneous activity of about 9 impulses per second. A similar postexcitatory depression was shown by a touch cell, spontaneously active at an arrhythmic frequency of about 18 imp/sec and with a typical response to electrical stimulation. The cell was excited with a series of repeated touch stimuli to the tongue lasting for 1.18 sec. During the period of stimulation the frequency was raised to 49 imp/sec. Immediately after cessation of the tactile stimulation, the cell stopped firing for a period of 0.5 sec and then the spontaneous activity reappeared at its previous frequency.

cortical cells sensitive to taste stimuli

Only 5 cells responding to taste solutions applied to the tongue have been observed. They were all found at depths between 1.8 and 2.3 mm below the surface of the cortex and within the area where the evoked surface potential showed a maximum, i.e. in the same area as the touch cells. The receptor field was investigated in two of the taste cells (5/3, 13/2) and was found to be the ipsilateral edge in the 5/3 animal and the ipsilateral edge and tip of the anterior half of the tongue in the 13/2 animal. In one of these experiments (13/2) the ipsilateral trigeminal component of the lingual nerve and the contralateral chordalingual nerve were cut. The following test solutions were applied to the tongue: Ringer's solution, 10% sucrose in Ringer's solution, 0.1 M acetic acid in Ringer's solution (pH 2.5), 0.5 M sodium chloride solution, 0.02 M quinine in Ringer's solution, water at 10°C and water at 40°C. Mechanical stimulation of the tongue was also tried. The results are summarized in the following table, where + indicates an increased discharge of the cortical cell and 0 stands for no effect on its spontaneous activity.

None of these cells responded to touch or Ringer's solution applied to the tongue. In

Table 4

Exp.	Depth mm	Touch	Ringer's solution	Sucrose	Acetic acid	NaCl	Quinine	H₂O +10°	H₂O +40°
9/5. 55...........		0	0						
13/2. 56...........	2.0	0	0			+	+	+	+
13/2. 56...........	2.2	0	0		+	+	+	0	0
16/2. 56...........	1.8	0	0		+	+	+	0	0
5/3. 56...........	2.3	0	0	0	+	+	+	+	+

two of the experiments touch cells were found very close to the taste cells and in still another the potential evoked by electrical stimulation showed the configuration typical for the touch cell pool. Taste cells are therefore probably closely intermixed with cells responding to touch of the tongue although they are found far below the depth where most of the touch cells were obtained and where the deep initially negative evoked potential due to tactile afferents had its maximum amplitude. This close approximation of taste and touch cells may indicate an interaction between touch and taste and this is in fact indicated by the clinical observations of Harris (27), who found that destruction of the trigeminal paths in humans caused a temporary abolition of taste even though the chorda tympani and glossopharyngeal pathways for taste fibres were intact.

The change in impulse activity due to the application of the taste solutions is shown in the diagram of Fig. 6 obtained from experiment 5/3. 56. The cell showed an arrhythmic spontaneous discharge varying from 4 to 17 imp/sec. The impulse frequency increased to 30 per sec when NaCl was applied and to about 50 per sec for quinine and acetic acid. Cold water gave an increase up to about 50 and warm water to 40 imp/sec indicating that both effects are due to stimulation of water receptors (45, 35). The acid seems to have been the strongest of the taste stimuli giving the highest frequency and longest duration of the response.

The facts that the amplitude of the taste cell spikes were much smaller than those of touch cells and that the former were much more difficult to find and record from without killing them suggest that the taste cells are smaller than the touch cells (33).

The possibility that the spikes evoked by taste stimuli were recorded from afferent axons and not from cortical cells cannot be excluded, particularly as the taste cells were found in the deepest layer of the cortex. A cortical response to taste stimuli was recorded by Gerebtzoff (25) from the surface of the cerebral cortex in the rabbit. No such response was obtained in the cat. As mentioned above the cortical taste cells in this animal seem to be rather small and situated deeply in the cortex and these observations may explain the lack of a taste response from the cortical surface in the cat.

Although the experimental evidence is still meagre, some conclusions can be drawn concerning the cortical organization of taste. First, it is apparent that fibres of the gustatory pathway do project to the cortical area excited by stimulation of the ipsilateral chorda tympani despite the fact that the most conspicuous components of the evoked potentials are due to afferent impulses in tactile fibres. Secondly, if the response of a cortical taste cell is compared to the response of a single chorda tympani taste fibre, it is seen that the single cortical cell responds to many more types of taste stimuli than any single primary afferent taste fibre (12). Thus the cortical taste cell appears to integrate afferent impulses from almost all the different types of peripheral taste receptors.

cortical cells sensitive to thermal stimuli

Two cells were found which could be stimulated by cooling the tongue but did not respond to warm water, touch or taste solutions. An exception was that one of the cells gave a weak response to 0.1 M acetic acid at body temperature. The temperature sensitive cells were both found within the touch projection area, one at a depth of 1.73 mm. The depth of the other is not known. The pattern

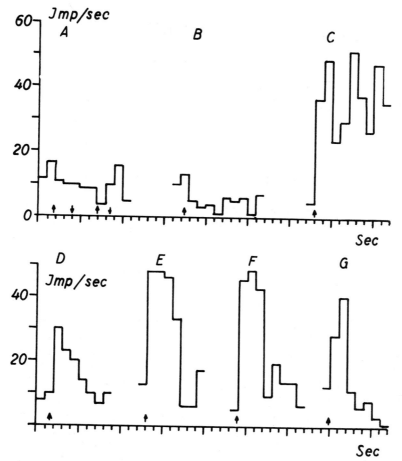

Fig. 6. Diagrams showing the impulse frequency of a cortical cell during application of taste solutions to the tongue. ↑ indicates application of the test solution. ↓ indicates end of application of the test solution. (*A*) Ringer's solution + 20° C. (*B*) 10% Sucrose in Ringer's solution. (*C*) 0.1 M acetic acid in Ringer's solution, pH = 2.5. (*D*) 0.5 M sodium chloride solution. (*E*) 0.02 M quinine in Ringer's solution. (*F*) Water at + 10° C. (*G*) Water at + 40° C.

of the response is shown in the diagrams of Fig. 7.

discussion

It is fully realized that data gathered from the cerebral cortex of an anaesthetized preparation may differ somewhat from the normal physiological picture. Nevertheless we feel that certain principles of cortical activity may be approached under conditions of controlled anaesthesia and therefore offer the following considerations.

the cortical representation of sensory modalities

The topographical distribution of cortical areas corresponding to certain receptive fields

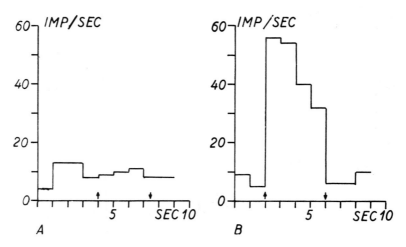

Fig. 7. Diagrams of the impulse frequency of a cortical cell responding to cooling of the tongue. (A) Application of warm water (+ 40° C) and (B) of cold water (+ 10° C) to the tongue. The arrows indicate the beginning and end of stimulus.

in the periphery is a well-established principle. It is in agreement with this principle that tactile stimulation of the tongue evokes a response in the same cortical area whether the impulses arrive via the chorda tympani or via the trigeminal component of the lingual nerve. Our findings further suggest that the different sensory modalities of the tongue are not projected to specific fields within the cortical tongue area, i.e. there is no specific area for taste, touch or temperature, but rather all the modalities are distributed together. Such an organization for the cortical representation of colours and also for skin modalities was suggested by Granit (26). We have found different cells responding to either touch, taste or thermal changes of the tongue within the same microelectrode track. However, with the exception of one thermosensitive cell yielding a weak response to acid, no cell was found responding to more than one sensory modality and it thus seems possible that the modalities could be differentiated by their reception in adjacent but discrete cell pools. There may be a segregation of these cell pools

in a vertical plane at different levels below the cortical surface as suggested by the fact that all the taste cells were found at a depth of about 2 mm while most touch cells were recorded at 0.7–1.5 mm.

In regard to receptive fields, Granit writes in his Silliman lectures (26): "I would not be surprised if the different central receivers were correspondingly organized, some to take care of large receptive fields and others of small ones." The present experiments have offered examples of such receivers. Cortical touch cells occur with large receptive fields covering both sides of the tongue and in one case not only the tongue but also a part of the nose. Other cortical touch cells have a receptive field restricted to a distinct area a few mm in diameter on the ipsilateral dorsal surface of the tongue. It may be that certain of the cortical cells with a large receptive field simply serve to denote the general area (tongue) and the specific modality (touch) involved. Other cortical cells, responding to a more localized receptive field could provide a "local sign" for the stimulus.

It was thought that a study of cortical potentials evoked by activity in the chorda tympani nerve would enable definite localization of the cortical taste area. It was found, however, that at least the initial and most conspicuous component of the potential evoked by ipsilateral and contralateral stimulation of the chorda was due to activity in pathways responding to tactile stimulation. The small late negative wave appearing as a hump on the falling phase of the deep negative focal potential may be a sign of gustatory activity but this remains to be verified. It is clear from single unit studies that the gustatory path does reach the cortical projection area of the chorda tympani but nothing can be said of the precise extent of the gustatory projection area.

the relationship between spontaneous and evoked cortical activity

The problem concerning the relationship between the slow spontaneous brain waves, the slow evoked cortical potentials and the activity of individual cortical cells is of great importance for the interpretation of the EEG. An observation often made during this study may throw some light on the correlation between the two first-mentioned types of brain waves. It was found that the fluctuations of the baseline due to slow spontaneous cortical potentials decreased during and immediately after the primary response evoked by a strong afferent volley. Thus the spontaneous waves invade less easily or do not originate in a cortical area during and just after the reception of an afferent volley. This suggests that the slow spontaneous potentials and the primary evoked response are due to activity in the same cortical structure.

In our records from single cortical touch cells there was a definite relationship between slow evoked potentials and propagated cell spikes. The spike discharge always appeared simultaneously with slow negative potentials and generally no spike discharge was seen during the slow positive potential following firing of the unit.

interpretation of evoked slow potentials

The similarity between our extracellular records and the intracellular ones obtained by Brock, Coombs and Eccles (5) from single motoneurones in the spinal cord and by Eyzaguirre and Kuffler (19) from the stretch receptor neurone of the crayfish, suggests that the slow negative waves are the summed result of synchronous excitatory postsynaptic potentials or dendritic generator potentials set up by the afferent volley in the touch cell pool. In fact the primary negative phase of the focal potential, which carries the initial burst of spike discharge, has generally been interpreted as a postsynaptic potential set up in the apical dendrites by the afferent volley (10, 16, 33). The true time course of this slow negative potential is difficult to assess as it seems to be cut short by a potential of opposite direction. It is, however, of a type similar to that of the excitatory postsynaptic potential of the motoneurone. The late deep negative wave carrying the delayed series of touch cell discharges seems to be built up by summation of smaller waves and reminds one of the long lasting generator potentials of the stretch receptor neurone of Crustacea (19).

It is also tempting to interpret the slow positive potential which always coincides with the pause in the propagated discharge as the expression of an inhibitory process analogous to the inhibitory process in the motoneurone, the crustacean muscle or the crustacean stretch receptor cell (5, 21, 19). The final proof must, however, await intracellular recording.

In this connection it is of interest to note the observation of Tasaki, Polley and Orrego (42) that an electric shock to the radiation fibres could give rise to a hyperpolarization of cells in the striate cortex. The "negative swing," which was recorded intracellularly, was able to stop a spontaneous injury discharge and appeared with a latency of 2–2.5 msec. Intracellular hyperpolarization of cortical cells appearing with a latency compatible with our extracellularly recorded positive wave and with the simultaneous inhibition of the spike discharge was also observed by Albe-Fessard and Buser (1).

Our observation that the surface negative potential following the initial response changes into a positive wave of similar time course (Fig. 5B and C) with increasing depth below the cortical surface, confirms the findings of Li, Cullen and Jasper (34). These authors described a similar turnover of a late negative potential recorded from the superficial layers of the somatosensory cortex in response to stimulation of the thalamic relay nucleus. They interpret the change of the positive-negative surface potential into a negative-positive deep potential as evidence of conduction of impulses along the apical dendrites from the fourth cortical layers towards the surface. However, the fact that local strychnine application enhances the later components of the evoked potentials far more than the initial response indicates that relayed interneuronal activity makes a major contribution to the surface negative and deep positive potentials. We are therefore inclined to interpret the negative superficial potential and its corresponding deep positivity as elicited in a pool of neurones superficial to the touch cells and with processes projecting down to them.

Chang (9) described the evoked potentials recorded from the surface of the motor cortex when stimulating the pyramidal tract. His late surface negative potential (component 4) was shown to be generated by interneurones activated via axon collaterals of the large pyramidal cells. Our late surface negative potential corresponds in time to Chang's component 4 and may therefore be of similar origin, i.e. generated by a superficial interneurone pool activated secondarily by the primary cortical touch cells.

the discharge pattern in single cortical cells

The pause in the touch cell discharge following the initial impulses is a very interesting feature independent of the role played by the slow positive potential in its creation. It is apparent that the pause is not due to a lack of recovery of the cell after its previous discharge as the cell is readily discharged at intervals of less than 2 msec. The fact that an injury discharge can be stopped for a definite period after the injured cell has received an afferent volley indicates that the inhibition must be acting on the cell itself. Thus the inhibition in these cortical cells appears to be an active process exerted directly on the cell and not merely due to a lack of stimulation or to refractoriness in the cell itself or in paths playing upon the cell.

Cells in the cat's cerebral cortex showing a pattern of activity similar to that of the present study have been repeatedly described in the recent literature. Thus Amassian (1953) described cells found in the somatosensory cortex which respond to electrical stimulation of the ulnar nerve with an initial burst of impulses, a silent period and then a delayed discharge. The length of the silent period was about 100 msec. Similar observations were made by Li, Cullen and Jasper (34) also on records from neurones in the somatosensory cortex and by Creutzfeldt, Baumgartner and Schoen (14) from cells found in the motor and in the visual cortex.

The excitability curve of a single cortical sensory neurone was drawn by Li et al. on the basis of experiments with conditioning and test shocks applied to the thalamic relay nucleus. This curve shows an initial hyperexcitability lasting for 5–10 msec after the arrival of the afferent volley. During the following 30–40 msec the cortical cell was depressed and thereafter a new period of hyperexcitability lasting for 100–150 msec appeared. The pattern of activity of the cortical touch cell discharge described in this series of experiments agrees well with the excitability curve of Li et al. and so do the results of our excitability tests.

Still more information concerning a delayed period of depression of cortical cells may be obtained from previous investigations. Thus Chang (7, 8) showed that the neurones of the auditory cortex were depressed during a period of 50 msec immediately following the primary response to a sound stimulus. Studying the cortical potential evoked by an antidromic volley in the axons of Betz cells, Chang (9) obtained evidence for a depression of excitability in the pyramidal cell. The depression was caused by two different processes, one of short duration corresponding to an absolute and relative refractory period of the cell and another starting with a latency of 10 msec and lasting for 60–100 msec. The later depression corresponds well in time to the period of inhibition of the touch cell. Clare and Bishop (11) have also provided evidence for a depression of neurones of the visual cortex following an initial facilitation.

It should finally be mentioned that Tasaki, Polley and Orrego (42) in cells of the lateral geniculate body found a similar silent period following the response to an afferent volley in the optic nerve.

The above-reviewed results show that a pattern of activity consisting of a short discharge and a silent period followed by a delayed burst of activity is typical of certain cortical neurones found in widely different parts of the cerebral cortex and also in lower integrating regions such as the lateral geniculate body. The question then arises whether the described pattern may be important in certain unknown functions of integrating neurones and whether the cortical neurones showing this pattern may belong to a functionally related group of cells appearing in the sensory as well as in the motor cortex. Some suggestions may be offered in response to the last of these questions.

In the case of the cortical cells responding to tactile stimuli from the tongue, two conclusions may be drawn. One is that these cells belong to the largest of the cortical neurones as judged from their large extracellularly recorded spike amplitude (33). They are most commonly found at depths between 0.7 and 1.5 mm below the cortical surface and thus probably belong to the group of large pyramidal cells of layers III and V.

It may secondly be concluded that the touch cells belong to the groups of cortical neurones which are first thrown into action by the afferent volley because their initial discharge is found on the rising phase of the primary cortical response. The observations of Chang referred to above indicate that the large pyramidal cells of the motor cortex may show a similar pattern. In regard to other observations made on single cortical cells using microelectrode recording it may be assumed that the technique would favour a selection of records from large cortical cells. It can therefore be suggested that the pattern of discharge shown by the cortical touch cell may be of importance for some function common to a certain group of large pyramidal cells appearing in functionally different areas of the cerebral cortex.

The following hypothesis is offered as a possible explanation of the functional role played by this particular cellular discharge pattern. The initial discharge, consisting of only one or two spikes, is assumed to start the cerebral elaboration of incoming information, i.e., to activate distant cortical and thalamic neurone pools. Its brief nature may be of importance in preventing the penetration of the input signal into the major efferent channels. The cerebral treatment is assumed to be occurring during the period of inhibition and consists of an activation of interneurone pools in the same cortical region as well as in the distant cortical association areas. The thalamic nuclei involved in cortico-thalamo-cortical reverberations would also be thrown into play at this time (28). The discharge of these distant cell pools is assumed to be reflected back upon the touch cell as excitatory or inhibitory impulses which reach final integration in the dendritic membrane of the touch cell. The delayed high frequency discharge following the period of inhibition may then be interpreted as the final result of the cerebral treatment. Because of its duration and high frequency, the terminal burst of impulses may be capable of penetrating through long chains of synapses and thereby force its way out into the efferent paths. The period of inhibition may thus be of importance in cutting short the initial discharge so that it penetrates only into the analyzing paths and not into the major efferent outflow channels. It would also prevent later afferent signals from disturbing the cortical elaboration under progress and lastly it may serve to keep the cortical cell in a state of preparedness for the integration of the reverberating activity.

cortical inhibition

Several mechanisms may be postulated for the inhibition following the initial discharge of the cortical touch cell. A most attractive analogy seems to be the Renshaw cell inhibition of the spinal motoneurones (17). This self-inhibitory mechanism implies that impulses in collaterals of the motoneurone axon excite interneurones (Renshaw cells) which return a series of inhibitory impulses to the motoneurone. On the basis of this analogy the inhibition of the cortical touch cell should be due to a negative feedback mechanism utilizing axon collaterals and short intracortical interneurone chains. Chang (9) has demonstrated the existence of self-excitation in the large pyramidal cells in the motor cortex via the axon collaterals of these cells. Axon collateral feedback is thus already shown to be part of the cortical mechanism. The length of the period of inhibition of the cortical touch cells requires a long lasting series of inhibitory discharge. Such a discharge is produced by the Renshaw cells of the spinal cord and may well be present in certain cortical interneurones.

The work of Chang (7, 8) demonstrating the existence of reverberating cortico-thalamic circuits suggests as an alternative possibility that the negative feedback may be mediated via these circuits. A latency of about 5 msec, which was observed for the inhibition of the touch cells, may be long enough to permit activation of an inhibitory cortico-thalamo-cortical path provided only a small number of interneurones are involved.

There are, however, several indications that something other than a simple negative feedback is involved in the delayed inhibition of the cortical touch cell. It has been seen that the initial discharge consists only of one or two impulses and is followed by a long period of inhibition, whereas during the after-discharges the cell may fire 10 or 20 times at frequencies up to 800 per sec and not inhibit itself during this burst. If only a negative feedback were involved, one would expect that inhibition should increase in parallel with the frequency of discharge from the cell and thus cause a gradual shortening of the number of spikes per burst rather than the observed lengthening. Another observation contrary to the negative feedback concept is the almost complete inhibition of the cortical touch cell resulting from relatively low frequency stimulation of the afferent path. A series of afferent volleys at a frequency of 25 per second can stop the delayed discharge of the cell even though the cell may fire at much higher rates when the after-discharge does occur and not inhibit itself. This again cannot be explained by a simple negative feedback system.

A mechanism which would explain the inhibition without invoking a negative feedback could be based upon a fractionation of the afferent inflow into a fast excitatory path and a slow inhibitory channel. A fractionation of the afferent inflow in the brain stem has been demonstrated by Starzl, Taylor and Magoun (41). These workers have shown that in addition to the classical path of the specific afferents, a portion of the sensory inflow termed the "collateral afferents" plays into the brain stem reticular formation and exerts an influence upon the cerebral cortex some time after impulses from the specific conduction pathways have arrived at the cortex. The influence exerted by this collateral afferent system upon cortical activity seems to be largely of an excitatory nature mediated through the ascending reticular activating system (41). The descending influence of the

reticular system is, however, known to cause inhibitory effects in the cord (36), and Li (32) has recently observed that the discharge of one thalamic nucleus, the nucleus ventralis lateralis, exerts an inhibitory effect upon the activity of the cortical motor neurones that may last from 80–400 msec.

The delayed cortical discharge of long duration and high frequency following the period of depression in a cortical cell seems also to depend on interaction between cortex and subcortical structures. A periodic variation of the excitability in cortical neurones was demonstrated in the auditory cortex by Chang (7, 8). The primary cortical response was followed by a series of depressions lasting approximately 50 msec and alternating with periods of facilitation lasting for 100 msec. The facilitation was shown due to impulses in reverberating cortico-thalamic circuits. Li, Cullen and Jasper (34) and Li (31) have shown that a major influence on the diffuse thalamic projection system upon cortical cell activity is to increase the number of times a cell may fire in response to a given volley arriving via the specific thalamic relay nuclei. Activity of the diffuse thalamic nuclei may facilitate the cortical cell without causing it to fire. The nature and time course of the diffuse thalamic effect strongly suggest that this system may contribute to the delayed bursts demonstrated in the cortical touch cell response pattern.

summary

1. Potentials evoked by stimulation of the chorda tympani and trigeminal component of the lingual nerve were studied by recording from the cerebral cortex of the cat. Single cortical cells influenced by these afferent

paths were also investigated using KCl filled glass pipette microelectrodes.

2. Both the chorda tympani and the trigeminal component of the lingual nerve project to essentially the same cortical region on the orbital surface of the brain. A surface positive-negative wave is evoked by electrical stimulation of either path and this changes to a negative-positive wave at a depth of 0.5–0.8 mm below the cortex surface.

3. Single cortical cells were observed which responded to electrical stimulation of both the chorda and trigeminal paths; other cells responded only to stimulation of the trigeminal component of the lingual nerve, and a very few cells were seen which responded only to stimulation of the chorda tympani.

4. The initial component of the slow potential evoked by electrical stimulation of either the chorda or the trigeminal path was shown to result from activity in pathways activated by tactile stimulation of the tongue.

5. The receptive field of 34 cortical cells responding to tactile stimulation of the tongue was determined. Certain single cortical cells responded to stimulation of large areas of tongue surface, frequently from ipsilateral and contralateral sides. Other cells responded to a restricted area of a few square millimeters. No cortical touch cells responded to gustatory or thermal stimulation of the tongue.

6. Five cells were found responding only to gustatory stimulation of the tongue. These cells responded to almost all types of gustatory stimulation and lacked the specificity of response known for the chemoreceptors of the tongue. The cortical taste cells did not respond to any other sensory modality.

7. Several cortical cells were observed which responded only to thermal stimulation of the tongue.

8. The cortical touch cells fired in a definite pattern which was the same whether the afferent path was activated electrically or physiologically. The cell fired once or twice on the rising phase of a deep negative potential. This was followed by a period of depressed activity accompanied by a slow positive wave lasting 40–60 msec and then the cell fired again with bursts of impulses at high frequency alternating with pauses in the activity. The sequence of afterdischarges may last from 100 to 800 msec.

9. The period of depression after the initial discharge lasted as long as 150 msec and was shown due to an inhibitory influence exerted directly on the cortical cell. The long period of depression was not due to the refractory period of the cell as these cells were observed to fire at frequencies greater than 600 per sec.

10. The possible inhibitory mechanism is discussed and the physiological implications of the cortical touch cell discharge pattern are considered with reference to interaction between various cortical and subcortical regions.

references

1. Albe-Fessard, D. and P. Buser, J. Physiol. Paris 1955. **47.** 67.
2. Amassian, V. E., EEG Clin. Neurophysiol. 1953. **5.** 415.
3. Benjamin, R. M. and C. Pfaffmann, J. Neurophysiol. 1955. **18.** 56.
4. Bremer, F., Arch. Int. Physiol. 1923. **21.** 308.
5. Brock, L. G., J. S. Coombs and J. C. Eccles, J. Physiol. 1952. **117.** 431.
6. Burns, B. D. and B. Grafstein, J. Physiol. 1952. **118.** 412.
7. Chang, H.-T., J. Neurophysiol. 1950. **13.** 235.
8. ——— Ibidem 1951. **14.** 95.
9. ——— Ibidem 1955. **18.** 452.

10. Chang, H.-T. and B. Kaada, J. Neurophysiol. 1950. **13**. 305.
11. Clare, M. H. and G. H. Bishop, EEG Clin. Neurophysiol. 1955. **7**. 85.
12. Cohen, M. J., S. Hagiwara and Y. Zotterman, Acta Physiol. Scand. 1955. **33**. 316.
13. Cragg, B. G., J. Physiol. 1954. **124**. 254.
14. Creutzfeldt, O., G. Baumgartner and L. Schoen, Arch. f. Psychiatr. u. Z. Neur. 1956. **194**. 592.
15. Curtis, H. J., J. Neurophysiol. 1940. **3**. 414.
16. Eccles, J. C., EEG Clin. Neurophysiol. 1951. **3**. 449.
17. Eccles, J. C., P. Fatt and K. Koketsu, J. Physiol. 1954. **126**. 524.
18. Eccles, J. C., P. Fatt, S. Landgren and G. J. Winsbury, J. Physiol. 1954. **125**. 590.
19. Eyzaguirre, C. and S. W. Kuffler, J. Gen. Physiol. 1955 a. **39**. 87.
20. ———— Ibidem 1955 b. **39**. 155.
21. Fatt, P. and B. Katz, J. Physiol. 1953. **121**. 374.
22. Forbes, A. and B. R. Morison, J. Neurophysiol. 1939. **2**. 112.
23. Frank, K. and M. G. F. Fuortes, J. Physiol. 1955. **130**. 625.
24. Gad, A. P., Arch. Anat. Physiol. 1891. **15**. 541.
25. Gerebtzoff, M. A., Arch. Int. Physiol. 1941. **51**. 199.
26. Granit, R., Receptors and Sensory Perception, 1955, Yale Univ. Press, New Haven.
27. Harris, W., British Med. J. 1952. **1**. 831.
28. Jasper, H. H. and C. Ajmone-Marsan, Res. Publ. Ass. nerv. ment. Dis. 1950. **30**. 493.
29. King, E. E., B. Minz and K. R. Unna, J. comp. Neurol. 1955. **102**. 565.
30. Lele, P. P., D. C. Sinclair and G. Wedell, J. Physiol. 1954. **123**. 187.
31. Li, C.-L., J. Physiol. 1956 a. **131**. 115.
32. ———— Ibidem 1956 b. **133**. 40.
33. Li, C.-L. and H. Jasper, J. Physiol. 1953. **121**. 117.
34. Li, C.-L., C. Cullen and H. Jasper, J. Neurophysiol. 1956. **19**. 111.
35. Liljestrand, G. and Y. Zotterman, Acta Physiol. Scand. 1954. **32**. 291.
36. Magoun, H., Physiol. Rev. 1950. **30**. 459.
37. Patton, H. D. and V. E. Amassian, J. Neurophysiol. 1952. **15**. 243.
38. Pfaffmann, C., J. cell. comp. Physiol. 1941. **17**. 243.
39. Phillips, C. G., Quart. J. exp. Physiol. 1956. **41**. 58.
40. Renshaw, B., A. Forbes and B. R. Morison, J. Neurophysiol. 1940. **3**. 74.
41. Starzl, T. E., C. Taylor and H. Magoun, J. Neurophysiol. 1951. **14**. 479.
42. Tasaki, I., H. Polley and F. Orrego, J. Neurophysiol. 1954. **17**. 454.
43. Zotterman, Y., Skand. Arch. Physiol. 1935. **72**. 73.
44. ———— Ibidem 1936. **75**. 105.
45. ———— Acta Physiol. Scand. 1949. **18**. 141.

9 gustatory nerve impulses in rat, cat, and rabbit *

Carl Pfaffmann

1. What advantages are there in using three different species of animals in an experiment?

2. What differences in response to the four stimuli were shown by the three different species? Can these differences be accounted for?

3. What are the similarities found in the gustatory nerve impulses in rat, cat, and rabbit? What are the implications of these similarities?

Electrophysiological studies of the peripheral nerves of taste have been carried out on the following mammals: cat (8, 12), dog (1)

* C. Pfaffmann, "Gustatory Nerve Impulses in the Rat, Cat, and Rabbit," *J. Neurophysiol.*, 18 (1955), 429–440. Reprinted with permission.

and rat (3, 10). These studies, however, were not concerned specifically with the quantitative differences among the species.[1] The adaptation of the integrator recording method by Beidler (3) provided a method well suited to the quantitative study of the intact chorda tympani nerve responses to taste stimuli. In the present study this method was combined with the method of single fiber analysis in order to compare the taste sensitivity of the cat, rat and rabbit under the same experimental conditions.

method

Four cats, 15 rabbits, and 25 albino Wistar stock rats were studied. Animals were anesthetized with nembutal or urethane. The trachea was cannulated and the head clamped in a vertical position so that the mouth and tongue were readily accessible from above. A deep dissection at the angle of the jaw exposed the chorda tympani nerve from the point where it leaves the bulla until it joins the lingual nerve. The deep incision formed a "natural" moist chamber for the nerve and electrode. Silver-silver chloride wick electrodes led to a Grass P-4 pre-amplifier, a Du Mont cathode-ray oscillograph and audio-monitoring circuit. The total nerve response was recorded with an integrator circuit and Esterline-Angus recording milliammeter. Single fiber discharges were photographed from the cathode-ray oscillograph by means of a Grass recording

[1] Two notes reporting a species difference, one a preliminary report of the present experiments, have appeared (2, 9). These two studies were initiated separately at about the same time and carried out independently. Subsequent personal communication revealed them to be in essential agreement where the same species were studied. Beidler's complete report (*Amer. J. Physiol.*, 1955, *181*: 235–239) has appeared since the preparation of this article for publication.

camera. Single functional nerve fibers as judged by the appearance of the action potential record were obtained by dissecting small strands of the chorda tympani nerve with the aid of sharpened needles and a binocular dissecting microscope.

Taste solutions of NaCl, KCl, HCl, sucrose and quinine hydrochloride at room temperature were applied to the tongue surface from a medicine dropper. At each presentation sufficient volume was used to flood the entire anterior tongue surface. In some rat preparations a flow system was used, but the response magnitudes were essentially similar with the two methods of application. Reagent quality chemicals in distilled water were employed except for sucrose which was of commercial household grade.

results

total nerve activity

The activity in the chorda tympani initiated by applying taste solutions to the tongue is typically an asynchronous discharge of impulses. For an electrolyte like sodium chloride, the latency of the discharge is of the order of 30 msec.; for sucrose, of the order of 300 msec. In the integrator records, the responses to salt (and acid) rise rapidly to a peak and then fall off to some steady resting level as long as the solution remains on the tongue. The response for sugar (and quinine) does not show the initial peak. This difference is well illustrated in Fig. 1 which compares the response to sodium chloride and sucrose in a rat preparation. Steady currents from 1 to 100 μA. with anode on the tongue will also elicit the typical asynchronous nerve activity. A polarizing current of approximately 10–20 μA. produces a response magnitude about equal to that elicited by 0.1 M NaCl. The latency of re-

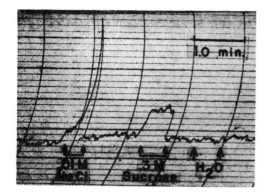

Fig. 1. Sample record of integrator response to sucrose and NaCl solutions. Note that water produces a negligible response. Read record from right to left.

sponse to electrical stimulation is short, in the neighborhood of less than 15 msec. Cathodal polarization of the tongue reduces or even stops completely any resting activity but at "break" may elicit a burst of impulses.

The effectiveness of different stimuli determined from the height of the integrator deflections for different stimulus concentrations is shown in Fig. 2. Response magnitudes are given in arbitrary units relative to the response to a standard NaCl solution. For any one stimulus the response is an increasing function from threshold to some maximal concentration. In terms of threshold, the five test substances fall in order from low to high: quinine, HCl, KCl, NaCl, and sucrose.

The responses of three preparations of each of three species, cat, rat and rabbit, are compared in Figs. 3 and 4. The ordinate values in arbitrary units are adjusted to give equal response heights for 0.1 N hydrochloric acid. Thresholds for each species lie close to 0.001 N HCl. In the cat, the thresholds for KCl and NaCl are approximately 1.25 log units above the threshold for HCl. The suprathreshold responses to the three stimuli rise in a roughly parallel manner (see Fig. 3).

In the rat, thresholds for all three stimuli are approximately the same (0.001 M or 0.001 N) and the suprathreshold acid and NaCl curves are very similar. Acids stronger than 0.1 N were not employed as they tended to inactivate the receptors. The response to KCl rises more slowly than that to NaCl, although at 1 M there is a sudden rise in the curve. The response to salts of 1 M concentration and above must be interpreted with caution. Repeated stimulation with strong salt leads to variable results. In the rabbit the order of effectiveness is HCl > KCl > NaCl. Furthermore, in the weaker concentrations NaCl tends to reduce the spontaneous resting activity. Water, on the other hand, produced a transient response. Continued rinsing with water led to great instability and fluctuation in the level of resting activity. For this reason, a solution of 0.01 M NaCl was used as a rinse to quiet and stabilize the baseline. In the other two species such water sensitivity was present to only a slight degree. Rinsing with water had primarily a quieting effect upon the baseline. Fig. 4 shows the differences among the

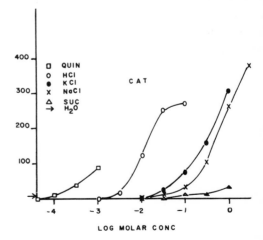

Fig. 2. Height of integrator deflections to stimuli of different concentrations in one cat preparation. Ordinate gives deflections in arbitrary units.

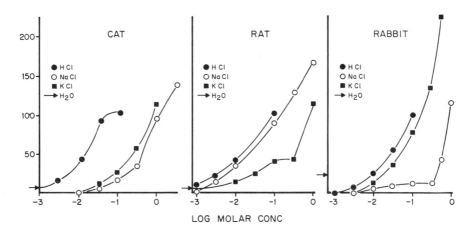

Fig. 3. Comparison of magnitude of integrator deflections to HCl, KCl, NaCl, and H₂O in cat, rat, and rabbit. Ordinate in arbitrary units adjusted to 100 units for the response to 0.1 N HCl.

three species for the non-electrolytes, quinine hydrochloride and sucrose. Quinine is quite effective in the cat, less so in the rat, and ineffective in the rabbit. Just the reverse relations hold true for sucrose.

These results show that in the chorda tympani nerves of all species the electrolytes elicit a more pronounced afferent neural discharge than do the non-electrolytes employed. Fur-

thermore, there is a striking difference in the relative effectiveness of HCl, NaCl, KCl, quinine and sucrose among the three species.

single elements in rat

A typical single unit discharge from the rat is shown in Fig. 5. The frequency of discharge in this case increases with an increase in NaCl concentration over the whole range of con-

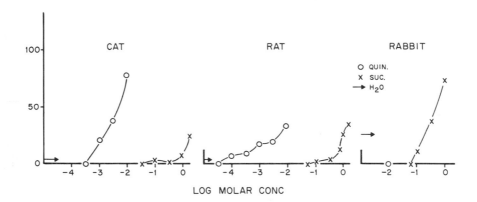

Fig. 4. Comparison of magnitude of integrator deflections for quinine and sucrose in cat, rat and rabbit. Same ordinates as in Fig. 3.

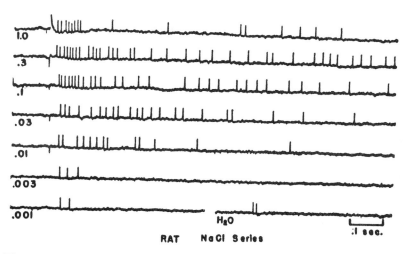

Fig. 5. Response of a single element from rat sensitive to NaCl. This element would also respond to HCl and KCl and corresponds to D in Fig. 7. Responses to quinine and sucrose were insignificant.

centrations to which the total rat nerve responds. The threshold for this fiber lies between 0.001 and 0.003 M. The very strong concentration of 1.0 NaCl produces a lower frequency than the next weaker stimulus. This "overload" phenomenon has been observed in a number of preparations although it does not always occur. The relation of stimulus intensity to afferent nerve discharge can be shown by plotting the frequency of impulses during the first second following the application of each stimulus for different concentrations. Figure 6 shows this relation for NaCl for several different elements in the rat. In the case of element I the frequency increases as a sigmoid function over three log units of concentration. This function resembles closely that obtained by integrating the total nerve response. Other units, however, have higher thresholds and therefore respond over a more restricted concentration range. Units with higher thresholds tend to have a lower maximal frequency of response. An increase in stimulus intensity therefore is associated with

an increase in both frequency of impulses per fiber and in the number of nerve fibers active.

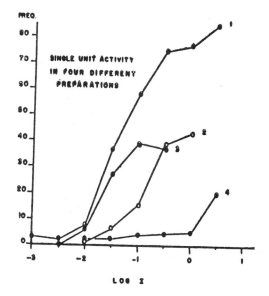

Fig. 6. Frequency of impulse discharge in the first second as a function of NaCl concentration in four different single elements of rat.

The relative effectiveness of the different stimuli is not always the same among the different fibers. Figure 7 shows the responses of nine different elements to five standard test solutions. Each solid histogram shows the frequency of discharge during the first second. The middle graph in cross hatching also shows the relative magnitude of the integrated total nerve response (in arbitrary units) to each test stimulus. The pattern of sensitivity varies widely from element to element and does not necessarily reflect the sensitivity found in the whole nerve preparation. Elements A, C, D, F, G, and I are characterized by a good response to NaCl; element A appears to be specific to that stimulus as does the weakly responding element E (high threshold fiber). Element B is especially sensitive to sugar. The response of this element is shown in Fig. 8. This is a noteworthy prepara-

tion for it is the only sugar-sensitive element obtained in the rat by the present author. The response to sugar in this case begins with a high frequency and shows the typical adaptation or decline in frequency. This fiber responds in a similar manner to glucose, maltose, Na saccharine and insol. saccharine. NaCl and HCl solutions also stimulate this element at concentrations higher than 0.01 HCl or 0.1 NaCl. In all other fibers sugar responses, when present, appeared to build up slowly. Element I is characterized by a general sensitivity to all stimuli but sugar.

single elements in cat and rabbit

Figure 9 summarizes the findings on four single elements in the cat and six units in the rabbit. The same test solutions were used except that 0.3 M NaCl and 0.3 KCl were

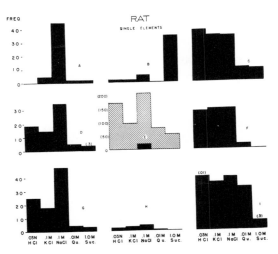

Fig. 7. Histograms summarizing frequency of response during the first second to five standard taste solutions in nine different single fiber preparations in rat. Sucrose of 0.3 M was used as test solution in elements D and I, 0.01 HCl in element I. In all other cases concentrations are as shown on abscissa. Cross-hatched histogram superimposed on figure for element E shows relative magnitude of integrator response for test solutions. Figures in parentheses give magnitudes in arbitrary units. Note that only elements D and G resemble the response of the total nerve.

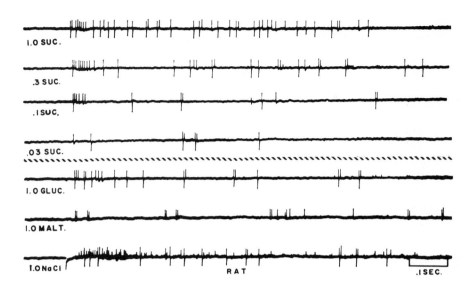

Fig. 8. A single element responsive to sugar. Responses to a series of sucrose solutions and to glucose, maltose and NaCl are shown. The latter stimulates other fibers in addition to sugar-sensitive element. Diphasic response of this element alternates with a monophasic response when inter-impulse interval is short. It is assumed that a phenomenon like "Wedensky inhibition" is occurring in stretch of nerve between recording electrodes.

employed because of the higher salt thresholds in the cat and rabbit. The four histograms (G, H, I, J) at the right of the figure show the responses in the cat. Although all elements responded similarly to 0.03 HCl, the combinations of other sensitivities associated therewith were not constant. In element J, both NaCl and KCl were effective; NaCl was ineffective in the other three preparations and KCl was ineffective in one of these (G). Slight responses to quinine and sugar were noted in the other preparations.

A new type of response was observed in the rabbit (elements A and B) in which the frequency of discharge for HCl and KCl was higher and the spacing between impulses somewhat more regular than in most other taste fibers studied. NaCl, on the other hand, elicited only a brief initial transient response followed by quiescence or inhibition of fur-

ther activity (Fig. 10). Water, quinine and sucrose solutions might be followed by gradually developing activity. Water rinsing was usually associated with a high resting level of activity. Rabbit elements C through F with a lower frequency and more irregular grouping of impulses were more typical of those fibers found in other species.[2]

discussion

One finding of particular interest is that of the species difference in the responses of the chorda tympani nerve. Although behavioral studies suggest that species differences in taste sensitivity are significant, no extensive docu-

[2] Elements A and B appear to resemble Liljestrand and Zotterman's water receptors (*Acta physiol. scand.*, 1954, *32:* 291–303).

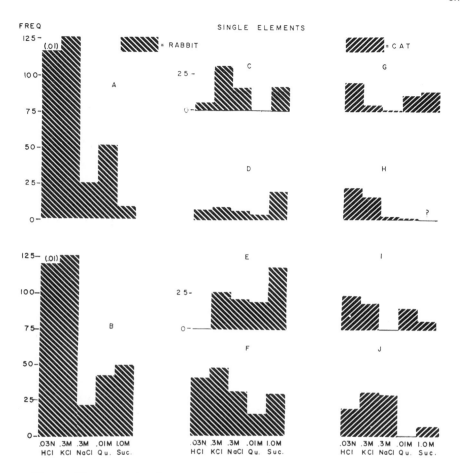

Fig. 9. Histogram showing response to standard test solutions in six single elements in rabbit and four in cat. Note that frequency of discharge for elements A and B is substantially in excess of that found in most other elements. 0.01 HCl used with elements A and B.

mentation has been presented (7). The tendency in comparative studies has been to emphasize similarities rather than differences (6, 11). Thus Frings (6) concluded that throughout the comparative scale, thresholds for ionic stimuli are directly related to the mobility of the different ions. Rejection thresholds in animals and psychophysical thresholds in man were used as criteria. The ions used in the present study rank in mobility as follows: H > K > Na. The taste effectiveness is in the

same order for the cat and rabbit. In the rat the order is different; H = Na > K for suprathreshold concentrations, although at threshold they all appear to be equally effective. The same relation was observed by Beidler in his more extensive study of ion series in the rat (3). Thus electrophysiological evidence shows that the order of stimulating efficiency is not the same in the different species. The weaker responses to the non-electrolytes in all species probably indicates

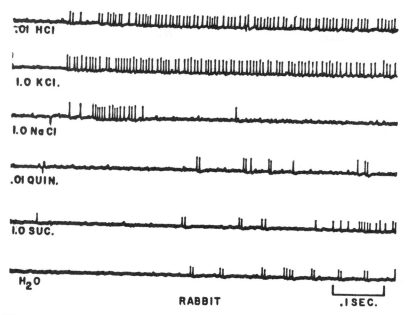

Fig. 10. Example of high frequency element from rabbit characterized by NaCl inhibition after a transient response.

that fewer sucrose- and quinine-sensitive fibers occur in the chorda tympani nerve. Thus the barely detectable response to quinine in the rabbit might indicate that there are very few quinine-sensitive fibers in the chorda tympani nerve of this animal, although no direct evidence on this point was obtained. When responses to sucrose and quinine were obtained in any of the three species, the nerve impulse spikes appeared to be similar in height and duration to those elicited by electrolytes.

The differences observed in total nerve activity among the three species studied are reflected only in a general way in the behavior of the single elements. Thus, in five rat single fiber elements, NaCl > KCl for equi-molar concentrations. However, in three preparations, NaCl and KCl were equally effective (see Fig. 7). In the rabbit, KCl is more effective than NaCl, especially in two instances (elements A and B, Fig. 9). Marked

water sensitivity characterized many but not all of the rabbit single elements. In the cat, HCl and KCl tended to be more effective than NaCl, yet in one case KCl and NaCl were approximately equal. Thus, even within a single species, Na, K and H do not have the same stimulating efficiency from element to element. The species differences with respect to sugar and quinine were not so obviously reflected in the single elements. Only one single element was found with what appeared to be a sensitivity to sugar. This was obtained in the rat, the species in which the largest number of elements was sampled. Quinine response when found was always associated with other sensitivity in the three species. Further work is needed to clarify the nature of the responses to sugar and quinine.

The present findings in general confirm earlier results on the cat (8), showing that some taste afferent nerve fibers are characterized by acid-salt sensitivity (J), and acid sensitivity (H). Whether elements I and K could be included under the earlier classification acid-quinine or acid types is not certain. When all three species are considered as a group, it is clear that the patterns of sensitivity do not fall readily into simple classes. Rather, there appears to be a wide variety of different combinations of reactivity. Further study of large populations of single elements from each of the several species is needed before a classification of receptor types can be attempted. However, whether definite classes or types will be found is questionable.

Chemical specificity of the receptor cells is not absolute but relative. Figure 11 shows the relation between concentration and frequency of discharge for different rat elements for two different stimuli. Both stimuli excite both elements. NaCl stimulates A more than it does B, sucrose stimulates B more than A. The discrimination of NaCl from sucrose could be

based upon such a quantitative difference between the activity in these two fibers. If this example is expanded to include many more fibers and many more chemicals, the basic outlines of a mechanism for discrimination among taste stimuli is suggested. The present evidence further indicates that the degree of specificity may be broad for some elements and narrow for others. The results of the single fiber analysis are not consistent with the classical view that taste sensitivity is compounded of four primary taste modalities. These results accord better with a concept like that of Frings (5) in which salty, sour, sweet and bitter are considered to be nodal points in a "taste spectrum." Ionic mobility, however, does not appear to be the basic stimulus dimension for such a spectrum.

The afferent nerve activity in taste is best described as a pattern of differences in the relative activity of different fibers. Such a pattern was proposed in an earlier paper as the

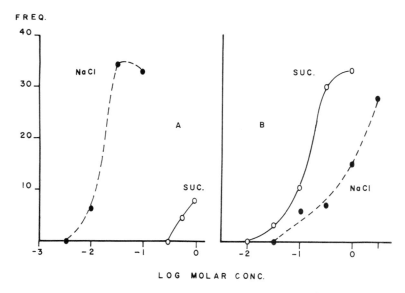

Fig. 11. Graph comparing relative specificities of two different elements in rat. Each is sensitive to NaCl and sucrose (as well as other stimuli). Element A is relatively more sensitive to NaCl, B is relatively more sensitive to sucrose. Ordinate gives frequency in the first second of discharge.

basis for discrimination (8). To quote: ". . . Sensory quality does not depend simply upon the 'all or nothing' activation of some particular fiber group alone, but on the pattern of other fibers active." Pattern in this sense may be distinguished from a temporal pattern in which different chemicals might be characterized by a difference in timing or grouping of impulses in any one fiber.

In the rabbit, diminution in neural activity (inhibition?) as a possible basis for discrimination of NaCl is suggested. Behavioral studies (4) show that in spite of the marked difference between the rat and the rabbit in the chorda tympani response to NaCl, the preference response to NaCl is almost the same in the two species. Concentrations of NaCl that reduce resting activity in the chorda tympani of the rabbit are discriminated and preferred to water by this animal. With further studies of taste sensitivity other substances may be found to have a similarly inhibiting effect. If this is the case, another dimension would be available by which the pattern of afferent activity could be modulated to mediate discrimination among taste stimuli.

conclusions

1. Taste solutions applied to the anterior tongue surface of rat, cat and rabbit elicit a maintained asynchronous discharge of impulses in the chorda tympani nerve. For all species the basic taste stimuli could be ranked from low to high in order of thresholds as follows: quinine, HCl, NaCl and sucrose. The magnitude of the total nerve response as recorded with an integrator circuit was typically an increasing sigmoid function of the logarithm of the stimulus concentration. The responses to NaCl and HCl were typically of larger magnitude than those to quinine and sucrose.

2. The relative effectiveness of three electrolytes HCl, KCl, and NaCl in suprathreshold concentrations was different in the three species as follows: rat, HCl = NaCl > KCl; cat, HCl > KCl > NaCl; rabbit, HCl >KCl ≫ NaCl. The order of effectiveness of sucrose and quinine was: cat, qu. > suc.; rat, qu. = suc.; rabbit, suc. > qu.

3. Recording from single nerve fiber elements of the chorda tympani nerve in the three species shows that thresholds for any one substance are different from one fiber to another. Frequency of discharge during the first second approximates a sigmoid function of the logarithm of the stimulus concentration. The order of effectiveness of HCl, KCl, and NaCl in the single elements did not always follow that found in the total response of that species. The stimulating effect of these electrolytes therefore may differ from one single element to another within the same species as well as between species.

4. Each single fiber preparation is characterized by a different pattern of sensitivity to the four basic taste stimuli. Every element isolated responded to more than one of the four basic taste stimuli but to varying degrees. No simple classification of receptors by types is obvious. Chemical specificity appears to be relative so that any one element might be characterized by the stimulus or stimuli for which it has the lowest threshold. Other stimuli at higher concentrations might be included in the group of chemicals to which it is sensitive.

references

1. Andersson, B., Landgren, S., Olsson, L., and Zotterman. Y. The sweet taste fibres of the dog. *Acta physiol. scand.*, 1950, **21**: 105–119.
2. Beidler, L. M. Our taste receptors. *Sci. Mon.*, 1952, **75**: 343–349.

3. Beidler, L. M. Properties of chemoreceptors of tongue of rat. *J. Neurophysiol.*, 1953, **16**: 595–607.
4. Carpenter, J. A. *Species differences in taste preferences.* Ph.D. thesis, Brown University, 1953.
5. Frings, H. Gustatory thresholds for sucrose and electrolytes in cockroach. *J. exp. Zool.*, 1946, **102**: 23–50.
6. Frings, H. A contribution to the comparative physiology of contact chemoreception. *J. comp. physiol. Psychol.*, 1948, **41**: 25–34.
7. Murray, E. J. Wells, H., Kohn, M., and Miller, N. E. Sodium sucaryl: a substance which tastes sweet to human subjects but is avoided by rats. *J. comp. physiol. Psychol.*, 1953, **46**: 134–137.
8. Pfaffmann, C. Gustatory afferent impulses. *J. cell. comp. Physiol.*, 1941, **17**: 243–258.
9. Pfaffmann, C. Species differences in taste sensitivity. *Science*, 1953, **117**: 470.
10. Pfaffmann, C. and Bare, J. K. Gustatory nerve discharges in normal and adrenalectomized rats. *J. comp. physiol. Psychol.*, 1950, **43**: 320–324.
11. Richter, C. P. and MacLean, A. Salt-taste thresholds of humans. *Amer. J. Physiol.*, 1939, **126**: 1–6.
12. Zotterman, Y. Action potentials in the glossopharyngeal nerve and in the chorda tympani. *Skand. Arch. Physiol.*, 1935, **72**: 73–77.

10 cutaneous impulses in the cat *

R. M. Gaze and G. Gordon

1. What method was used by the experimenters for the anatomical studies of the thalamus?

* R. M. Gaze and G. Gordon, "Some Observations on the Central Pathway for Cutaneous Impulses in the Cat," *Quart. J. exp. Physiol.*, 40 (1955), 187–194. Reprinted with permission.

2. What experimental evidence is available for the conclusion that "the dorsal columns carry cutaneous impulses"?

3. How could an investigator design an experiment to discover whether or not an entirely ipsilateral pathway exists through the medium of the ventrolateral columns?

4. What are the limitations of the experiment?

In a previous paper (3) we described some of the functional characteristics of those single neural units in the thalamus which respond to stimulating the skin. Small stimuli such as the bending of hairs usually activated pathways whose peripheral fibres were for the most part large and rapidly conducting (α and β fibres principally); stronger stimuli such as pinching, pricking or tapping usually activated slowly conducting pathways which involved peripheral fibres of smaller size (δ fibres and some β or γ fibres). The majority of the thalamic responses were contralateral, but some were ipsilateral.

The present paper describes an attempt to identify some of the central paths concerned in the excitation of the different groups of thalamic neural units. Lesions were made in different parts of the afferent pathways in the spinal cord, and the thalamic responses were studied a few weeks afterwards when the animals had recovered.

methods

General procedure. All the experiments were done with cats. In each animal a lesion was made in some part of the spinal cord under deep pentobarbitone anæsthesia and with full aseptic precautions, and a period of at least two weeks was allowed for recovery and healing. The animal was then again anæsthetized with pentobarbitone (35 mg./kg. body weight) and an investigation made of the responses of single thalamic units to stimulating the saphenous nerve and its skin area. The methods used in this type of investigation, including the subsequent anatomical studies of the thalamus, have already been described in full (3). The essence of the method is that a regularly repeated electrical stimulus is given to the saphenous nerve while a fine steel electrode is slowly pushed into the thalamus: when a single thalamic unit is found which responds consistently to the stimulus, it can be discovered, from a record of the action potential of the nerve, which group or groups of saphenous fibres must be excited in order for that thalamic unit to respond. Finally, the electrical stimulus is removed and the saphenous skin area is stimulated mechanically in the hope of finding an appropriate stimulus for the same unit.

Operative technique and assessment of lesions. The fibres of the cat's saphenous nerve are derived largely from the fifth and sixth lumbar roots (5), and in order to be certain that no saphenous fibres could have entered the cord above the lesion, we have made all the spinal lesions at levels above the 13th thoracic segment.

The lesions were made in the lower thoracic region by removing the arch of one or sometimes two vertebræ, opening the dura and cutting through the appropriate part of the cord. Large lesions were best done with a fine ophthalmic knife, but when cutting only the dorsal columns it was quicker and more accurate to make a single snip with a pair of fine sharp-pointed scissors.

At the end of the final experiment each brain and spinal cord was fixed *in situ* by perfusion with 5 per cent formaldehyde. The tissue containing the lesion was removed and fixation completed in 10 per cent formaldehyde. Serial transverse sections were then cut at 20 μ thickness throughout the relevant region, and were stained with iron-hæmatoxylin and eosin. In assessing the size and position of a lesion, a tracing was made from a transverse section of normal spinal cord near the lesion, and the region of the cord completely destroyed was marked on this tracing after careful study of the series of sections. This method of assessment does not take full account of destruction of nervous tissue other than that produced at the time of the operation: œdema and ischæmia must produce some additional disturbance of function. The method therefore assesses the *minimal* extent of the lesion. We have reported here only those experiments in which the lesion proved, on examination, to be of the size and in the position intended.

Nomenclature. The words "ipsilateral" and "contralateral" are used throughout this paper to describe central phenomena with respect to the side of the peripheral stimulus. "Latency" always refers to the time-interval between the delivery of a stimulus to the saphenous nerve at the knee and the earliest response to the stimulus made by a thalamic unit.

results

Section of the whole spinal cord except for the dorsal columns. This operation was carried out successfully on two animals, though the lesions were somewhat more extensive than was intended [see Fig. 1 (*a*)]. In the first (Cat 1), no thalamic responses were found on stimulating the hind legs, although the relevant region was explored on each side of the thalamus. In the second (Cat 2), four thalamic units were identified which responded to saphenous stimulation, three contralateral and one ipsilateral [see Table 1 (*a*)]. The responses of all these units were mediated by saphenous fibres of the $\alpha\beta\gamma$ group; only two of

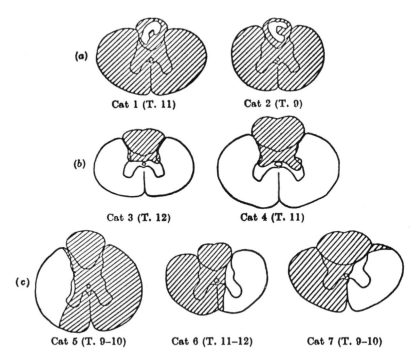

Fig. 1. The figure shows the position of the spinal lesion (shaded area) in each of the seven animals referred to in the text. The segmental level of each lesion is given in brackets.

them responded clearly to skin stimulation, and in these the appropriate stimulus was the bending of hairs. The latencies for three of these units were longer than would be expected for corresponding units in normal animals: the mean latency figures for normal animals, taken from experiments described in our previous paper (3), are shown in parentheses in the table.

Section of both dorsal columns. The dorsal columns were cut in two animals, and in each the lesion was satisfactory [see Fig. 1 (*b*)]. Only one side of the thalamus was investigated, that contralateral to the stimulated nerve. In the first (Cat 3), no responses were found although the relevant region of the thalamus was explored. In the second (Cat 4),

responses were found in four contralateral thalamic units. A response was also found on moving hairs on the hind leg opposite to that prepared for saphenous stimulation: this response was not further investigated, but it was ipsilateral with respect to the skin stimulus. The details of these five responses are shown in Table 1 (*b*). It is clear that a considerable variety of responses, including tactile responses, are mediated by fibres other than those of the dorsal columns.

Section of the whole cord except for one ventrolateral column. The particular object of these experiments was to determine, with respect to the level of the lesion, the level of the crossing made in those pathways which reach the contralateral thalamus through the

	Cat	Saphenous fibre-group	Latency (msec.)	Skin stimulus	Side
(a) Section of whole cord except dorsal columns	2	$\beta\gamma$	35·8 (20·0)	Hairs	C.
		$\beta\gamma$	29·4 (28·0)	N.I.	C.
		α	56·0 (28·0)	N.I.	C.
(b) Section of both dorsal columns	4	$\beta\gamma$	39·2 (20·0)	Hairs	I.
		α	—	—	C.
		$\beta\gamma$	31·0 (32·9)	Light tap	C.
		$\beta\gamma$	23·1	—	C.
		δ	70·1 (44·1)	Pinch	C.
		—	—	Hairs	I.
(c) One ventrolateral column alone surviving:					
(i) L. column surviving	5	$\beta\gamma$	43·0 (30·1)	Touch not hairs	I.
		δ	43·5 (44·1)	Tap	I.
(ii) R. column surviving	6	α	12·6 (17·6)	Hairs	C.
	7	$\beta\gamma$	—	Hairs	C.
		α	18·6 (17·6)	Hairs	C.

ventrolateral columns of the cord, and also to find whether impulses reaching the ipsilateral thalamus remain always on one side or whether they can cross and recross the midline on their way to the brain.

(i) *Left ventrolateral column alone surviving.* The column surviving was of the side opposite to that of the saphenous nerve stimulated. The lesion in the only animal of this kind (Cat 5) is shown in Fig. 1 (*c*). The thalamus of each side was explored thoroughly. No contralateral responses were found, but two ipsilateral units responded: the details of these two are shown in Table 1 (*c*).

(ii) *Right ventrolateral column alone surviving.* The column surviving was of the same side as the saphenous nerve stimulated. The lesions in the two animals of this group are shown in Fig. 1 (*c*) (Cats 6 and 7). In both animals the thalamus was explored thoroughly on each side, and in neither animal was any response found in the thalamus ipsilateral to the nerve. Two contralateral responses were found in one animal (Cat 7) and one in the other (Cat 6): the details of these are set out in Table 1 (*c*).

Nature and anatomical position of thalamic responses. The thalamic responses referred to

in this paper were composed of trains of impulse-spikes similar in every respect to those seen under the same conditions in normal animals. They were all recorded from the ventrolateral nuclear region of the thalamus where cutaneous responses are to be found in normal animals.

discussion

When a lesion has been made in some part of the afferent pathway, the subsequent experiment must be looked upon as an attempt to test the functional capacity of that part of the pathway which remains intact. It seems likely, in view of the immediate depression caused by acute lesions of the central nervous system (e.g. spinal shock), that the functional capacity of the intact pathways will be greater when two or three weeks have been allowed for recovery from the initial lesion; and this was our reason for preferring the chronic to the acute lesion in these experiments.

If no responses are recorded from a region of the thalamus in which responses would be expected under similar conditions in normal animals, then it is possible to make an estimate of the probability that this is the result of making the lesion. We have several instances where a high probability exists; but such information is difficult to interpret because it is not known how the fibres destroyed by the lesion would have acted in producing the response in a normal animal. They might, for instance, have acted by facilitating an effect mediated primarily by other fibres not destroyed by the lesion: the absence of the tonic stretch reflex in a spinal animal, in which the reflex arc remains intact, is an example of such a situation. For this reason we have refrained from drawing conclusions from negative evidence.

The recording of responses from single units in the thalamus after a lesion has been made in the afferent pathway, although providing definite evidence that impulses have travelled in the intact pathways which remain, does not show that the whole nervous mechanism normally concerned in activating these units is still intact. These responses may be compared in latency, in number and frequency of impulses, and in anatomical position with corresponding responses from normal animals; and if they do not differ greatly from the normal, then it is probable that the afferent pathway in question had not been seriously affected by the lesion. In fact, the only experiment in which the responses were strikingly different from the normal was that in which the whole cord was cut except for the dorsal columns (Cat 2), and here the latencies for three of the four units were so long as to be somewhat outside the range which we have found in normal animals.

The experimental evidence allows certain definite conclusions. In the first place, it has been shown that the dorsal columns carry cutaneous impulses (Cat 2). This fact was demonstrated in the rabbit by Schiff (10), who found that an animal with only its dorsal columns intact still responded with movements of the face and head when the skin below the lesion was touched or blown upon. Lloyd and McIntyre (7) have measured the conduction velocity of the fibres of this cutaneous component in the cat's dorsal columns. The only type of cutaneous response which we showed to be mediated by the dorsal columns was that brought about by moving hairs, the peripheral fibres concerned being those of the saphenous $\alpha\beta\gamma$ group.

It is also clear, from those experiments in which the dorsal columns were cut (Cats 4, 5, 6 and 7), that cutaneous responses of a number of kinds can be mediated otherwise than by the dorsal columns. The pathway for these responses must have been in the ventrolateral columns, since the view that afferent impulses could travel for any distance through the spinal grey matter seems to be untenable (11). A cutaneous sensory pathway in the ventrolateral columns was recognized clearly by Gowers (4) as a result of his own observations and those of Woroschiloff (13), and its existence has since been supported by a large amount of additional evidence. In our experiments, the thalamic units which were active after the dorsal columns had been cut included some responding to hair movement whose responses were mediated by peripheral $\alpha\beta\gamma$ fibres; so that, considering also the evidence from Cat 2, it appears that the impulses concerned with units of this type can travel both within and without the dorsal columns. A unit responding to touch without hair movement (peripheral $\beta\gamma$ fibres) and two units responding to strong skin stimuli (peripheral δ fibres) were also identified after cutting the dorsal columns; no such units were found in Cat 2 where the ventrolateral columns had been cut. The "strong stimuli" referred to here might be deemed to have excited the receptive mechanism called by

Sherrington "nociceptive," and the fact that the impulses travelled in the ventrolateral columns calls to mind the pathway in the lateral columns described by Woodworth and Sherrington (12) for nociceptive reactions in the cat. It is worth remark that the spino-thalamic tract which is commonly supposed to carry impulses mediating pain in man has not been identified in the cat: it appears from the work of Patrick (8), and from much subsequent work, including unpublished observations of our own, that few if any myelinated fibres degenerate in the upper brain-stem of this animal after lateral semi-section of the cord. The ventrolateral pathway may be a simple unmyelinated or thinly myelinated pathway, therefore, or it may be a complicated pathway containing synapses. This second possibility is supported by the fact that nociceptive reactions can still occur when the spinal pathway has been interrupted by two lateral semi-sections at different levels, one on each side of the cord (6, 9). Bohm (1) has found that the electrical wave responses elicited in the cat's cerebral cortex by stimulating cutaneous fibres of low threshold are abolished when the dorsal columns are cut in the course of the experiment, whereas cerebellar responses are not affected by this procedure. Our experimental evidence conflicts with Bohm's conclusion that the fibres in the ventrolateral region of the cord which are activated by stimulating low threshold cutaneous fibres are connected with systems projecting not to the thalamus but exclusively to the cerebellum.

There seems to be no ground for distinguishing two simple pathways, one leading to the ipsilateral and one to the contralateral thalamus. For instance, the evidence from Cat 5 leads to the conclusion that the ventrolateral fibres concerned in an *ipsilateral* response, entering the cord on the right, had crossed to the left below the lesion and had crossed back to the right at some point above it. This sort of arrangement was also found by Gardner and Haddad (2) on stimulating muscular, articular and mixed nerves of the cat's hind limb and recording from the cerebral cortex, though their results do not apply specifically to cutaneous pathways. There is no means of deciding from their experiments, or from ours, whether an entirely ipsilateral pathway exists through the medium of the ventrolateral columns. We have shown that there is also an ipsilateral pathway through the dorsal columns; Gardner and Haddad also found such a pathway for impulses set up in muscle nerves and mixed nerves.

It is commonly believed that the ventrolateral cord pathway concerned with *contralateral* cerebral activity arises by crossing to the side opposite to that of the peripheral stimulus within one or two segments of entry into the cord. On this basis we should have expected to find contralateral responses in Cat 5, where the contralateral ventrolateral column alone remained intact at the 9th thoracic segment, though little significance can be attached to our failure to do so in one experiment. Gardner and Haddad (2) found contralateral cerebral responses to mixed nerve stimulation after this type of spinal lesion, but our experiment may not be comparable with theirs owing to their lesions having been made higher up in the spinal cord. We have, on the other hand, definite evidence from Cat 7, in which the ipsilateral ventrolateral column alone remained intact between the 9th and 10th thoracic segments, that some fibres ran ipsilaterally past a lesion which was some seven segments above the level of entry of the afferent fibres into the cord, and only crossed to the opposite side higher up. Gardner and Haddad also report experiments of this type.

Our experimental results do not allow any

simple diagrammatic representation of the paths taken by afferent cutaneous impulses: impulses from one hind limb can reach the thalamus of either side by quite a variety of methods. Nor has it been possible, from this rather limited investigation, to allot impulses aroused by any particular kind of stimulus to one exclusive path; although it is perhaps worth attention that no responses other than tactile were shown to be mediated by the dorsal columns.

summary

1. The responses of single neural units in the cat's thalamus to electrical stimulation of the saphenous nerve, and to mechanical stimulation of the saphenous skin area, have been studied after chronic lesions had been made in various parts of the spinal pathway.

2. Thalamic responses to stimulating hairs, mediated by saphenous fibres of the $\alpha\beta\gamma$ group, were found after the whole spinal cord had been cut except for the dorsal columns. These were both ipsilateral and contralateral to the peripheral stimulus.

3. Thalamic responses to a variety of cutaneous stimuli were found after cutting the dorsal columns, one or both ventrolateral columns having been left intact. These included responses to stimulating hairs, mediated by saphenous fibres of the $\alpha\beta\gamma$ group, and responses to stronger stimuli, mediated by the saphenous δ group.

4. In experiments in which the spinal cord was cut across except for the ventrolateral column of one or other side, it was found that impulses can activate the ipsilateral thalamus by crossing the midline below the lesion and crossing back at some point above it. Impulses activating the contralateral thalamus can cross the midline at some point above the lesion. These are probably only examples of a variety of possible paths for such impulses.

5. These results do not support any simple diagrammatic representation of the afferent cutaneous pathway.

acknowledgments

We would like to express our thanks to Mr. P. Philbin for constant technical help; to Mr. T. A. Marsland, who prepared the microscopic sections of the lesions; and to Mr. A. Austin for his photographic work.

references

1. Bohm, E. (1953). "An electro-physiological study of the ascending spinal anterolateral fibre system connected to coarse cutaneous afferents," *Acta physiol. scand.* **29**, Suppl. 106, 106.
2. Gardner, E. and Haddad, B. (1953). "Pathways to the cerebral cortex for afferent fibres from the hindleg of the cat," *Amer. J. Physiol.* **172**, 475.
3. Gaze, R. M. and Gordon, G. (1954). "The representation of cutaneous sense in the thalamus of the cat and monkey," *Quart. J. exp. Physiol.* **39**, 279.
4. Gowers, W. R. (1880). The Diagnosis of Diseases of the Spinal Cord, pp. 14–15. London: Churchill.
5. Heinbecker, P., O'Leary, J. and Bishop, G. H. (1933). "Nature and source of fibers contributing to the saphenous nerve of the cat," *Amer. J. Physiol.* **104**, 23.
6. Karplus, J. P. and Kreidl, A. (1914). "Ein Beitrag zur Kenntnis der Schmerzleitung im Rückenmark," *Pflüg. Arch. ges. Physiol.* **158**, 275.

7. Lloyd, D. P. C. and McIntyre, A. K. (1950). "Dorsal column conduction of Group I muscle afferent impulses and their relay through Clarke's column," *J. Neurophysiol.* **13**, 39.

8. Patrick, H. T. (1896). "On the course and destination of Gowers' tract," *J. nerv. ment. Dis.* **23**, 85.

9. Ranson, S. W. and Billingsley, P. R. (1916). "Afferent spinal paths and the vasomotor reflexes," *Amer. J. Physiol.* **42**, 16.

10. Schiff, J. M. (1858). *Lehrbuch der Physiologie des Menschen. I. Muskel- und Nervenphysiologie*, pp. 252–254. Lahr: Schauenburg.

11. Sherrington, C. S. (1900). *In* Schäfer, E. A., Textbook of Physiology. Vol. 2, p. 978. Edinburgh and London: Pentland.

12. Woodworth, R. S. and Sherrington, C. S. (1904). "A pseudaffective reflex and its spinal path," *J. Physiol.* **31**, 234.

13. Woroschiloff (1874). "Der Verlauf der motorischen und sensiblen Bahnen durch das Lendenmark des Kaninchen," *Arb. physiol. Anst. Leipzig.* Neunter Jahrgang, p. 99.

11   the corpus callosum in contralateral transfer in cats *

John S. Stamm and R. W. Sperry

1. Do the findings in this study substantiate previous findings for the sense of vision?

* J. S. Stamm and R. W. Sperry, "Function of the Corpus Callosum in Contralateral Transfer of Somesthetic Discrimination in Cats," *J. comp. physiol. Psychol.*, 50 (1957), 138–143. Reprinted with permission.

2. When "savings scores" are used, what assumptions are made about retention?

3. What anatomical checks were made by the experimenters?

Monocularly learned visual discriminations transfer readily to the untrained eye in cats with midsaggital division of the optic chiasma (3). However, if the corpus callosum has also been sectioned, the animals are unable to recognize the patterns with the untrained eye (4) and can only relearn the discriminations at rates similar to the original learning with the first eye (6). These findings appear to demonstrate an important role for the corpus callosum in integrating the two hemispheres in visual learning and memory.

In an attempt to obtain further evidence concerning the function of the callosum we have investigated contralateral transfer from one forepaw to the other of trained tactile discriminations. Cats were trained to push the correct one of two pedals which could be reached only with one forepaw and which the cats could not see, but had to discriminate by touch alone. Transfer to the contralateral paw of roughness, softness, and form discriminations in unoperated cats was compared with that obtained in cats with midsaggital section of the corpus callosum.

method

animals

Eight cats were used. They were 8 to 12 months old at the start of the experiment and had been reared in the laboratory from the age of approximately 2 months. The corpus callosum was sectioned in four of the cats at least 3 weeks before the beginning of training. With the exception of one cat, *Hrr*, the *S*s had received no previous training. *Hrr*, in which the optic chiasma as well as the callosum was sectioned, had been used in a previous experiment on visual discrimination (6).

apparatus

Training box. The discrimination box was designed to permit the cat to reach through a hole to press two test pedals with the right but not the left forepaw, and conversely. The cat was closely confined in the choice chamber. A set of interchangeable sliding screens allowed the cat complete, partial, or no view of the test pedals. A vertical partition inside the chamber helped to prevent the cat's using the wrong paw. The pedals, mounted in a separate box, were pulled out of reach between trials. Duplicate pairs of pedals mounted side by side in the pedal box were used for reversing the right-left placement of correct and incorrect discriminanda. Adjustments could be made so the four pedals had equal strokes and countertensions, and the proper height for individual cats. When a pedal was completely depressed, it closed a microswitch which activated electric circuits to release a food pellet after a correct response, or to sound a buzzer after a wrong response. An observation window in the top of the box made it possible to observe the cats while they were working.

The discriminanda could be attached interchangeably to the ends of the pedals. After preliminary tests with discriminations of varying difficulty, three problems were selected that could be learned with a moderate amount of training. In order to reduce generalization and interference effects between the problems, each pair of discriminanda was made distinct in shape or surface characteristics. The following problems were used:

Form. A triangular prism with a 90° edge on top, placed crosswise, versus a flat square block. Both pieces were made of wood and were covered with plastic cloth.

Softness. Three degrees of softness were used: a foam rubber block 2 cm. high, a foam rubber block ½ cm. high mounted on wood, and a wooden block 2 cm. high, all covered with cotton cloth. The two discriminanda selected for each cat are listed in Tables 1 and 2.

Roughness. Two half-cylinders of wood, placed crosswise with rounded surfaces up, one covered with No. 2 sandpaper, the other sanded smooth.

procedure

Preliminary training. The cat was trained first to press a wood block (2 cm. high), mounted on a pedal directly in front of the choice chamber. At the beginning S could view the pedal, but vision was restricted increasingly as training progressed. Toward the end of preliminary training, with vision now excluded entirely, the block was shifted at random to the right and left positions until S learned to discriminate between the block and the blank pedal. After this habit had been learned, S was trained to do the same with the other forepaw. Except at the start of this introductory training, vision of the pedals by the Ss was completely excluded.

Experimental training. The training schedule as a rule consisted of six daily sessions per week, with 70 to 120 trials per day. The right-left placement of the two discriminanda was alternated in accordance with Gellermann's principles (2), except when a position habit developed. When S had consistently pressed the right or the left pedal for as many as 10 trials, the correct discriminandum was placed at the nonpreferred side until S made two consecutive correct responses. If, then, 4 successive incorrect responses were made, move-

Table 1. Summary of Training Sequence and Results for Unoperated Cats

Subject[†]	Problem[‡]	Paw Trained First	Total Trials with First Paw	No. Trials to Reach Criterion		Saving Score (%)
				Learn	Relearn	
Hnr	s_1*	L	680	260	110	58
	r	R	890	360	50	86
	f	L	630	90	90	0
Jsp	r	R	750	340	80	76
	f	L	480	100	30	70
	s_3	R	750	170	10	94
Frn	f	R	600	110	40	64
	s_2	L	450	90	10	89
	r	R	1,250	820	10	99
Gdf	f	L	600	90	20	78
	s_2	R	660	330	120	64

* Negative stimuli.
† The table is arranged according to the order of training of Ss and discrimination problems.
‡ Discriminations: s—softness; r—roughness; f—form. The positive stimulus is the softer pedal, the sandpaper surface, or the edge, except where an asterisk (*) indicates that these were the negative stimuli. For softness discrimination the positive and negative stimuli were, respectively: s_1, 2-cm. rubber pad vs. wood; s_2, ½-cm. rubber pad vs. wood; s_3, 2-cm. vs. ½-cm. rubber pad.

ment of the incorrect pedal was blocked until S pressed the correct one. It was found that most cats developed a position habit on beginning a new discrimination. After this had been broken, they tended to form the opposite position habit, after which they would learn to touch both pedals before responding and generally showed no further position preferences.

The Ss were trained on each discrimination until they responded correctly for at least 50 successive trials or until the response level no longer rose during 200 or more trials. A minimum of six daily training sessions was given for each discrimination with each paw. Retraining with the second paw always started one day after training with the first paw had been terminated. Two days prior to the first transfer trial, S received at least 30 trials with the second paw on a previously learned discrimination. The order in which Ss were trained on successive problems, the paws used for initial training, and the total number of training trials with the first paw are given in Tables 1 and 2.

The apparatus permitted E to watch S's

Table 2. Summary of Training Sequence and Results for Cats with Sectioned Callosum*

Subject	Problem	Paw Trained First	Total Trials with First Paw	No. trials to Reach Criterion		Saving Score (%)
				Learn	Relearn	
Bnj	f	R	420	170	210	−23
	s_2	L	510	110	80	+27
	r	R	840	270	380	−41
Crr	f	R	980	300	340	−13
	s_2*	L	500	150	200	−33
	r	R	610	270	200	+26
Drl	s_2	L	600	240	260	− 8
	f	R	500	210	180	+14
Hrr	r	R	1,350	680	260	+62
	f	L	620	350	330	+ 6
	s_2	R	650	180	270	−50

* See footnotes of Table 1.

paw during the response process, so it was easy to see when the pedals were being selected by touch. That learning was achieved on the basis of touch was evident throughout with a single exception as follows: On the roughness discrimination *Drl* attained an above-chance performance without appearing to feel both pedals, whereupon it was noticed that this cat, being smaller than the other *S*s, was moving sufficiently far back in the chamber to enable it to see the pedals through the hole for the forepaw. Proper precautions were then taken to be certain that *Drl* learned all subsequent discriminations by touch. The other *S*s, when watched through the observation windows, kept their heads above the opaque screen and did not attempt to view the pedals.

The use of auditory and incidental somesthetic cues was prevented by moving the pedal box forward and sideways in a random manner between trials and by attaching the discriminanda to different pedals between successive training sessions. In order to make valid comparisons between the two groups, we attempted to apply similar training procedures and schedules to all cats.

treatment of data

The *S*s' responses were recorded in groups of 10 trials. The criterion of learning selected was 17 or more correct responses within two successive groups, provided the performance remained above the .01 probability level during overtraining. The first of these 20 trials was taken as the point at which learning had occurred and where overtraining started.

The degree of contralateral transfer is expressed by the "saving score," which is the ratio of the trials saved in relearning to the trials required in initial learning, stated as a percentage. A negative "saving score" indicates that more trials were required to reach criterion during retraining than during the original training.

The mean percentage of correct responses for the number of trials to criterion with the first paw was computed for training and for retraining. The difference is stated as the "transfer level." Its significance was evaluated by computing the t ratio for the difference between proportions of right and wrong responses. A negative "transfer level" signifies that *S*'s performance was lower with the second than with the first paw.

results

transfer tests with corpus callosum intact

Substantial transfer, as expressed by the saving scores listed in Table 1, was evident in all four cats. The saving scores were, with one exception, between 58 per cent and 99 per cent, with a median of 76 per cent. The only exception was *Hnr*'s zero saving score on the form discrimination. This *S* made consistently fewer errors, however, during retraining than during training with the first paw. If one applies the .05 criterion level (15 correct responses in 20 trials) to this performance, 80 trials were required with the first paw, but only 30 with the second, giving a saving score of 62 per cent.

Positive transfer effects were also revealed by the learning curves. The curves for *Jsp*, shown in Figure 1, are representative for this group. When the shift was made to the second paw, the performance level dropped somewhat, but remained considerably above the initial performance with the first paw and reached the final level more rapidly. This was observed for every discrimination which these *S*s learned. The terminal performance levels

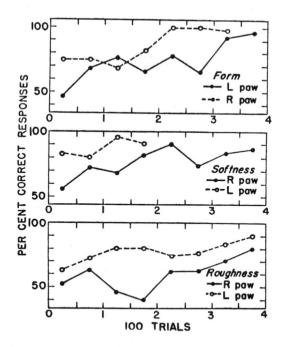

Fig. 1. Learning (solid) and relearning (dotted) curves for three discriminations by *Jsp* with callosum intact. The terminal portions of some of the curves are omitted.

were approximately equal for both paws at 85 per cent to 100 per cent correct responses.

According to the *t* ratios for the transfer levels, the cats gave significantly more correct responses with the second than with the first paw on all tasks, except *Hnr*'s form discrimination. One *t* was slightly above the .01 probability level, while nine ratios fell well beyond this criterion.

transfer tests with corpus callosum sectioned

No cat in this group showed consistent transfer, as indicated by the saving scores listed in Table 2. Five saving scores were positive and six were negative, with a group median of —8 per cent. An appreciable positive

saving score was obtained only by *Hrr* on the roughness problem. This is accounted for by the exceptionally long training with the first paw. *Hrr* did not reach criterion with the first paw until trial 260, which is more than twice the highest number of trials needed by any of the unoperated *Ss* to attain criterion during retraining.

The lack of transfer in these cats is apparent also from their learning curves. The curves of *Bnj*, shown in Figure 2, are representative for this group. When the shift was made to the second paw, the performance dropped to chance level and the relearning curves then followed the course of the curves for the first paw. The marked agreement between the two curves of each task was evident in the majority of discriminations of the other three cats. The final performance was also 85 to 100 per cent correct responses. For three cats the right

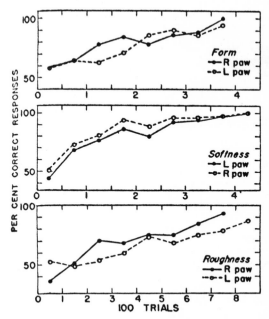

Fig. 2. Learning (solid) and relearning (dotted) curves for three discriminations by *Bnj* with callosum sectioned.

and left curves for each discrimination ended at about the same level, but *Crr* responded better with the left paw during final training on each task, regardless of the paw with which it was first trained.

The transfer levels for this group were consistently low, varying little from the group median of —0.2 per cent and the corresponding *t* ratios did not fall beyond chance, except for *Hrr*'s roughness and *Crr*'s form discrimination. The latter *t* was negative beyond the .01 probability level because *Crr* gave somewhat better than chance responses during training with the first paw and responded below chance for over 250 trials with the second paw.

comparisons between the two groups

The number of training sessions for the three tasks required with the first paw were 6 to 10 for the unoperated and 6 to 11 for the operated group, except for one discrimination in each group which needed longer training. The group medians for the total number of training trials with the first paw were 660 for the unoperated and 610 for the operated *Ss*. *Frn* and *Hrr* required exceptionally long training on the roughness discrimination. *Frn* attained the .05 criterion level on this problem after 310 trials, but then responded slightly below the .01 criterion for over 500 trials. This was the first discrimination on which *Hrr* was trained, and *S* did not begin to test the discriminanda until after almost 600 trials, when its learning curve finally rose from chance level.

The unoperated group appeared to learn somewhat faster than the operated group, the respective medians being 170 and 240 trials to criterion. This difference is entirely accounted for in the scores for form discrimination, which required medians of 95 trials for the unoperated and 255 trials for the operated

cats. The other two discriminations, however, were learned somewhat more rapidly by the callosum-sectioned cats.

In the performance with the second paw, there was a marked difference between the two groups, with the median number of trials to reach criterion being 260 for the operated, but only 40 for the unoperated group. The difference in the degree of transfer is illustrated in Figure 3.

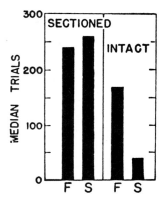

Fig. 3. Median number of trials required to attain criterion for the callosum-sectioned and callosum-intact groups during training with the first paw (F) and retraining with the second paw (S).

There was little overlap between the saving scores for the two groups. Only one score of the unoperated *Ss* was below 58 per cent, and only one score in the operated group was above 27 per cent, while ten scores in each of the groups were clustered about the respective medians. For this distribution of scores a chi-square coefficient of 11.6 ($p < .001$) was obtained, further illustrating the significantly higher degree of transfer in the operated cats.

anatomical checks

In view of the nature of the results, anatomical checks seemed uncalled for, and the operated cats have been retained for other investigations. On the basis of the results one would infer that the callosum has been successfully sectioned in all cases. Examination of other brains similarly operated has regularly shown the callosum to have been completely sectioned along with the hippocampal commissure and occasional remnants of the fornix on one or, rarely, both sides.

discussion

Substantial contralateral transfer was evident in all four cats with intact callosum, the saving score averaging 76 per cent. This is a somewhat lower degree of transfer than was obtained for visual discrimination in a previous investigation (3). The lower degree of transfer in the somesthetic discriminations may be related to the use of different motor patterns in shifting from one limb to the other, whereas the motor response remained the same during the visual testing with right and left eye.

In contrast with the unoperated group, no cat with sectioned callosum showed consistent transfer. The distribution of saving scores, which in this group varied between +62 per cent and —50 per cent (with a median of —8 per cent) on different discrimination tasks, is similar to that obtained for interocular transfer in cats with sectioned chiasma and callosum (6). Since the positive and negative scores were of approximately equal magnitude and since the complete learning curves indicated a lack of transfer, it may be concluded that transfer was absent in the callosum-sectioned cats.

As was found for visual discriminations (6), the independent learning curves from the separated hemispheres of the same animal were much more alike in character than were those from different cats. Also for each individual, variations between right and left curves for the same discrimination problem were small compared with the differences between curves for different tasks. These observations suggest that the individual variability in learning tends to be determined to a surprising degree by intrinsic features of brain organization as opposed to adventitious events in the learning process and general situation.

There was some evidence, not well quantified, that the motor learning involved in pushing the pedals in the present study transferred to a higher degree in the normal than in the callosum-sectioned cats. The learning to press a pedal, which took place prior to the discrimination training, required at least seven days with the first paw. Three callosum-sectioned cats needed as much training with the second as with the first paw. By contrast, all unoperated Ss were able to press the pedal during the first retraining session.

The present findings are in keeping with an earlier report (1) that cutaneous conditioned responses fail to show the usual spread to contralateral homologous areas in dogs in which the corpus callosum has been sectioned. The apparent disagreement with the observation on human patients that stylus maze learning transfers readily from one hand to the other after section of the callosum (5) remains unaccounted for and may reflect a species difference.

summary

An apparatus was devised in which cats were trained to press with one forepaw the correct one of two pedals which they could not see and had to distinguish on the basis of touch. Four normal cats and four cats with sectioned corpus callosum were trained to make three discriminations involving differences in form, softness, and roughness. After the discriminations had been learned and overtrained with one forepaw, the cat was retrained to make the same discrimination using the other forepaw.

The group of unoperated cats attained the criterion of 17 or more correct responses in 20 consecutive trials after a median of 170 trials with the first paw, and only 40 with the second paw. The medians for the operated group, on the other hand, were 240 trials for the first paw and 260 for the second. The degree of transfer was expressed by saving scores for which the medians were +76 per cent for the unoperated group and —8 per cent for the group with the callosum sectioned.

It is concluded that in cats the corpus callosum is essential for the contralateral transfer of somesthetic discriminations from one to the other forepaw.

references

1. Bykoff, K. Versuche an Hunden mit Durchschneiden des Corpus Callosum. *Zbl. ges. Neurol. Psychiat.*, 1924, **39**, 199.
2. Gellermann, L. W. Chance orders of alternating stimuli in visual discrimination experiments. *J. genet. Psychol.*, 1933, **42**, 206–208.
3. Myers, R. E. Interocular transfer of pattern discrimination in cats following section of crossed optic fibers. *J. comp. physiol. Psychol.*, 1955, **48**, 470–473.
4. Myers, R. E. The corpus callosum and hemispheric interaction. Ph.D. thesis, Univer. of Chicago, 1955.
5. Smith, K. U. Experimental analysis of the associative mechanisms of the human brain in learning functions. *J. comp. physiol. Psychol.*, 1952, **45**, 66–72.
6. Sperry, R. W., Stamm, J. S., & Miner, Nancy. Relearning tests for interocular transfer following division of optic chiasma and corpus callosum in cats. *J. comp. physiol. Psychol.*, 1956, **49**, 529–533.

chapter 4

emotion

In the first reading in this chapter (Reading 12), E. Gellhorn reviews the theories of emotion discussed in Part II of the Introduction. He finds especially useful the Papez theory of emotion based on the "visceral brain," which was discussed in Chapter 1 as the "limbic system." Gellhorn finds the limbic system (including the hypothalamus) more important than the RAS in explaining emotions. Of course, he does not discount the role of the RAS in arousal of the organism. Gellhorn does an excellent job of marshaling the evidence in support of the importance of the visceral brain and the hypothalamus in emotion. Gellhorn believes that an understanding of the antagonism between the neocortex and the paleocortex together with an understanding of hypothalamic balance will lead to an explanation of abnormal as well as normal emotional behavior. He concludes with the note that Joseph Wolpe's reciprocal inhibition psychotherapy can be best understood in these terms.

The second reading (Reading 13, by Daniel Funkenstein) is discussed by Gellhorn in his article. Funkenstein was one of the first to show that fear and anger can be differentiated physiologically. Fear is correlated with the production of adrenalin (epinephrin) by the adrenal medulla and anger turned outward is related to the adrenal production of noradrenalin (norepinephrin). An interesting experimental breakthrough was the development of the mecholyl reaction test, which Funkenstein discusses.

In the final reading in this section (Reading 14), José Delgado and his co-workers report on their implanting of an assembly of six electrodes in each monkey subject to find which brain areas in and near the limbic system will elicit a conditioned fear response. Among the several areas that elicited the response was the medial nucleus of the amygdala. The amygdala has now been established as important in both fear and anger.

For many years the physiology of emotions was poorly understood. The breakthrough in this area has occurred only in the last decade. This is not to say that earlier theoretical speculations were valueless; they formed the foundation upon which to build. However, until the discovery of the importance of the reticular formation and the limbic system, it was not established that emotional behavior is differentiated by neural mechanisms.

12 prolegomena to a theory of the emotions *

E. Gellhorn

1. What is the present status of the James-Lange theory of emotion? Of the Cannon-Bard thalamic theory?

2. What is the relation between the reticular formation (RAS) and the limbic system in emotional behavior?

* E. Gellhorn, "Prolegomena to a Theory of the Emotions," *Perspectives in Biology and Medicine*, 4, No. 4 (1961), 403–436. Reprinted with permission.

3. What does Gellhorn mean by "body feelings"? Do they exist in civilized man?

4. How does Gellhorn use data from clinical cases (hospital patients) to extrapolate from animal findings to human beings?

5. Does this article present a complete theory of emotions? What limitations exist in this presentation?

Sieh', so ist Natur ein Buch lebendig,
Unverstanden, doch nicht unverstaendlich.
(So it is that nature is a living book,
not understood but not beyond understanding.)
Goethe

i. current theories

Before we comment on some important aspects of the theories of the emotions, we will review briefly the main points of those theories which still form the basis of our thoughts in this area.

a. the james-lange theory

The James-Lange theory held that emotional feeling really was the perception of changes in the activity of viscera and skeletal muscles. In other words, emotion was the result rather than the cause of visceral and muscle response.

Sherrington (1) objected to this theory in 1906. His objections were based on the observation of "emotional behavior" in animals deprived of a large part of the sensory input from body structures. Since that time considerable additional evidence, based chiefly on Cannon's work, has accrued which makes the theory appear untenable. Hebb disagrees with those who purport to refute the James-Lange theory on the basis of experiments which prevent the central nervous system from receiving signals from responding organs. Hebb (2) states that "such an argument is totally irrelevant; James did not say that emotional *behavior* depends on sensations from the limbs and viscera." To agree with Hebb, one must deny that behavioral signs of emotion are valid indicators of emotional feeling. However, they are the only signs we have that *any* animal or person (except one's self) experiences emotion, and common sense dictates that we accept them as valid indicators.

b. the cannon-bard thalamic theory

One of the foremost theories to emerge as an alternative to that of James and Lange was the Cannon-Bard theory. According to this theory (3, 4) a "thalamic process" was essential to the experiences of emotion. As originally postulated by Cannon, a simple relay of impulses to the cortex via the thalamus resulted in awareness of the stimulus object but no emotion. However, if the arrival of impulses at the cortex resulted in thalamic release from cortical inhibition, the released "thalamic process" added to the perception the "peculiar quality of emotion." It was also held that the "thalamic process" could be aroused directly by afferent impulses reaching it from the receptors. Unlike the James-Lange theory, the motor responses of emotion were thought to arise as the *result* of the emotional "thalamic process" rather than being the *cause* of the *emotional feeling*. Bard (5) insisted that the "thalamic process" was, of itself, inadequate. It must send signals back to the cortex to confer the emotional quality on the perception. The complete Cannon-Bard theory, therefore, considers perception with emotional coloring to depend on direct projections from thalamus to cortex plus activation of a thalamic process which secondarily

affects the cortex in such a way as to give rise to emotional experience. In view of the facts that Cannon and Bard showed emotional behavior to be virtually abolished by destruction of the posterior hypothalamus, and that Hess (6) demonstrated various types of emotional behavior with stimulation of the hypothalamus in the unanesthetized cat, it is the hypothalamus and not the thalamus which forms the core of the modern version of the Cannon-Bard theory.

c. lindsley's activation theory of emotion

Lindsley's (7) "activation theory" of emotion retains the basic framework of the Cannon-Bard but expands it to include the reticular activating system. The theory relates not only to emotional but also to cortical arousal, sleep-wakefulness, and certain types of abnormal behavior. It is based on the following experimental evidence: (1) The electroencephalogram shows an "activation pattern" in emotion. (2) Cortical activation can be evoked by stimulation of the brain stem reticular formation. (3) Destruction of the rostral end of the reticular system abolishes cortical activation and leads to apathy, somnolence, etc. (4) The reticular activating system which can arouse the cortex "is either identical with or overlaps" the mechanism whose "downward" discharge causes the motor activity of emotional expression.

d. the papez theory of emotion and the visceral brain

Papez (8), in a speculative paper published in 1937, proposed a theory of emotion in which the limbic system assumes a paramount role. The cortical emotive process was presumed to originate in the hippocampal formation. From the hippocampal formation impulses pass via the fornix to the hypothalamic mammillary bodies, thence to the anterior thalamic nucleus, from which impulses are relayed to the cingulate gyrus. He considered the cingulate gyrus to be the receptive region for the experiencing of emotion. "Radiation of the emotive process from the gyrus cinguli to other regions of the cerebral cortex would add emotional coloring to psychic processes occurring elsewhere." In support of his thesis Papez cited a number of investigations to show that preservation of this circuit is essential to a state of vigilance and wakefulness and suggested that it constitutes a mechanism capable of emotional expression and experience.

On the basis of Papez' theoretical paper and the important experimental studies of Klüver and Bucy (9), MacLean (10) developed the theory that the limbic system serves as a "visceral brain." By "visceral brain" he does not imply that the limbic system has functions related exclusively to the internal organs but that it is an organ which interprets experience in terms of *feeling* rather than in terms of "intellectualized" symbols. The "experience" which it interprets is in the form of information received from "the body viscus," by which he apparently means all body structures, both somatic and visceral. He points out that the visceral brain is strategically located to correlate every form of internal and external perception; for bringing into association not only oral (smell, taste, mouth) and visceral sensations, but also impressions from the sex organs, body wall, eye, and ear. He stresses the fact that "in contrast to the neopallium, the rhinencephalon has many and strong connections with the hypothalamus for discharging its impressions." Whereas intellectual expression may be carried out by the use of verbal symbols which require a well-developed neocortex, emotional expression can be achieved by the more primitive neural mechanisms of the limbic system, using a sort of "organ language" instead of words. He considers that the "visceral brain" is of special importance in emotional phenomena and the neocortex is essential to mental operations involving verbal symbols.

This theory seems to us to be an excellent framework within which the experimental material accumulated in the last decades fits without difficulty and which provides fruitful concepts for future work. We would like to add, however, a few remarks, the first of which concerns the relation of the reticular formation to the visceral brain.

ii. the visceral brain and the reticular formation

MacLean's visceral brain consists of a number of structures such as the hippocampus, amygdala, cingulum, septum, and hypothalamus. Obviously, stimulation or destruction of any one of these structures will alter the functional state of the whole system and will have repercussions in the neocortex as well. They will appear, in addition to other phenomena, as changes in emotional responsiveness and in the expression of emotional behavior. The prerequisite for the normal and abnormal functioning of the visceral brain is the activity of the reticular formation. It supplies the tonic impulses not only for the neocortex—without them coma supervenes (11)—but also for the hypothalamus and the other parts of the visceral brain.

Although we emphasize this dominant role of the reticular formation, we believe that the hypothalamus should be separated conceptually from the reticular formation. The hypothalamus controls hypophyseal functions, regulates various instinctual drives (hunger, thirst, sex activity), integrates sympathetic and somatic activity into the characteristic patterns of the ergotropic system, and is responsible for the maintenance of a balance between the parasympathetic (trophotropic) functions of the anterior hypothalamus and the sympathetic (ergotropic) division of the posterior hypothalamus. Moreover, the hypothalamus has a far-reaching influence on the reactivity of the neocortex, as indicated by experiments in which lesions were placed in the posterior hypothalamus while the reticular formation remained intact (12). These are functions which are not mediated by the more basic but less differentiated reticular formation.

In support of this interpretation, we like to quote from Herrick's (13) discussion of autonomic integration: "It is very important to recognize that all levels of integration interpenetrate, and one never operates independently of the others. Each higher level is derived from the lower and can work only with the instrumentation provided by the lower levels. Nonetheless, each level has its own distinctive qualities and the laws of its operation are peculiar to it."

It is obvious since ascending and descending pathways connect the reticular formation with the hypothalamus that under experimental conditions similar effects may be produced by stimulation of either structure (14), but this fact should not obscure the fundamental functional difference between the two structures.

iii. arousal and emotion

Hypothalamus and reticular formation are closely interrelated, anatomically and physiologically. It is, therefore, not surprising that stimulation causes arousal and emotional reac-

tions whereas lesions produce somnolence and coma regardless of whether the posterior hypothalamus or the reticular formation is subjected to these procedures. Both are multisynaptic structures and are blocked by small concentrations of barbiturates (15, 16). Yet, there is some evidence which suggests that the prevalent tendency in modern neurophysiology and psychology to attribute arousal and emotion to the reticular formation has gone too far.

Thus, the study of the action of drugs on arousal has shown that alterations in the reactivity of the reticular formation does not necessarily influence arousal. Physostigmine causes cortical asynchrony (as in arousal), and atropine produces synchrony of cortical potentials (as in sleep), yet the state of wakefulness is not altered by these drugs (17, 18). Neither do they influence the threshold of behavioral arousal (indicated by opening of the eyes, movements of ears, jaw, etc.) through stimulation of the reticular formation or afferent nerves. In sharp contrast to these findings, atropine raises and physostigmine lowers the threshold of the reticular formation for the alerting reaction of the EEG. These drugs, therefore, create conditions of a discrepancy between the behavioral and electroencephalic manifestations of stimulation of the reticular formation. A synchronizing drug such as atropine lessens the effectiveness of stimulation of the reticular formation on the EEG and behaves thereby as other synchronizing drugs (barbiturates) but is without effect as far as behavior is concerned, while physostigmine causes an asynchrony of cortical potentials (like amphetamine) without producing arousal. Bradley's recent work (19) shows clearly that the effectiveness of altering cortical potentials through electrical stimulation of the reticular formation may be changed to a high degree by atropine and (in the opposite direction) physostigmine without influencing the state of alertness. *This suggests that under certain conditions reticulo-neocortical relations do not determine the state of arousal.*

Anatomical studies showing that one path projects from the mesencephalic tegmentum "through the medical thalamus in the intralaminar zone while another descends ventrolaterally and continues, rostrad in the zona incerta of the hypothalamus" (20) offer an alternative interpretation: that arousal is primarily due to an excitation of the hypothalamus directly and reflexly, and also via the reticular formation and through afferent nerves impinging on the latter (21, 22). Arousal and emotion appear, therefore, chiefly as the result of an activation of the visceral brain.

The reticulo-neocortical system plays an important role in modifying the state of arousal. Thus, the change from relaxation to attention is linked with corticofugal effects on the reticular formation which lead to a specific filtering of afferent impulses (23). The failure of arousal seen when the same sound is presented repeatedly (habituation) involves likewise the reticular formation (24).

Only a few physiological and pharmacological investigations supporting our interpretation that hypothalamus and visceral brain play the primary role in arousal and emotion can be cited. Ranson (25) considered the posterior hypothalamus as the center of wakefulness which, as Nauta (26) showed, is inhibited by the anterior hypothalamus. Stimulation of the amygdaloid region in cats elicits initially an arousal (attention) response before signs of fear and anger appear (27). Furthermore, the arousal induced by the presence of an observer (28, 29) alters the potentials of the hippocampus of an experimental animal. Finally, certain drugs which have profound effects on the state of arousal seem to alter

hypothalamic functions more than the reactivity of the reticular formation. Bradley and Key (30) report that chlorpromazine has minimal and LSD no effect on the arousal reaction produced by stimulation of the reticular formation while other workers have clearly shown that the hypothalamic reactivity is greatly altered by these drugs (31–34) and that sectioning of the brain stem in front of the mammillary bodies eliminates their characteristic action (35–37).

These data seem to show that an animal can be aroused from the visceral brain and also from the reticular formation. There is a gradual transition from arousal to emotional reactions which corresponds to the close psychological relation existing between certain forms of arousal and emotions. It would, indeed, be difficult to decide whether the reaction of a rabbit to the presence of an observer is arousal or emotion. Whereas a crude form of arousal is maintained through the tonic activity of the reticular formation and the hypothalamus and its effect on the visceral brain, the production of finer degrees of attention required for perceptual and complex mental processes seems to be due to the interaction between the neocortex and the reticular formation.

iv. reflexes, feeling, and emotion

It is generally assumed (13, 38) that during the phylogenetic development, feelings of a primitive kind become associated with reflexes. At a later stage sensations become individuated and, with further development of the brain that is closely associated with the function of the distance receptors (1), perception of the environment emerges. From the very beginning sensory events are accompanied by movements. As a matter of fact, one important school of thought represented by Coghill (39) and Herrick (13) assumes that in "embryological and phylogenetic development intrinsically activated motility precedes reaction to external stimulation." These movements can be divided into two groups: those which result in retraction from the stimulating object, and those which lead to a turning to it. The former tend to minimize the (harmful) contact with the object, the latter increase it.

Physiological research has devoted more attention to the withdrawal reaction typified by the retraction of the foot and leg on contact with a painful stimulus than to the second group of reflexes, which are in general not elicited by electrical stimulation of sensory cutaneous end organs but by contact with broad smooth surfaces. Thus, pressure on the sole of the foot elicits the extensor thrust (the basis of the supporting reaction), and a similar stimulus to the palm of the hand calls forth a grasping reflex which fulfills a corresponding role in birds, monkeys, etc. A biologically most important reflex of this type is the oral reflex, which elicits a turning of the mouth to the mammilla and secures the intimate contact that is needed for suckling. A further familiar example of movements belonging to this group is evoked by stroking and similar forms of fondling.

It is characteristic that reflexes and actions resulting in a movement toward the stimulating object are accompanied by a feeling of well-being in contradistinction to those resulting in withdrawal. Pain and pleasure seem to have been developed on this basis. Although they have been enriched and intensified by the cerebral cortex, they are demonstrable through behavioral reactions in infants born without cerebral hemispheres. Thus, stroking may halt crying, whereas a loud noise was found to produce a cringing reaction even in

the absence of the cerebral hemispheres (40).

The prototype of unpleasant body feelings arises in conjunction with the withdrawal reflexes in response to stimuli which are sharp, rough, and irregular while the motor response becomes associated with that of the autonomic system. Thus, the ergotropic system comes into being. Its activation furnishes characteristic expressions of unpleasant feelings and, at higher stages of development, of emotions which accompany aggressive action and flight. On the other hand, in response to stimuli which are round, soft, and smooth, the *Zuwendungsreflexe* (positive thigmotactic reflexes) become associated with pleasant feelings and form the basis of the pleasant emotions (38). The relaxation of the muscle tone and the tendency to fall asleep on stroking suggest that the feeling of well-being is associated with an inhibition of the ergotropic system and an increase in tone of the parasympathetic division of the autonomic system.

The complex superstructure of the emotions has been built on the basis of the diffuse body feelings originally formed with withdrawal- and approach-reflexes and demonstrable in lower species and decerebrate infants. Nevertheless, these feelings retain a profound influence on the emotional and intellectual behavior of man. We designate them no longer as body feelings but as moods. There is little doubt that the hypothalamus is involved in them (see also 41). It is suggested that its tonic state is the basis of the moods where its phasic response is associated with the emotions.

The genetic relation which seems to exist between body feelings and certain reflexes on one side and hypothalamic function and emotions on the other is reflected in corresponding patterns of physiological organization. Emotions are thought to be associated with hypothalamic up- and downward discharges, the former in their manifold types being the physiological basis of the various emotions (41*a*). Similarly, it has been pointed out (38) that although most visceral, circulatory, and respiratory functions do not reach the level of consciousness, the food intake and the excretory functions are associated with feelings of hunger and thirst and of pressure in bladder and rectum, respectively, which dominate consciousness and action under appropriate conditions. There is a parallelism between the intensity of the reflexes of evacuation of bladder and rectum and the corresponding feelings[1] which is comparable to the intensity of nociceptive reflexes and emotional excitation. Likewise, if under experimental or clinical conditions the supply of oxygen becomes deficient, the increase in respiratory and circulatory reflexes is paralleled by the intensity of the air hunger. This parallelism is further illustrated by the fact that when in hypoxia the reflexly increased excitability of the respiratory apparatus is lessened by swallowing, the feeling of air-hunger is likewise reduced.

It seems to follow that in conjunction with visceral reflexes and the development of mechanisms by which the constancy of the internal environment for oxygen, water, glucose, etc. was assured, certain subjective phenomena have arisen which, depending on their degree of complexity, are designated as body feelings and emotions. Their primary purpose seems to have been to intensify and accelerate the motor phenomena which restore homeostasis. (Those who object to this teleological formulation may ponder the following quotation from Sherrington: "Physiology pursues

---

[1] The feelings are separated from the sensations. Both are aroused by stimulation of sensory end organs, but the former mediate information on the state of the body whereas the latter furnish data on the environment particularly through the distance receptors.

analyses of the reactions of the body considered as physical and chemical evidence; but, further, it aims at giving reasoned accounts of the acts of an organism in respect of their purpose and use to the organism qua organism. This may be called a teleological aim, yet belongs to a teleology not foreign to the scope of natural science.") This is true for the emotion as an aid in fight in animals of prey. It is obvious that in man, due to hypothalamic-cortical interrelations, the emotions have transgressed this function and have acquired a great importance in his mental existence.

v. drugs, feeling tone, and mood

The extensive experimental work on man and animals with psychopharmacological agents has furnished valuable material for the exploration of the physiological basis of feelings and mood. Chlorpromazine and morphine (and derivatives) are chosen as representatives of depressants and amphetamine and congeners as representatives of analeptic drugs. In spite of minor differences between morphine and the tranquilizers (42), they reduce the excitability of the reticulo-hypothalamic system, shift the hypothalamic balance to the parasympathetic side, decrease the intensity of the diffuse discharges from the reticular formation and hypothalamus to the neocortex, and lower the threshold for the spindle or recruiting response from thalamus and caudate nucleus (43). As a consequence, the EEG shows large slow potentials as in sleep, and the trophotropic system dominates. On the contrary, amphetamine and similar drugs act in opposite manners leading to an alerting reaction (asynchrony) in the EEG, sympathetic discharges, and increased general activity, indicating a dominance of the ergotropic system as far as the hypothalamic balance is concerned.

Studies on animals in which the mood was inferred from behavior showed that in cats and monkeys chlorpromazine and methamphetamine are antagonists: contentment (inferred in cats from washing, kneading, purring, rubbing, etc. and in monkeys from playing, grooming, and eating) is increased and "defensive and aggressive hostility" is diminished by chlorpromazine, while methamphetamine acts in an opposite manner (44). The fundamental difference in mood and behavior produced by the two types of drugs is obvious also from the work on humans although the results are not identical with the animal experiments. Chlorpromazine produces dysphoria (feeling sad) and sedation (drowsiness), and the response to morphine and heroin in normals causes a state described for different persons as sad, melancholy, relaxed, sleepy, serene, dizzy, uncomfortable, shaky, tired, grouchy. On the other hand, amphetamine and its congeners produce euphoria (happiness) and alertness (45). The subjects are in a happy, enthusiastic, and optimistic state while objectively they appear tense, jumpy, and talkative (46), indicating a dominance of the ergotropic system. Conversely, the frequently observed sleepiness, nausea, vomiting, and dizziness testifies to the dominance of the trophotropic system after administration of morphine and chlorpromazine. It should be added that with small doses of morphine, sleepiness and a feeling of calm and contentment were observed. This seems to indicate that slight shifts in the hypothalamic balance to the parasympathetic side result in calm and contentment apparently similar to the state before falling asleep, whereas more marked alterations lead to a depressive mood. A change in the balance to the sympathetic side leads to a happy and alert state, whereas in the animal only the increased aggressiveness appears. The subjective awareness of the mental stimulation leads in man to a state of elation. Increased hypothalamic-cortical discharges may be related in the animal to greater aggressiveness and hostility and in man to enhanced psychomotor activity and manic behavior.

Caffeine and amphetamine accelerate and increase conditioned reactions (47) and lessen the effect of conditioned extinction, whereas depressing drugs such as alcohol and sodium amytal have the opposite effect.

The observations support the hypothesis that depressive moods are linked to the preponderance of the trophotropic system and elation to that of the ergotropic system. Eysenck (48) believes that these states are related to certain characteristics of personality such as introversion and extroversion, and also to neurotic disorders.

It seems to us probable that the individual differences in the reaction to these drugs (49) depend on the state of hypothalamic balance, but further experiments are needed to prove it.

The heuristic importance of these inferences for neuropsychiatric problems is obvious. One would expect that certain states of depression would be associated with an increased central parasympathetic and decreased sympathetic reactivity. The Mecholyl test seems to confirm the latter, but no data are available to judge the former. On the other hand, in states of aggressiveness and hostility, the expected increased sympathetic reactivity has, indeed, been found, as studies on the excretion of noradrenalin and the reaction to Mecholyl show. The observation that the excretion of noradrenalin is greater in the manic than in the depressive phase is likewise in agreement with our theoretical concepts (50).

vi. the basis of qualitative differences in the emotions

A theory of the emotions which does not provide an understanding of the mechanism upon which the qualitative and quantitative changes in the emotions are based seems incomplete in important theoretical and practical aspects. Let us, therefore, first consider the physiological foundations of the qualitative differences in the emotions.

As a starting point, we choose not the central processes underlying the emotions but the peripheral autonomic discharges which accompany them. Allport (51) in 1924 related the pleasurable and unpleasurable emotions to the parasympathetic and sympathetic systems, respectively. It is, indeed, well established that the sight and smell of food elicit parasympathetic effects on the gastrointestinal system and the glands lining it, and that in the state of postprandial contentment the activity of the ergotropic system is reduced and that of the parasympathetic system is increased. But we have not to search far to find glaring exceptions. Sadness causes weeping through parasympathetic impulses, whereas resentment is associated with increased peristalsis, vasodilatation of the mucous membranes, and related symptoms (52). Not only good food but also bad odors elicit secretions controlled by parasympathetic nerves and may lead to vomiting. On the other hand, increased motor activity of bladder and rectum are characteristic parasympathetic signs accompanying fear and anxiety.

Since Cannon's work, it is generally recognized that fright leads to sympathetic or sympathetico-adrenal discharges or, to use Hess's terminology, it causes an activation of the ergotropic system; but the examples cited here and elsewhere (52) show that this statement is not inclusive enough in some instances and wrong in others. Thus, severe emotional disturbances induce sympathetic *and* parasympathetic discharges, the former indicated by the vascular reactions, the latter by changes in the intestinal system (and sometimes in the sex organs). And, to cite only one example of abnormal tuning of the hypothalamus (53), neurotics may react to emotional stress with a fall of the blood sugar (via the vago-insulin system) instead of with a rise (52).

If we confine the discussion at present to the normal reactions, it seems to be fair to state that emotions of moderate intensity are predominantly associated with parasympathetic discharges when they are pleasurable and with sympathetic discharges when they are unpleasant and painful. As the degree of emotional excitation increases, the hypothalamic downward discharge does not remain restricted to one division of the autonomic system. The most impressive example for the pleasurable emotions of high intensity which elicit this type of reaction is the orgasm, during which vascular and somatic changes indicate activation of the ergotropic system, whereas the changes of the sex organs disclose corresponding parasympathetic discharges. This twofold action reflects the double nature of this process: it occupies the limbo between pleasure and pain.[2] But severe (unpleasant) emotional excitement has also been shown to involve both sympathetico-adrenal and vago-insulin systems, with the former predominating in the normal organism. In states of extreme fright and terror, however, the circulatory collapse and slowing of the heart may

[2] Chordotomy (sectioning of the spino-thalamic tracts in the anterolateral funiculus of the spinal cord) causes loss of orgasm although reflexly induced erection and ejaculation persist.

occur due to markedly increased parasympathetic activity while pupillary dilatation, sweat secretion, etc. disclose increased sympathetic discharges. In this case there is also a dissociation between the sympathetic activity and the tone of the skeletal muscles.[3]

The most significant result derived from these considerations is the fact that the emotions show a rather complex relation to the autonomic nervous system, particularly at high intensities. Although in the organism at rest the changes in autonomic balance at the hypothalamic level are determined by the principle of reciprocal innervation (54), deviations from it occur in strong emotional excitement (and also in other conditions involving intensive central autonomic excitation as, for instance, in electroshock-induced convulsions [55, 56]).

Since changes in autonomic balance induced in the hypothalamus of the experimental animal by stimulation, injection of a drug, or lesion result in alterations of hypothalamic up- and downward discharges (12, 53, 57, 58), and since the former were linked to corresponding "psychic" changes, the question arises as to what characteristic relations exist between the type of autonomic downward discharges and the quality and intensity of the emotions.

In support of the specific relation between "unpleasant" emotion and sympathetic discharges, the reader is reminded of experiments on rage: (1) under natural conditions; (2) as the result of stimulation of the sympathetic division of the hypothalamus by various procedures; and (3) following the release of this division through removal of the inhibitory influence of the ventromedial hypothalamic nucleus (59). Similar releases have been

---

[3] See also the occurrence of nausea and vomiting to a pain-signifying conditioned stimulus in the near-neurotic cat (50).

effected through lesions in the septum (60). Conversely, the relation between the parasympathetic system and pleasant emotions is evident from Hess's studies on stimulation of the septum and the anterior hypothalamus (61) in which grooming and behavioral reactions suggesting pleasure occurred. Such effects have also been obtained from various parts of the visceral brain, as, for instance, from the hippocampus (particularly on chemical stimulation [62]). Furthermore, stimulation of the hippocampus is followed first by a period of afterdischarges associated with signs of sympathetic excitation (pupillary dilatation, piloerection) and then by a phase of "well-being" characterized by grooming reactions and maternal behavior toward a kitten to which the animal had shown an aggressive attitude before stimulation (63). Here again it is a shift in autonomic balance which accompanies a fundamental alteration in emotional behavior. The close association of pleasure and sexual reactions and the diminished reactivity to painful stimuli under these conditions was frequently noted in stimulation experiments on the limbic brain (64).

Whereas stimulation of the amygdala causes behavioral changes signifying fear and anger (65), removal of the amygdaloid complex in cats leads to a hypersexed state and to an "increase in pleasure reactions to stroking and petting" (66). At the same time, emotional reactions related to increased discharges of the sympathetic division of the hypothalamus such as fear and aggressive behavior as well as responsiveness to nociceptive stimuli are diminished. But these characteristic changes do not occur if the ventromedial hypothalamic nuclei are destroyed bilaterally prior to amygdalectomy; and they are abolished if these nuclei are destroyed subsequent to amygdalectomy. Such animals showed the savage behavior characteristic for cats with these hypothalamic lesions. It seems to follow that amygdalectomy leads to an increased activity of the ventromedial nuclei, which are known to inhibit the sympathetic division of the hypothalamus. These experiments show that lesions in the visceral brain alter emotional behavior by changing the hypothalamic balance.

It should, however, not be forgotten that the experimental results involving stimulation and lesions of the limbic system are far from uniform. To what extent these discrepancies are due to species differences (9, 67) and inequalities in lesions (65) is uncertain. The lability of these functions suggests to Gloor (68) that "the amygdala and other parts of the rhinencephalon modulate activities integrated in subcortical structures." Since the action of the limbic system is closely related to, if not completely dependent on, the hypothalamus, it should be remembered that the state of hypothalamic reactivity is variable and that the hypothalamic balance may be altered within wide limits (53).

The assumption that stimulation or lesions of certain parts of the limbic system alter emotional behavior through a change in the balance of the hypothalamus is supported further by experiments in which septal and amygdaloid lesions were successively produced in rats. We have seen that stimulation of the septum elicits pleasurable reactions and inhibits the ergotropic system, whereas stimulation of the amygdala produces fear and rage (69). Conversely, destruction of the amygdala reduces emotionality—this is seen particularly well in unmanageable wild rats which become tame after the operation (70)—whereas septal lesions caused a striking increase in emotionality (71). This effect is completely abolished by the subsequent removal of the amygdala, whereas a control group subjected to neocor-

tical and cingulate damage suffered only an insignificant loss in emotional reactivity. Furthermore, the increase in emotionality due to septal lesions was much less in the amygdalectomized than in the control-operated rats.

If our thesis is correct—that changes in the autonomic balance of the hypothalamus are associated with alterations in the emotional state—one would expect that pathological processes in man which lead to increased sympathetic or parasympathetic discharges would be accompanied by different emotional states. Thus, the verbal expressions of the patients would supplement our information on emotion and its relation to the hypothalamic system, which so far has been chiefly based on the observation of the emotional behavior of animals. Observations on patients with diencephalically induced cardiovascular disturbances seem particularly pertinent. As discussed elsewhere (50), such patients may suffer sudden attacks leading to extreme vagal excitation (slowing or cessation of the heart beat and fall in blood pressure) or sympathetic excitation (maximal heart rate, rise in blood pressure). The behavior of the two groups of patients is fundamentally different (72). Patients with vago-vasal attacks appear quiet, rather relaxed, and report objectively the symptoms such as weakness, dizziness, and blackout and do not seem to be particularly perturbed by the repeated occurrence of these phenomena although they may have caused injuries. Those suffering from sympathetic attacks, on the contrary, complain vividly about extreme states of anxiety and terror (*Vernichtungs-gefühl*) regardless of medical assurance of the relative harmlessness of the condition. The first group shows a state related to relaxation and sleep, the second group that of maximal emotional excitation despite the fact that the disquieting symptoms seem to be greater in the first group. This linkage between hypo-

thalamic parasympathetic discharges and relaxation, on the one hand, and sympathetic discharges and emotional excitation on the other,
are confirmed in experiments in which these
shifts in autonomic activity were induced
reflexly in man by the injection of noradrenalin and Mecholyl, respectively (50, 73). The
injection of noradrenalin led to reflexly increased parasympathetic activity and relaxation and, in some patients, to sleep, whereas
the Mecholyl-induced sympathetic discharges
were accompanied by feelings of tension and
irritability. These observations confirm our
hypothesis that central (hypothalamic) discharges presumably involving different parts
of the hypothalamus lead to fundamentally
different up- and downward-discharges. It is
thought that the type of the upward discharge
which determines to an important degree the
character of the emotion depends not only on
the hypothalamic site that is involved but also
on the feedback from the activated autonomi-
cally innervated organs. It is in this sense only
that the peripheral autonomic effect influences
the state of the hypothalamus and thereby of
the emotions.

In addition, this discussion shows that
different emotions cannot be explained by
considering only the factor of intensity, as the
activation theory does. At present it seems
that the qualitative differences between the
emotions which, on the basis of the psychological analysis, require a three-dimensional
representation (74), involve physiologically at
least states of parasympathetic, sympathetic,
and mixed discharges with correspondingly
differentiated forms of activation of the visceral brain and the neocortex. Furthermore, it
must be borne in mind that emotional excitement leads to the liberation of noradrenalin,
adrenalin, and insulin, at least when higher
degrees of excitation are involved, and also of
the hypothalamically controlled hypophyseal

hormones. It is highly probable that not only
adrenalin and noradrenalin—whose action on
the reticulo-hypothalamic system has been
studied extensively (75)—but also other hormones released as the result of hypothalamic-
hypophyseal activity (76) contribute to a
change in the pattern of the hypothalamic-
cortical discharge.

With increasing degree of hypothalamic
excitation there is also a change in quality of
the emotion as, for instance, from fear to rage
(69). It is suggested that this change is not
solely the result of an increasing firing rate
and an increased number of discharging neurons, but also of an alteration in the pattern of
discharge that is related to the change in tone
and activity of the striated muscles. The
feedback from the somatic nervous system is
different in fear and terror compared to rage,
and the role of proprioceptive impulses for
the maintenance of hypothalamic excitability
and the intensity of hypothalamic-cortical
discharges has been stressed elsewhere (50).
This accounts for the fact that light curariza-
tion tends to change the emotional response
from rage to fearlike behavior by virtue of a
reduction in proprioceptive activity in the
relaxed muscles (73).

vii. on the significance of the intensity of the emotions

Thus far we have emphasized the qualitative changes in the peripheral autonomic discharges which accompany different kinds of
emotional excitation, but the quantitative aspects are equally important. As Lindsley (7)
and others have emphasized, there is a continuous transition in the state of awareness from
sleep to emotional excitement which parallels
electroencephalographic changes and indicates

increasing degrees of activity of the reticulo-hypothalamic system. Whereas the degree of arousal seems to show a continuous increase as we pass from "alert attentiveness" to a strong emotion such as fear or rage, such progressive increases throughout the range of arousal states do not occur in all behavioral, autonomic, and EEG changes. Thus, when a person becomes emotionally excited, attention to a particular object (stimulus) becomes difficult, and the responsiveness to a stimulus of the sympathetic system (probably at the hypothalamic level) is lessened while the spontaneous activity is increased (77). These phenomena studied in man on the basis of the palmar sweat secretion (psychogalvanic reflex) seem to be related to the increased spontaneous sympathetic discharges indicated by contraction of the nictitating membrane which occur in the experimental animal after intravenous (78) or intrahypothalamic injection of metrazol (79). Apparently, states of greatly increased hypothalamic sympathetic excitation are characterized by repetitive "spontaneous" sympathetic discharges.

It is suggested that in "strong" emotions the hypothalamus starts firing nearly maximally under the combined influence of discharges from the reticular formation and the sense organs, the latter impinging on the reticular formation and hypothalamus not only directly but also via the neo- and limbic cortex. Under these circumstances the differentiation in activation pattern and function which exists between various cortical areas under strictly physiological conditions is lessened (80). The resulting "functional" decortication is not the result of a "cortical conflict" leading to a subcortical release, as Darrow (81) suggested, but is due to an *excessive excitation of the hypothalamic system which is incompatible with the differentiated action of the cortex necessary for attention (82) and the higher mental processes.*

With a further increase in hypothalamic excitation, neurotic phenomena occur.

viii. the hypothalamic system in experimental neurosis

A profound change in emotional behavior and autonomic activity precedes and accompanies states of experimental neurosis. If relatively mild conditions of frustration are chosen and no lasting neurosis develops, the conditioned stimulus elicits first the typical sympathetic symptoms but later marked parasympathetic discharges such as vomiting (83). It was shown elsewhere (50) that when nausea and vomiting prevail, the parasympathetic system is dominant and the ergotropic system is inhibited. This shift in autonomic balance which accompanies severe emotional disturbances may be looked upon as a homeostatic reaction: the responsiveness to environmental stimuli in general and to the perturbing stimuli in particular is eliminated. When the conditioned stimulus is no longer reinforced, the vomiting disappears and the normal autonomic balance is restored. On the other hand, if the appropriate reaction to the food-signifying conditioned stimulus is prevented for some time, or if other neurosis-producing procedures are used, a pathological conditioned reflex develops either in the form of a general excitation or an inhibitory state. Under these conditions, autonomic dysfunctions are common and irregularities and increased responses of the heart rate may persist for years (84). It seems to follow that when a severe emotional disturbance is produced in the experimental animal, it leads either to very strong sympathetic reactions or a reversal of the autonomic balance. In either case the total behavior is abnormal.

It is important that external factors which cause a considerable increase in the reactivity of the sympathetic system such as electro-shock, insulin coma, and metrazol convulsions lead likewise to alterations in conditioned reflexes. A few of these episodes may restore previously inhibited conditioned reflexes (85, 86), but a series of ten or more cause an abolition of a conditioned fear reaction (87) or a reversal in the response to previously enforced and non-reenforced conditioned stimuli (88). On this basis, it is suggested that abnormal behavior follows from autonomic disturbances at the hypothalamic level. They are characterized either by excessive sympathetic discharges or by a reversal in the autonomic balance resulting from a conflict situation or "treatment" with shock-producing procedures. It is believed that these processes are causally related and that the altered behavior depends to an important degree on the alteration of the hypothalamic-cortical discharges.

ix. excitatory and inhibitory processes of the central nervous system

Our emphasis on the importance of the hypothalamus and visceral brain for the emotions should not prevent us from viewing the neurological apparatus activated in these conditions within a larger framework.

Important experimental findings of recent years indicate that certain parts of the central nervous system exert a diffuse excitatory, other parts an inhibitory, influence on brain and spinal cord. The ascending reticular activating system of Magoun (7, 11, 21, 22), which on stimulation induces wakefulness and asynchrony in the EEG, is the classical example of the excitatory system. Similar effects can be produced from the posterior hypothalamus and various parts of the visceral brain. Reflex stimulation of the hypothalamus through nociceptive and proprioceptive nerves (57), or release of the posterior hypothalamus from the restraining action of the sino-aortic baroreceptors, likewise causes arousal in both its behavioral and electroencephalographic aspects (89). A diffuse activation of the cortex accompanied by arousal follows also the stimulation of the medial thalamic nuclei and the caudate, provided that relatively high frequencies of stimulation (100/sec) are used. Since these structures likewise increase the movements induced by stimulation of the motor cortex and augment spinal reflexes (90), it may be said that an excitatory system exists within the brain which involves cortical and subcortical structures and activates the sensory as well as the motor system. Arousal and emotional reactions share these characteristics: they can be evoked from cortical and subcortical structures and enhance movements (91) as well as sensory phenomena (perception [92]).

Conversely, there is an inhibitory system which reduces movements and the state of activity of the cerebral cortex. It comprises the bulbar reticular apparatus, which exerts inhibitory effects on spinal reflexes (93). In addition it is known that some cerebral nuclei such as the intralaminar nuclei of the thalamus (94) and the caudate nucleus (95) produce effects of synchrony on the potentials of the cerebral cortex and of subcortical structures particularly when single shocks or low frequencies of stimulation are applied. Under these conditions, "arrest" reactions (not unlike the temporary loss of consciousness seen during a petit mal attack) and sleep (96) occur on thalamic stimulation, whereas stimulation of the caudate nucleus lessens spontaneous activity (97) and suppresses cortically induced movements (98). Stimulation of the hippocampus at low voltage (99) and of the anterior hypothalamus (100) may also elicit synchronous potentials in the cerebral cortex.

Recent investigations have disclosed an even greater extension of the inhibitory system. Studies on the EEG of animals with section of the brain stem in front of the entrance of the fifth nerve (pretrigeminal, midpontine, cats) have furnished evidence for a synchronizing action originating in the caudal part of the brain stem (101, 102), probably in the inhibitory bulbar apparatus of Magoun (93).

The physiological significance of this work is evident from the fact that sleep can be produced not only on stimulation of Hess's hypnogenic zone closely related to the intralaminar thalamic nuclei, but also from the anterior hypothalamus (103), and even from the reticular formation in the midbrain (104). It is remarkable that stimulation of the same site in the reticular formation elicited in the monkey yawning and sleep with 0.2 volts, awakening with 0.4 volts, and extreme panic with signs of maximal sympathetic excitation with 0.65 to 0.9 volts (105). The form of stimulation is often more important than the site. Thus, stimulation of the caudate and of the intralaminar nuclei of the thalamus produce cortical synchrony with low and asynchrony with high frequencies of stimulation.

It is of interest that the excitatory processes are accompanied by symptoms of sympathetic discharges, whereas the inhibitory states are associated with signs of increased parasympathetic activity (106). The data suggest that the functional concepts of the ergo- and trophotropic systems extend beyond the boundaries of the hypothalamus.

The balance between the excitatory and inhibitory system is undoubtedly altered during the sleep-wakefulness cycle. Their behavior in emotional states is less clear. Is it possible that the inhibitory system has some power to limit the activity of the excitatory system and vice versa? To explore this possibility, we shall discuss the reactivity of the inhibitory system at different degrees of activity of the excitatory system.

x. the inhibitory system at various states of activity of the hypothalamus and the reticular formation

The threshold of a spindle burst (as in sleep) following a single shock or of a recruiting response consisting of waxing and waning of synchronous cortical potentials of high voltage in correspondence with the low frequency of stimulation may serve as an indicator of the activity of the inhibitory system[4] while the threshold of the reticular formation or the posterior hypothalamus reflects the sensitivity of the diffuse excitatory system. The latter is discharging to increasing degrees as the organism passes from sleep to wakefulness, to attention and, finally, to emotional excitement (7). On testing the threshold of a spindle burst at increasing degrees of hypothalamic or reticular activity, it is found that the threshold increases in a parallel manner (108). Conversely, on lowering the state of activity of the posterior hypothalamus by lesions confined to the posterior hypothalamus or by injection of barbiturates into this structure, the threshold for the spindle burst is lowered. Administration of metrazol in subconvulsive doses or of carbon dioxide, which increases hypothalamic-cortical discharges, raises the spindle threshold, whereas drugs such as barbiturates and chlorpromazine or procedures such as the lowering of the temperature of the body, which diminish these discharges, have the opposite effect on the spindle threshold (43). These results occur with great regularity regardless of whether the spindle burst or

[4] For further anatomical description see reference 107.

the recruiting response is chosen as the indicator of the state of the inhibitory system. It is also immaterial whether the caudate nucleus (43,108) or the intralaminar thalamic nuclei (109) are tested, and whether the state of the posterior hypothalamus or the reticular formation is altered by direct stimulation, through nociceptive reflexes or by changing the internal environment (inhalation of carbon dioxide). The importance of the state of the posterior hypothalamus is further illustrated by the fact that the marked lowering of the threshold of the caudate nucleus with decrease in body temperature was virtually abolished after lesions had been placed in the posterior hypothalamus (79).

Experiments show that the inhibitory system, exemplified by the caudate nucleus—which on stimulation exerts a quieting effect (97), abolishes aggressiveness (110), reduces or inhibits cortically induced movements (98) and even convulsions (110)—is without a restraining action on states of increased excitation of the reticulo-hypothalamic-cortical system.

The reason for this finding seems to lie in the close relation between arousal and emotion. We know that a reciprocal relation exists between sleep and wakefulness, as between anterior and posterior hypothalamus, from which these states can be evoked. Moreover, the synchronization of cortical potentials in sleep is accompanied by a lessening of the activity of the reticular formation (111). This reciprocal relation between the excitatory and inhibitory systems is retained in widely different states of activity of the hypothalamus and the reticular formation, as indicated by the progressively lessened inhibitory action (synchrony) of the caudate nucleus with increasing excitation of the reticulo-hypothalamic apparatus and vice versa (108).

The inability of the inhibitory system to curb excessive emotional excitement is also understandable if we take the chief biological significance of the emotions into consideration.

The forms of emotion in which the activity of the posterior hypothalamus is increased are primarily related to fight and flight, and any homeostatic mechanism which would tend to reduce these actions would endanger the organism. On the contrary, we see under these circumstances a synergistic action between the somatic nervous system and the sympathetic division of the hypothalamus which characterizes the ergotropic system. Cortically induced movements are intensified from the hypothalamus (91), and this facilitation takes place at cortical and spinal levels (90, 91, 112). In addition, the adrenomedullary secretion tends to delay muscular fatigue (113).

Nevertheless, inhibitory processes play an important role in certain emotional processes. In fear and terror the skeletal muscles show a loss of tone; a person in this condition is unable to move and animals "freeze," yet signs of sympathetic discharges are clearly present. This syndrome—sympathetic excitation combined with relaxation of the muscles—may be evoked by stimulation of a portion of the amygdala (27) and also of the cingulate gyrus (114); removal of this area results in loss of fear (115). But it is hardly explainable on the basis of an excitation of the posterior division of the hypothalamus, which results in ergotropic activity—i.e., sympathetic excitation *plus* activation of the skeletal muscles. Analysis suggests that the relative part played by the neurogenic and the hormonal (adrenomedullary) components of sympathetic excitation varies in different emotional states. In states of ragelike reactions—"anger out" (Funkenstein, 116)—the neurogenic, hypothalamically controlled activity predominates, whereas in "anger in," the hormonal phase, chiefly influenced by the medulla oblongata, prevails (117). This accounts for the fact that the cardiovascular reactions and the excretion of the catecholamines show a prevalence of noradrenalin in anger but of adrenalin in fear (118).

xi. antagonism between neo- and paleocortex

Numerous data show that stimulation of, and lesions in, various parts of the visceral brain have a profound influence on the hypothalamus and emotional reactivity. The relation of neocortex and visceral brain with respect to emotional reactivity seems to be antagonistic: removal of the neocortex tends to create placidity whereas removal of limbic brain structures induces ragelike behavior (67). It is not improbable that the general excitability of the neocortex is limited by certain parts of the visceral brain. Green and Arduini (119) discovered that arousal induced by stimulation of various sense organs or occurring spontaneously is associated with slow synchronous potentials in the hippocampus (about 3–5/sec. theta potentials). This contrast between paleo- and neocortex indicated by the asynchronous fast potentials of low amplitude in the neocortex and the theta rhythm in the hippocampus is seen also after stimulation of the reticular formation and hypothalamus, and after application of visceral stimuli, carbon dioxide, and other stimuli which cause arousal (120). With increasing intensity of these stimuli, the amplitude of the synchronous hippocampal potentials increases and their frequency is raised slightly (from 2.5/sec. to 4/sec., for instance). Since hippocampal stimulation inhibits spontaneous movements and conditioned reflexes (121), it is conceivable that the increased synchrony is the expression of an augmented inhibitory

action of the hippocampus on the reticulo-hypothalamic system.

The placidity of cats which results from neocortical ablation is abolished when the fornix is sectioned. Apparently, the restraining influence of the hippocampus on the hypothalamus is abolished and the rage threshold is lowered (122).

xii. factors facilitating emotional and hypothalamic responses from the neocortex

Since emotional reactions in the higher vertebrates depend on individual experience and are aroused in man, in addition, by complex symbols, one would expect that the hypothalamus could be excited from the cortex. In experiments with topical application of strychnine on the cerebral cortex (123), the transmission of impulses from the cortex to the hypothalamus was demonstrated. Moreover, the responsiveness of the hypothalamus to nociceptive stimulation is greatly increased under these conditions (124). Even more complex and obviously cortically induced forms of emotional arousal could be elicited in monkey A on seeing monkey B (but not a rabbit) in emotional stress. A previously extinguished conditioned reaction was restored in monkey A and was associated with typical signs of emotional excitement including sympathetic discharges (125).

It seems to follow that by and large an antagonism exists between the paleo- and the neocortex as far as emotional reactivity is concerned, and that the balance between the two systems determines the emotional responsiveness of the organism. In addition, the neocortical-hypothalamic relations play a great role in primates, as Mirsky's interesting experiment on the "communication of affect" demonstrates (126). But even in relatively primitive laboratory animals such as the rat, sex activity closely identified with the hypothalamus and the visceral brain is enhanced by the neocortex (127).

MacLean (128) stressed correctly the importance of the visceral brain for preservation of the individual and the species, as evidenced by the influence of the limbic brain (including the hypothalamus) on emotions related to fight and flight and also on sexual functions. It should be added that in man neocortical-hypothalamic interrelations probably play a role in the fusion of emotional processes with those underlying perception, memory, imagination, and creativity.

Previous experiences are obviously of great importance for the qualitative and quantitative emotional response. The visceral brain as well as the neocortex is known to contribute to memory (128, 129), but this topic is beyond the scope of this paper.

xiii. hypothalamic balance and its significance

After this brief discussion of neo-, paleocortical, and cortico-hypothalamic relations, let us return once more to the problem of hypothalamic balance and its physiological and pathological significance. Facilitatory processes take place between neocortex and hypothalamus via ascending and descending pathways. Thus cortico-fugal discharges induced by topical application of strychnine to a minute area in the neocortex summate with spikes present in the hypothalamus and cause increased convulsive discharges. On the other hand, the temporary reduction in hypothalamic excitability through the injection of a barbiturate into the posterior hypothalamus causes a lessening in frequency and amplitude of cortical strychnine spikes until the hypothalamic excitability is restored (124). Apparently, a positive feedback exists between the posterior hypothalamus and the cerebral cortex. Consequently, if for any reason the hypothalamic excitability falls below the physiological level, the lessened hypothalamic-cortical discharges lead to a diminished state of activity in the cortex with consequent reduction in the cortico-fugal discharges. Obviously, a vicious cycle develops. This tendency can be broken either by restoring hypothalamic excitability directly or via cortico-hypothalamic pathways. It is believed that drug therapy and electroshock involve the former and psychotherapy the latter mechanism.

Before we comment further on these pathological conditions, we should remember that changes in the state of the hypothalamus within physiological limits distinguish sleep from wakefulness. Thus, a low intensity of hypothalamic-cortical discharges prevails in sleep and a high one during wakefulness, resulting in synchronous EEG potentials in the former and asynchrony in the latter condition. Moreover, the dominance in parasympathetic action (with reciprocal inhibition of the sympathetic) at the hypothalamic level induces, by its peripheral action, the autonomic symptoms of sleep and, by its action on the cortex, a lessening in the reactivity of the sensory and motor apparatus of the somatic nervous system. With the dominance of the sympathetic division of the hypothalamus, the opposite changes occur. Since electrical stimulation of the posterior hypothalamus produces the effects of wakefulness while stimulation of the anterior hypothalamus (103) induces sleep, it may be said that the reactivity of the whole organism is altered by a change in the autonomic reactivity of the hypothalamus. Similar effects can be induced reflexly via the baroreceptor reflexes in man (79) and animals (89).

Of particular importance is the study of the actions of drugs in this respect. Although no drugs act exclusively on the hypothalamus or a part of it, there is sufficient specificity to distinguish drugs which shift the hypothalamic balance to the sympathetic side from those which produce a parasympathetic dominance. The former comprise analeptic and psychoactive drugs, the latter the tranquilizers. Specific differences exist in the action of different drugs belonging to the same group as, for instance, between reserpine and chlorpromazine. Important as these differences are, they should not obscure the basic fact that by shifting the hypothalamic balance sufficiently to the parasympathetic side, we produce depressions, whereas a shift in the opposite direction causes excitatory effects and, eventually, maniclike changes. The emotional states produced by drugs influence the cortical potentials in a characteristic manner; synchrony prevails in the EEG of the experimental animal after administration of tranquilizers, but asynchrony after application of analeptic and psychoactive drugs (50).

The shock therapies act likewise on the hypothalamic balance (52). Physiological experiments and clinical observations have shown that these procedures influence the hypothalamically controlled hypophyseal secretions and increase sympathetic discharges. They shift the hypothalamic balance to the sympathetic side. This explains the beneficial effect of electroshock therapy in certain depressions and a shift in the reaction from hypo- to normal reactivity of the sympathetic system as shown by the Mecholyl test. Some investigators have found a parallelism between remissions and return of the sympathetic reactivity of the hypothalamus to the normal level as indicated by the Mecholyl test and, conversely, between clinical impairment and in-

creasing deviation of this test from the norm (50). Nevertheless, the theory that the determining influence of the hypothalamic balance has a profound influence on the clinical behavior of neuropsychiatric patients has not yet been tested on an adequate number of patients. The Mecholyl and noradrenalin tests applied with certain precautions are reliable indicators of this central autonomic balance (130), but for the sake of correlating autonomic and clinical states, and of studying the effect of certain therapeutic procedures on central autonomic reactions, additional tests seem to be desirable.

It was assumed that the shift in autonomic hypothalamic balance occurring spontaneously in neuropsychiatric patients or resulting from the application of certain therapeutic procedures follows the pattern known from the sleep-wakefulness cycle. A change in the balance to the parasympathetic side leads in the normal individual to sleep or, in special circumstances, to cardiovascular collapse or nausea and vomiting. In both conditions the emotional and perceptual sensitivity is diminished, but no depression occurs such as is seen clinically or may be produced in normal persons by drugs. The fundamental differences between physiological and pathological states of parasympathetic (and also of sympathetic) dominance remain to be elucidated.

Perhaps a clue to these and related problems lies in the fact that changes in the intensity of hypothalamic discharges which are associated with changes in its balance lead also to *qualitative* alterations in reactivity. A state of parasympathetic "tuning" of the hypothalamus (131, 132) induced experimentally causes not only an increase in the parasympathetic reactivity of this structure to direct and reflexly induced stimuli, but leads also to an autonomic reversal: a stimulus acting sympathetically under control conditions elicits in this state of tuning a parasympathetic response (53)! Furthermore, conditioned reactions are fundamentally altered when the hypothalamic sympathetic reactivity is augmented beyond a critical level, and several types of behavioral changes probably related to the degree of central autonomic "tuning" are observed. If, for instance, such a change is produced by one or a few insulin comas or electroshocks, previously inhibited conditioned reactions reappear (85, 86). However, if these procedures are applied more often, conditioned emotional responses are temporarily abolished (87). In other studies, loss of differentiation in previously established conditioned reflexes resulted from repeated convulsive (metrazol) treatments (88), suggesting a fundamental disturbance in the balance between excitatory and inhibitory cerebral processes.

It has further been shown that: (1) an experimental neurosis in its initial stages is associated with a reversible shift in the central autonomic balance (83); (2) drugs altering the hypothalamic balance alter conditioned reactions (47); (3) in a state of depression, the positive conditioned stimulus may fail to elicit a conditioned reaction but cause an increased synchrony instead of the excitatory desynchronizing (alerting) effect on the EEG (133). These are few and seemingly disjointed data, but they illustrate the important fact that fundamental alterations in conditioned reactions occur in a variety of states in which the hypothalamic balance has been altered by physiological experimentation, pharmacological action, or clinical processes.

xiv. on the physiological basis of some form of psychotherapy

The foregoing remarks imply that the hypothalamic balance plays a crucial role at the crossroads between physiological and pathological forms of emotion. If this is the case, one would expect that not only the various procedures just mentioned which alter the hypothalamic balance would influence emotional state and behavior but that emotion itself would act likewise. We pointed out that emotional excitement may lead to psychosomatic disorders and neurotic symptoms, particularly in certain types of personality, but it is also known that the reliving of a strong emotion ("abreaction") may cure a battle neurosis (134, 135). This phenomenon raises the question whether the guidance of the emotions for therapeutic ends may not have an even wider application in the area of the neuroses. Being a strictly physiological procedure, one may expect from such a study additional information on the nature of the emotional process itself.

Wolpe's (136) experiments and therapeutic work lie in this area. He showed convincingly that anxiety is a learned (conditioned) reaction and is the basis of experimental and clinical neuroses and assumed, therefore, that the neuronal changes which underlie the neuroses are functional and reversible. An important observation of Pavlov served as a guide post to achieve such a reversibility by physiological means. In a conditioning experiment, he demonstrated the antagonism between feeding and pain. A mild electrical shock served as a conditioned stimulus and was followed by feeding. The pain became thus the symbol for food and elicited salivary secretion (conditioned reflex). Even when the intensity of the shocks was increased gradually, it failed to evoke any signs of pain. Since strong nociceptive stimuli produce an experimental neurosis during which the animals fail to eat in the experimental situation, Wolpe thought that he could utilize the feeding-pain antagonism to inhibit the neurotic symptoms through feeding. Appropriate experiments showed that this is, indeed, possible. He then applied this principle of reciprocal inhibition to human neuroses. He took advantage of the antagonism between aggressive assertiveness and anxiety and found a relatively rapid disappearance of anxiety when the former attitude was established (cf. 137).

For the interpretation of these significant investigations, it should be remembered that reciprocal relations exist in the hypothalamus with respect to autonomic and somatic functions which are closely associated with the emotions. The feeding-pain antagonism seems to be based on this reciprocal relation between the tropho- and ergotropic systems. Furthermore, a functional antagonism exists between an aggressive attitude and a state of anxiety. Although in both emotions sympathetic symptoms are present, different autonomic-somatic patterns underlie aggression and anxiety, respectively, as indicated by the rate of the excretion of the catecholamines, the state of the muscle tone, and the Mecholyl test (50, 77, 117). The psychological incompatibility of these emotional states seems to be reflected in, or based on, this marked difference.

xv. concluding remarks

In our attempt to interpret the emotions in their physiological and pathological range, we emphasized the importance of the degree of activity of the parasympathetic divisions of the hypothalamic system and their influence on the inhibitory and excitatory systems, respectively. We stressed the reciprocal relation of these systems with respect to the autonomic-somatic downward discharge as well as regarding the hypothalamic-cortical discharge. Although we are still far from a complete understanding of these problems, as a

first approximation, it is suggested that alterations in the hypothalamic balance with consequent changes in the hypothalamic-cortical discharges account for major changes in behavior seen in various moods and states of emotions in man and beast under physiological circumstances, in experimental and clinical neurosis, and as the result of psychopharmacological agents. In view of the important role which emotional disturbances play in the genesis of neurotic and psychotic disorders (138) and the parallelism observed between autonomic states and psychological behavior in several instances (50), it is further suggested that a hypothalamic imbalance may play an important role in initiating mental changes.

This theoretically and experimentally founded framework appears to be compatible with the experiments and clinical data of Wolpe's important work. In addition, his studies suggest to us a further refinement in the organization of the hypothalamic system. A reciprocal relation seems to exist not only between the parasympathetic and sympathetic divisions of the hypothalamic system, but also within each of the two subdivisions. This is illustrated for the sympathetic division by the antagonism between aggression and anxiety. Its validity for the parasympathetic division is apparent from the incompatibility of eating and vomiting and the psychological states associated with these processes.

The medical applications of the study of the emotions comprise the psychosomatic disorders and the neuroses and functional psychoses. Our discussion (50) has shown that, in all groups, hypothalamic disturbances leading to autonomic imbalances are related to these diseases. Why such an imbalance leads to a gastric ulcer in some persons and to a psychosis in others remains a mystery and, therefore, one of the most challenging problems.

references

1. C. Sherrington. The integrative action of the nervous system. New Haven: Yale University Press, 1906.
2. D. O. Hebb. Organization of behavior. New York: Wiley, 1949.
3. W. B. Cannon. Amer. J. Psychol., **39**: 106, 1927.
4. ———. Psychol. Rev., **38**: 281, 1931.
5. P. Bard. *In:* C. Murchison (ed.), Handbook of general experimental psychology, p. 264. Worcester, Mass.: Clark University Press, 1934.
6. W. R. Hess. Das Zwischenhirn. Basel: Schwabe u. Co., 1949.
7. D. B. Lindsley. *In:* S. S. Stevens (ed.), Handbook of experimental psychology, p. 473. New York: Wiley & Sons, 1951.
8. J. W. Papez. Arch. Neurol. & Psychiat., **38**: 725, 1937.
9. H. Klüver and P. C. Bucy. J. Psychol., **5**: 33, 1938.
10. P. D. MacLean. Amer. J. Med., **25**: 611, 1958.
11. D. B. Lindsley, L. H. Schreiner, W. B. Knowles, and H. W. Magoun. Electroenceph. Clin. Neurophysiol., **2**: 483, 1950.
12. W. P. Koella and E. Gellhorn. J. Comp. Neurol., **100**: 243, 1953.
13. C. J. Herrick. The evolution of human nature. Austin: University of Texas Press, 1956.
14. E. Gellhorn, H. M. Ballin, and M. Kawakami. Epilepsia, **1**: 233, 1960.
15. E. Gellhorn. Arch. Int. Pharmacodyn., **93**: 434, 1953.
16. J. D. French, M. Verzeano, and H. W. Magoun. Arch. Neurol. & Psychiat., **69**: 519, 1953.
17. A. Wikler. Proc. Soc. Exp. Biol. Med., **79**: 261, 1952.
18. P. B. Bradley and J. Elkes. Brain, **80**: 77, 1957.
19. P. B. Bradley and B. J. Key. Electroenceph. Clin. Neurophysiol., **10**: 97, 1958.
20. M. E. Scheibel and A. B. Scheibel. Ann. N.Y. Acad. Sci., **89**: 857, 1961.
21. T. E. Starzl, D. W. Taylor, and H. W. Magoun. J. Neurophysiol., **14**: 461, 1951.
22. ———. *Ibid.* 479, 1951.
23. J. D. French, R. Hernández-Peón, and R. B. Livingston. J. Neurophysiol., **18**: 74, 1955.
24. S. Sharpless and H. Jasper. Brain, **79**: 655, 1956.
25. S. W. Ranson. Arch. Neurol. & Psychiat., **41**: 1, 1939.
26. W. J. Nauta. J. Neurophysiol., **9**: 285, 1946.
27. H. Ursin. Acta Psychiat. Scand., **35**: 378, 1960.
28. W. T. Liberson and K. Akert. Electroenceph. Clin. Neurophysiol., **7**: 211, 1955.
29. H. Gangloff and M. Monnier. Electroenceph. Clin. Neurophysiol., **8**: 623, 1956.
30. P. B. Bradley and B. J. Key. Brit. J. Pharmacol., **14**: 340, 1959.
31. N. N. Das. Arch. *In:* Pharmacodyn., **97**: 149, 1954.
32. D. Bovet, V. G. Longo, and B. Silvestrini. *In:* S. Garattini and V. Ghetti (ed.), Psychotropic drugs, p. 193. Amsterdam: Elvesier Publ. Co., 1957.
33. S. Courvoisier, J. Fournel, R. Ducrot, M. Kolsky, and P. Koetschet. Arch. Int. Pharmacodyn., **92**: 305, 1953.
34. D. de Wied and R. Jinks. Proc. Soc. Exp. Biol. Med., **99**: 44, 1958.
35. G. Hiebel, M. Bonvallet, P. Huvé, and P. Dell. Sem. Hop. Paris, **30**: 1, 1954.
36. V. G. Longo. J. Pharmacol., **116**: 198, 1956.
37. K. Neuhold, M. Taeschler, and A. Cerletti. Helv. Physiol. Pharmacol. Acta, **15**: 1, 1957.
38. U. Ebbecke. Physiologie des Bewusstseins in entwicklungsgeschichtlicher Betrachtung. Stuttgart: G. Thieme, 1959.
39. G. E. Coghill. Anatomy and the problem

of behavior. London: Cambridge University Press, 1929.

40. L. Edinger and B. Fischer. Arch. ges. Physiol., **152**: 535, 1913.

41. F. Kennedy. Res. Publ. Ass. Nerv. Ment. Dis., **20**: 864, 1940.

41*a*. E. Gellhorn. Proc. Amer. Psychopath. Ass., **39**: 205, 1949.

42. H. Gangloff and M. Monnier. J. Pharmacol. Exp. Ther., **121**: 78, 1957.

43. T. Tokizane, M. Kawakami, and E. Gellhorn. Arch. Int. Pharmacodyn., **113**: 217, 1957.

44. S. Norton. *In:* Psychotropic drugs, p. 73.

45. D. R. Hawkins, R. Pace, B. Pasternak, and M. C. Sandifer. J. Nerv. Ment. Dis., **2**: 1, 1961.

46. L. Lasagna, J. M. von Felsinger, and H. K. Beecher. J.A.M.A., **157**: 1006, 1955.

47. N. Finkelstein, E. B. Alpern, and W. H. Gantt. Bull. Johns Hopkins Hosp., **73**: 287, 1943.

48. H. J. Eysenck. The dynamics of anxiety and hysteria. New York: F. A. Praeger, 1957.

49. J. M. von Felsinger, L. Lasagna, and H. K. Beecher. J.A.M.A., **157**: 1113, 1955.

50. For the literature see: E. Gellhorn and G. N. Loofbourrow. Emotions and emotional disorders. New York: P. B. Hoeber, 1962.

51. F. H. Allport. Social psychology. New York: Houghton Mifflin, 1924.

52. For the literature see: E. Gellhorn. Physiological foundations of neurology and psychiatry. Minneapolis: University of Minnesota Press, 1953.

53. E. Gellhorn. Autonomic imbalance and the hypothalamus. Minneapolis: University of Minnesota Press, 1957.

54. E. Gellhorn, H. Nakao, and E. Redgate. J. Physiol. (Lond.), **131**: 402, 1956.

55. M. Kessler and E. Gellhorn. Proc. Soc. Exp. Biol. Med., **46**: 64, 1941.

56. E. Gellhorn, R. Cortell, and J. Feldman. Amer. J. Physiol., **133**: 532, 1941.

57. M. Bernhaut, E. Gellhorn, and A. Rasmussen. J. Neurophysiol., **16**: 21, 1953.

58. E. Gellhorn and H. M. Ballin. Arch. Int. Pharmacodyn., **122**: 265, 1959.

59. M. D. Wheatley. Arch. Neurol. & Psychiat., **52**: 296, 1944.

60. J. V. Brady and W. Nauta. J. Comp. Physiol. Psychol., **46**: 339, 1953.

61. A. E. Meyer and W. R. Hess. Helv. Physiol. Pharmacol. Acta., **15**: 401, 1957.

62. P. MacLean. Arch. Neurol. & Psychiat., **78**: 128, 1957.

63. P. Passouant, T. Passouant-Fontaine, and J. Cadilhac. Rev. Neurol. (Par.), **94**: 292, 1956.

64. F. Alonso-de Florida and J. M. Delgado. Amer. J. Physiol., **193**: 223, 1958.

65. C. D. Wood. Neurology, **8**: 215, 1958.

66. A. Kling and P. J. Hutt. Arch. Neurol. & Psychiat., **79**: 511, 1958.

67. P. Bard and V. B. Mountcastle. Res. Publ. Ass. Nerv. Ment. Dis., **27**: 362, 1947.

68. P. Gloor. *In:* Handbook of Physiology, section I, **2**:1395, 1960.

69. H. Gastaut. J. Physiol. (Par.), **44**: 431, 1952.

70. J. W. Woods. Nature, **178**: 869.

71. F. A. King and P. M. Meyer. Science, **128**: 655, 1958.

72. F. Broser. Nervenarzt, **31**:·289, 1960.

73. E. Gellhorn. A.M.A. Arch. Intern. Med., **102**: 392, 1958.

74. H. Schlosberg. Psychol. Rev., **61**: 81, 1954.

75. A. B. Rothballer. *In:* O. Krayer (ed.), Symposium on catecholamines, p. 494. Baltimore: Williams & Wilkins, 1959.

76. D. M. Woodbury. Recent Progr. Hormone Res., **10**: 65, 1954.

77. S. I. Cohen, A. J. Silverman, and N. R. Burch. J. Nerv. Ment. Dis., **124**: 352, 1956.

78. E. Gellhorn and C. W. Darrow. Arch. Int. Pharmacodyn., **62**: 114, 1939.

79. E. Gellhorn. Unpublished observations.

80. D. B. Lindsley. *In:* Handbook of Physiology, section I, **3**: 1553, 1960.
81. C. W. Darrow. Psychol. Rev., **42**: 566, 1935.
82. E. D. Adrian. The physical background of perception. Oxford: Clarendon Press, 1947.
83. E. Jacobsen and Y. Skaarup. Acta Pharmacol. (Kbh.), **11**: 117, 1955.
84. W. H. Gantt. Ann. N.Y. Acad. Sci., **56**: 143, 1953.
85. E. Gellhorn and H. Minatoya. J. Neurophysiol., **6**: 161, 1943.
86. E. Gellhorn. Ann. N.Y. Acad. Sci., **56**: 200, 1953.
87. H. F. Hunt. Fed. Proc., **19**: 629, 1960.
88. V. H. Rosen and W. H. Gantt. Arch. Neurol. & Psychiat., **50**: 8, 1943.
89. H. Nakao, H. M. Ballin, and E. Gellhorn. Electroenceph. Clin. Neurophysiol., **8**: 413, 1956.
90. S. M. Peacock and R. Hodes. J. Comp. Neurol., **94**: 409, 1951.
91. J. P. Murphy and E. Gellhorn. J. Neurophysiol., **8**: 341, 1945.
92. E. Gellhorn. Brain, **77**: 401, 1954.
93. H. W. Magoun and R. Rhines. J. Neurophysiol., **9**: 165, 1946.
94. E. W. Dempsey and R. S. Morison. Amer. J. Physiol., **135**: 293, 1942.
95. T. Shimamoto and M. Verzeano. J. Neurophysiol., **17**: 278, 1954.
96. J. Hunter and H. H. Jasper. Electroenceph. Clin. Neurophysiol., **1**: 305, 1949.
97. K. Akert and B. Andersson. Acta Physiol. Scand., **22**: 281, 1951.
98. F. A. Mettler, H. W. Ades, E. Lipman, and E. A. Culler. Arch. Neurol. & Psychiat., **41**: 984, 1939.
99. K. Iwata and R. S. Snider. Electroenceph. Clin. Neurophysiol., **11**: 439, 1959.
100. C. von Euler and U. Söderberg. Electroenceph. Clin. Neurophysiol., **9**: 391, 1957.
101. M. Mancia, M. Meulders, and G. Santibanez. Arch. Int. Physiol., **67**: 661, 1959.
102. J. P. Cordeau and M. Mancia. Electroenceph. Clin. Neurophysiol., **11**: 551, 1959.
103. T. Ban, H. Masai, A. Sakai, and T. Kurotsu. Med. J. Osaka U., **2**: 145, 1951.
104. H. Caspers and K. Winkel. Arch. ges. Physiol., **259**: 334, 1954.
105. L. D. Proctor, R. S. Knighton, and J. A. Churchill. Neurology, **7**: 193, 1957.
106. E. Grastyán, K. Lissák, and L. Molnár. Acta Physiol. Acad. Sci. Hung., **4**: 261, 1953.
107. R. Hodes, S. M. Peacock, Jr., and R. G. Heath. J. Comp. Neurol., **94**: 381, 1951.
108. T. Tokizane, M. Kawakami, and E. Gellhorn. Arch. Int. Physiol., **65**: 415, 1957.
109. E. E. King. J. Pharmacol. Exp. Ther., **116**: 404, 1956.
110. J. M. Delgado. Psychiat. Res. Rep. Amer. Psychiat. Ass., **12**: 259, 1960.
110a. W. Umbach. Arch. Psychiat. Nervenkr., **199**: 553, 1959.
111. H. Wehmeyer and H. Caspers. Pflueger. Arch. ges. Physiol., **266**: 99, 1957.
112. E. Gellhorn. Nervenarzt, **29**: 385, 1958.
113. For the literature see: A. Kuntz. The autonomic nervous system, p. 360. Philadelphia: Lea & Febiger, 1953.
114. W. K. Smith. J. Neurophysiol., **8**: 241, 1945.
115. A. A. Ward. Res. Publ. Ass. Nerv. Ment. Dis., **27**: 438, 1948.
116. D. H. Funkenstein. Sci. Amer., **192**: 74, 1955.
117. E. Gellhorn. Psychiat. Res. Rep. Amer. Psychiat. Ass., **12**: 209, 1960.
118. S. I. Cohen and A. J. Silverman. J. Psychosom. Res., **3**: 185, 1959.
119. J. D. Green and A. Arduini. J. Neurophysiol., **17**: 533, 1954.
120. T. Tokizane, M. Kawakami, and E. Gellhorn. Electroenceph. Clin. Neurophysiol., **11**: 431, 1959.
121. K. Lissák, E. Grastyán, A. Csanaki, F. Kekesi, and G. Vereby. Acta Physiol.

Pharmacol. Neerl., **6**: 451, 1957 and Physiol. Bohemosloven., **7**: 9, 1958.

122. L. Rothfield and P. Harman. J. Comp. Neurol., **101**: 265, 1954.
123. J. P. Murphy and E. Gellhorn. J. Neurophysiol., **8**: 431, 1945.
124. E. Gellhorn. Acta Physiol. Pharmacol. Neerl., **6**: 111, 1957.
125. I. A. Mirsky, R. E. Miller, and J. V. Murphy. J. Amer. Psychoanal. Assoc., **6**: 433, 1958.
126. R. E. Miller, J. V. Murphy, and I. A. Mirsky. Arch. Gen. Psychiat., **1**: 480, 1959.
127. F. A. Beach. J. Comp. Psychol., **29**: 193, 1940.
128. P. D. MacLean. Handbook of Physiol., section I, **3**: 1723. Washington, D.C.: American Physiological Society, 1960.
129. W. Penfield. *In:* Neurological basis of behavior, G. E. Wolstenholme (ed.), p. 140. London: Churchill, 1958.
130. E. Gellhorn and A. D. Miller. A.M.A. Arch. Gen. Psychiat., **4**: 371, 1961.
131. E. Gellhorn. Acta Neuroveg. (Wien), **20**: 490, 1960.
132. ———. *Ibid.*, 514, 1960.
133. L. Alexander. Arch. Neurol. & Psychiat., **80**: 629, 1958.
134. R. R. Grinker and J. P. Spiegel. War neurosis in North Africa. New York: J. Macy, Jr. Foundation, 1943.
135. R. L. Swank. J. Nerv. Ment. Dis., **109**: 477, 1949.
136. J. Wolpe. Psychotherapy by reciprocal inhibition. Stanford: Stanford University Press, 1958.
137. H. J. Eysenck (ed.). Behaviour therapy and the neuroses. New York: Pergamon Press, 1960.
138. R. Walther. Das vegetativ-affektive Syndrom und seine Bedeutung für die Psychiatrie. Berlin: VEB Verlag, 1956.

13 the physiology of fear and anger *

Daniel H. Funkenstein

1. How did Cannon differentiate rage and fear physiologically?
2. What is the mecholyl test?
3. What does Funkenstein mean by the statement "man . . . has within him the lion and the rabbit"?

When the late Walter B. Cannon, by his historic experiments nearly half a century ago, showed a connection between emotions and certain physiological changes in the body, he opened a new frontier for psychology and medicine. His work, coupled with that of Sigmund Freud, led to psychosomatic medicine. It also made the emotions accessible to laboratory measurement and analysis. Within the last few years there has been a keen revival of interest in this research, because of some important new discoveries which have sharpened our understanding of specific emotions and their bodily expressions. It has been learned, for instance, that anger and fear produce different physiological reactions and can be distinguished from each other. The findings have given us a fresh outlook from which to study mental illnesses.

The best way to begin the account of this recent work is to start with Cannon's own summary of what he learned. Cannon found that when an animal was confronted with a situation which evoked pain, rage or fear, it responded with a set of physiological reactions which prepared it to meet the threat with "fight" or "flight." These reactions, said Cannon, were mobilized by the secretion of adrenalin: when the cortex of the brain perceived the threat, it sent a stimulus down the sympathetic branch of the autonomic nervous system to the adrenal glands and they secreted the hormone. Cannon graphically described the results as follows:

"Respiration deepens; the heart beats more rapidly; the arterial pressure rises; the blood is shifted away from the stomach and intestines to the heart and central nervous system and the muscles; the processes in the alimentary canal cease; sugar is freed from the reserves in the liver; the spleen contracts and discharges its content of concentrated corpuscles, and adrenin is secreted from the adrenal medulla. The key to these marvelous transformations in the body is found in relating them to the natural accompaniments of fear and rage— running away in order to escape from danger, and attacking in order to be dominant. Whichever the action, a life-or-death struggle may ensue.

"The emotional responses just listed may reasonably be regarded as preparatory for struggle. They are adjustments which, so far as possible, put the organism in readiness for meeting the demands which will be made upon it. The secreted adrenin cooperates with sympathetic nerve impulses in calling forth stored glycogen from the liver, thus flooding the blood with sugar for the use of laboring muscles; it helps in distributing the blood in abundance to the heart, the brain, and the limbs (*i.e.,* to the parts essential for intense physical effort) while taking it away from the inhibited organs in the abdomen; it quickly abolishes the effects of muscular fatigue so

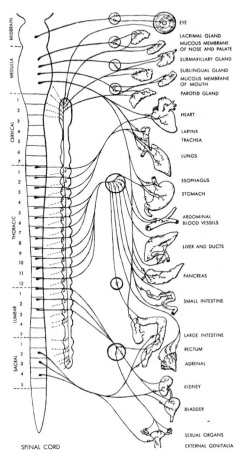

The autonomic nervous system is represented by this diagram. The parasympathetic branches arise from the brain and sacral vertebrae; the sympathetic branches arise from the thoracic and lumbar vertebrae.

that the organism which can muster adrenin in the blood can restore to its tired muscles the same readiness to act which they had when fresh; and it renders the blood more rapidly coagulable. The increased respiration, the redistributed blood running at high pressure, and the more numerous red corpuscles set free from the spleen provide for essential oxygen and for riddance of acid waste, and make a setting for instantaneous and supreme action.

In short, all these changes are directly service-able in rendering the organism more effective in the violent display of energy which fear or rage may involve."

Cannon recognized that among all these physiological changes there were a few which could not be ascribed directly to the action of adrenalin. He therefore postulated that the hormone was supplemented by two additional substances from the sympathetic nerves. An active agent, distinguishable from adrenalin, was eventually identified in 1948, when B. F. Tullar and M. L. Tainter at length succeeded in preparing the optically active form of the substance. It proved to be a second hormone secreted by the adrenal medulla. Called nor-adrenalin, it differs markedly from adrenalin in its physiological effects. Whereas adrenalin elicits profound physiological changes in al-most every system in the body, nor-adrenalin apparently has only one important primary effect: namely, it stimulates the contraction of small blood vessels and increases the resistance to the flow of blood.

An animal exhibits only two major emo-tions in response to a threatening situation: namely, rage and fear. A man, however, may experience three: anger directed outward (the counterpart of rage), anger directed toward himself (depression) and anxiety, or fear. In studies of physiological changes accompany-ing various emotional states among patients at the New York Hospital, H. G. Wolff and his co-workers noticed that anger produced effects quite different from those of depres-sion or fear. For example, when a subject was angry, the stomach lining became red and there was an increase in its rhythmic contrac-tions and in the secretion of hydrochloric acid. When the same subject was depressed or frightened, the stomach lining was pale in color and there was a decrease in peristaltic movements and in the hydrochloric acid se-cretion.

The experiments of Wolff, the evidence that the adrenal medulla secreted two sub-stances rather than one and certain clinical observations led our group at the Harvard Medical School to investigate whether adrena-lin and nor-adrenalin might be specific indica-tors which distinguished one emotion from another. The clinical observations had to do with the effects of a drug, mecholyl, on psychotic patients. We had been studying their blood-pressure responses to injections of adrenalin, which acts on the sympathetic nervous system, and mecholyl, which stimu-lates the parasympathetic system. On the basis of their blood-pressure reactions, psychotic patients could be classified into seven groups. This test had proved of value in predicting patients' responses to psychiatric treatments, such as electric shock and insulin: certain groups responded better to the treatments than others. But more interesting was the fact that psychotic patients with high blood pres-sure reacted to the injection of mecholyl in two distinctly different ways. In one group there was only a small drop in the blood pressure after the injection, and the pressure returned to the usually high level within three to eight minutes. In the other group the blood pressure dropped markedly after the injection and remained below the pre-injection level even after 25 minutes. Not only were the physiological reactions quite different, but the two groups of patients also differed in person-ality and in response to treatment. Thirty-nine of 42 patients whose blood pressure was sharply lowered by mecholyl improved with electric shock treatment, whereas only three of 21 in the other group improved with the same treatment. Further, the two groups showed distinctly different results in projec-tive psychological tests such as the Ror-schach.

All this suggested that the two groups of patients might be differentiated on the basis of

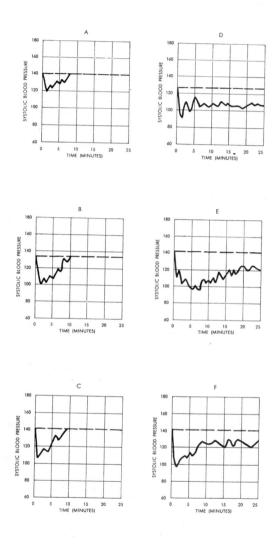

emotions. Most psychotic patients in emotional turmoil express the same emotion constantly over a period of days, weeks or months. Psychiatrists determined the predominant emotion expressed by each of 63 patients who had been tested with mecholyl, without knowing in which physiological group they had been classified. When the subjects' emotional and physiological ratings were compared, it turned out that almost all of the patients who were generally angry at other people fell in Group N (a small, temporary reduction of blood pressure by mecholyl), while almost all those who were usually depressed or frightened were in Group E (sharp response to mecholyl). In other words, the physiological reactions were significantly related to the emotional content of the patients' psychoses.

The next step was to find out whether the same test could distinguish emotions in normal, healthy people, using medical students as subjects. They were studied at a time when they were under stress—while they were awaiting the decisions of hospitals on their applications for internships. As the competition among the students for the hospitals of their choice is keen, the period just prior to such announcements is a time of emotional turmoil for the men. A group of students who responded to this situation with elevated blood pressure was given the standard dose of mecholyl. The results were the same as for the psychotic patients: students who were angry at others for the situation in which they found themselves had a Type N physiological reaction; those who felt depressed (angry at

Type N response to the injection of mecholyl is traced by the heavy line. The broken line represents the basal blood pressure. The response is shown for three kinds of subject: (A) healthy individuals under stress who respond with anger toward others, (B) healthy individuals whose blood pressure has been elevated with nor-adrenalin and (C) psychotic individuals with elevated blood pressure and anger toward others.

Type E response to the injection of mecholyl is similarly traced by the heavy line. In these charts the response is shown for three different kinds of subject: (D) healthy individuals under stress who respond with anger directed inward, or depression, (E) healthy individuals whose blood pressure has been elevated with adrenalin and (F) psychotic individuals with elevated blood pressure and depression.

themselves) or anxious showed a Type E physiological reaction. The reaction was related only to their temporary emotional state; after the internships were settled and their blood pressures had returned to pre-stress levels, all the students reacted the same way to the injection of mecholyl.

It was at this point that we undertook to investigate the comparative effects of adrenalin and nor-adrenalin. A group of workers at the Presbyterian Hospital in New York had shown that injections of nor-adrenalin and adrenalin produced two different types of rise in blood pressure, one due to contraction of blood vessels and the other to faster pumping by the heart. Upon learning of this work, we designed experiments to test the hypothesis that the two types of elevated blood pressure, differentiated by us on the basis of mecholyl tests, indicated in one instance excessive secretion of nor-adrenalin and in the other excessive secretion of adrenalin. Healthy college students were first given a series of intravenous injections of salt water to accustom them to the procedure so that it would not disturb them. Then each subject was tested in the following way. He was given an injection of nor-adrenalin sufficient to raise his blood pressure by 25 per cent. Then, while his blood pressure was elevated, he received the standard dose of mecholyl, and its effects on the blood pressure were noted. The next day the subject was put through the same procedure except that adrenalin was given instead of nor-adrenalin to raise the blood pressure.

Ten students were studied in this way, and in every instance the effect of nor-adrenalin was different from that of adrenalin [see charts on this page]. When the blood pressure was elevated by nor-adrenalin, mecholyl produced only a small drop in pressure, with a return to the previous level in seven to 10

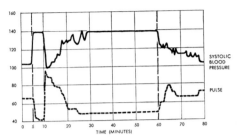

Effect of nor-adrenalin was observed by administering an infusion of the hormone for 60 minutes. After 5 minutes the blood pressure of the subject rose. After 10 minutes mecholyl was injected and the blood pressure fell. Then it rose in a Type N response.

minutes. This reaction was similar to the Type N response in psychotic patients and healthy students under stress. In contrast, when the blood pressure was elevated by adrenalin, mecholyl produced the Type E response: the pressure dropped markedly and did not return to the previous level during the 25-minute observation period.

These results suggested, in the light of the earlier experiments, that anger directed outward was associated with secretion of nor-adrenalin, while depression and anxiety were associated with secretion of adrenalin. To check this hypothesis, another series of experiments was carried out.

A group of 125 college students were sub-

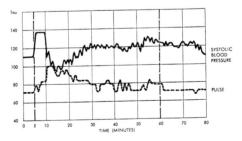

Effect of adrenalin was observed by the same procedure. After the injection of mecholyl the systolic blood pressure of the subject remained depressed in a Type E response.

jected to stress-inducing situations in the laboratory. The situations, involving frustration, were contrived to bring out each student's habitual reaction to stresses in real life; that the reactions actually were characteristic of the subjects' usual responses was confirmed by interviews with their college roommates. While the subjects were under stress, observers recorded their emotional reactions and certain physiological changes—in the blood pressure, the pulse and the so-called IJ waves stemming from the action of the heart. This test showed that students who responded to the stress with anger directed outward had physiological reactions similar to those produced by injection of nor-adrenalin, while students who responded with depression or anxiety had physiological reactions like those to adrenalin.

There remained the question: Does the same individual secrete unusual amounts of nor-adrenalin when angry and of adrenalin when frightened? Albert F. Ax, working in another laboratory in our hospital, designed experiments to study this question. He contrived laboratory stressful situations which were successful in producing on one occasion anger and on another occasion fear in the same subjects. His results showed that when a subject was angry at others, the physiological reactions were like those induced by the injection of nor-adrenalin; when the same subject was frightened, the reactions were like those to adrenalin. This indicated that the physiology was specific for the emotion rather than for the person.

In all these experiments the evidence for excessive secretion of nor-adrenalin and adrenalin was based on the physiological changes being similar to those which can be produced by the intravenous injection of nor-adrenalin and adrenalin. Since the substances involved have not been identified chemically, and the evidence is entirely physiological, at the present time we prefer to limit ourselves to the statement that the reactions are *like* those to the two hormones. However, nothing in our experiments would contradict the hypothesis that these substances are actually adrenalin and nor-adrenalin.

What is the neurophysiological mechanism whereby different emotions evoke different adrenal secretions? Although no conclusive work in this area is yet available, some recent investigations suggest a possible answer. U.S. von Euler in Sweden found that stimulation of certain areas of the hypothalamus caused the adrenal gland to secrete nor-adrenalin, whereas stimulation of other areas caused it to secrete adrenalin. These areas may correspond to those which the Nobel prize winner W. R. Hess of Zurich stimulated to produce aggressive behavior and flight, respectively, in animals. The experiments suggest that anger and fear may activate different areas in the hypothalamus, leading to production of nor-adrenalin in the first case and adrenalin in the second. Until more experiments are made, these possibilities must remain suppositions.

Some of the most intriguing work in this field was recently reported by von Euler. He compared adrenal secretions found in a number of different animals. The research material was supplied by a friend who flew to Africa to obtain the adrenal medullae of wild animals. Interpreting his findings, J. Ruesch pointed out that aggressive animals such as the lion had a relatively high amount of nor-adrenalin, while in animals such as the rabbit, which depend for survival primarily on flight, adrenalin predominated. Domestic animals, and wild animals that live very social lives (*e.g.*, the baboon), also have a high ratio of adrenalin to nor-adrenalin.

These provocative findings suggest the theory that man is born with the capacity to react with a variety of emotions (has within him the lion and the rabbit), and that his early childhood experiences largely determine in which of these ways he will react under stress. Stated in another way, the evolutional process of man's emotional development is completed in the bosom of the family. We have found in other studies that individuals' habitual emotional reactions have a high correlation with their perceptions of psychological factors in their families.

This entire series of experiments yielded data which can be understood in the frame of reference of psychoanalytical observations. According to theory, anger directed outward is characteristic of an earlier stage of childhood than is anger directed toward the self or anxiety (conflicts over hostility). The latter two emotions are the result of the acculturation of the child. If the physiological development of the child parallels its psychological development, then we should expect to find that the ratio of nor-adrenalin to adrenalin is higher in infants than in older children. Bernt Hokfelt and G. B. West established that this is indeed the case: at an early age the adrenal medulla has more nor-adrenalin, but later adrenalin becomes dominant.

Paranoid patients show a greater degree of regression to infantile behavior than do patients with depression or anxiety neurosis. And it will be recalled that in our tests paranoid patients showed signs of excessive secretion of nor-adrenalin, while depressed and anxious patients exhibited symptoms of adrenalin secretion.

These parallels between psychological and physiological development suggest further studies and some theories for testing. Standing on the shoulders of Cannon and Freud, we have extended our view of human behavior and discovered fertile fields for exploration.

14   conditioned fear by electrical stimulation of the monkey brain *

José M. R. Delgado, H. Enger Rosvold, and Edmund Looney

1. Why do the authors refer to the behavior produced by hypothalamic stimulation as "pseudo-emotion"?

2. What differences from MacLean's findings are reported in this article?

3. Does this experiment support (in general) the Papez view of emotion?

The work of Hess (9, 10), Ranson and Magoun (18), Kaada (11), MacLean and Delgado (12), Gastaut and collaborators (8), and Masserman (14) has demonstrated that the mesencephalon, diencephalon, and rhinencephalon play important roles in the integration of emotional reactions. Electrical stimulation of all these subcortical structures has elicited a wide variety of the behavioral components usually associated with fear, rage, and anger. Masserman (14), however, was unable to condition an escape response to hypothalamic stimulation, or even to elicit an escape response by such stimulation in animals which had already been conditioned to escape to auditory stimuli. He concluded, therefore, much as Bard had done earlier in connection with lesions placed in the hypothalamus, that "these pseudo-affective responses differ from those in integrated emotional states in that the hypothalamic reactions are not adapted to

* J. M. R. Delgado, H. E. Rosvold, and E. Looney, "Evoking Conditioned Fear by Electrical Stimulation of Subcortical Structures in the Monkey Brain," *J. comp. physiol. Psychol.*, 49 (1956), 373–380. Reprinted with permission.

external circumstances" (1, p. 633). Delgado (6), on the other hand, observed that animals in which emotional responses were being evoked by stimulating in subcortical structures other than the hypothalamus soon began to exhibit anxiety-like responses when placed in the apparatus prior to stimulation. These observations were incidental to the main purpose of that study, and the phenomenon may have been an artifact of certain uncontrolled variables. The present study was designed to determine whether electrical stimulation in these same subcortical structures would evoke a fear response which had been conditioned to an auditory stimulus. Positive results would suggest that the emotional behavior mediated by these subcortical structures, unlike that mediated by the hypothalamus, can be adapted to external circumstances.

subjects

Ten monkeys (*Macaca mulatta*), ranging in weight from 2.0 kg. to 3.0 kg., were housed in individual cages and maintained on a standard synthetic diet calculated to provide 80 cal/kg of body weight daily. One-half orange three times a week supplemented the diet. Upon completion of preoperative training, an assembly of six needle electrodes was permanently implanted within each hemisphere at the positions in the rhinencephalon, diencephalon, and mesencephalon from which Delgado (6) had previously elicited emotional behavior.

apparatus

needle electrodes

Enameled or Teflon-coated stainless steel wire, 0.005 in. in diameter, was straightened by stretching and cut into six graduated lengths: the first 10 cm. long, and each succeeding piece 4 mm. shorter. Each wire was scraped bare of insulation for 1 mm. at the tip, and for about 5 mm. at the socket end. Six such wires were then cemented together side by side with Plexiglas dissolved in dichlorethylene, each bare tip 4 mm. from the next. The socket ends were soldered to a seven-pin miniature radio tube socket in an identifiable order. A bare stainless steel wire was soldered to the middle pin to serve as the indifferent lead. These seven wires were insulated from one another by flooding the soldered ends with INSLX-E33 clear. This assembly provided a six-point multilead electrode by means of which the brain could be stimulated at six vertical levels.

electrical stimulator

The two-channel Hols-Delgado stimulator providing bidirectional rectangular pulses was connected to the electrode by means of a light-weight, flexible multilead cable. Frequency was kept constant at 100 cycles per second, and pulse duration at .35 msec.; amplitude was varied from 1 to 10 v. Monitoring the current with a dual-beam oscilloscope (DuMont Type 322) indicated that current of 0.25 to 4 ma. passed through the brain when 1 to 10 v. was applied. Stimulation was unilateral and monopolar. In some cases bipolar stimulation between adjacent points was also used to check the results of monopolar stimulation. In each stimulation trial the animals were continuously stimulated until they responded or until 40 sec. had elapsed.

testing apparatus

The animal was carried to an air-conditioned, soundproofed, darkened testing room, where it was released into the testing cage. On stimulation days before being released into the testing cage the multilead cable was plugged into the electrode socket. The animal was free to move about in the testing cage even when the multilead cable was plugged in. The testing cage was a Wisconsin General Test Apparatus (WGTA) modified by Waterhouse (20) to contain an electric grid floor through which shock could be administered to the animal's feet as described by Beck, Runyon, and Waterhouse (2). The level of shock was regulated so that it produced apparent signs of discomfort in the monkey without producing tetany. Lifting the one-way vision screen started a timer and, either immediately or after 2 sec., electrified the grid. Lifting the screen also initiated either the high tone, the low tone, the no-tone, or the electrical stimulation. In addition, lifting the screen exposed to the animal two cups placed 12 in. apart, each fastened to a separate slide. Turning over a cup stopped the timer, the current in the grid, and the tones or the electrical stimulation. The time elapsed between the raising of the screen and the turning of the cups was called the "response time." The monkeys were trained to pull in and overturn the left cup in response to the high tone to stop (escape) and later to avoid, the shock to the feet, and the right cup in response to the low tone to obtain a peanut reward. This training proceeded as described below.

procedure

training

Twenty-five trials of each of the two responses were distributed at random over the day's 50 trials. The trials were separated by 5 to 10 sec. The training was continued until the animal was correct on all trials and avoided shock by anticipating fear (high-tone) trial on five successive days. Then 10 trials preceded by no-tone were presented at random among the other 50 trials for a total of 60 trials. The no-tone trial consisted at first of confronting the monkey with various stimuli such as blinking lights, trainer's gloves, and banging noises as the screen was raised. Gradually these novel stimuli were omitted so that finally the no-tone condition consisted in simply raising the screen. Training continued under these conditions until on three successive days the animal responded to the left cup only for the conditioned fear stimulus, and to the right cup for everything but the conditioned fear stimulus, i.e., on both the low-tone and no-tone trials. The electrodes were then implanted. Training was resumed within a few days after operation and was continued until on three successive days the animals did not make an error either by going to the wrong cup or by failing to avoid shock.

testing

Selection of the stimulation intensity. The animal was placed on the observation stage described by MacLean and Delgado (12), and all the leads of both electrodes were plugged into a flexible cable leading to the stimulator. With frequency and pulse duration constant at 100 cps and .35 msec., respectively, the voltage was varied in 0.1-v. intervals from 1.0 to a maximum of 10.0 v., repeating each level three times in one ascending and one descending series for each lead. The E recorded whether or not he observed an effect and on the basis of earlier investigations categorized the behavior into fear responses, motor effects, or inhibition of movement. The lowest voltage at which an effect was apparent every time in both series (six out of six) was called the "effective threshold" for that lead. This was the intensity of the stimulation used for that lead in the systematic testing.

Systematic testing. Each day that the animal was placed in the Waterhouse apparatus only three leads were plugged in, one in one hemisphere and two in the other. The leads were selected so that (*a*) on any one day stimulation was applied through one lead from which fear responses had been elicited, one from which either motor effects or inhibition had been elicited, and one from which there had been no apparent effect. (*b*) The same lead was selected on three different days, separated by as many days as possible, usually three.

A day's session consisted of 60 trials—15 stimulation (5 through each of three leads), 20 low-tone, 20 high-tone (fear), and 5 no-tone trials—presented in a balanced order such that neither (*a*) two stimulation trials, nor (*b*) a fear trial and a stimulation trial expected to elicit a fear response, were juxtaposed. The systematic testing was completed in 12 testing days and provided observations on a total of 15 stimulation trials through each lead.

Testing the limits. Upon completion of the 12 days of systematic testing, several variations in procedure were introduced. In one of these, the low (food) tone, was sounded simultaneously with applying stimulation through a lead from which fear had been elicited. A conditioned fear response in the presence of this competing drive was considered a definitive demonstration of the capacity of the stimulation to evoke fear responses. In another of these variations, the high tone or low tone was sounded simultaneously with applying stimulation through a lead from which inhibition had been elicited. Failure to respond in the presence of these competing drives was considered a definitive demonstration of an inhibitory effect of stimulation. Toward the end of this testing period, stimulation was applied only through leads from which fear responses had been elicited. Thus,

an animal received a total of approximately 40 trials in which the conditioned fear response was elicited by substituting electrical stimulation for the conditioned stimulus.

surgical procedure

Surgical procedures, construction of electrodes, and the method of implantation have been reported by Delgado (3, 5) and Rosvold and Delgado (19). Briefly, the method was as follows: with the animal under anesthesia and placed in the Horsley-Clarke instrument, the assembly of needle electrodes was lowered through holes in the skull drilled at points designated by Olszewski (16) to locate the various intracerebral structures to be investigated. The electrodes were secured in place by dental cement and steel wire ties through the skull. Electrodes thus implanted remained in place over many months and permitted daily testing of the unanaesthetized animal while it was being stimulated.

anatomical procedure

Following completion of the behavioral observations, the animals were sacrificed and the brains prepared for histological examination as described by Rosvold and Delgado (19). Cells were stained by the method of Nissl, fibers by the method of Spielmeyer.[1] As a check, the Klüver method of staining cells and fibers simultaneously was used in some brains. Sections were examined to determine the anatomical location of the electrode leads. The sections in the plane of the electrode were photographed, and the enlarged prints were examined to identify the structures surrounding the leads. Each histological section was then magnified through a photographic enlarger and the image traced, marking the

[1] Miss Beatrix Egli prepared the histological slides.

channel of the electrode and location of the leads. These findings, together with tissue changes, were verified microscopically. A final drawing of the section was prepared by comparing the tracing and the photograph.

results

responses to the conditioned stimuli

The interpolation of stimulation trials during the testing sessions did not alter significantly either the accuracy or the response times of the conditioned responses. Pulling in and overturning the left cup in response to the high tone (conditioned fear response, henceforth called CFR) continued to be a very energetic, fast response with a mean response time of 1.78 sec. Pulling in and overturning the right cup in response to the low tone (conditioned food response) and in response to the no-tone (also a conditioned food response—the rising screen served as the conditioned stimulus) continued to be identical and relatively slow responses, each with a mean response time of 4.24 sec.

responses to the electrical stimulation

Stimulation trials were identical to the no-tone trial (i.e., the only external stimulus was the rising screen) except that electrical stimulation was applied through one of the leads. The effect of the stimulation was to elicit one of five responses: (*a*) A response identical to that which had been made to the high-tone. This response was indistinguishable from the CFR with respect to response time and accompanying autonomic signs. It was therefore called an "elicited fear response" (FEAR). (*b*) A response identical to that which had

been made to the low-tone or no-tone. This response was indistinguishable from the conditioned food response with respect to response time and absence of autonomic signs. However, the interpretation of a response to the food cup during stimulation is equivocal; i.e., it could be interpreted as indicating that stimulation elicited a food response, or that stimulation had no effect, the response to the food cup being simply the CR to the rising screen in the absence of the high (fear) tone. Therefore, the more conservative interpretation was made, namely, that a response to the right cup indicated that the stimulation had "no apparent effect" (NAE). (*c*) A response to the food cup which was accompanied by pronounced "motor effects" (MOTOR). (*d*) A response to neither cup. The monkey sat motionless in the cage slowly turning its head from side to side for the 40 sec. during which the current was on, after which it moved abruptly to the food cup. Such a failure to respond while the current was on was called an "inhibited response" (INHIBIT). (*e*) A response in which the animal did not overturn either cup for 10 to 39 sec., but moved cautiously about the cage, frequently as though searching the floor. This response was called "a slow response" (SLOW).

Every time a stimulating current was passed through a particular lead, the same response was invariably elicited. Even in those trials which tested the limits, i.e., in which a CS was sounded during the stimulation, the type of response that resulted was related to the structure being stimulated rather than the CS, always being different from that to be expected in response to the CS.

anatomical results

The structures from which these responses were elicited are identified in Figure 1, which

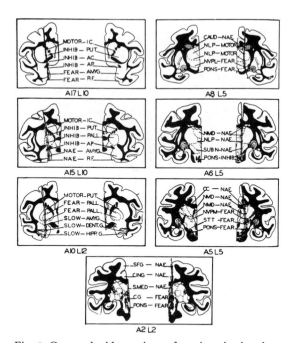

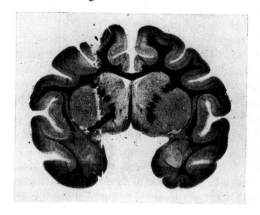

Fig. 1. Camera lucida tracings of sections in the plane of the electrode from at least one animal implanted at each of the Horsley-Clarke positions investigated in this study. *A:17* indicates the anterior H-C coordinate of the electrode placement, *L:10*, the lateral. The black dots in the channel of the electrode represent the points of stimulation. Their positions within the brain appear somewhat distorted as a result of fixing and cutting processes. *INHIB* = inhibitory response; *NAE* = no apparent effect. *IC* = internal capsule, *PUT* = putamen, *AC* = anterior commissure, *AP* = ansa peduncularis, *AMYG* = amygdala, *RF* = rhinal fissure, *PALL* = pallidum, *DENTG* = dentate gyrus, *HIPPG* = hippocampal gyrus, *NLP* = nucleus lateralis posterior of the thalamus, *NVPL* = nucleus ventralis posterolateralis of the thalamus, *NMD* = nucleus medialis dorsalis of the thalamus, *NVPM* = nucleus ventralis posteromedialis of the thalamus, *SUBN* = substantia nigra, *CC* = corpus callosum, *STT* = spinothalamic tract, *SFG* = superior frontal gyrus, *CING* = cingulate gyrus. *SMED* = striae medullaris, *CG* = central gray.

contains reproductions of the sections in the plane of the electrode tracts from seven different hemispheres. Reproductions of sections from the 13 other hemispheres (bilateral implantation in 10 animals, making 20 hemi-

spheres) are not shown because they are similar to one or another of the seven. Thus, the sections in Figure 1 which are designated by A:17 L:10, A:15 L:10 and A:10 L 12 each represent an N of 2. The other sections represent N's as follows: A:8 L:5, N = 3; A:6 L:5, N = 4; A:5 L:5, N = 1; and, finally, A:2 L:2, N = 6. The three reproductions on the left of Figure 1 are at different anterior-posterior levels in the amygdala, that at the top being most anterior. The remaining four are at four different anterior-posterior levels through the pons and thalamus, that at the top right being most anterior. The anatomical structure in which each lead was found to be located is identified by familiar abbreviations. The label for the particular behavior elicited by electrical stimulation is shown prefixed to the abbreviation of the structure from which the behavior was elicited. Stimulating in the following structures elicited the CFR:

The amygdaloid-hippocampal complex. The complicated arrangement of nuclei within the amygdala makes it difficult to determine for certain from which of the amygdaloid nuclei the CFR was obtained. However, as illustrated in Figure 2 and in the sections on

Fig. 2. Photograph of the section in the plane of the electrode of one of the brains represented as A:17 L:10 in Figure 1.

the left of Figure 1, it is probable that the CFR was elicited only from the medial amygdaloid nucleus and from tissue adjacent to this nucleus in the superior bank of the rhinal fissure. That these effects were specific to this nucleus is suggested by the fact that they were not obtained, as illustrated in A:15 L:10, 2 mm. posterior to it (probably in basal amygdaloid nucleus), nor 4 mm. superior to it (probably in central amygdaloid nucleus). Stimulating the anterior portion of the hippocampus resulted in the slow response, not the CFR.

The corpus striatum. As illustrated in the three sections on the left of Figure 1, the CFR was elicited from the corpus striatum only when the lead was in the posterior portion of the pallidum or in the external medullary lamina surrounding the pallidum. Stimulation 2 to 4 mm. anterior to these structures in the striatum, particularly in the putamen, inhibited responses.

Thalamus. The only thalamic nuclei from which the CFR was elicited were, as illustrated in A:8 L:5 and A:5 L:5 of Figure 1, the *ventral* nuclei VPL and VPM. Motor effects were obtained from the lateral thalamic nuclei while no apparent effect was observed during stimulation in medialis dorsalis.

Mesencephalon. The CFR was elicited from several structures in the mesencephalon. Whenever the trigeminus nerve was involved, this response was very frantic, and the monkey screamed and rubbed its face. This was apparent from stimulating (*a*) where the root of the nerve appears, as in A:8 L:5 just lateral to the pons (Gasserian ganglion); (*b*) where it enters the pons through the superolateral aspect of the brachium pontis (not illustrated, but 1 mm. posterior and medial to the tract shown in A:8 L:5); and (*c*) where the mesencephalic root of the nerve runs close to periaqueductal central gray, as illustrated in Figure 3 and A:2 L:2.

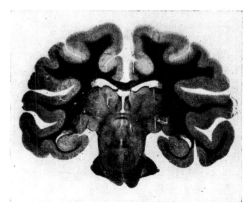

Fig. 3. Photograph of the section in the plane of the electrode of one of the brains represented in A:2 L:2 in Figure 1.

Similarly, whenever stimulation in the pons may have involved the spinothalamic tract, as in A:5 L:5 and in A:2 L:2, the CFR was elicited, sometimes accompanied by screaming.

However, when, as in A:2 L:2, the lead was clearly in periaqueductal central gray, where it probably did not involve either spinothalamic tract or trigeminus nerve, the CFR was always elicited accompanied by autonomic signs but *never* by screaming or face-rubbing.

Other structures. The CFR was *not* elicited from sensorimotor cortex, sensorimotor pathways, n.VL and pulvinar of the thalamus, substantia nigra, or tegmentum inferior to central gray.

It is apparent in Figure 1 that the motor effects followed stimulation mainly of sensorimotor pathways and thalamic nuclei projecting to the motor cortex, while responses were inhibited by stimulating primarily in corpus striatum but also in ansa peduncularis.

discussion

Many investigators have elicited fearful reactions in animals by electrically stimulating in some subcortical structures. In this study a conditioned fear response invariably followed electrical stimulation in certain of these structures in the monkey. More recently, Delgado, Roberts, and Miller (7) have demonstrated that stimulation in some of these structures in cats leads to fear-like behavior which can be conditioned, can be used to motivate trial-and-error learning, and can function as punishment to make hungry animals avoid food. It may be concluded, therefore, that responses resulting from this stimulation, unlike those elicited by stimulating in the hypothalamus, are not "pseudo-affective" responses but, instead, are responses which have the characteristics of learned behavior in that they can be adapted to external circumstances.

There is a question, however, as to whether these elicited responses are actually fear responses. In the present study there are three other possible interpretations: (a) One alternative is that the stimulation was in "pain fibers" and therefore elicited a pain-escape response rather than a pain-avoidance response (CFR). This is a plausible interpretation, since overturning the left cup was the conditioned response for both conditions. Indeed, in the case of stimulation of structures related to sensory fibers, such as trigeminal nerve, spinothalamic tract, pallidum, and ventral thalamus, it is a likely interpretation. Such is probably not the case for stimulation in amygdala and central gray, however, for these structures are not related to sensory fibers. (b) A second, less likely alternative is that stimulation was in auditory structures involved in the transmission of the conditioned fear stimulus (high tone). Two factors argue against this interpretation: First, it is unlikely that stimulation would selectively evoke responses to the high tone; second, the structures from which the fear responses were evoked are remote from those related to the auditory system. (c) Finally, it is possible that the stimulation resulted merely in a novel sensation to which the animal responded with the fear response. This interpretation is quite unlikely since the animals had learned to respond to the other (left, not the right) cup when confronted with novel external stimuli (the no-tone condition). It seems reasonable, therefore, to advance the interpretation that electrical stimulation, at least in the amygdala and central gray, induces in the animal a condition similar to that which is present when it is anxious or afraid of being hurt.

Papez (17) and more recently, MacLean (13), have summarized the evidence to support the conclusion that emotional expression is mediated through the related cerebral structures called the limbic system. It is well established that the amygdala is included in this system. Further, Nauta (15) has recently demonstrated that periaqueductal central gray is also related to the limbic system by way of collateral fibers from the fornix. These considerations perhaps provide a rationale for the findings that fearful behavior was elicited by stimulating in central gray and medial nucleus of the amygdala.

A difficulty for this formulation is that fear was not elicited by stimulating in other amygdaloid nuclei or in the anterior hippocampus, i.e., structures which are also included in the limbic system. Kaada (11), and MacLean and Delgado (12), however, have reported "fear" responses following stimulation in these structures. Some of the factors which might be responsible for these discrepant results can be pointed out. Stimulating at two different points within what appears to be the same anatomical structure may produce different behavioral effects. Thus, in the present study, stimulation in the corpus striatum through one lead resulted in motor effects but through an adjacent lead resulted in inhibitory effects. Secondly, what appear to be minor variations in the parameters of stimulation produce different behavioral effects. Thus, stimulating in the putamen with 100-cps current in the present study resulted in inhibition, but stimulating in the putamen with 60 cps in an earlier study (19) resulted in hyperactivity. The resolution of these problems would require a systematic analysis of the effect on behavior of point-by-point stimulations throughout a structure in question, varying all the parameters of the stimulating current. Until such systematic studies are undertaken, assigning functions to structures based on the results of electrical stimulation is hazardous.

At present, however, it seems profitable to include the results of the present study among those which support the notion that the limbic system is involved in the expression of emotions.

summary

1. An assembly containing six electrodes was implanted in mesencephalic, diencephalic, and rhinencephalic structures in the brains of 10 monkeys (*Macaca mulatta*), which had been trained to avoid shock to the feet.

2. Electrical stimulation of some structures evoked a response identical to the response to avoid shock; of other structures, an inhibitory response; of other structures, motor effects; and of some structures no apparent response.

3. Stimulation of the following structures elicited the conditioned fear response: medial nucleus of the amygdala and adjacent tissue in rhinal fissure, trigeminal nerve at the Gasserian ganglion, rostral part of the pons, medial part of the mesencephalon in the vicinity of the central gray, nucleus ventralis posteromedialis, external part of the nucleus ventralis posterolateralis of the thalamus, and external medullary lamina of the pallidum.

4. Electrical stimulation of the following structures did not evoke the avoidance response: sensorimotor cortex, sensorimotor pathways, nucleus ventralis lateralis of the thalamus, pulvinar of the thalamus, substantia nigra, part of the tegmentum inferior to the central gray, anterior hippocampus, posterior portions of the amygdaloid nucleus, and the putamen.

5. A great variety of motor effects affecting head, eyes, face, forelimbs, hindlimbs, and also the tail were evoked by stimulation. In some instances responses were inhibited by stimulation.

6. The results suggest that fear may be induced by electrical stimulation of some structures, not others. The structures from which fear was elicited appear to be related to the limbic system.

7. These results are interpreted as indicating that electrical stimulation of some subcortical structures elicits fear responses which may be adapted to external circumstances.

references

1. Bard, P. Central nervous mechanisms for emotional behavior patterns in animals. *Res. Pub. Ass. nerv. ment. Dis.* 1939, **19**, 190–218.

2. Beck, L. H., Waterhouse, I. K., & Runyon, R. P. Practical and theoretical solutions to difficulties in using Licklider's rat shocker. *J. comp. physiol. Psychol.*, 1953, **46**, 407–410.

3. Delgado, J. M. R. Permanent implantation of multilead electrodes in the brain. *Yale J. biol. Med.*, 1952, **24**, 351–358.

4. Delgado, J. M. R. Responses evoked in the waking cat by electrical stimulation of motor cortex. *Amer. J. Physiol.* 1952, **171**, 436–446.

5. Delgado, J. M. R. Evaluation of permanent implantation of electrodes within the brain. *EEG clin. Neurophysiol.*, 1955, **4**, 637–644.

6. Delgado, J. M. R. Study of some cerebral structures related to transmission and elaboration of noxious stimulation. *J. Neurophysiol.*, 1955, **18**, 261–275.

7. Delgado, J. M. R., Roberts, W. W., & Miller, N. Learning motivated by electrical stimulation of the brain. *Amer. J. Physiol.*, 1954, **179**, 587–593.

8. Gastaut, H., Naquet, R., Virourous, R., & Corriol, J. Provocation de comportements émotionnels divers par stimulation rhinencéphalique chez le chat avec électrodes à demeure. *Rev. Neurol.*, 1952, **86**, 319–327.

9. Hess, R. W. Hypothalamus und die Zentren des autonomen Nervensystem: Physiologie. *Arch. Psychiat. Nervenkr.*, 1936, **104**, 548–557.

10. Hess, W. R. *Das Zwichenhirn*. Basel: Benno Schwabe, 1949. Pp. 187.

11. Kaada, B. R. Somato-motor, autonomic and electrocorticographic responses to electrical stimulation of rhinencephalic and other structures in primates, cat, and dog. *Acta Physiolog. Scand.* 1951, **24**, 1–285 (Supplement 83).

12. MacLean, P. D., & Delgado, J. M. R. Electrical and chemical stimulation of frontotemporal portion of limbic system in waking animal. *EEG clin. Neurophysiol.*, 1953, **5**, 91–100.

13. MacLean, P. D. Psychosomatic disease and the "visceral brain." *Psychosom. Med.*, 1950, **11**, 1949.

14. Masserman, J. H. The hypothalamus in psychiatry. *Amer. J. Psychiat.*, 1942, **98**, 633–637.

15. Nauta, W. J. H. An experimental study of the fornix system in the rat. *J. comp. Neurol.* 1956, in press.

16. Olszewski, J. *The thalamus of the Macaca mulatta*. Basel: Karger, 1952. Pp. 93.

17. Papez, J. W. A proposed mechanism of emotion. *Arch. Neurol. Psychiat.*, 1937, **38**, 725–743.

18. Ranson, S. W., & Magoun, H. W. The hypothalamus. *Ergebn. Physiol.*, 1939, **41**, 56–163.

19. Rosvold, H. E., & Delgado, J. M. R. The effect on delayed-alternation test performance of stimulating or destroying electrically structures within the frontal lobes of the monkey's brain. *J. comp. physiol. Psychol.* 1956, **49**, 365–372.

20. Waterhouse, I. K. Effects of prefrontal lobotomy on conditioned fear and food responses in monkeys. *J. comp. physiol. Psychol.* 1956, **49**, in press.

motivation 1

In the first article in this section (Reading 15), Clifford Morgan presents a "central theory" of motivation. Rather than a narrow set of specific formulations, this theory provides a broad frame of reference for understanding the many and diverse physiological experiments in this area. Morgan also attempts to correlate physiological research with behavioral work such as that of Clark Hull and his followers. Of importance to the student is the useful set of operational definitions given in this article. These definitions include such terms as "need," "drive," and "motivated behavior."

After a discussion of the excitatory and inhibitory systems of the brain, Morgan indicates that there has been an upsurge of research on central motivational mechanisms. He only mentions the "exciting work of Olds and Milner." Since Morgan's article was written, sufficient research on self-stimulation has been published to establish its importance to motivation theory. Beginning in the 1950s, James Olds and P. M. Milner showed that electrodes implanted in various areas[1] of a rat's brain could be used to "reward" the animal.

[1] Especially the areas in the limbic system, which was described in the article by MacLean (1958) in Chapter 1.

Once the importance of an area of research (such as self-stimulation) is established, the detailed analysis of the many implications and ramifications concerns the experimenter. Three (17, 18, and 19) of the following four articles that comprise this section involve explorations of some of the parameters of the basic self-stimulation work.

In Reading 16, H. W. Magoun reviews several experiments concerned with "non-specific brain mechanisms," which lie between the much-studied sensory and motor nervous systems and are complexly interconnected with them. These mechanisms are involved in the arousal of an organism to wakefulness and in alerting it to attention. Magoun begins his article by examining early research on the "reticular activating system" (RAS).[2] The RAS provides some of the substratum of wakefulness necessary to the functioning of more specific centers in the cortex. Magoun also indicates that future research on these non-specific brain mechanisms may explain such behavioral phenomena as habituation.

In the next reading in this section (17), Ben Bursten and José Delgado report an experiment that extends to monkeys the self-stimulation results obtained with rats and cats. In addition to the fact that this phenomenon can occur in primates, Bursten's and Delgado's most important finding is that self-stimulation is less "rewarding" in monkeys than in the lower animals previously studied.

The article by Warren Roberts (Reading 18) makes an interesting extension of self-stimulation research by showing that the same electrode and the same intensity can be both "rewarding" and "punishing" to cats. Roberts implanted an electrode in the posterior hypothalamus of the brain and discovered that the animal could learn to turn on stimulation ("reward") and then turn it off (avoidance of "punishment"). The effect of dual reinforcement helps explain some of the contradictory results obtained in previous work on the punishment effects of self-stimulation.

The final reading of this section (19) is by James Olds, one of the pioneers in the study of self-stimulation. In this article, Olds explores satiation effects in self-stimulation of the brain. His results show no satiation effects for hypothalamic stimulation, but show marked effects for electrodes implanted in the telencephalon (in the septal and amygdaloid regions).[3]

Although these "exciting" lines of research have revolutionized the study of motivation, they are limited by the necessity of using infrahuman subjects. Care must be exercised in extrapolating such animal results to human beings. As in other areas of physiological psychology, students of motivation must wait until data from clinical cases of brain-injured human beings are available to corroborate animal findings.

15   physiological theory of drive*

Clifford T. Morgan

1. What does Morgan mean to imply by the phrase "central theory of drive"?

2. What are the functions of a "central motive state"?

[3] See the article by MacLean (1958) in Chapter 1.

* From *Psychology: A Study of a Science*, Study 1, Vol. 1, edited by S. Koch. Copyright © 1958, McGraw-Hill, Inc. Used by permission of McGraw-Hill Book Company.

[2] RAS is described in the article by French (1957) in Chapter 1.

3. What are the differences between Morgan's and Hull's concepts of "drive reduction"?

4. What direct and what indirect evidence does Morgan marshal in support of a central theory of drive?

5. What neural centers are known to be important in motivation?

6. How do the "sensory drives" fit into Morgan's scheme?

My task in this paper is to analyze my physiologically oriented theory of motivational mechanisms. This theory was presented most explicitly in *Physiological Psychology* (38), but certain aspects of it appear in research papers published before and afterward, as well as in the revision of *Physiological Psychology* (44) and in *Introduction to Psychology* (39). The theory has been restated and related to recent literature in a paper published in the 1957 *Nebraska Symposium on Motivation* (40).

The theory is a rather modest one, lacking many of the refinements and elegancies of more mature theories such as Hebb's (24) or such as have been elaborated in the field of learning (26). For that reason, some of the rubrics suggested for the systematic analysis appearing in this series of volumes do not fit this particular paper, but to the extent that it is appropriate, I shall follow the same general scheme of organization that has been employed in other papers.

background factors

The events of the 1930s form the backdrop for my physiological analysis of motivation, both because I took my undergraduate and graduate training during this period and because new physiological methods of studying motivational problems were making their ap-

pearance at this time. In my first three undergraduate years, my major studies were in the natural sciences and philosophy. Only in my senior year did I choose psychology as my field, and this because psychology seemed to offer the scientific approach of the natural sciences to the problems talked about in philosophy, religion, and the social sciences. Under the influence of Paul E. Fields, who recruited me into psychology, I became interested in the neo-behaviorism of Hull and Weiss. After reading the early papers of Hull on learning theory, I chose for my first research a problem in the effect of preliminary feeding on the anticipatory goal tendencies of rats running a maze (41). Among the results of this study were the findings that rats given a little food before running a maze increased their speed of locomotion and that fully fed rats would run it about as speedily as those on regular 24-hr. deprivation. Neither result jibed particularly well with the local theory of hunger then in vogue.

This theory had been argued eloquently by Walter B. Cannon in his chapter in the Murchison handbook of experimental psychology (17). In graduate school, where the handbook was the mainstay for seminars in comprehensive examinations, I took the trouble to consult some of the original literature cited by Cannon. Much of it did not seem to fit in with his notion of hunger as an experience arising from stomach contractions. He seemed to have trouble explaining the report by Wangensteen and Carlson (67) of the hunger reported by a gastrectomized patient and of such work as Montgomery's (37) in which dogs deprived of parotid secretions exhibited only a normal amount of thirst. Then, too, Adolph's work on thirst in fistulated dogs was going on a few blocks away at the Medical School campus. I saw this (2), and wondered how such data could possibly be explained in terms of a local theory of hunger and thirst.

My first experiments on the problem, done at that time, were suggested by Cannon's account (17) of the action of insulin on the contractility of the stomach. Research cited by him indicated that insulin increased stomach contractility and did this primarily by way of the vagus nerve. I therefore did a series of experiments in which hunger, as measured by food ingested, was studied under the influence of insulin injections, first in normal rats (42) and then in rats in which the vagus nerve had been sectioned (43). Although the vagotomized rats, as one might predict from knowing that vagotomy glutted the gut, did not behave exactly like normal rats, insulin nevertheless did cause them to increase their food intake, and this was difficult to explain with Cannon's theory. About the time these experiments were being written up for publication, Bash (8) independently published similar results except that he used an obstruction method rather than a Skinner box technique for measuring hunger motivation.

During this period, other investigators were publishing results that pointed to central factors in physiological motivation. Bard and his collaborators had shown that cats deprived of sensory innervation of the genitals were quite capable of sexual behavior (5) and that a center for sexual motivation existed in the brain stem (6). The fact that estrogenic hormones could induce heat so long as this "center" was intact led him to suggest (6) that sexual motivation is aroused by the erotization of the brain stem by sex hormones. Lashley (29) surveyed existing data on instinct and concluded that "physiologically all drives are no more than expressions of the activity of specific mechanisms" and that hormones "activate some central mechanism which maintains excitability and activity." From his studies of sexual behavior, Beach

(10) came to believe that "sexual arousal depends upon the creation and maintenance in the central nervous system of a condition analogous to Sherrington's central excitatory state" and to "postulate the existence of a Central Excitatory Mechanism." I had these various ideas in mind, as well as the facts on which they were based (see later section on Initial evidence) when I was writing the chapters on motivation in *Physiological Psychology* (38). I merely arranged the facts, and the inferences to be drawn from them, in an orderly scheme. At the time, the scheme had no name, but in order to have something brief to refer to throughout this paper, I shall call it the *central theory of drive*.

structure of the central theory

The central theory of drive attempts to provide a physiological explanation of the motivated behavior ordinarily considered to stem from physiological drives. Thus the term *motivated behavior* in this paper is restricted to behavior that is aroused and maintained by internal conditions within the body. For the most part, it refers to hunger, thirst, and sex. The problem is to state what these internal conditions are, how they are related to each other, and how they control motivated behavior. For our purposes, the term *drive* may be used to refer to any internal conditions that arouse and maintain behavior, either independently or in conjunction with external stimuli. *Motivated behavior*, by definition, is behavior impelled by a drive. *Need* will refer to any condition of deficit within the organism that impairs the health or efficiency of the organism. It is not, as we shall see, synonomous with drive. Restated in terms of these definitions, the purpose of the central theory is to understand the relation of need to drive, the nature of drive, and the physiological machinery through which drive regulates behavior.[1]

The central theory of drive stands in contrast to older peripheral theories (17). These assumed drive to consist of internal stimuli, such as dryness of the throat, contractions of the stomach, or tension in sexual organs. Having assumed this, they made little or no attempt to examine the events intervening between drive stimuli and behavior. Motivated behavior was considered to wax and wane with drive stimuli.[2] It is a premise of central theory that drives are aroused in other ways than by the stimulation of receptors and that they should be regarded as states in the nervous system that may be aroused and abated in a variety of ways.

Central motive state. To stress the central locus of these states, I proposed the concept of "central motive state" or cms for short (cf. Beach's Central Excitatory Mechanism, 10). Such a state is one of nervous activity in a system of centers and pathways concerned in one particular kind of motivation. Different drives involve different systems, but there may be, and probably is, considerable overlap of these systems. As originally postulated, a

central motive state has the following general properties:

1. Once a state is set up, it is regarded as persisting, at least for a time, without outside support from sensory inputs or other kinds of excitation. By reverberation, or perhaps by "tonus" supplied by other centers that are in constant activity, it can coast and perseverate in such a way that it does not depend directly on outside influences.

2. A central motive state predisposes the organism to react in certain ways to particular stimuli and not to react to others. If, for example, the central motive state concerns hunger, it sets or primes the organism to react by approaching certain odors, tastes, and textures and to ingest food having certain characteristics. Theoretically, there is no limit to this selectivity. It may prime an animal to accept (react by ingestion) salt and nothing else, or foods containing vitamin B, etc. It is only an empirical matter to determine the limits of selectivity much as one measures stimulus generalization in an experiment on sensory discrimination. The important point is that the cms functions as a selective valve or switch for certain S-R relationships and not others.

3. Besides being self-perpetuating and predisposing the organism to certain reactions to stimuli, the cms may also directly emit certain patterns of behavior. It is responsible for the general bodily activity that almost always precedes and accompanies other more specific forms of motivated behavior. In fact, by emitting general activity, the cms makes it possible for the organism to come into the vicinity of stimuli for which it is selectively primed to act. In addition, the cms may emit certain rather specific forms of behavior. A female cat in heat, for example, often emits distinctly sexual patterns, such as treading, rubbing, and crying, without being near a male cat or in the vicinity of sexually arousing

---

[1] Some of the contributors to this series of papers have been able to employ effectively the language of variables in describing the structure of their theories. After trying to do the same thing, I gave it up because the discussion becomes so cluttered with "intervening variables" and "dependent variables" that the facts are obscured and the reasoning confused. I have therefore chosen to present the system in the terms commonly used in physiological psychology, with only an occasional reference to "variables."

[2] Although some are inclined to use the term *stimulus* as any physical disturbance of the sense organs or the nervous system, I feel that our thinking can be kept clearer by restricting the term *stimulus* (as early psychologists did) to that which excites a sense organ. It is used in this way throughout this paper.

stimuli. The theory does not rule out the possibility that some of this "emitted" behavior is evoked by external or internal stimuli and consequently that it may be in part "released" behavior merely primed by the cms. By "emitted" behavior, the theory simply refers to behavior that is not elicited by any specific, obvious stimulus.

Arousal of drive. These are the general properties assigned to central motive states. The theory also deals with the conditions arousing and diminishing these states. In regard to arousal, it is admitted, as peripheral theorists would have it, that external or internal stimuli can and do arouse central motive states. A person in an environment that is too hot or too cold is motivated by external temperatures. Internal stimuli in the mouth and stomach undoubtedly do have motivating power and may affect the level of activity in the cms. On the other hand, it is postulated that drives such as hunger, thirst, and sex depend more on chemical and hormonal conditions of the blood than on such stimuli. It is held that humoral factors can directly activate the central nervous system, arousing central motive states without the operation of stimulus factors. Moreover, in most circumstances, they are a prior condition for such stimuli, for they determine whether the mouth will be dry or the stomach contract. In any case, if and when stimuli arouse central motive states, they represent only one factor, along with humoral and chemical factors[3] that can arouse drive.

Drive reduction. The theory, finally, attempts to explain the ways in which central motive states, once aroused, can be diminished or eliminated. This is the problem of "satisfac-

---

[3] To stress this possibility, I originally used the term "humoral motive factor" to refer to all chemical and hormonal conditions of the blood assumed to "erotize" the central nervous system.

tion" and, when considered in connection with learning theory, the problem of "reinforcement." It was assumed that there are several ways in which the "satisfaction" of a central motive state can take place. Just as the peripheral theorist would hold, the elimination of the stimulus or humoral motive factor which originally aroused the central motive state can reduce it. It is doubtful, however, whether the elimination of hunger, thirst, or sex drive takes place in this way.

Another possibility is that some humoral messenger, different from those arousing the drive, can directly reduce the cms. For example, when an organism eats food, some hormone that can act as an inhibitor on the cms may be liberated from the stomach or intestine (see 9).

Still a third possibility is that stimulation of receptors in the course of drive-instigated behavior may reduce the cms. For example, when a hungry rat starts out a cafeteria meal choosing sugar, then tires of it and turns to wheat (69), the "sweet" stimulation may be the factor that reduces selectively the part of the cms predisposing the rat to eat sugar.

Still another alternative is that the behavior resulting from central motive states may itself reduce these states. In this case, we might assume that the mere ingestion of food or water, as a behavioral act considered independently of its consequences or of its stimulus value, might terminate the central motive state. Drive reduced in this way would be like a clock running down (see 38, p. 443). (It would also be comparable to Skinner's reflex reserve.)

initial evidence for the theory

At the time the central theory was formulated, there was relatively little positive evidence for the states or factors assumed to be important in motivation, but there was some. The most cogent arguments for the theory were based partly on negative evidence and partly on circumstantial evidence. I shall consider these three kinds of evidence—negative, circumstantial, and positive—in turn.

Against peripheral theory. Negative evidence in this case refers to data that seemed to limit or disprove the peripheral theory of drive. Such evidence consisted of any phenomena in which motivated behavior seemed relatively independent of the peripheral stimulus factors assumed to be important in such theories.

In the field of hunger motivation, there were just a few cases in which hunger, as defined in terms of a craving for food or in terms of food ingestion, could be said to be in some degree independent of stomach contractions. The case study by Wangensteen and Carlson (67) previously mentioned was one. Then, within the space of two years three studies with rats appeared to confirm this finding. Tsang (66) completely removed the stomachs of rats and found that they still were as highly motivated to run a maze, overcome an obstruction, and as active at the time of feeding as normal animals. The only trouble with gastrectomized rats was that they could not eat as much at one time as normal animals and had to eat more frequently (as one might expect when there is no stomach in which to store food). The other two studies by Bash (8) and Morgan (43), already mentioned, obtained comparable results following section of the vagus nerve, which (presumably) reduced stomach motility and eliminated afferent messages from the stomach. Such studies made it clear that hunger drive could function largely unabated after the removal or reduction of peripheral events in the stomach.

Rather parallel research on the thirst drive

pointed in the same direction. Montgomery (37) had removed the salivary glands from dogs, thereby making their mouths chronically dry. Such dogs, however, had the same average intake of water as normal dogs, something one would not expect if dryness of the throat figured prominently in thirst drive. Then, Adolph (1, 2) and Bellows (12) came along with their studies of drinking behavior in fistulated dogs compared with normal animals. They worked with the other side of Montgomery's coin; letting ingested water run out a fistula rather than deposit in the stomach, they separated local sensory factors from the subsequent effects of water ingestion. Dogs prepared in this way and allowed *ad libitum* drinking drank barrels of water a day, despite the fact that this made their mouths about as wet as anything can get. The experiments by Adolph and by Bellows have other important aspects, which we will come to below, but their point, so far as the peripheral theory is concerned, was that thirst drive does not appear to depend upon local buccal stimulation.

Similar results had been obtained by Bard and his associates in the area of sexual motivation. Ball (4) found removal of the vagina and uterus, which might be expected to be sources of sensory stimulation, to have no effect on the sexual inclinations of the female rat in estrus. Bard (5) sectioned the sensory fibers innervating the cat's female genitalia without disrupting in the slightest the cat's mating behavior. And Root and Bard (53), after sectioning the lower afferent pathways of the spinal cord in the male cat, noted no decline in sexual aggressiveness. All these studies seem to lay to rest any ideas that erogenous stimulation is necessary for sexual motivation (though common experience indicates that such stimulation facilitates sexual arousal).

Indirect evidence. These three lines of experimental evidence argued against the peripheral theory of drive. By implication, they also provided circumstantial evidence for humoral and central factors in motivation. Such evidence was also to be found, however, in other quarters.

Perhaps the most compelling fact came from the work on sex hormones (10). By the middle 1930s, extracts of estrogen and androgens had become generally available to research workers, and dozens of experiments relating these hormones to sexual behavior soon appeared in the literature. In contrast to the negative results with sensory factors in sex drive, these experiments made it clear that sex drive depended almost entirely on the level of sex hormones in the blood. In female animals (at that time, mostly rodents and carnivora) estrogenic hormone was a *sine qua non* for sexual behavior. In male animals, the dependence was not so all-or-none, but it was nevertheless great. Since there was not then, nor is there now, any clear evidence for the mediation of this effect through sensory structures, we could only presume that the hormones exerted their influence, as Bard suggested, through the "erotization" of the nervous system.

There was also presumptive evidence that hormones might play a role in hunger (9). It had been shown that stomach muscle, completely detached from the stomach and transplanted elsewhere, began contracting when the intact stomach did—this without any neural innervation. Such muscle also stopped contracting after sugar had been introduced into the intact stomach, although sugar in the blood had no such effect (44, pp. 449–450). Such effects presumably could be accomplished only through a humoral mediator. And if such an agent could directly control muscular tissue, why not nervous tissue too?

Perhaps the most puzzling data being published in the 1930s were those on specific hungers. Richter (51) had already reported extensively on his cafeterial feeding experiments, and Young (69) similarly had described in detail the food preferences of the rat. Although subsequent research (44, pp. 395–396) requires us to make some reservations about the "wisdom of the body," it was clear then, and still is, that animals often can detect, select, and ingest in the biologically appropriate quantities a dozen or more rather specific dietary materials. And when they are deficient in any one of these materials, they avidly crave it and take it in preference to other things offered to them. Such results pointed to many hungers, not one, and only humoral factors seemed sufficiently different to convey enough "information" to the nervous system to explain such "wisdom." (The theory that humoral factors altered sensory thresholds seemed rather lame at the time and has since been contradicted.)

In the case of thirst, Adolph (2) had demonstrated that water left in the stomach for only a few minutes could fully reduce it. Fistulated dogs subjected to severe dehydration stopped showing any interest in water (at least for a while) when water sufficient to offset the dehydration lay in the stomach for 15 minutes. Since little water was absorbed in that time, something else must have "told the nervous system to stop drinking." That something else, by inference, would be some sort of hormonal message to the nervous system.

For central theory. So much for the negative and circumstantial evidence. The positive evidence for humoral factors directly activating central motive states was sparse, but there were a few straws in the wind. It had long been known that chemical conditions of the blood, later identified as increased carbon dioxide, directly affect respiratory centers of the medulla. If carbon dioxide can erotize simple behavior patterns, why could not other substances erotize more complex patterns?

In the case of sexual behavior of the female cat, Bard (6) located a region in the midbrain and rear of the hypothalamus that was critical in the appearance of sex drive. With this region intact *and* injection of appropriate hormones, cats could be brought into heat. With either of these conditions lacking, they could not. It was these results that led Bard to suggest the idea of "erotization" of the nervous system. About the same time, Ranson (49) established what we now call the "waking center," a region in the posterior hypothalamus where lesions cause somnolence. It was not until some years later that other motivational centers[4] were added to this list—a "sleep center," "hunger center," "starvation center," and "thirst center,"—but this early work established two such regions and made it seem likely that relatively specific systems (or "central excitatory mechanisms") might be found for the physiological drives.

recent developments

In the years elapsing since the explicit formulation of the central theory of drive, research relevant to the theory has poured forth in ever increasing volume. In general, the research supports and extends the theory, giving it a more solid foundation than it had when it was first presented.

Guiding influences on research. Though much of this research was guided vaguely by the feeling of many experimenters that humoral and central factors in motivation would prove to be important, the research probably was not directed specifically by intentions to

[4] The term *center* is used here to mean any region or combination of regions in the nervous system participating in a certain function. The problem of centers is discussed later in this paper.

test the theory, in the sense that research, say, in the field of learning has so often been designed to test specific predictions generated by theory. Rather, in this case, there seem to have been three somewhat different guiding influences on such research.

One, interestingly enough, comes not from physiological theory per se but rather from neo-behavioristic learning theory. Hull's formal learning theory (26), of course, leaned heavily on the concept of reinforcement. Although no definite commitments were made about the nature of reinforcement, it was implied by Hull, and explicitly stated by others (45), that reinforcement consisted of drive reduction. (Some said need reduction.) Several learning theorists, particularly Neal E. Miller and his students, (33, 34, 35) interested themselves in this proposition and attempted to analyze physiologically the nature of reinforcement. In the course of their work, they have studied animals with hypothalamic lesions in hunger "centers," animals prepared with stomach fistulas, animals motivated by centrally placed electrodes, and the effects of preloading the stomach with various materials on the drive level of animals. These various experiments all contribute, as we shall see below, data relevant to central theory.

A second group of experiments bearing on central theory has come from neurophysiologists who have not concerned themselves particularly with the over-all problem of understanding motivation. They have merely pressed their search for clues to the functions of various structures of the brain. In the course of their search, they have discovered new "centers" and new phenomena, which they promptly followed up with systematic explorations. In this way, additional "centers" in the hypothalamus for hunger, thirst, and sleep have been found, and the role of the reticular formation as an activation system has been uncovered and explored. These findings have confirmed and extended the idea of central "excitatory" or motivating mechanisms.

A third group of experiments was probably more influenced by the implications of central theory than the other two groups. These experiments were done by investigators whose interests and training were primarily in physiological psychology. Appreciating the phenomena turned up by experiments in the first two groups, they have attempted to explore and analyze in detail the meaning of these phenomena for motivational theory. I refer particularly to work by Pfaffmann (48), Stellar (60), and their respective colleagues. They have studied the effect of changes in the humoral system on preference and aversion for dietary materials, and Stellar's group has also analyzed the mode of action of the hypothalamic centers concerned in hunger.

Though it is interesting to observe how different groups of investigators contribute knowledge in an area for their own individual reasons, more important is the net effect of their work on our knowledge of motivational mechanisms. This, I believe, strengthens considerably the tenets of the so-called central theory of physiological drives. In the next few paragraphs, I shall review their experiments, showing in each case the bearing of the experiment on central theory. I shall begin at the periphery and move toward the central nervous system.

Peripheral factors in drive. When Richter had established the existence of several specific hungers in the rat, he proposed a peripheral basis for such hungers (51). This was in keeping with the thinking of the times, which was strongly flavored by peripheral theory. More specifically, Richter proposed that changes in the internal environment were reflected in altered taste thresholds, and that these accounted for the animal's preference for the foods that met the needs of its internal environment. He implied that there might be some general hunger drive regulated by any deficit in the internal environment, but that the drive was "directed" toward specific foods merely because the animal was more sensitive to certain tastes than to others. In support of this view, Richter had the fact that animals in dire need of salt showed preferences for salt in much lower concentrations than did normal animals.

This particular theory has now been tested and found wanting. With electrodes in the gustatory nerve of the rat, Pfaffmann and Bare (48) were able to obtain physiological thresholds for salt solutions placed on the rat's tongue. Separately they (7) checked Richter's observation that adrenalectomized rats had very low preference thresholds, while normal rats had high ones. But they found that the physiological thresholds measured electrically for these two kinds of rats were just the same, and were precisely of the order of preference thresholds obtained for the adrenalectomized, salt-deficient rat. These findings were also checked out by Carr (18) in a discrimination experiment. When forced to detect minimal concentrations of salt by being shocked for doing otherwise, normal rats yielded thresholds for salt that were the same as those of adrenalectomized rats. From such interlocking experiments, only one conclusion could be drawn: salt deficiency in adrenalectomy does not change an animal's sensitivity to salt; it merely changes the craving for salt. Thus the idea that humoral factors altered motivation through peripheral taste channels was in this case ruled out.

That is not to say, however, that there is never a peripheral mechanism for humoral influences. It seems possible that in some cases a hormonal or chemical condition of the blood may have some local effect that results in peripheral stimulation. Lehrman (30), for example, has studied the parental regurgitation-feeding of the ring dove induced by the hormone prolactin. At the same time that prolactin induces such feeding, it also causes engorgement of the crop, and Lehrman suggests (though he did not prove) that engorgement of the crop may act as the stimulus for regurgitation-feeding. Beach and Levinson (11) make a similar suggestion concerning genital papillae. They note that the number of genital papillae in castrated rats is closely related to levels of androgen supplied to the rat, and also that changes in the genital papillae correlate with sexual performance. From these correlations, they propose that "the genital papillae may act as accessory sensory structures, by stimulating tactile nerve endings that lie beneath them." Hence it may be possible for humoral factors to have an influence on drive by a route leading through effectors and receptors, but there is no reason to believe that this is either the only route or the major one.

Humoral factors in drive. The fact that humoral factors somehow influence drive, and often quite rapidly and markedly, has been demonstrated in a great variety of recent experiments. These experiments may be divided into two general groups: those in which the dependent variable is rate of learning or extinction, and those in which simple preference between two materials, or the rate of ingesting such materials, is the dependent variable. Both types of experiment have made use of the stomach tube or fistula for getting food into the stomach without the animal's eating or drinking it, although in some cases the material has been introduced directly into the internal environment by hypodermic needle.

Those of the first type, using rate of learn-

ing as a measure of effect, have issued mostly from Miller's laboratories at Yale. Through a permanent fistula, fluid food has been delivered directly into the stomach whenever the rat performed a correct response (28). The general problem has been to determine how reinforcement administered in this way compares with normal reinforcement. Although there are many interesting results of these experiments, two facts stand out: food administered directly into the stomach is reinforcing, though probably not as much so as food ingested in the normal way. When nonnutritive materials are introduced into the stomach, the result is not one of reinforcement, and distention of the stomach by a balloon is negatively reinforcing (13, 34). Although it is risky to interpret such results until we understand better the nature of reinforcement and its relation to learning, they indicate that mere stimulation of the stomach is not enough to change whatever must be changed to effect learning and that there are some specific humoral effects of food that are important in bringing about this change.

The second group of experiments, with preloading of the stomach, points even more clearly in this direction (32, 60). With the single stimulus method developed by Stellar and Hill (59), it is possible to measure relatively small changes in rate of ingestion, which presumably reflect drive level, within a very few minutes after loading the stomach with any desired material. Several different materials have been used prior to animals' drinking solutions of salt and sugar. Both the kind of preloaded material and its concentration make an important difference in rates of ingestion immediately following preloading. And the striking thing about the results is that they follow so quickly upon preloading, long before the material in the stomach has had a chance to be absorbed into the blood stream.

McCleary (32) has suggested a specific theory to account for such results, but for our purposes they seem to mean that some humoral messenger is released into the blood, or in some cases water is withdrawn from the blood thereby changing its chemical balance, and that this directly modifies activity in a "central motive state." Confirming this interpretation is the fact that substances injected directly into the blood stream cause about the same effects as the same substances placed in the stomach (60).

Neural centers. No less important for the central theory than these experiments on sensory and humoral factors are the increasing number of studies on drive "centers" in the central nervous system. In the early studies of the 1930s, the only such centers that had been positively identified were those for "waking" and sex. Since then, several more have been discovered and studied at some length.

Logically, though not chronologically, we should begin with the reticular activating system (RAS), which has recently been getting so much attention (31). This system, extending through much of the brain stem between thalamus and pons, is set into activity by incoming sensory stimuli. Through its own pathways to the hypothalamus, thalamus, and cortex, it in turn sets up activity in these other centers. Some of the centers feed back impulses to the RAS, thus setting up a reverberatory system that is self-sustaining unless it is interrupted by other influences. Lesions in this system are followed by somnolence, and the system quite clearly functions as a general activator of many processes in the brain. Its role has been compared to that of a biasing voltage in an amplifier, for on its level of activity seems to depend the responsiveness of other systems of the brain. In the original language of the central theory, this RAS would seem to be the most general kind of "central motive state" determining the predisposition of the animal to react to stimuli and perhaps to develop more specific "central motive states."

Besides the "waking" center (49) first discovered in the posterior hypothalamus (not far from RAS), another center farther forward for "sleep" has recently been described by Nauta (46). So far it has been confirmed only in the rat. Destruction of this center is followed by insomnia and incessant activity, resulting finally in death due to exhaustion. It is interesting, according to Nauta, that when both the "waking" and "sleep" centers are destroyed, the sequel is somnolence, the same as the destruction of the "waking" center. This finding fits in with what is becoming a general rule, that when centers work in opposing pairs the destruction of both has the same outcome as the destruction of the "active," not the "inhibitory," center. In this case, the "waking" center seems to provide positive influences for waking, and the "sleep" center appears to inhibit or reduce these influences.

A similar pair of centers has now been demonstrated for hunger. In the ventromedial nucleus of the hypothalamus near the midline is a pair whose destruction causes hyperphagia (15, 61). Rats in this condition eat incessantly, putting away several times their normal intake and gaining weight rapidly until they reach about three times normal size. A little lateral to these centers whose destruction causes hyperphagia is another pair with opposite functions (62). Injuring them electrolytically produces animals that have no interest in food and eventually starve to death if they are not maintained by stomach feeding or "trained" to eat again (62). Both conditions, of hyperphagia and of aphagia, are dramatic and unequivocal.

It would not be surprising, of course, if we should encounter a similar pair of centers (really a pair of a pair) involved in thirst. It once seemed as though a "thirst" center had been found when certain lesions in the hypothalamus caused animals to drink inordinate amounts of water. It later was established, however, that such lesions had these effects, not because of injury to the hypothalamus, but because they also involved the posterior pituitary gland (50). This gland, it turned out, secretes an antidiuretic hormone normally aiding in the retention of water in the body; without it, the animal becomes dehydrated, and this is why it drinks. As of this writing, we still have not found centers whose *destruction* causes changes in`drinking behavior.

Quite dramatic, however, are two pilot experiments in which *stimulation* of the hypothalamus causes animals to drink. In one such experiment (3), a permanent pipette was imbedded in the head of a goat so that its tip was in the hypothalamus. Squirting in very small quantities of salt solution to stimulate directly the hypothalamus caused the goat to drink, and drink a lot. (This experiment, incidentally, is the only one so far to confirm directly the proposition of central theory that direct chemical stimulation of brain can "erotize" a "central motive state.") In another experiment (22), an electrode similarly placed in the hypothalamus of the rat caused it to drink when weak currents were administered through the electrode. These are preliminary experiments and need to be followed up, but they do indicate that certain restricted regions of the brain are concerned in thirst drive.

A more detailed review and discussion of experiments of this kind, as well as an elaboration of the central theory of drive, may be found in a recent paper by Stellar (58). All the evidence that is accumulating continues to point to central mechanisms directly controlled by humoral factors in the internal environment.

some implications of central theory

In this section I shall discuss some of the conclusions to be drawn from the central theory of drive and also the relation of the theory to other recent developments in the general field of motivation. In this way, I hope both to enlarge the scope of application of the theory and to show how it can assist those engaged in building theories of learning, motivation, and behavioral development.

Drives and needs. One of the important implications of central theory, and one that is brought out by some of the work just reviewed, is that we must clearly distinguish between needs, drives, and satisfiers. A drive, regarded as that which gives an impetus to behavior, is an activity or state of the central nervous system (a cms). A need, defined as some sort of deficit, may or may not give rise to a drive, and drive does not necessarily arise from a need. Thirst drive, for example, is most closely correlated with the degree of dehydration of bodily tissues (21), and it would seem that the dehydration of regions of the brain can directly arouse the corresponding drive. In the case of hunger, however, some needs arouse drive and others do not. An animal deprived of vitamin D, for example, seems to have no specific hunger for vitamin D, nor any great degree of drive associated with the deficiency (68). On the other hand, mild deprivation of vitamin B, or of proteins (55, 56), is accompanied by specific hungers for these substances. Sexual drive, on the other hand, cannot be said to be due to a need, for no lack accompanies it. It correlates well, at least in lower animals, with level of hormones, and these, rather than any deficits, arouse drive. Hence needs do not always arouse drives, and drives are not always aroused by needs. Some learning theorists have come to recognize this distinction and are now using the term drive, rather than need, in their analysis of reinforcement (33).

It is necessary also to distinguish between need reduction and satisfaction. (Satisfaction is used here to refer to drive reduction.) The satisfaction or reduction of drives does not necessarily depend on the reduction of the need giving rise to the drive, nor even to changes in the factor that aroused drive. In the case of hunger, for example, it appears that chemical messengers different from those involved in arousing drive and generated by consummatory responses may be the important factors in reducing drive. In other cases, mere sensory stimulation or behavior resulting from the operation of a drive may reduce it. Sex drive is perhaps the best example of this. Although sex hormones play a crucial role in sexual drive, the act of copulation and its concomitant neural discharge reduce, at least temporarily, the sex drive. This, of course, is not due to any reduction in sex hormones nor, so far as we know or can imagine, to any other chemical messengers. (Below I shall consider in detail the role of sensory and behavioral factors in drive and drive reduction.) The distinction, then, between needs, drives, and the events that reduce drive is one important implication of central theory.

Exploratory and sensory drives. In recent years, research has brought out several facts and generated other theories that need to be considered in the light of the central theory of drives. These developments may be classified broadly into two general categories: one concerns curiosity, exploration, manipulation, and activity; the other concerns instinctive behavior and particularly the concept of "releasers" given to us by the European ethologists.

Fifteen or twenty years ago, when central theory was being formulated, psychologists generally regarded such things as "interest" and "curiosity" as derived or learned somehow from basic, physiological motives. Central theory, therefore, took no especial account of such motives and was restricted to what were then the primary physiological drives—hunger, thirst, sex. Now it is becoming clear that such drives constitute only one class of drive, which might better be called "visceral drives" because they are concerned directly or indirectly with visceral events. To this we must add another general class, one perhaps that is more important in understanding human behavior than the class of visceral drives. In keeping with the distinction neurological scientists make between visceral and somatic functions, we might call these the "somatic drives."

It is not yet clear how somatic drives may be subdivided and further classified, if indeed they can be, so we shall not try. The kinds of data, however, that may be subsumed under somatic drives are as follows: first is what Montgomery (36) has called exploratory drive, and Berlyne (14) curiosity drive. This is an impetus to move around in one's environment and to be stimulated by it. Montgomery seems to have demonstrated beyond reasonable doubt that this sort of drive can exist independently of other drives and that it is sufficiently strong to motivate and maintain learned behavior. Harlow (23) has similarly shown a manipulative drive in monkeys, a drive not obviously derived or learned from other drives, to handle, manipulate, and "solve" puzzles. Closely related, secondly, is considerable evidence for "sensory drives," drives to see and experience the environment. Harlow (23), for example, has reported experiments in which a "peek" at the environment is sufficient incentive for a monkey to learn other discriminations, ordinarily formed on the basis of physiological rewards. And Thompson and Solomon (64) have demonstrated convincingly that rats are interested enough in their environment to form visual discriminations without being motivated or rewarded in any other way. Some learning theorists have not given up hope that they may find some way to explain such facts in terms of derived or learned drives. To me, however, it seems clear that we must recognize unlearned somatic drives, that are just as primary and underived as the more familiar visceral drives.

The second major development, mentioned above, has been contributed by the work of European ethologists on instinctive behavior. Much of this work is with physiological drives such as hunger and thirst and presents no special problems for physiological theory. The work, however, emphasizes and dramatizes the role of the stimulus as a "releaser" of instinctive movements (65). Certain reactions are preset or primed by drives so that they are released when the appropriate stimulus is present. I like this concept because it is precisely what I was trying to say in presenting the central theory when I wrote of "central motive states" priming or predisposing the organism to react to certain stimuli. The ethologists, using instinctive behavior, have given us many nice examples of this sort of predisposition and a good word, "releaser," to refer to it.

In their work with releasers, however, the ethologists have supplied an additional notion not anticipated or adequately dealt with in central theory. This is the idea that the "threshold" for releasing an instinctive movement is raised by "exercise." They find, for example, that it is more difficult to release the attack reaction of the male stickleback fish to the red belly of another male immediately

after the reaction has occurred than in the normal, "rested" animal. And they have other examples. The general point is that the ability of a releaser stimulus to release a reaction depends upon how recently the same reaction has been released.

Placing these two general developments side by side, we may say that the work of Montgomery, Harlow, and others gives us the concept of "sensory hunger" or some drive to experience the environment, and the work of the ethologists indicates that sensory experience and its effects may itself be drive reducing. These points are important ones to be dealt with by central theory. Before attempting to do that, we may note recent work with sensory deprivation, which fits in here (25, 63). Both animals and people whose sensory environment is restricted show signs of deficit comparable to those of the hungry or thirsty organism. Only in this case the drive expresses itself as an avid interest in, and "hunger" for, sensory experience. The research appears to demonstrate rather powerful "sensory" drives, which are ordinarily kept in such reasonable balance that we do not notice them.

Origin of sensory drives. If there be "sensory drives," as I believe there are, two things are implied: first, that drives (cms) build up because of a lack of sensory stimulation, and secondly, that sensory stimulation can reduce these drives. Actually, these are merely two sides of the same coin, for one could hardly be true without the other also being true. Both implications, however, raise additional questions. Why should drives arise because of a lack of sensory stimulation? There are two possible general answers to this question.

One is that a so-called sensory drive really is an activity drive in the sense that lack of activity in an organism whose nervous system is in continuous activity builds up a tendency for activity to be "released." In this case, sensory stimulation would be "needed" only because it releases this activity. Such a proposition is difficult, if not impossible, to test directly, for it requires us somehow to separate the effects of stimulation from those of activity although the two are inextricably bound together in the organism's structure and function. Recent research on activity, however, tends to support the idea. Campbell and Sheffield (16), studying general activity in rats, found that it waxed and waned with the amount of sensory stimulation. In experiments in which certain lesions of the nervous system were followed by augmented activity (27), the activity depended upon the level of external environmental stimulation. In certain other experiments (54), however, a methodical pacing following lesions in a restricted area of the monkey's frontal lobe did not seem to depend upon environmental stimuli. It is probably true, therefore, that sensory drives may be due in part to activity drives that require stimuli for the release of the activity.

The second possibility for "explaining" sensory drives is to assume that sensory drives or sensory hunger may develop without reference to activity, merely because of the interplay of events in the nervous system. This possibility receives some support from everyday observation of human behavior, for individuals with rather low activity drives may have strong sensory drives. Witness the workingman who spends the evening reading the paper and watching television without stirring from his easy chair, and also the enormous amount of "looking" that people do in reading, movies, touring, etc.—while activity is resisted or kept to a minimum. From a physiological point of view, moreover, this possibility is not unreasonable. Internal stimuli are at all times bombarding the organism's afferents, pouring impulses into the brain and particularly the reticular activating system. Impulses

leaving the RAS take a different route to the cerebral cortex than those in the direct afferents and there are neurophysiological reasons, which I will not go into, for believing that these two sorts of impulses must somehow be coordinated (31). One can think then of drive states being set up in the brain by internal stimuli and perhaps by the internal rhythms of the brain, and of these particular drive states being reduced only by sensory stimulation. At present, such a possibility is somewhat hazy, but electrophysiological research now in progress may clear it up in the not too distant future.

Sensory stimulation and drive reduction. The idea that stimuli may be drive reducing in and of themselves is one that has not heretofore been considered very seriously; yet it has interesting possibilities for a theory of motivation. It is particularly applicable to some of the phenomena of food preference, described by Young, which are otherwise quite baffling. Young (69, 70) has shown that a hungry animal has a hierarchy of food preferences. When first put in a feeding situation with several choices before it, it may select sugar and eat this for a while. After a few minutes, it may turn to protein, and then later to fat, or salt, or some other dietary component. Put another way, the animal shows several different specific hungers at the same meal and in rapid succession. The time involved is so short that it is hard to believe any change in the internal environment could account for changes in preference. If it is assumed, however, that mere stimulation with one type of food gradually reduces the drive related to that food, the phenomenon is readily explained. In order to test such a possibility, however, it would be necessary to combine the techniques of the esophageal fistula with those of preference testing so that the effects of sensory stimulation could be separated from those of the internal environment. At this writing, such experiments have not been carried out.

For sensory stimulation to be capable of reducing drive, it would be necessary to assume some sort of inhibitory influences on central motive states, and not merely a reduction in whatever it is that builds up drive in the first place. Such influences, however, are already implied by the conclusion, stated earlier, that humoral messengers different from those generating a drive can reduce the drive. Moreover, it has already been well demonstrated in the case of sleep and hunger that there are pairs of centers in the brain, one of which is "excitatory" and the other "inhibitory." Hence there is no physiological reason why sensory stimulation may not "inhibit" and thus reduce drive strength.

Sensory regulation of drive. While on the subject of the role played by stimuli in regulating drive, there are a few other points that ought to be made in passing. First of all, Hebb has emphasized the steering and cue functions of stimuli in motivated behavior (25). The motivated animal, he points out, is steered or directed in its behavior by stimuli that it would otherwise not heed. This, I think, is another way of describing the releaser function of stimuli. If certain stimuli selectively release behavior under the influence of drive, this is the same thing as saying that they steer behavior or act as cues.

Secondly, it is quite clear from experiments on the nervous system, that no increase in drive level can ever be considered independently of the releaser functions of stimuli. Hypothalamic lesions, for example, that produce hyperphagia do not indiscriminately increase an animal's hunger for all foods under all conditions. Teitelbaum has made this point convincingly in a series of experiments on what hyperphagic animals will and will not

eat (61). He followed up on an experiment by Miller et al. (35) in which it was demonstrated that hyperphagic animals were not so hyperphagic when they had to do some work to get their food rather than eat it freely. Teitelbaum found that hyperphagics are more finicky about their food than normal animals when they are presented with foods of unusual texture or bitter taste. He concluded that the sensory aspects of the food were quite important in whether or not they were hyperphagic. Stated another way, his results show that increased hunger following hypothalamic lesions is largely a "release" phenomenon but limited to certain stimulus situations.

Finally, in considering the relation of stimulation to drives, we must recognize that stimuli sometimes "amplify" drives as well as release drive-primed behavior or reduce drives. Feeding a rat a little food increases its speed of running and, presumably, its level of motivation (41). In the case of sex drive, stimuli associated with sex objects and with the erogenous zones enhance the intensity of sex motivation—a fact so well known that it needs no experimental demonstration. Though this paper has steered clear of the problem of reinforcement because it is one that would take it too far afield, the fact that stimuli amplify drives and yet can serve as reinforcers (57) is one that needs to be seriously considered by theorists who try to define reinforcement in terms of drive reduction.

some additional comments on central theory

In a sense, all of this paper is an attempt to evaluate critically the status of the central theory of motivation, and the theory, in my opinion, comes off well. Recent research has on the whole more than lived up to the expectations that central theory led us to entertain. We have had to give sensory factors more credit than we did originally, but only as regulators of drive, not as the instigators or sources of it. Otherwise, research has continued to uncover specific physiological mechanisms, both humoral and central, which at first were mere speculations based on fragments of evidence. We now are fully justified, it would seem, in accepting the central theory as a satisfactory scheme for encompassing the physiological facts of motivation.

In this concluding section, I should like to consider some special problems raised by the theory and also its relationship to psychological theory in general. The section will consequently be a potpourri, but only in this way can many of the points be included that are to be covered in this series of papers but that in this case did not merit more extended treatment.

Central neural activities. First a comment on the use of the term *central motive state*. When the central theory was first presented, this term was employed primarily as a teaching and heuristic device, because it served to emphasize central, rather than peripheral, activities in physiological motivation. I have used it relatively little throughout this paper because it is really synonomous with drive, if one understands drive in the physiological sense to be those central neural activities that give rise to behavior. Once this concept is established, it is probably just as well to avoid using such a vague term as central motive state.

Another problem involved in this area is an old one. How is one to talk about the function of different regions of the nervous system? Is it proper to refer to "centers" for this and that? Many physiological psychologists avoid this term because it smacks of old faculty psychology and phrenology, which implied a neat packaging of functions into pigeonholes of the brain. The modern neurologist, however, manages to use the term "center" to mean nothing more than a place containing cell bodies arranged in one or more nuclei and participating in one or more functions. It does not mean that this is the *only* region concerned in this function or even that this region has only one function. (Sophisticated scientists ought to take it for granted that such neat packages of functions or variables are never found in the real world.) Thus, in using the term "center" throughout this paper, I have meant to indicate that a region or a place in the nervous system was distinctively, but not exclusively, implicated in a particular function.

Speaking of motivational functions of centers, Hebb has raised the question whether the hypothalamic centers involved in motivation really represent motivational mechanisms (25). His criterion for answering the question is whether or not these centers "energize other mechanisms." If one is looking for a *single* source of energy, the answer is probably "no." For these centers certainly do not energize behavior all by themselves. Undoubtedly systems, not centers, are required for such energizing. Probably all motivational systems depend generally on activities in other parts of the brain and perhaps more specifically on the reticular activating system. Moreover, they involve more than just one specific region of the brain. Respiration, for example, which has a crucial center in the medulla, whose destruction is lethal unless the organism is put in an iron lung, has several centers including a region in the frontal lobe of the cerebral cortex. Hyperphagia, in moderate degrees, can be produced by lesions of the cerebral cortex (again frontal lobes) as well as by lesions in the hypothalamus (52, 54). And there are other examples. The point is that the "central excitatory mechanisms," as Beach calls them, consist of several "centers" associated in a complex system. It appears, however, that in certain cases, particularly those for hunger, thirst, and sleep, the hypothalamic centers are the crucial ones in their respective systems.

General properties of the central theory. Turning now to more general considerations of the theory, it is probably plain to the reader that the theory is not a formal, hypothetico-deductive system. It has no explicit axioms, postulates, or theorems, nor does it make any specific predictions about what will happen under such and such circumstances. It is rather a descriptive system that attempts to arrange in a coherent scheme the known facts about the physiological basis of motivation and to provide hooks on which to hang new facts as they are generated or discovered in subsequent research. It is more like the scheme a man might develop if, unfamiliar with engines, he were given the task of figuring out how an automobile works. By puttering and trying first one thing then another, he would eventually discover what the fuel is, how it is mixed with air, how it is conveyed to the engine, discharged by spark, and so on through the differential and steering gear. He would gradually develop a description of the events taking place in the operation of the automobile. That is what we are doing, I think, in the case of physiological events in motivated behavior.

Whether such a physiological theory will, or should, eventually be elaborated into a formal system, I do not know. If so, it will probably depend in large part on the development of satisfactory formal systems in neighboring areas. Behavior theorists will have to provide systems that account for behavior, and especially motivated behavior, before it will be possible to incorporate the central theory, which is basically a physiological explanation, into a more formal scheme. Not being optimistic about the short-term success of efforts to devise a satisfactory formal behavior theory, I have my reservations about the contingent possibility of devising a formal physiological theory of motivation. Certainly there is much to be done in straightforward empirical research, following up leads we already have, before it will be feasible or profitable to attempt a rigorous, formal system.

Since formality and rigor are part and parcel of any quantitative theory, it follows that the central theory is far from being a quantitative theory. To be sure, most of the facts upon which the theory was based are quantitative facts, and techniques for the measurement of both physiological and behavioral events in motivation are becoming increasingly refined. So far, however, it is hardly possible to tie together quantitatively such closely related measures of motivation as rate of free eating and rate of instrumental responses to obtain food, let alone establish any more complex mathematical relationships between motivational phenomena. More empirical research, of the same type that has characterized the last few decades, on the qualitative conditions under which motivational phenomena take place is necessary before we are ready to consider putting any quantitative terms into our theory.

For the foreseeable future, I suspect that we will see the present outlines being filled in by experiments that resolve the sorts of problems that have been raised in this paper. More "centers" will be found, some of them at higher levels in the brain, the general functions of these centers in relation to each other will be described, the role of stimuli as releasers will be studied in more detail, the question of activity and its relation to environmental stimuli will be straightened out, the role of stimuli as "satisfiers" or inhibitors will be explicated, the particular humoral factors concerned in such drives as hunger and thirst will be ferreted out, and perhaps the exact way in which such factors "erotize" the brain will be worked out. These, in any event, are the kinds of problems toward which current research is being directed, and they probably need to be solved to make central theory explicit enough to quantify it, formalize it, and relate it to other theoretical endeavors.

Relation to other theories. To wind up this paper, I shall make a few brief comments about the relation of central theory of drive to theory in other areas of psychology. The point at which the central theory and neo-behavioristic learning theory most clearly come in contact is on the problem of reinforcement. Although Hullian theorists have staked much of their theory on the idea that reinforcement (as an intervening variable) represents a reduction in drive strength, my guess is that some combination of Tolman's and Guthrie's views will turn out to be more nearly correct. It seems most likely to me that drive level only determines what an organism will do (or what behavior will be released) and thus determines the acts that will be terminal in a series, or conversely those that are less likely to occur again. This has so far proved to be a difficult issue to settle, largely because one cannot find ways of separating reinforcement per se from the releaser functions of stimuli. It is possible, however, that further physiological work on the mechanisms of motivation may contribute to its solution. Certainly some of the work done by Miller and his associates on the nature of reinforcement has contributed information of value for central theory.

The possibility, finally, that somatic drives —sensory hunger, curiosity, exploratory drive, and manipulative drives—are built-in physiological mechanisms has important implications for personality theory. If it is characteristic of people that they are motivated to explore, manipulate, and experience their environment, then personality theory need not indulge in any great gyrations to explain the seemingly complex motives found in people. The problem addressed by "functional autonomy," for example, largely disappears through the "canalization" of built-in physiological drives. This is putting the matter too simply, perhaps, but the point is that the more we find included in the physiological realm of motives, the less difficult is the job of the personality theorist. Consequently, in time, these two areas of theory are likely to have a better speaking acquaintance than they do at present.

As a postscript, I ought to mention why I have omitted from discussion a topic that many readers might have expected to find here. This is the topic of emotion. In explaining central theory in 1943 (38), I brushed it off quickly by saying simply that emotion follows the same rules as other kinds of motivation. By this I meant that emotional drives have a central locus, that they perseverate as other drives do, and that they prime certain reactions to certain stimuli. Such a statement still seems to be justified. In recent years, we have witnessed an upsurge of research on central motivational mechanisms. (It indicates, incidentally, that there are both excitatory and inhibitory systems of the brain imposing their influences on the more basic hypothalamic centers.) Little of this work, however, has a direct bearing on the concepts of central theory, and most of it is so tied up with problems in reinforcement, anxiety, and other aspects of learned behavior that I felt that it would unnecessarily complicate this paper to undertake to discuss it. The exciting work of Olds and Milner (47) on self-stimulation has not been discussed, partly for this reason and partly because the mechanism of the self-reinforcement effect has not been analyzed in sufficient detail to interpret it within the framework of the present discussion. The same is true for the avoidance learning described for shocks applied electrically deep within the brain (19).

references

1. Adolph. E. F. Measurements of water drinking in dogs. *Amer. J. Physiol.*, 1939, **125**, 75–86.

2. Adolph, E. F. *Physiological regulations.* Lancaster, Pa.: Jaques Cattell Press, 1943.

3. Anderson, B. The effect of injections of hypertonic NaCl solutions into different parts of the hypothalamus of goats. *Acta Physiol. Scand.*, 1953, **28**, 188–201.

4. Ball, Josephine. Sex behavior of the rat after removal of the uterus and vagina. *J. comp. Psychol.*, 1934, **18**, 419–422.

5. Bard, P. The effects of denervation of the genitalia on the oestrual behavior of cats. *Amer. J. Physiol.*, 1935, **113**,·5.

6. Bard, P. The hypothalamus and sexual behavior. *Res. Publ. Ass. nerv. ment. Dis.*, 1940, **20**, 551–579.

7. Bare, J. K. The specific hunger for sodium chloride in normal and adrenalectomized white rats. *J. comp. physiol. Psychol.*, 1949, **42**, 242–253.

8. Bash, K. W. An investigation into a possible organic basis for the hunger drive. *J. comp. Psychol.*, 1939, **28**, 109–134.

9. Bash, K. W. Contribution to a theory of the hunger drive. *J. comp. Psychol.*, 1939, **28**, 137–160.

10. Beach, F. A. Analysis of factors involved in the arousal, maintenance and manifestation of sexual excitement in male animals. *Psychosom. Med.*, 1942, **4**, 173–198.

11. Beach, F. A., & Levinson, G. Effects of androgen on the glans penis and mating behavior of castrated male rats. *J. exp. Zool.*, 1950, **114**, 159–171.

12. Bellows, R. T. Time factors in water drinking in dogs. *Amer. J. Physiol.*, 1939, **125**, 87–97.

13. Berkun, M. M., Kessen, Marion L., & Miller, N. E. Hunger-reducing effects of food by stomach fistula versus food by mouth measured by a consummatory response. *J. comp. physiol. Psychol.*, 1952, **45**, 550–554.

14. Berlyne, E. E. The arousal and satiation of perceptual curiosity in the rat. *J. comp. physiol. Psychol.*, 1955, **48**, 238–246.

15. Brobeck, J. R., Tepperman, J., & Long, C. N. H. Experimental hypothalamic hyperphagia in the albino rat. *Yale J. Biol. Med.*, 1943, **15**, 831–853.

16. Campbell, B. A., & Sheffield, F. D. Relation of random activity to food deprivation. *J. comp. physiol. Psychol.*, 1953, **5**, 320–322.

17. Cannon, W. B. Hunger and thirst. In C. Murchison (Ed.), *A handbook of general experimental psychology.* Worcester, Mass.: Clark Univer. Press, 1934.

18. Carr, W. J. The effect of adrenalectomy upon the NaCl taste threshold in rat. *J. comp. physiol. Psychol.*, 1952, **45**, 377–380.

19. Delgado, J. M. R., Roberts, W. W., & Miller, N. E. Learning motivated by electrical stimulation of the brain. *Amer. J. Physiol.*, 1954, **179**, 587–593.

20. Dempsey, E. W., & Rioch, D. McK. The localization in the brain stem of the oestrous responses of the female guinea pig. *J. Neurophysiol.*, 1939, **2**, 9–18.

21. Gilman, A. The relation between blood osmotic pressure, fluid distribution, and voluntary water intake. *Amer. J. Physiol.*, 1937, **120**, 323–328.

22. Greer, M. A. Suggestive evidence of a primary "drinking center" in hypothala-

mus of the rat. *Proc. Soc. exp. Biol.,* *N.Y.,* 1955, **89,** 59–62.

23. Harlow, H. F. Motivational factors underlying learning. In Kentucky Symposium, *Learning theory, personality theory, and clinical research.* New York: Wiley, 1954. Pp. 36–53.

24. Hebb, D. O. *The organization of behavior: a neurophysiological theory.* New York: Wiley, 1949.

25. Hebb, D. O. Drives and the CNS (conceptual nervous system). *Psychol. Rev.,* 1955, **62,** 243–254.

26. Hull, C. L. *Principles of behavior.* New York: Appleton-Century-Crofts, 1943.

27. Kennard, Margaret A., Spencer, S., & Fountain, G., Jr. Hyperactivity in monkeys following lesions of the frontal lobes. *J. Neurophysiol.,* 1941, **4,** 512–524.

28. Kohn, M. Satiation of hunger from food injected directly into the stomach versus food ingested by mouth. *J. comp. physiol. Psychol.,* 1951, **44,** 412–422.

29. Lashley, K. S. Experimental analysis of instinctive behavior. *Psychol. Rev.,* 1938, **45,** 445–471.

30. Lehrman, D. S. The physiological basis of parental feeding behavior in the ring dove (*Streptopelia risoria*). *Behaviour,* 1955, **7,** 241–286.

31. Lindsley, D. B. Physiological psychology. *Annu. Rev. Psychol.,* 1956, **7,** 323–348.

32. McCleary, R. A. Taste and post-ingestion factors in specific-hunger behavior. *J. comp. physiol. Psychol.,* 1953, **46,** 411–421.

33. Miller, N. E. Learnable drives and rewards. In S. S. Stevens (Ed.), *Handbook of experimental psychology.* New York: Wiley, 1951.

34. Miller, N. E., & Kessen, Marion L. Reward effects of food via stomach fistula compared with those of food via mouth. *J. comp. physiol. Psychol.,* **45,** 555–564.

35. Miller, N. E., Bailey, C. J., & Stevenson, J. A. F. Decreased "hunger" but increased food intake resulting from hypothalamic lesions. *Science,* 1950, **112,** 256–259.

36. Montgomery, K. C. The role of exploratory drive in learning. *J. comp. physiol. Psychol.,* 1954, **47,** 60–64.

37. Montgomery, M. F. The role of the salivary glands in the thirst mechanism. *Amer. J. Physiol.,* 1931, **96,** 221–227.

38. Morgan, C. T. *Physiological psychology.* New York: McGraw-Hill, 1943. Pp. 458–465.

39. Morgan, C. T. *Introduction to psychology.* New York: McGraw-Hill, 1956. Pp. 58–69, 540–545.

40. Morgan, C. T. Physiological mechanisms of motivation. In M. R. Jones (Ed.), *Nebraska symposium on motivation.* Lincoln, Neb.: Univer. Nebraska Press, 1957.

41. Morgan, C. T., & Fields, P. E. The effect of variable preliminary feeding upon the rat's speed of locomotion. *J. comp. Psychol.,* 1938, **26,** 331–348.

42. Morgan, C. T., & Morgan, J. D. Studies in hunger: I. The effects of insulin upon the rat's rate of eating. *J. genet. Psychol.,* 1940, **56,** 137–147.

43. Morgan, C. T., & Morgan, J. D. Studies in hunger: II. The relation of gastric denervation and dietary sugar to the effect of insulin upon food intake in the rat. *J. genet. Psychol.,* 1940, **57,** 153–163.

44. Morgan, C. T., & Stellar, E. *Physiological psychology* (Rev. ed.) New York: McGraw-Hill, 1950.

45. Mowrer, O. H. On the dual nature of learning—a reinterpretation of "conditioning" and "problem solving." *Harv. educ. Rev.,* 1947, **17,** 102–148.

46. Nauta, W. J. H. Hypothalamic regulation of sleep in rats: an experimental study. *J. Neurophysiol.,* 1946, **9,** 285–316.

47. Olds, J., & Milner, P. Positive reinforcement produced by electrical stimulation of septal area and other regions of rat brain. *J. comp. physiol. Psychol.,* 1954, **47,** 419–427.

48. Pfaffmann, C., & Bare, J. K. Gustatory

nerve discharges in normal and adrenalectomized rats. *J. comp. physiol. Psychol.*, 1950, **43**, 320–324.

49. Ranson, S. W. Somnolence caused by hypothalamic lesions in the monkey. *Arch. Neurol. Psychiat.*, 1939, **41**, 1–23.

50. Richter, C. P. The primacy of polyuria in diabetes insipidus. *Amer. J. Physiol.*, 1935, **112**, 481–487.

51. Richter, C. P. Total self-regulatory functions in animals and human beings. *Harvey Lectures*, 1942–43, **38**, 63–103.

52. Richter, C. P., & Hawkes, C. D. Increased spontaneous activity and food intake produced in rats by removal of the frontal poles of the brain. *J. Neurol. Psychiat.*, 1939, **2**, 231–242.

53. Root, W. S., & Bard, P. Erection in the cat following removal of lumbo-sacral segments. *Amer. J. Physiol.*, 1937, **119**, 392–393.

54. Ruch, T. C., & Shenkin, H. A. The relation of area 13 of the orbital surface of the frontal lobe to hyperactivity and hyperphagia in monkeys. *J. Neurophysiol.*, 1943, **6**, 349–360.

55. Scott, E. M., and Quint, Eleanor. Self-selection of diet. III. Appetites for B vitamins. *J. Nutrit.*, 1946, **32**, 285–292.

56. Scott, E. M., & Quint, Eleanor. Self-selection of diet. IV. Appetite for protein. *J. Nutrit.*, 1946, **32**, 293–302.

57. Sheffield, F. D., Wulff, J. J., & Backer, R. Reward value of copulation without sex drive reduction. *J. comp. physiol. Psychol.*, 1951, **44**, 3–8.

58. Stellar, E. The physiology of motivation. *Psychol. Rev.*, 1954, **61**, 5–22.

59. Stellar, E., & Hill, J. H. The rat's rate of drinking as a function of water deprivation. *J. comp. physiol. Psychol.*, 1952, **45**, 96–102.

60. Stellar, E., Hyman, R., & Samet, S. Gastric factors controlling water-and salt-solution drinking. *J. comp. physiol. Psychol.*, 1954, **47**, 220–226.

61. Teitelbaum, P. Sensory control of hypo-
thalamic hyperphagia. *J. comp. physiol. Psychol.*, 1955, **48**, 156–163.

62. Teitelbaum, P., & Stellar, E. Recovery from the failure to eat produced by hypothalamic lesions. *Science*, 1954, **120**, 894–895.

63. Thompson, W. R., & Heron, W. The effects of early restriction of activity in dogs. *J. comp. physiol. Psychol.*, 1954, **47**, 77–82.

64. Thompson, W. R., & Solomon, L. M. Spontaneous pattern discrimination in the rat. *J. comp. physiol. Psychol.*, 1954, **47**, 104–107.

65. Tinbergen, N. *The study of instinct.* London: Oxford Univer. Press, 1951.

66. Tsang, Y. C. Hunger motivation in gastrectomized rats. *J. comp. Psychol.*, 1938, **26**, 1–17.

67. Wangensteen, O. H., & Carlson, A. J. Hunger sensations in a patient after total gastrectomy. *Proc. Soc. exp. Biol., N.Y.*, 1931, **28**, 545–547.

68. Wilder, C. E. Selection of rachitic and antirachitic diets in the rat. *J. comp. Psychol.*, 1937, **24**, 547–577.

69. Young, P. T. The experimental analysis of appetite. *Psychol. Bull.*, 1941, **38**, 129–164.

70. Young, P. T. Food-seeking drive, affective process, and learning. *Psychol. Rev.*, 1949, **56**, 98–121.

16   nonspecific brain mechanisms *

H. W. Magoun

1. How does Magoun define "nonspecific brain mechanism"?

* H. W. Magoun, "Non-Specific Brain Mechanisms," *Biological and Biochemical Bases of Behavior* (University of Wisconsin Press, 1958), 25–36. Reprinted with permission.

2. What information about the RAS is given by Magoun that is an addition to that given by French (Chapter 1)?

3. What are the central influences on afferent transmission?

Within recent years, interest in spinal reflexes or specifically sensory or motor systems of the brain has been extended to include study of relatively nonspecific neural mechanisms involved in functions previously receiving attention chiefly from investigators in psychology. As a result, boundaries between neurophysiology and psychology are in some areas commencing to lose sharp definition and increasingly to overlap. One program in this development has utilized electrical recording techniques to examine features of the brain's activity during arousal to wakefulness or alerting to attention.

ascending reticular system and wakefulness

This work began with the chance observation that direct stimulation of the central reticular core of the brain stem (Plate 1) reproduced those alterations in cortical electrical activity encountered in awakening from sleep or alerting to attention, in which patterns of high voltage, slow waves, and spindle bursts in the EEG become replaced by low-voltage fast discharge (41). This evoked electrocortical alteration was manifest over wide areas of the hemisphere, being most pronounced and persisting longest in frontal regions. It was mediated by diffusely distributed ascending connections, some of which appeared to reach the cortex through relays in the nonspecific thalamic nuclei, while the remainder traversed extra-thalamic routes through the subthalamus and internal capsule.

The functional significance of this ascending reticular system for behavior was tested by exciting it through chronically implanted electrodes in naturally sleeping animals with consequent behavioral awakening or arousal (42). Conversely, the production of large experimental lesions in its cephalic portion resulted in chronic loss of wakefulness, the animals appearing as though asleep, anesthetized, or comatose for as long as they could be nursed to survival. Serial EEGs of monkeys with such central cephalic lesions of the brain stem were of the coma or stupor type and, though classical afferent paths to the cortex were intact and viable, peripheral stimulation of the most vigorous sort was no longer capable of evoking generalized EEG or behavioral arousal (8, 9, 10, 11).

This latter observation suggested that the arousing properties of afferent stimulation might be mediated by collateral connections from direct lemniscal paths, turning into the ascending reticular system in the brain stem (Fig. 1 and Plate 2). In preparations without central anesthesia, potentials evoked by somatic and auditory stimulation could be recorded widely through the central brain stem, and further exploration has shown that all sensory modalities make such collateral reticular connections. While early work emphasized the long latency, wave-like form, and prolonged recovery time of these evoked potentials, together with the interaction of discharge initiated from various peripheral sources, more recent study suggests that several component types may be differentiated. By direct test, these extralemniscal connections with the reticular formation can be shown to mediate generalized EEG arousal, though this change may also be induced in the circumscribed sensory regions of the cortex by excitation of each of the classical afferent paths (27).

Unit analysis of excitation induced in the

ascending reticular system by single afferent shocks (Fig. 2) has revealed a complex cycle of repetitive discharge associated with the evoked potential, subsequent increased frequency of firing, or a reduction of spontaneous activity (32). Most commonly, brief repetitive afferent stimulation led to prolonged increased frequency of unit firing, to rates of 30–60/sec, together with the recruitment of previously silent units.

corticifugal projections to central brain stem

An ascending reticular system subserving arousal or attention would seem likely to receive inflows from central as well as peripheral sources. Corticifugal projections to the central brain stem have been demonstrated both by Jasper and his associates (26) and by Bremer and Terzuolo (4). Further investigation by French, Hernández-Peón, and Livingston (7) has shown that associational areas of frontal, cingulate, parieto-occipital, and temporal cortex, as well as sensory and motor regions, project diffusely to common portions of the central cephalic brain stem. Considerable overlap exists in these projections, and interaction of discharge initiated from different parts of the cortex, and from peripheral

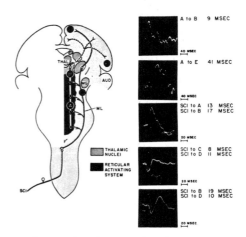

Fig. 1. Diagram showing somatic afferent path making collateral connections with ascending reticular system (black) in brain stem, with potentials evoked and recorded at labeled sites with latencies indicated. From French, Verzeano, and Magoun (9).

sources as well, can readily be demonstrated (22). More focal facilitation or inhibition of reticular transmission can be observed, however (1). When conditions are appropriate for its testing, generalized EEG arousal can be induced by stimulating certain of these cortical areas, in particular, those of the temporal lobe (44).

With the use of chronically implanted electrodes, stimulating these cortical areas in naturally sleeping monkeys evoked behavioral awakening. Their stimulation in the waking

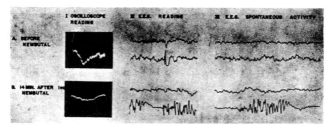

Plate 1. Oscilloscopic and ink-written records showing effect of barbiturate anesthesia upon potentials evoked in the central brain stem (heavy beam and upper EEG trace) and somatic cortex (light beam and lower EEG trace) by single sciatic shocks. From French, Verzeano, and Magoun (10).

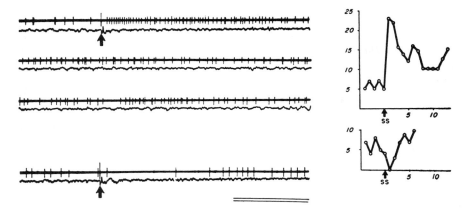

Fig. 2. Unit activity in central cephalic brain stem (upper) and cortical EEG (lower beam) upon single-shock sciatic stimuli. Graphs show spikes per second (vertical) and time in seconds (horizontal). From Machne, Calma, and Magoun (32).

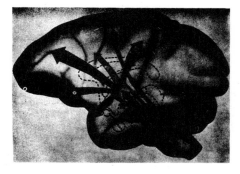

Plate 2. View of monkey brain showing ascending reticular system receiving collaterals from somatic afferent pathway in the brain stem and projecting diffusely to the cortex. From Magoun (38).

monkey caused it to behave as though confronted with an alerting or alarming situation. Exciting the somatic or visual sensory cortex in the wide-awake animal induced behavior suggesting the experience of subjective impressions. The same or far more intense stimuli applied to these functionally specific areas during sleep were, by contrast, devoid of any obvious consequence. It would appear, therefore, that excitation of cortical sensory areas is not by itself sufficient either to induce arousal or to cause sensation. For the latter to occur, a

simultaneous background of wakefulness appears indispensable (42).

central influences on afferent transmission

From the classical studies of Adrian and others, it is clear that variations in the frequency of receptor discharge signal intensity of afferent stimulation and, if such stimulation is maintained, accommodation. Transmission of afferent impulses from receptors to receiving areas of the cortex has been conceived as stereotyped, however, and little subject to central neural influences. Demonstrations by Granit and Kaada (14) of pronounced centrifugal effects upon afferent discharge from the muscle spindle, led Hagbarth and Kerr (21) to explore the effect of excitation of the brain-stem reticular formation, or of cortical or cerebellar regions projecting to it, upon somatic afferent transmission at the first central relay in the spinal cord. A pronounced reduction of amplitude of afferent potentials was encountered, and similar inhibitory influences upon transmission have since been observed in the olfactory bulb (28) and in the posterior column nuclei, nucleus of the spinal fifth tract, and dorsal cochlear nucleus (24). Except in the retina, where Granit (12) has observed potentiation, nonspecific influences thus seem generally capable of reducing afferent transmission at the first central relay, and this influence is evidently a tonic one, for enhancement of evoked afferent discharge at these sites follows central brain stem injury or anesthesia.

In addition to lower relays in the neuraxis, transmission in each of the classical afferent pathways (except the olfactory one) has the common feature of relay to the cortex by a specific thalamic nucleus. By contrast with lower stations, reticular influences upon thalamic transmission in the somatic pathway led to more pronounced alterations in temporal features than in amplitude (30). Reticular stimulation induced abbreviation of latency, as well as duration of discharge and recovery time, together with obliteration of facilitatory periods in the recovery cycle, the latter raising some question of the importance in alert wakefulness of the 10/sec excitability cycle which augments in-phase afferent signals during anesthesia (6).

While the functional significance of these novel observations will require much further study, it appears that they may contribute to understanding of the mechanisms of focus of attention and habituation. With chronically implanted electrode techniques, Hernández-Peón, Scherrer, and Jouvet (25) have observed that discharge evoked in the dorsal cochlear nucleus of the cat by serially repeated clicks becomes markedly reduced in amplitude during an interval when the animal's attention is attracted by visual or olfactory stimulation. If nonspecific influences are involved in this effect, they may provide a means by which the brain is able to exclude irrelevant afferent information during the focus of attention.

Possibly allied to this is a type of learning called "habituation," by which the brain ultimately ceases to attend to monotonously repeated, afferent information. Nonspecific brain mechanisms have been shown to be involved by Sharpless and Jasper (45), and Hernández-Peón and Scherrer (23) have found that reduction in evoked potentials at the dorsal cochlear nucleus, associated with habituation to repeated clicks, is reversed by central brain-stem lesions or anesthesia. These latter categories of experimentation particularly emphasize the great desirability of increasing the scope of interdisciplinary research in the field between neurophysiology and physiological psychology.

subcortical relations with rhinencephalic structures

Antedating the cerebral development of the neocortex was the phylogenetically old establishment of the paleocortical hippocampus, which, with its basal ganglion, the amygdala, served as the highest forebrain mechanism regulating subcortical function (Fig. 3).

The work of Green and Arduini (17) has shown that when electrical patterns of the neocortex and hippocampus are recorded simultaneously in the rabbit, the two often exhibit inverse relationships, fast discharge in the neocorticogram being associated with large, slow-wave activity in the hippocampus and vice versa. The contrasting patterns of spontaneous activity in these two parts of the forebrain are more striking still during arousal to afferent stimulation (Plate 3). Neocortical desynchronization is invariably accompanied

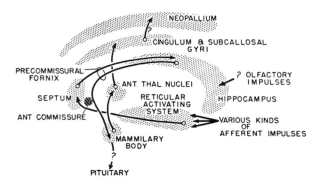

POSSIBLE PATHWAYS IN HIPPOCAMPAL
AROUSAL REACTION

Fig. 3. Diagram showing possible pathways in hippocampal arousal. From Green and Arduini (17).

in the hippocampus by a train of sinusoidal slow waves of large amplitude and 3–6/sec rhythm. This response is generalized in the hippocampus and identical for all modalities of stimulation. It is obtained most readily in the rabbit, is often partially obscured by fast activity in the cat, and is difficult to observe at all in the monkey.

Like that of the neocortical EEG, this hippocampal arousal pattern can readily be evoked by direct stimulation of the central cephalic brain stem, as well as by excitation of the preoptic region and septum. It appears to be mediated by a cephalic projection of the ascending reticular system directed through the dorsal fornix to the hippocampus. The slow-wave discharge is reflected centrifugally through the fornix proper and can be recorded from the mammillary body, the mammillothalamic tract, and, with wide pickups, from areas of the neocortex.

Functional relationships between the hippocampus and entorhinal area are greatly in need of study as potentially direct links between paleo- and neocortex. Recent observations by Carreras et al. (5) indicate that delimited

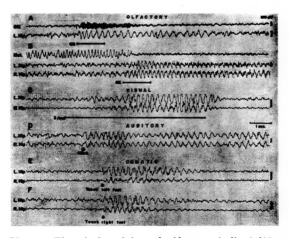

Plate 3. Electrical activity of olfactory bulb (olf.), hippocampus (hip.), and motor cortex (mot.) of rabbit, showing alterations induced by arousing stimuli (signal) of several modalities. From Green and Arduini (17).

ablation of the entorhinal cortex in the rabbit converts the slow-wave pattern of hippocampal arousal to low-voltage fast discharge like that of the neocortex. Green and Arduini (17) earlier concluded that the hippocampal arousal pattern was uninfluenced by total decortication, however, and more recent study has not revealed specific influences of entorhinal ablations upon it.

The high-frequency electrical activity of the deep-lying nuclear masses of the amygdala is relatively imperturbable and shows no conspicuous alteration with EEG changes between relaxation and arousal (2). Afferent or central brain-stem stimulation fails to evoke clear-cut changes, but prolonged increase in the rate of unit-firing can be observed with microelectrode recording (33). It would appear that the amygdala may secondarily be subject to afferent or central influences through the hippocampus (16) or neocortex of the superior gyrus and tip of the temporal lobe (43).

As observed with electrical recording techniques, experimentally induced amygdaloid seizures propagate most conspicuously to the basal forebrain and cephalic brain stem. Such seizures propagate also to the hippocampus and to the temporal cortex outside the auditory area. Striking, indeed, is their failure to involve the large remainder of the cerebral cortex (2). At present the amygdala would appear potentially able to command somatic, visceral, and endocrine regulating mechanisms of the cephalic brain stem and to be itself subject to influence both by the hippocampus and temporal cortex.

summary

From a number of recent studies, conceptions of brain organization have been enlarged by identification of nonspecific neural mechanisms lying between the sensory and motor systems of classical neurophysiology and richly interconnected with them. Reciprocal ascending and descending connections between these nonspecific neural mechanisms in the brain stem and wide areas of the hemi-spheres, including both neo- and paleocortex, are involved in arousal to wakefulness and alerting to attention. Further study of these nonspecific neural mechanisms may be expected to be rewarding in relating brain organization and behavior.

references

In an effort to limit the bibliography, reference has been made primarily to papers from this laboratory. Most of these contain extensive references to related work by others.

1. Adey, R. W., R. B. Livingston, and J. P. Segundo. Corticifugal influences on intrinsic brain stem induction in the cat and monkey. *J. Neurophysiol.*, 1957, **20**: 1–16.
2. Arana-Iníguez, R., D. J. Reis, R. Naquet, and H. W. Magoun. Propagation of amygdaloid seizures. *Acta Neurol. Latino-Amer.*, 1955, **1**: 109–22.
3. Arduini, A., and M. G. Arduini. Effect of drugs and metabolic alterations on brain stem arousal mechanism. *J. Pharmachol.*, 1954, **110**: 76–85.
4. Bremer, F., and C. Terzuolo. Nouvelles recherches sur le processus physiologique du réveil. *Arch. int. Physiol.*, 1953, **61**: 86–90.
5. Carreras, M., G. Macchi, F. Angeleri, and M. Urbani. Sull' attività elettrica della formazione Ammonica. Effetti determinati dall'ablazione della corteccia entorinale. *Boll. Soc. ital. Biol. sper.*, 1955, **31**: sep.
6. Chang., H.-T. The repetitive discharges of corticothalamic reverberating circuit. *J. Neurophysiol.*, 1950, **13**: 235–58.
7. French, J. D., R. Hernández-Peón, and R. B. Livingston. Projections from cortex to cephalic brain stem (reticular formation) in monkey. *J. Neurophysiol.*, 1955, **18**: 74–95.

8. French, J. D., and H. W. Magoun. Effects of chronic lesions in central cephalic brain stem of monkeys. *Arch. Neurol. Psychiat., Chicago,* 1952, **68:** 591–604.

9. French, J. D., M. Verzeano, and H. W. Magoun. An extralemniscal sensory system in the brain. *Arch. Neurol. Psychiat., Chicago,* 1953, **69:** 505–18.

10. ———. A neural basis of the anesthetic state. *Arch. Neurol. Psychiat., Chicago,* 1953, **69:** 519–29.

11. French, J. D., F. K. von Amerongen, and H. W. Magoun. An activating system in brain stem of monkey. *Arch. Neurol. Psychiat., Chicago,* 1952, **68:** 577–90.

12. Granit, R. Centrifugal and antidromic effects on ganglion cells of retina. *J. Neurophysiol.,* 1955, **18:** 388–411.

13. ———. *Receptors and sensory perception.* New Haven: Yale Univer. Press, 1955.

14. Granit, R., and B. R. Kaada. Influence of stimulation of central nervous structures on muscle spindles in cat. *Acta physiol. scand.,* 1952, **27:** 130–60.

15. Green, J. D. Neural pathways to the hypophysis. Chap. I in *Hypothalamic-hypophysical interrelations.* Springfield, Ill.: Charles C. Thomas, 1956.

16. Green, J. D., and W. R. Adey. Electrophysiological studies of hippocampal connections and excitability. *Electroenceph. clin. Neurophysiol.,* 1956, **8:** 245–63.

17. Green, J. D., and A. A. Arduini. Hippocampal electrical activity in arousal. *J. Neurophysiol.,* 1954, **17:** 533–57.

18. Green, J. D., and X. Machne. Unit activity of rabbit hippocampus. *Amer. J. Physiol.,* 1955, **181:** 219–24.

19. Green, J. D., and T. Shimamoto. Hippocampal seizures and their propagation. *Arch. Neurol. Psychiat., Chicago,* 1953, **70:** 687–702.

20. Gunn, C. G., S. Eliasson, and J. D. French. Cortical projections to the septum. *Fed. Proc.,* 1955, **14:** 66 (Abstract).

21. Hagbarth, K.-E., and D. I. B. Kerr. Central influences on spinal afferent conduction. *J. Neurophysiol.,* 1954, **17:** 295–307.

22. Hernández-Peón, R., and K.-E. Hagbarth. Interaction between afferent and cortically induced reticular responses. *J. Neurophysiol.,* 1955, **18:** 44–55.

23. Hernández-Peón, R., and H. Scherrer. "Habituation" to acoustic stimuli in cochlear nucleus. *Fed. Proc.,* 1955, **14:** 71 (Abstract).

24. ———. Inhibitory influence of brain stem reticular formation upon synaptic transmission in trigeminal nucleus. *Fed. Proc.,* 1955, **14:** 71 (Abstract).

25. Hernández-Peón, R., H. Scheerer, and M. Jouvet. Modification of electric activity in cochlear nucleus during attention in unanesthetized cats. *Science,* 1956, **123:** 331–32.

26. Jasper, H., C. Ajmone-Marsan, and J. Stoll. Corticofugal projections to the brain stem. *Arch. Neurol. Psychiat., Chicago,* 1952, **67:** 155–71.

27. Jaspar, H., R. Naquet, and E. E. King. Thalamocortical recruiting responses in sensory receiving areas in the cat. *Electroenceph. clin. Neurophysiol.,* 1955, **7:** 99–114.

28. Kerr, D. I. B., and K.-E. Hagbarth. An investigation of olfactory centrifugal fiber system. *J. Neurophysiol.,* 1955, **18:** 362–74.

29. King, E. E. Differential action of anesthetics and interneuron depressants upon EEG arousal and recruitment responses. *J. Pharmacol.,* 1956, **116:** 404–17.

30. King, E. E., R. Naquet, and H. W. Magoun. Alterations in somatic afferent transmission through the thalamus by central mechanisms and barbiturates. *J. Pharmacol.,* 1957, **119:** 48–63.

31. Lindsley, D. B., L. H. Schreiner, W. B. Knowles, and H. W. Magoun. Behavioral and EEG changes following chronic brain stem lesions in the cat. *Electroenceph. clin. Neurophysiol.,* 1950, **2:** 483–98.

32. Machne, X., I. Calma, and H. W. Magoun. *Unit activity of central cephalic brain stem in EEG arousal. J. Neurophysiol.*, 1955, **18**: 547–58.

33. Machne, X., and J. P. Segundo. Unit activity in the amygdaloid complex of the cat. *Fed. Proc.*, 1955, **14**: 96 (Abstract).

34. Magoun, H. W. Caudal and cephalic influences of the brain stem reticular formation. *Physiol. Rev.*, 1950, **30**: 459–74.

35. ———. The ascending reticular activating system. *Res. Publ. Ass. nerv. ment. Dis.*, 1952, **30**: 480–92.

36. ———. An ascending reticular activating system in the brain stem. *Harvey Lect.* Ser. 47, 1951–52. New York: Academic Press, 1953, p. 53–71.

37. ———. Physiological interrelationships between cortex and subcortical structures. *Electroenceph. clin. Neurophysiol.*, 1953, Suppl. No. 4, 163–67.

38. ———. The ascending reticular system and wakefulness. In J. F. Delafresnaye (Ed.), *Brain mechanism and consciousness.* Oxford: Blackwell, 1954, p. 1–20.

39. ———. A neural basis for the anesthetic state. In *Symposium on sedative and hypnotic drugs.* Baltimore: Williams and Wilkins, 1954, p. 1–19.

40. ———. Ascending reticular system and anesthesia. *Neuropharmacology:* transactions of the first conference, 1955, **1**: 145–61.

41. Moruzzi, G., and H. W. Magoun. Brain stem reticular formation and activation of the EEG. *Electroenceph. clin. Neurophysiol.*, 1949, **1**: 455–73.

42. Segundo, J. P., R. Arana, and J. D. French. Behavioral arousal by stimulation of the brain in the monkey. *J. Neurosurg.*, 1955, **12**: 601–13.

43. Segundo, J. P., R. Naquet, and R. Arana. Subcortical connections from temporal cortex of monkey. *Arch. Neurol. Psychiat. Chicago*, 1955, **73**: 515–24.

44. Segundo, J. P., R. Naquet, and P. Buser. Effects of cortical stimulation on electro-

cortical activity in monkeys. *J. Neurophysiol.*, 1955, **18**: 236–45.

45. Sharpless, S., and H. H. Jasper. Habituation of the arousal reaction. *Brain*, 1956, **79**: 655–80.

46. Shimamoto, T., and M. Verzeano. Relations between caudate and diffusely projecting thalamic nuclei. *J. Neurophysiol.*, 1954, **17**: 278–88.

47. Starzl, T. E., and H. W. Magoun. Organization of the diffuse thalamic projection system. *J. Neurophysiol.*, 1951, **14**: 133–46.

48. Starzl, T. E., C. W. Taylor, and H. W. Magoun. Ascending conduction in reticular activating system, with special reference to the diencephalon. *J. Neurophysiol.*, 1951, **14**: 461–77.

49. ———. Collateral afferent excitation of reticular formation of brain stem. *J. Neurophysiol.*, 1951, **14**: 479–96.

50. Starzl, T. E., and D. G. Whitlock. Diffuse thalamic projection system in the monkey. *J. Neurophysiol.*, 1952, **15**: 449–68.

17 positive reinforcement induced by intracerebral stimulation in the monkey *

Ben Bursten and José M. R. Delgado

1. What is the importance of extending self-stimulation experimentation to monkeys?

2. In self-stimulation experiments, what similarities were shown in the performance of mon-

* B. Bursten and J. M. R. Delgado, "Positive Reinforcement Induced by Intracerebral Stimulation in the Monkey," *J. comp. physiol. Psychol.*, 51 (1958), 6–10. Reprinted with permission.

keys to that of rats and cats? What differences? How can these differences be explained?

The fact that intracerebral electrical stimulation can have positive reinforcing value for animals has been a matter of considerable interest since it was reported by Olds and Milner in 1954 (13). They required rats to press a bar in a Skinner box in order to be "rewarded" with stimulation of various parts of the brain. This phenomenon could be demonstrated by stimulating the septal area, the cingulate gyrus, the mammillothalamic tract, and a point in the tegmentum.

In a more comprehensive review of the work Olds (12) noted that a rat could learn to go to any part of a cage where it would receive the stimulation, and that maze learning could also be induced, using intracerebral stimulation as the reward. In a "conflict of motives" situation a hungry rat preferred the brain stimulation to food.

Sidman et al. (15), working with cats, employed a bar-pressing technique similar to that used by Olds and Milner and demonstrated that the positively reinforcing value of the stimulation increases with its intensity. In their cats results were obtained by stimulating the caudate nucleus, a fact which assumes considerable interest in view of Olds' formulation that the limbic system is a "reward system in the brain." In a personal communication of work in progress, J. V. Brady indicated that he had been successful in an attempt to train monkeys to press a bar for self-stimulation. Brady et al. (1) showed that food and water deprivation tended to increase bar-pressing scores when the animals were reinforced with septal stimulation. Conrad and Brady (3) have shown that conditioned "anxiety" responses were not elaborated while septal stimulation was being received.

A previous attempt in this laboratory to train monkeys to turn a lever in order to receive septal stimulation had failed. The parameters of the stimulation were such that, in general, they did not produce observable movement effects. Choice of parameters was further governed by the "optimal" ranges found by Mihailović and Delgado (10) in other stimulation experiments. Because of the possibility that the lever-turning technique might not be sensitive enough to detect an effect under these stimulation conditions, we devised an alternate method to elicit the phenomenon, using the same parameters.

method

subjects

The experimental Ss were six adult rhesus monkeys. The five females had been ovariectomized and used in physiological studies unrelated to the present problem. The male, no. 971, had undergone no surgical procedure prior to the implantation of the electrodes. Two Ss, 971 and 16, had been used in the previously unsuccessful attempt to train the animals to turn a lever to receive intracerebral stimulation; the others were naive.

The monkeys were implanted with multilead needle electrodes (4) through which the brain could be stimulated at any one of up to 12 different points in each animal. The needles consisted of three to six stimulation points arranged linearly. The intention was to locate some of the stimulation points within the limbic system and some points in the neighboring non-limbic structures. All the animals were allowed at least ten days to recuperate. During the course of the experiments they appeared to be in good health and behaved generally as they had before the operation. After the experiment was completed, the monkeys were sacrificed and histological studies made of sections of the brains in order to insure accurate localization of the stimulation points.

apparatus

A Grass stimulator, S-4, with isolation unit, was set to deliver unidirectional square waves, 100 cps. and 0.25 msec. of pulse duration. Monopolar stimulation with the negative pole as the active electrode was used. The stimulus intensity was kept between 0.8 and 1.0 ma. and was monitored during the stimulation by a Du Mont oscilloscope, 304H. A timing mechanism allowed the stimulus to pass through in bursts of 0.34 sec. with pauses of 3.46 sec. between bursts. It was calculated that each burst delivered a maximum of 8.5 microcoulombs to the animal.

procedure

The experiment was carried out on a table 25 by 60 in. The monkey was attached by a harness to a ring that fitted loosely around a bar running lengthwise, which permitted the animal to move freely on the table but prevented escape. The leads from the stimulator were brought up through the grid, which comprised the table top, were attached to the harness and then plugged into the electrode sockets; in this way there was no interference with movement. During a testing session E could test any of the points on an electrode by switching the point into the circuit. The monkey was separated from the observer by a one-way-vision screen fitted with chutes through which peanuts could be rolled to feeding pans at both sides of the table. The animals were trained to get peanuts at either side. The experimental trials were composed of a series of "blocks" lasting 5 min. each. The monkey, food-deprived 16 to 24 hr., was

placed on the testing table and left alone for several minutes. Thirty seconds after each testing block began the monkey was "forced" to cross the mid-line of the table by rolling a peanut to the more distant feeding pan. Throughout the test the animal was free to move to either side of the table. While the monkey was on one predetermined side (e.g., the right) a manually operated switch turned on the cerebral stimulation and energized a clock. If the monkey remained for $2\frac{1}{2}$ consecutive minutes on one side it was "forced" to cross the mid-line again by rolling a peanut the other way. Thus, if the monkey did not move spontaneously during the 5-min. block it spent $2\frac{1}{2}$ min. on each side and would have sampled both sides (stimulating and nonstimulating). The side of the table on which the animal was stimulated, and the point stimulated, varied at random from block to block. Thirteen blocks constituted a series. One control block, without any stimulating on either side, was included in each series.

The time spent on the stimulating side for each block was recorded. This figure represented two factors: the amount of time spent on that side because of the extraneous side-preference factors (approximated by the amount of time spent on that side when neither side was stimulated) and the preference due to the effect of the stimulation. Thus, to obtain a measure of the stimulation effect, we subtracted the extraneous side-preference score from the total time recorded by our clock. With this method of calculation, a *preference* due to stimulation was recorded as a plus figure, while an *aversion* was recorded as a minus figure. In general, each monkey was given one series daily for four or five days, and each point was tested approximately ten times, except in the case of a monkey which broke some of the connections.

Table 1. Effect of Stimulation

S	Location	N	Mean (sec.)	σ	p	S	Location	N	Mean (sec.)	σ	p
16	LSN	9	+42.7	39.3	<.02	71	MSN	10	+12.1	33.5	>.05
	LSN	10	+34.3	27.7	<.02		MSN and LSN	9	-1.6	67.9	>.05
	SG	4	+34.0	17.6	<.02		LSN	7	+27.9	101.5	>.05
							LSN	7	+35.0	36.2	.05
17	MSN (M)	10	-22.0	26.2	<.05		CC	8	+16.9	70.1	>.05
	MSN and LSN	10	-2.3	27.4	>.05		LAN	10	-14.7	63.3	>.05
	LSN	10	+41.5	42.6	<.02		LAN and BAN	10	+7.3	40.3	>.05
	LV and LSN	10	+24.2	59.8	>.05		LAN and AAA	6	-36.2	68.9	>.05
	BAN	10	+37.8	39.8	<.02		DBB and LOT	10	+12.4	50.9	>.05
	AAA	10	+1.7	42.4	>.05		AC	10	+56.2	54.3	<.02
	PC	10	+24.7	44.5	>.05		P	10	-1.3	93.3	>.05
	P	10	-11.5	69.8	>.05						
18	P	10	+1.9	62.6	>.05	78	EMT	4	-68.8	29.1	<.02
	P	10	+12.1	48.3	>.05		EMT	4	-28.3	44.5	>.05
	P	10	-26.4	63.8	>.05		TO and PC	4	-45.5	92.7	>.05
	CR	10	+26.5	35.4	.05		AC	4	+85.0	41.0	<.05
	CL	10	-40.0	59.3	>.05						
	RH	10	+75.1	46.5	<.01	971	MSN	10	+3.3	29.4	>.05
	T	10	-2.7	58.1	>.05		LSN	10	+29.7	32.4	.02
	WP	10	+27.9	73.9	>.05		LV and LSN	10	+20.0	33.0	>.05
							CN	10	-2.7	42.5	>.05
71	MSN (M)	9	-30.9	20.3	<.01		CC	10	+42.0	57.7	.05
							CG	10	+22.1	32.9	>.05

KEY

AAA	anterior amygdaloid area		AC	anterior commissure
BAN	basal amygdaloid nucleus		CC	corpus callosum
CG	cingulate gyrus		CL	common limb of parieto-occipital and calcarine fissures
CN	caudate nucleus		CR	corona radiata
DBB	fibers of diagonal band of Broca		EMT	external to brain on medial surface of temporal lobe
LAN	lateral amygdaloid nucleus		LOT	lateral olfactory tract
LSN	lateral septal nucleus		LV	lateral ventricle
M	meninges		MSN	medial septal nucleus
NDB	nucleus of diagonal band of Broca		P	putamen
PC	prepyriform cortex		RH	posterior rudiment of hippocampus
SG	supracallosal gyrus		TO	tuberculum olfactorium
WP	white matter of inferior parietal lobe			

results

Table 1 shows the location of all the stimulating points in each monkey along with the respective mean times spent on a side due to stimulation. The means and standard deviations have been calculated from results of all the testing blocks for each point. The number of blocks during which a particular point was tested is indicated by N. The probability indicates a level of confidence from a t table

based on a Z score between the mean time and zero (the mean score we would have obtained if there were only extraneous preference factors with no stimulation effect). The location of points given shows only the chief structure within which the stimulation point lay. It is highly probable that adjacent structures were also stimulated. Eleven points gave significant results indicating positive reinforcement; of these, nine were in the limbic system, one in the *corona radiata*, and one in the *corpus callosum.* Three significant results showed negative reinforcement; all these points lay at least partly in the meninges.

It is of some interest to consider whether the phenomenon under study can be elicited from any part of the brain or is one obtained primarily from points in the limbic system. Inasmuch as we are dealing here with data drawn from different parts of the brain, we can make no assumptions regarding the shape of distribution of these data. Hence, following the suggestions made by Moses (11), we used nonparametric statistics to attempt to draw inferences about the limbic system in general. We considered as limbic points only those which fell *entirely* within limbic structures, while the non-limbic points were those falling entirely outside the limbic system. Points included in both systems were discarded.

Using the Dixon-Mood (7) sign test, we paired each mean score from the table with zero (the expected mean score if there were no stimulation effect). We found that 16 of 21 limbic points gave positive results. Thus, there is a probability, at the .05 level of confidence, that stimulation of points in the limbic system would have positively reinforcing qualities. Considering non-limbic structures, we found 5 of the 10 points to be positive. Therefore, random stimulation in non-limbic areas seems just as likely to give results in a negative as in a positive direction. We attempted to compare limbic points directly with non-limbic points, using Festinger's test (8). Although there was a tendency for limbic points generally to have more positively reinforcing value than non-limbic points, the differences were not statistically significant.

Thus, we have some support for the hypothesis that the phenomenon is primarily a function of the limbic system, but the probability that some extra-limbic structures could also be positively reinforcing, when electrically stimulated, cannot be ruled out.

discussion

It will be recalled that two monkeys (971 and 16) of the present study had previously failed to learn to turn a lever to stimulate themselves. This would suggest that, in our experimental setup at least, the table-test method was more sensitive than the lever-turning technique. Olds (12) reported that positive reinforcement in hungry rats was dominant over food reward. With our method there was a conflict of motives, and in no instance did the monkey choose to remain on the stimulating side and forego the peanut. Two explanations of this divergence can be offered. It is difficult to compare our data with the Olds work because intensity of stimulation in milliamperes was not mentioned in his paper, but the intensity of our stimulation was low, and perhaps Olds was using higher levels of stimulation. We must remember that, according to Sidman et al. (15) the strength of reinforcement diminishes as the intensity of the brain stimulation decreases. Olds used rats and we used monkeys. Another interpretation could be that the dominance of the phenomenon under study might be diminished as the phylogenetic scale is ascended.

The point might be raised that since our results do not demonstrate the same effect as those of other workers, our stimulation may have somehow rendered the animal less able to move, thus forcing it to remain for long periods of time on the stimulating side. Indeed, many workers (9, 13, and others) have described "arrest" reactions due to intracerebral stimulation. These reactions were characterized by the animal's maintaining a "waxy flexibility" and a lack of movement or defensive responses, even when pricked with a pin. We have evoked this arrest response by stimulation of septal points, using levels of stimulation considerably higher (3 to 5 ma.) than those used in the present experiment. However, we never observed arrest during experimental trials when we used lower intensities (0.8 to 1.0 ma.). In addition, we kept records of the animals' spontaneous crossings; these records indicate that when positively reinforcing stimulation was given, the motility of the animals was not modified.

Regarding the location of points producing positive reinforcement, our data generally agreed with those offered by Olds. The limbic system seemed to be more consistently involved in this phenomenon, although positively reinforcing points were also found in the *corpus callosum* and the *corona radiata*. It should be noted that these two non-limbic points were in fiber systems rather than in cellular nuclei, and thus we cannot say where the actual site of action lay in these cases. Although Sidman et al. (15) were able to show positive reinforcement by stimulating the caudate nucleus in cats, we were unable to do so with our monkeys. Olds suggested that within the limbic system the phenomenon could be best produced from System II of the Pribram and Kruger classification (14). System III (according to Olds) gave less satisfactory results, while no evidence of positive reinforcement could be obtained by stimulating System I. Although several of our positive points were located in System II, we were also able to show positive reinforcement when we stimulated a System III structure. Concerning System I, we have obtained a positive result from a point lying chiefly in the anterior commissure. This structure is not listed in Pribram and Kruger's classification, but since its fibers stem chiefly from the corticomedial nuclei of the amygdala (with only a very few

connections to the basolateral group), we feel it proper to call this commissure a System I structure. Regarding the septal area we have found positive results from stimulation of the lateral septal nucleus, but not from stimulation of the medial septal nucleus. This suggests that reference merely to the septal area (without specifying the particular nuclear groups) may be masking differences to be found within this region.

Although negatively reinforcing results were obtained from three points, each of these points lay partly in the meninges, and this may account for their aversive properties. We should note, nevertheless, that work by Delgado et al. (5, 6), Cohen et al. (2), and Olds and Milner (13) indicates that there are cerebral areas which will produce aversive behavior upon electrical stimulation. The areas found by these workers, however, were generally in lower regions of the brain.

summary

We have shown that there are areas within the brains of monkeys which, when stimulated through implanted electrodes, have positively reinforcing value. In our experiment, the monkeys were "forced" to sample both sides of a table on which they could move freely. They were stimulated only on one side of it, varied at random. By recording the time spent on the stimulating side (and correcting for extraneous side-preference effects), we were able to localize cerebral points of positive reinforcement. Most of these were located in the limbic system, although there is evidence that some extra-limbic areas also produce these responses. Our results are attributable to the reinforcing value of the stimulus and not to any effect which might inhibit movements of the animal. In our experiments, in contrast to previous reports, food had more reward value than the electrical stimulation. Possible explanations for this are offered.

references

1. Brady, J. V., Boren, J. J., Conrad, D. G., & Sidman, M. The effect of food and water deprivation upon intracranial self-stimulation. Paper read at East. Psychol. Ass., Atlantic City, March, 1956.
2. Cohen, B. D., Brown, G. W., & Brown, M. L. Avoidance learning motivated by hypothalamic stimulation. *Fed. Proc.*, 1956, **15**, 37.
3. Conrad, D. G., & Brady, J. V. Conditioned anxiety as a function of intracranial self-stimulation. Paper read at East. Psychol. Ass., Atlantic City, March, 1956.
4. Delgado, J. M. R. Evaluation of permanent implantation of electrodes within the brain. *EEG clin. Neurophysiol.*, 1955, **7**, 637–644.
5. Delgado, J. M. R., Roberts, W. W., & Miller, N. E. Learning motivated by electrical stimulation of the brain. *Amer. J. Physiol.*, 1954, **179**, 587–593.
6. Delgado, J. M. R., Rosvold, H. E., & Looney, E. Evoking conditioned fear by electrical stimulation of subcortical structures in the monkey brain. *J. comp. Physiol.*, 1956, **49**, 373–380.
7. Dixon, W. J., & Mood, A. M. The statistical sign test. *J. Amer. statist. Ass.*, 1946, **41**, 557–566.
8. Festinger, L. The significance of difference between means without reference to frequency distribution function. *Psychometrika*, 1946, **11**, 97–106.
9. Goldzband, M. G., Goldberg, S. E., & Clark, G. Cessation of walking elicited by stimulation of forebrain of unanesthetized dog. *Amer. J. Physiol.*, 1951, **167**, 127–133.
10. Mihailović, M., & Delgado, J. M. R. Electrical stimulation of the monkey brain with various frequencies and pulse durations. *J. Neurophysiol.*, 1956, **19**, 21–36.
11. Moses, L. Non-parametric statistics for psychological research. *Psychol. Bull.*, 1952. **49**, 122–143.
12. Olds, J. Physiological mechanisms of reward. In M. R. Jones (Ed.), *Nebraska Symposium on Motivation. 1955*. Lincoln. Univer. of Nebraska Press, 1955.
13. Olds, J., & Milner, P. Positive reinforcement produced by electrical stimulation of the septal area and other regions of the rat brain. *J. comp. physiol. Psychol.*, 1954, **47**, 419–428.
14. Pribram, K., & Kruger, L. Function of the olfactory brain. *Ann. N.Y. Acad. Sci.* 1954, **58/2**, 109–138.
15. Sidman, M., Brady, J. V., Boren, J. J., Conrad, D. G., & Schulman, A. Reward schedules and behavior maintained by intracranial self-stimulation. *Science*, 1955, **122**, 830–831.

18 rewarding and punishing effects from stimulation of posterior hypothalamus of cat *

Warren W. Roberts

1. What experimental behavior in cats led Roberts to design this experiment?

2. What innovations in experimental procedures were introduced in these experiments?

3. What was the necessity for the second experiment?

* W. W. Roberts, "Both Rewarding and Punishing Effects from Stimulation of Posterior Hypothalamus of Cat with Same Electrode at Same Intensity," *J. comp. physiol. Psychol.*, 51 (1958), 400–407. Reprinted with permission.

4. What is the explanation for the findings in these experiments?

The purpose of this study was (*a*) to investigate the possibility that stimulation of the same brain electrode at the same intensity might have dual rewarding and punishing[1] effects, (*b*) to determine if such dual effects could explain a previous finding (9) that stimulation in the posterior hypothalamus would motivate prompt learning of escape responses but would not produce learning of avoidance responses, and (*c*) to rule out the possibility that the termination (rather than the onset) of the stimulation might be the cause of the reward effect.

A recent study (8) has shown that stimulation in certain areas of the brain can have rewarding effects on behavior. Animals learn to perform responses which are closely and regularly followed by the *onset* of the stimulation. Other studies (1, 9) have shown that stimulation in other areas of the brain has punishing effects. Animals learn responses which are closely and regularly followed by the *termination* of the stimulation. The possibility that both onset and termination of stimulation of the same electrode at the same voltage might be reinforcing has not been investigated.

The hypothesis of dual rewarding and punishing effects was originated to explain the paradoxical result of a preceding study (9) in which a "flight-like" emotional response evoked by stimulation in the posterior hypothalamus was used as the aversive stimulus in avoidance training. Cats stimulated in this area learned rapidly to *escape* the stimulation, but did not learn to *avoid* it in 270 trials. Control animals stimulated in the thalamus and mid-

brain needed only one-sixth as many trials to learn both escape and avoidance habits. If both the onset and the termination of the posterior hypothalamic stimulation were reinforcing, the animals would be rewarded (*a*) for *not* avoiding the aversive stimulus, i.e., for sitting still during the avoidance interval and allowing the stimulation to be turned on, and (*b*) for making the correct response to *escape* (turn off) the aversive stimulus after it was applied. It is also possible that the conditioning of fear (or "aversion") to the warning stimulus, viewed as an essential element in avoidance learning by current avoidance theories, might be interfered with by even a relatively weakly rewarding onset.

This hypothesis of dual effects was tested in the present experiment by combining bar-pressing tests showing that cats would learn to turn the stimulation on, with avoidance training tests showing that the *S*s would also learn to turn off the same stimulation at the same voltage.

A second experiment was performed to rule out the possibility that the *termination* of the stimulation might be the reinforcement for the learning of both the turning-on and turning-off habits. In this experiment, the animals learned two different but analogous responses to turn on and turn off the stimulation. The voltage was varied to bring out certain functional differences between the reinforcing effects of the onset and the termination.

experiment i

method

Subjects. Seven adult cats, five males and two females, were given the behavioral tests. Data from three exploratory animals are included in the anatomical findings.

Operative technique. Multiple electrodes

---

[1] Following traditional usage, "punishing" is used in this report to describe stimuli which an animal will learn to turn off or avoid, or both. "Escape" will refer to the turning-off response itself.

were implanted in the posterior hypothalamus under aseptic conditions with the aid of a Horsley-Clarke stereotaxic instrument. The technique and electrodes were the same as described previously (9), except that each wire was only 1 mm. shorter than the next longer one, and the uninsulated area at the tip was only .5 mm.

Apparatus. The stimulator was a Grass S-4 rectangular wave generator set for a undirectional pulse width of .2 ms. and a frequency of 100 pps. Stimulation was applied between a negative brain electrode and a positive indifferent electrode.

The bar-pressing apparatus for testing the reward effects of stimulation was a rectangular box with an interior 24 in. long, 10 in. wide, and 17 in. high. The "bar" was a metal plate that extended across the width of the box at one end and protruded 6 in. from the wall at a height of 5 in. above the floor. A downward movement of ⅝ in. at the front edge of the plate, requiring a force of 12 gm., closed the microswitch which started the .5 sec. of brain stimulation which followed each bar press. An electronic timer signaled when 2 min. had gone by without a bar press, the criterion of extinction. All bar presses were recorded with a Gerbrands cumulative recorder, and a .01-sec. clock and a counter were used to obtain precise measures during the test periods.

The apparatuses used in avoidance testing have been described in detail in the preceding study. A 66-in. alley was used for preliminary escape training before the avoidance training proper. The two avoidance training apparatuses were a T maze and a unidirectional hurdle box. Both were constructed so that time and error score could be obtained automatically.

Procedure. In brief, the order of procedure was (*a*) observation of unlearned responses elicited by stimulation, (*b*) tests for reward effects of stimulation on bar pressing, (*c*) avoidance training with stimulation as the US, (*d*) avoidance training with peripheral shock as the US, and (*e*) retests of reward effects.

In the first observation sessions, the points were classified in three categories, depending on the unconditioned response pattern elicited by stimulation. The first category of responses, termed "flight," consisted at low intensities of "visual searching," looking around the environment with quick, darting glances, and at high intensities of locomotor activity, searching every crack and cranny as if looking for a hole through which to escape. This was the emotional response pattern which produced escape learning but failed to motivate avoidance learning in the previous study, and was therefore of primary interest in the present investigation.

The second, more heterogeneous category was called "alarm" and included rage, painlike, and fearlike behavior.

The third group of responses, termed "motor" responses, consisted of localized motor responses such as unilateral eye closure, or repetitive stereotyped activities such as continuous circling or rolling on the floor. All these responses interfered markedly with the performance of learned habits.

Following the observation and classification sessions, the points were tested for reward effects by giving the animals repeated reconditioning-extinction cycles with a food reward and administering a brief burst (.5 sec.) of stimulation after each bar press during the extinction phase. When compared with normal extinction without stimulation, "rewarding" effects appeared as marked increases in the number of responses made during extinction. If the rewarding effects were strong enough to prevent extinction altogether, the stimulation reward was discontinued after 5 min. of responding, and the animal allowed to extinguish. When the stimulation of a point markedly decreased the number of responses during extinction, sometimes down to only one or two, it was classified as "disrupting."

The reconditioning portion of each cycle consisted of seven reinforcements of .7 gm. of mashed sardines delivered on a variable-interval schedule which averaged 12 sec. and ranged from 6 to 18 sec. The extinction phase was carried to a criterion of no response for a continuous 2-min. period. The number of responses during extinction and the time required to reach the criterion were recorded.

One electrode point was tested each day at four or five voltages. Each voltage was tested during the extinction phase of a different reconditioning-extinction cycle. The order of voltages was ascending. Two control cycles were given daily to determine the normal rate of extinction in the absence of stimulation.

As measured by the calibrated oscilloscope, the average voltage and current[2] at the lowest intensity were 2.0 v. and .5 ma., and at the highest intensity, 5.7 v. and 1.7 ma.

The number of bar presses during the extinction tests at the three highest voltages was averaged for each point. Six categories of effects were formulated from comparisons of mean scores with stimulation with mean scores without stimulation: strong and mild disruption, neutral, and mild, moderate, and strong reward.

After the tests for rewarding effects, two points in each animal were selected for avoidance training. These points included nine rewarding and five disrupting points. Stimulation of each point was used as the aversive stimulus in one of the two avoidance apparatuses.

For all rewarding points, the voltages used

[2] Averaging was over animals and points. Readings were taken as in previous report (9).

in avoidance training were within the range of rewarding effects. Mean voltage and current were 5.6 v. and 1.4 ma. During the last 15 trials, the voltages were raised about 20% to the highest possible value short of eliciting responses so strong that they would interfere with escape behavior.

The animals received 30 avoidance training trials per day for three days. This total of 90 trials was well beyond the number of trials [57] found sufficient in the preceding study for even the slowest learners to learn avoidance of peripheral shock or central stimulation in certain midbrain and thalamic structures. The general training procedure was the same as that described in the preceding study.

After completion of the avoidance testing with brain stimulation, the animals were given 30 additional trials in the T maze with peripheral shock as the US.

Lastly, the animals were retested for reward effects in the bar-pressing box with all points used in the avoidance tests and with most of the other points, particularly those with borderline effects.

Anatomical controls. The histology and localization procedures were similar to those described in the preceding study.

results

Unconditioned responses to stimulation. Of the 84 electrode points in the seven Ss, 48 elicited integrated emotional behavior patterns. These were divided into 39 points eliciting "flight" behavior and 9 eliciting "alarm" behavior. The latter group included 7 points eliciting rage, 1 eliciting fearlike cowering, and 1 eliciting painlike withdrawal. In Figure 1, the different types of URs are indicated by distinctive symbols on the left side of the midline. The URs elicited by 11 rewarding points from three exploratory ani-

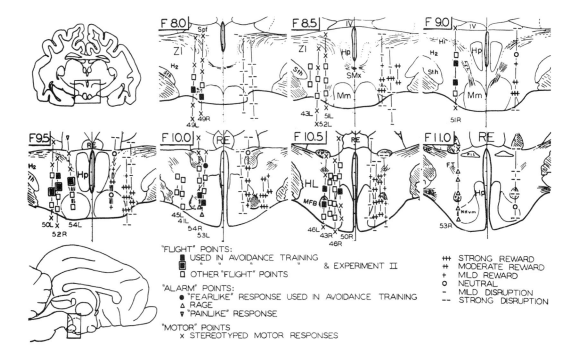

Fig. 1. Localization of unlearned responses and reward effects elicited by stimulation. Box in upper left diagram indicates area shown enlarged five times in following diagrams (4). Unlearned responses shown on left of midline; rewarding and disrupting effects from same electrodes shown on right. Each column is a single multiple electrode, with cat's number and hemisphere indicated below. Eleven rewarding points from three exploratory animals (Cats 41, 43, 45) are also plotted. Last diagram shows sagittal midline view with box indicating area covered by diagrams. Dotted lines inside box mark upper and lower boundaries of reward effects. Abbreviations: *HL, hypothalamus lateralis; Hp, hypothalamus posterior; MFB, median forebrain bundle; Mm, corpus mamillare; NHvm, n. hypothalami ventromedialis; SMx, supramammillary commissure; Sth, n. subthalamicus; ZI, zona incerta.*

mals were also plotted on the diagrams. Previous findings localizing the densest concentration of "flight" points in the posterior hypothalamic area (3, 9) are replicated in the present study.

The third, or "motor" category consisted of the remaining 36 points. Eleven of these were outside the brain in the ventral midline vascular tissue. They elicited tight closing of the ipsilateral eye, pulling the head and shoulders back rapidly, and at high intensities, clawing

in the air with the ipsilateral paw. Direct stimulation of the third nerve in about half the cases was evidenced by turning inward of the ipsilateral eye. Most of the 25 "motor" points inside the brain were in the dorsal hypothalamus, dorsomedial subthalamus, or ventromedial thalamus. In most cases they elicited circling in a contralateral direction or rolling in an ipsilateral direction or both.

Reward tests. Twenty-nine of the 84 points were rewarding in the bar-pressing test, 50 had disrupting effects, and 5 could not be clearly assigned to either group. The average optimal response rates for the rewarding points ranged from 6 to 35 responses per minute, with a median of 17.

Five of the seven Ss showed reward effects, and each of these had at least one rewarding point on each of the two electrodes. The other two animals showed no reliable reward effects despite the fact that some of their points were very close to locations where other animals showed strong reward effects. Whether these differences were due to slight variations in location, to individual differences in strength of fear aroused by strange stimuli, or to too much experience with disrupting stimulation in the earlier testing sessions is not clear from the available data.

The rewarding and disrupting effects of stimulation of the various points are plotted anatomically on the right side of the midline in the diagrams of Figure 1. In the limited region sampled in this behavioral study, there was considerable overlap of the area of the reward effects and the area where the "flight" response can be elicited. Two-thirds of the "flight" points were rewarding, while only 7% of the "alarm" and "motor" points showed any reward effects (and these were relatively weak). Most of the "flight" points having disrupting effects were located near the periphery of the principal cluster of "flight" points. However, any final conclusion regarding the relationship between the "flight" response and the rewarding effects must await more extensive mapping of the two phenomena. Reward effects have been obtained in the rat (7) in a variety of areas where "flight" responses are not obtained in the cat. This suggests that the association in the present study may be adventitious. It is of interest in this regard that all eight points having the strongest reward effects were lo-

cated in the lateral hypothalamus in the region where the medial forebrain bundle passes through on its way to the midbrain. Because of its connections with most of the areas where reward effects are found, it has been suggested that this fiber system may play an important role in the mechanism of centrally elicited reward.

The disrupting effects were obtained dorsal to the reward area in the subthalamus and ventromedial thalamus and ventrally, beneath the brain in the midline vascular tissue. Most of the "alarm" and "motor" points (87%) were disrupting.

Avoidance training. The points selected for avoidance training included 1 strongly rewarding point, 4 moderately rewarding, 4 mildly rewarding, 2 mildly disrupting, and 3 strongly disrupting. All points elicited "flight" behavior, with the exception of one strongly disrupting point which evoked fearlike "alarm" behavior. These points are indicated in Figure 1 by solid black symbols.

In the upper left graph of Figure 2 are plotted the percentages of avoidance responses during training with brain stimulation. Thirteen of the 14 points in the seven cats failed to motivate a single avoidance response in the course of 90 training trials. The animal motivated by stimulation of the fourteenth point (which was the single "alarm" point) made 15 avoidance responses in the first 40 trials and none thereafter.

The course of learning of the escape response is shown in terms of response times in the lower left graph. Steady improvement is apparent in the first 20 trials, by the end of which most animals had achieved a prompt escape response which was maintained through the remaining 70 trials. When the voltages were turned up to a maximum during the last three blocks of trials, the slower animals responded faster, but no animals made

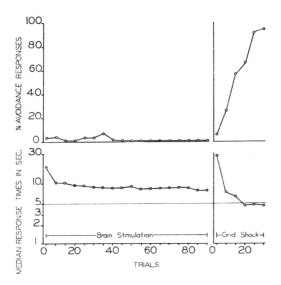

Fig. 2. Avoidance training with brain stimulation and grid shock. Upper graph shows percentage of avoidance responses. Left curve for brain stimulation, right curve for peripheral shock. Lower graph shows median response times. Fine horizontal line indicates point when US was given if animal was not already responding.

any avoidance responses. Additional evidence of learning of the escape response is found in a comparison of errors in the first and second halves of training, where 13 of 14 points showed a reduction in errors.

Following the avoidance training with brain stimulation, the animals were given 30 additional trials in the T maze with peripheral shock as the US. The prompt learning of avoidance under this condition, shown in the curves on the right in Figure 2, indicates that implantation of the electrodes had not destroyed some area essential to avoidance learning, and that the general procedure was favorable for conditioning.

Still left unanswered by these findings is the question of what was the critical reinforcing event or events which produced learning of both bar-pressing and escape responses. The fact that the cats would learn the escape

response, which was immediately followed by termination of the stimulation and a 4- to 8-min. intertrial interval, proves that the *termination* was one reinforcing event. However, the demonstration that the animals would learn to press a bar to obtain .5 sec. of the same level of stimulation cannot be taken as conclusive evidence that the *onset* was also rewarding. Since the termination of the stimulation followed the bar pressing by only .5 sec., the possibility remains that the termination might have been the reinforcing event for this response too. Conceivably, the motivation aroused by the stimulation might have a rewarding termination without a punishing onset, as is commonly believed to be the case with the sex drive. Or a physiological state following the termination of brain stimulation, such as an afterdischarge, might have rewarding properties. Alternatively, an effect similar to that reported by Miller (5) and Gwinn (2) may have been involved, where painful shocks given during the performance of a response facilitated the performance of the response for a large number of trials. The unusual character of the findings in the present and preceding studies argued that all logical alternative explanations should be ruled out before concluding that both onset and termination were rewarding. To determine whether the onset possessed rewarding properties separate from the termination, a second experiment was performed. In this test, separate turning-on and turning-off responses were used to obtain separate measures of the reinforcing properties of the onset and the termination of the stimulation.

experiment ii

method

Subjects. Three of the above *S*s which showed reward effects (Cats 50, 52, 54) were tested with one of the rewarding points used in avoidance training.

Apparatus. The apparatus was a symmetrical Y maze with distinctively painted arms 30 in. long, 12 in. wide, and 20 in. high. At the entrance to each arm was a guillotine door which could be used for detaining the animal after it had entered the arm. Response times were recorded with an automatic .01-sec. clock or an Esterline-Angus multichannel recorder, depending on whether a detention or free-responding procedure was used.

Procedure. In brief, the test consisted of turning the stimulation *on* when the cat entered one arm (the "on arm"), turning it *off* when it entered another arm (the "off arm"), and making no change in the stimulation if it entered the third arm (the "no-change arm"). From the results of the bar-pressing and escape learning tests, it was predicted that the animals would learn to oscillate back and forth between the on and off arms. The no-change arm served as an opportunity for the animal to make errors so that both error and time scores might be obtained.

The on and off arms were selected so that they would be contrary to the animal's initial preferences, as evidenced in its first choices. The reinforcements (onset and termination of stimulation) were applied at the moment when the last hind foot stepped across the threshold of the appropriate arms. In the detention procedure, the door was closed behind the animal when it entered the correct arm, and it was confined for 3 min. before being allowed to make the next choice. The stimulation was left on or off (depending on the arm) throughout this period. This increase of 180 sec. in the interval between the turning-on response and the termination of stimulation was deemed sufficient to be highly unfavorable for any possible reinforcement of the turning-on response by the termination. In

the free-responding procedure, S was allowed to oscillate freely between the on and off arms.

The design of the apparatus eliminated any need to handle the animals between trials. They received 15 turning-on and 15 turning-off trials daily for 7 days (Cat 52), 10 days (Cat 54), or 2 days (Cat 50). On Days 1, 2, 4, 5, 7, 8 and 10, the intensity of the emotional response elicited by the stimulation was relatively low, with median stimulus parameters of about 3.4 v. and .8 ma. On Days 3, 6 and 9, the voltage was increased about 50% for each animal.

results and discussion

All three animals learned to turn on and turn off the brain stimulation by choosing the correct arms. Cat 52, tested with a point having a stronger reward effect on bar pressing than the points used with the other two cats, learned and maintained a high level of performance with the 3-min. detention procedure. The other two cats (50 and 54) showed conflict, hesitation, and eventual avoidance toward the on-arm under the detention procedure. When switched to the free-responding procedure, both learned to oscillate back and forth between the on- and off-arms. Because of a generally weak reward effect, Cat 50 was not included in the later Y maze tests in which the stimulation voltage was varied.

Three principal findings in this second experiment are relevant to the question whether the onset of stimulation possessed a reinforcing property separate from that occurring at the termination. The first principal finding was that Cat 52 learned the turning-on response promptly despite the 3-min. detention period which was used to reduce to a minimum any possible reinforcing effect from the termination. Figure 3 presents the course of

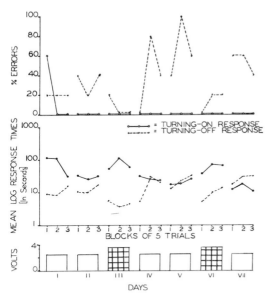

Fig. 3. Performance of turning-on and turning-off responses by Cat 52. Upper graph shows percentage of errors in blocks of five trials. Middle graph shows average response times.

learning and performance of Cat 52 in terms of response times and errors. On Days 1 and 2, the turning-on response shows significant improvement in both response times ($p = .02$) and errors ($p = .01$). Since it is very unlikely that the prompt learning of the turning-on response could be produced by reinforcement from the termination which was delayed for 3 min., this finding is taken as support for the hypothesis that the onset of stimulation can have an independent reinforcing effect.

The second principal finding was that at low voltages the turning-on response was learned much better than the turning-off response. In Figure 3, while Cat 52 was learning the turning-on response on Days 1 and 2, it failed to show any improvement in the turning-off response. On Day 2 and each low-voltage day thereafter, it performed the turning-on response with significantly fewer errors than the turning-off response (all

$ps < .02$). Similar results were obtained for Cat 54. The over-all superiority of the turning-on response at the low voltage was evidenced by the fact that after Day 1, each cat made very few or no turning-on errors, while the over-all performance of each on the turning-off response approximated the 50% chance level. Comparison of response times between the two responses would not be meaningful because the fast walking elicited by the stimulation artificially reduced the turning-off response times, despite numerous errors.

If the termination were the sole reinforcing event, the turning-off response would have been learned best, because it occurred closer in time to the termination. The two Ss' near-perfect performance of the turning-on response and near-chance performance of the turning-off response indicate that the onset was reinforcing at low voltage levels where the termination was not.

Since the previous demonstration of escape learning with these electrode points in Experiment I was with a considerably higher intensity than was used in this second experiment, the voltages were increased about 50% on certain days. Both animals made significantly fewer turning-off errors on each of the high voltage days (over-all $ps < .001$). This finding shows that the animals were not prevented from making the correct turning-off response by the stimulation, but could learn to do so if the termination were made sufficiently reinforcing by increasing the voltage.

The third principal finding was that the increased voltage had opposite effects on the turning-on and turning-off responses. The marked improvement in the *turning-off* response was accompanied by significantly slower response times for the *turning-on* response (over-all $ps < .001$ for each animal). However, the reward effect was still evident at this higher voltage, for the animals continued to respond, although more slowly and with evident conflict. Since both responses would be expected to improve together if there were only one reinforcing event, this inverse relationship furnishes additional support for the hypothesis of two reinforcing events.

The general conclusion drawn from these three principal findings is that both the onset and termination of stimulation in the posterior hypothalamus can exert separate reinforcing effects which can be elicited by the same electrode at the same intensity. For Ss of Experiment II, the reinforcing effect of the onset had a lower threshold than the reinforcing effect of the termination.

The results of this study support the original hypothesis that posterior hypothalamic stimulation initially elicits a positively reinforcing state, followed by a transition to an aversive state as the train of stimulation continues. One predictable consequence of such a close temporal succession of reward and punishment is that conflict behavior should appear in the turning-on response. This was observed in both Cats 52 and 54 in the second experiment. The increased time the animals took to turn on the stimulation at the higher voltage consisted, for the most part, of conflictful hesitation halfway into the on-arm. A second prediction would be that longer durations of stimulation, by lengthening the duration of the aversive component, should increase the strength of the conflict. This was confirmed with three cats [51, 52, 54] which were tested on bar-pressing with gradually increasing fixed durations of stimulation. They showed increasing conflict and finally stopped pressing altogether (at durations of 3, 6, and 18 sec.). The aversion for 3-min. durations shown by Cats 50 and 54 in Experiment II may be similarly explained.

These positively and negatively reinforcing states might be due to excitation of two overlapping neuronal systems having different recruiting or fatigue rates, or to sequential changes within a single system due to overexcitation or fatigue. While the findings give no specific indication of the nature of the mechanism by which the onset produces learning, they do rule out any explanation in terms of a reduction in general drive level (6). The marked increase in skeletal and autonomic excitation accompanying the "flight" response appeared immediately after the onset of the stimulation with no perceptible delay. The reward effects obtained from the flight points could not, therefore, be due to decreased excitation, but occurred in spite of greatly increased excitation.

All 14 points used in the avoidance training motivated learning of escape, but failed to produce stable avoidance. For the 9 of these points which showed reward effects, it is highly probable that these effects were important contributing factors in causing the animals to fail to avoid the stimulation. This is supported by the demonstration in Experiment II that three cats would learn to go to one arm of the Y maze to turn on the stimulation and to another arm to turn it off. Moreover, it was noted in the protocols of the original avoidance training with Cats 52 and 54 (motivated by the same points used later in Experiment II) that the animals crossed back to the starting box 35 and 9 times, respectively, soon after making the escape response.

The remaining five points having mild to strong disrupting effects, which also failed to motivate avoidance, raise the possibility that other factors than the reward effect may also have been involved. The finding in the preceding study that stimulation in certain parts of the thalamus and midbrain is capable of motivating both escape and avoidance learning, provides evidence that failure to learn avoidance is not a general characteristic of brain stimulation and that the procedure and apparatus were not unfavorable for avoidance learning. The locations of these five disrupting points were very close (within a radius of 1 mm.) to the locations of points in other cats which did have reward effects. If the reward component were relatively weak compared with the aversive component, it might not be strong enough to maintain bar pressing, yet be sufficient to interfere with the process of fear conditioning and avoidance learning.

Since both rewarding and punishing effects may be elicited by stimulation of the same point, some caution should be exercised in the use of bar-pressing rates alone as indices of the strength of the reward component. If the animals could learn to avoid successfully the punishing state by pressing the bar for shorter durations, they would show an increase in over-all rate if the interresponse times remained constant. On the other hand, if the punishing state could not be avoided, a conflict would be likely to occur, decreasing the over-all rate to a degree dependent on the intensity of the aversive state.

summary

Two experiments were performed showing that both rewarding and punishing effects can be elicited by stimulation of the posterior hypothalamus of cats with the same electrode at the same voltage.

In Experiment I, the cats learned (*a*) to press a bar to turn on the stimulation, and (*b*) to perform a locomotor escape response to turn off the same stimulation at the same voltage. They did not learn to avoid the stimulation by responding to a preceding CS, although given a large number of trials after acquisition of the escape response.

In Experiment II, some Ss were trained to oscillate back and forth between two of the three arms of a symmetrical Y maze to turn on the stimulation in one arm and turn it off in the other. At a low voltage, the turning-on response was performed with few or no errors, but the turning-off response was performed at a chance level. At a higher voltage, the turning-off response improved markedly, while the turning-on response deteriorated, being performed more slowly and with evident conflict.

The second experiment ruled out the possibility that the termination of the stimulation might be the cause of the reward effect. It was concluded that both the onset and the termination of stimulation of the same electrode at the same intensity can have separate reinforcing effects.

The finding that the rewarding intensities of stimulation elicited a marked general excitation of the animal in the form of vigorous "flightlike" activity rules out drive reduction as an explanation of the rewarding effect of the onset. The reinforcement at the termination appears to be due to the cessation of an aversion drive which does not become effective until after the initial rewarding effect of the onset.

It appears highly probable that the finding in the preceding study (9) that cats would learn to escape, but not to avoid, posterior hypothalamic stimulation may be attributed in most, if not all cases, to the dual reinforcing effects of the onset and termination of the stimulation.

references

1. Delgado, J. M. R., Roberts, W. W., & Miller, N. E. Learning motivated by electrical stimulation of the brain. *Amer. J. Physiol.*, 1954, **179**, 587–593.

2. Gwinn, G. T. The effects of punishment on acts motivated by fear. *J. exp. Psychol.*, 1949, **39**, 260–269.
3. Hess, W. R. *Das Zwischenhirn: syndrome, lokalisationen, funktionen.* (2nd ed.) Basel: Schwabe, 1954.
4. Jasper, H. H., & Ajmone-Marsan, C. *A stereotaxic atlas of the diencephalon of the cat.* Ottawa: National Research Council of Canada, 1954.
5. Miller, N. E. Learnable drives and rewards. In S. S. Stevens (Ed.), *Handbook of experimental psychology.* New York: Wiley, 1951. Pp. 435–472.
6. Olds, J. Physiological mechanisms of reward. In M. R. Jones (Ed.), *Nebraska symposium on motivation.* Lincoln: Univer. Nebraska, 1955.
7. Olds, J. A preliminary mapping of electrical reinforcing effects in the rat brain. *J. comp. physiol. Psychol.*, 1956, **49**, 281–285.
8. Olds, J., & Milner, P. Positive reinforcement produced by electrical stimulation of septal area and other regions of rat brain. *J. comp. physiol. Psychol.*, 1954, **47**, 419–427.
9. Roberts, W. W. Rapid escape learning without avoidance learning motivated by hypothalamic stimulation in cats. *J. comp. physiol. Psychol.*, 1958, **51**, 391–399.

19   satiation effects in self-stimulation of the brain*

James Olds

1. What is the difference between a "positive feedback system" and a "negative feedback system"?

2. What implications do these findings have for learning theory?

3. How can the positive-feedback data be explained in terms of physiological efficiency of the organism?

4. What does Olds mean when he says "intrinsic satiation effects"?

* J. Olds, "Satiation Effects in Self-Stimulation of the Brain," *J. comp. physiol. Psychol.*, 51 (1958), 675–678. Reprinted with permission.

In self-stimulation experiments (2, 3), electrodes are chronically implanted to stimulate small regions of the brain. A circuit is arranged so that the animal can stimulate itself by manipulating a switch. If electrodes are placed in a system which includes most of the hypothalamus and rhinencephalon and parts of the tegmentum, thalamus, and basal ganglia, animals will stimulate themselves at rates far above operant levels (1). Rates often range above 5,000 responses an hour with electrodes in the ventral posterior hypothalamus (just in front of the mammillary body). Much lower rates (about 200 an hour) occur in most parts of limbic and rhinencephalic cortex. The question arises whether or not satiation will occur if animals are allowed to self-stimulate for long periods of time.

The present experiment was designed to study the stability of response rates from day to day when animals were allowed access to self-stimulation for 1 hr. a day for several weeks, and the changes in these stable rates which occurred when animals were then allowed to self-stimulate for 48 consecutive hours.

method

In these experiments, 32 animals were prepared with electrodes chronically implanted in parts of the hypothalamus and in parts of the septal and amygdaloid regions of the telencephalon. One pair of bipolar silver electrodes of 0.01-in. diameter was implanted in each rat. Electrodes were insulated all the way down; only the cross section of the tip was bared. The two electrodes were side by side in the brain, separated by a distance of .002 to .004 in.

After implantation and a four-day recovery period, Ss were trained to self-stimulate in Skinner boxes. A sine wave current of 60 cycles per second was used for the stimulus; the level of stimulation was constant for all Ss: 1 v. r.m.s. As the resistance of the electrodes was about 12,000 ohms, the current was about 83 μa. (In subsequent experiments, we have found it more rigorous to control electric current instead of voltage.) In the Skinner box each depression of a pedal caused a stimulus to the brain which was turned off automatically after $\frac{1}{2}$ sec. if S held the lever that long. The S had to release the lever and press it again to get more.

After about two weeks of pretraining, Ss were tested for an hour a day for a month to determine stability of response rates over time. Then all Ss were allowed 48 hr. of continuous self-stimulation. In the course of the 48-hr. tests, Ss were unattended during about 8 hr. of every day. Some Ss became disconnected owing to continuous twisting of cords, and others chewed through their cords. Sixteen of the total group of 32 animals came through the 48-hr. test without becoming disconnected; the data on these Ss is reported below. Two facts about the selectivity involved here should be mentioned: (a) Extremely rapid self-stimulators were apt to become disconnected because their movement often involved turning and therefore twisting; (b) extremely slow responders were apt to chew cords. Thus, animals self-stimulating in a middle range of 1,000 to 2,000 responses per hour were the ones that tended to come through the 48-hr. test intact. In an effort to rule out changes that might be caused by hunger or

thirst, food pans and water bottles were available in the Skinner boxes all during the 48-hr. test period. After testing, Ss were sacrificed and brains were sliced and examined microscopically to determine the exact location of the electrode track.

results

one-hour daily test

During the one month of testing 1 hr. a day, all Ss achieved relatively stable self-stimulation rates. Table 1 shows the mean rate for the final 12 days for each animal (only animals that completed 48-hr. tests are included) and the standard deviation as a percentage of the mean rate. The standard deviations range from less than 10% to more than 30%. The average for Ss with hypothalamic electrodes was 16%; for Ss with telencephalic electrodes, 21%. Some of the faster Ss which did not complete the 48-hr. test gave even more stable rates, as indicated by the top half of Figure 1. This shows cumulative response curves for 15 consecutive days for one S. Here the slope represents the response rate (each saw tooth indicates 500 responses, and each block represents an hour of responding). The rate at the top of Figure 1 is about 5,000 an hour for an S with electrodes in the posterior hypothalamus. Shown in Figure 1 is a much slower rate of 750 an hour obtained with electrodes in the ventral septal area. In other experiments it has been found that such stability can be maintained for periods of six months to a year if Ss are tested every day.

forty-eight-hour test

In the 48-hr. test, Ss with hypothalamic electrodes maintained rapid rates until slowed by sheer physical exhaustion; Ss with telen-

Table 1. Rates, Standard Deviations, and Endurance Scores

Locus of Electrodes	Mean hourly rate for last 12 test days 1 hr. a day		SD of 12 daily scores as % of mean	Highest hourly rate in 2nd 24 hr. of 48-hr. test as % of 1st-hr. rate
Hypothalamus Group				
L. post	1,925		20	67
	985		17	90
L. mid.	927*	10	12*	167
	1,959*	6	19*	100
L. ant.	730*	5	2*	167
	1,036		6	133
M. mid.	2,740		32	40
	205		15	67
M. ant.	1,413		8	67
	1,306		13	69
Mean	1,343		16	97[a]
Telencephalon Group				
L. sept.	1,167		29	18
	893		13	23
M. sept.	821		11	100
	716		29	50
	1,121		12	35
Amyg.	575		34	35
Mean	882		21	44[a]

Note.—Means based on fewer than 12 observations are indicated by an asterisk followed by the actual number of observations. The corresponding standard deviations were, therefore, not used in computation of the hypothalamic mean.

[a] The difference between these two scores is significant at the .05 level.

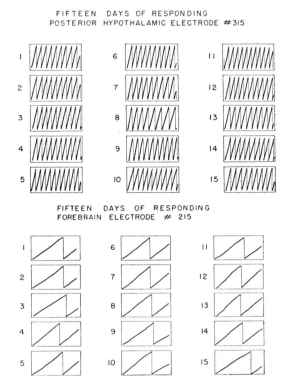

FIFTEEN DAYS OF RESPONDING
POSTERIOR HYPOTHALAMIC ELECTRODE #315

FIFTEEN DAYS OF RESPONDING
FOREBRAIN ELECTRODE # 215

Fig. 1. See text for explanation.

cephalic electrodes often showed sharp slowing after 4 to 8 hr. The difference between the two groups is indicated in the last column of Table 1 by the difference between average endurance scores of 97 for the Ss with hypothalamic electrodes and 44 for Ss with telencephalic electrodes. Such a large difference would occur by chance less than once in 20 trials.

The endurance score for each rat was determined by selecting the highest hourly rate during the second day of continuous testing and stating it as a percentage of the rate for the first hour of the first day of continuous testing. A score of 100 thus indicates that the S came back up to its first-hour rate on the second day.

The difference between the two groups indicates a satiation effect with telencephalic electrodes that does not occur with hypothalamic ones. The difference is demonstrated more clearly in Figures 2 and 3. Figure 2 shows 48 hr. of responding for one S with hypothalamic electrodes. A rate of more than 2,000 responses per hour was maintained con-

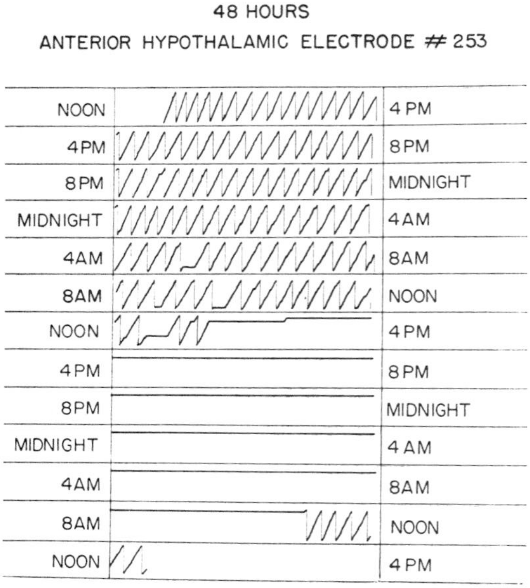

48 HOURS
ANTERIOR HYPOTHALAMIC ELECTRODE # 253

NOON	///////////////	4 PM
4 PM	///////////////	8 PM
8 PM	///////////////	MIDNIGHT
MIDNIGHT	///////////////	4 AM
4 AM	///////////////	8 AM
8 AM	///////////////	NOON
NOON	/ / /\	4 PM
4 PM		8 PM
8 PM		MIDNIGHT
MIDNIGHT		4 AM
4 AM		8 AM
8 AM	////	NOON
NOON	//	4 PM

Fig. 2. See text for explanation.

tinuously for the first 26-hr. period. This rate did not continue through the second day. Instead, the S slept for almost 20 hr.; upon awakening it went back to responding at a rate of 2,000 an hour. The electrodes in this case were in the anteroventral hypothalamus (just behind the preoptic area), stimulating a region slightly medial and dorsal to the fornix.

The data for some other Ss are given in Figure 3. Here the 48 hr. of the experiment run along the abscissa and cumulative response totals along the ordinate. The dotted line represents the end of the first 24-hr. period. The shaded areas on the abscissa represent periods of darkness from 8 P.M. to 6 A.M. Data for Ss with hypothalamic electrodes are shown on the right; for those with telencephalic electrodes, on the left. There is a striking difference between self-stimulation rates for these two groups; Ss with hypothalamic electrodes produced self-stimulation

rates in the same order of magnitude on the second day as on the first, while almost all Ss with telencephalic electrodes showed sharp slowing after 4 to 8 hr. In almost all records for Ss with telencephalic electrodes, that is, there is a sharp inflection point occurring about 8 hr. after the beginning of the continuous test. These Ss apparently began at their old 1-hr.-a-day rates and then shifted to a new 24-hr.-a-day rate. Thus, there appears to be a daily satiation effect in the case of telencephalic stimulation which does not occur when electrodes are implanted in the hypothalamus.

discussion

Drive-reduction theories of reinforcement have considered satiation to occur as the drive state declines. Thus, motivated behavior, by reducing drive, would tend to turn itself off. Such a negative feedback principle would be functional because it would permit allocation of the organism's time and energy to a wide variety of needs.

The demonstration of strong positive motivation apparently uncoordinated with drive reduction raises the possibility of a positive feedback system in which the result of a behavior would lead to more and more of the same behavior. This would endanger the organism by causing a neglect of other needs.

In nature, the scarcity of reward objects probably affords some protection, as possibly also do biological shutoff mechanisms such as the full stomach or the empty seminal vesicle. Finally, some mechanism apparently functions to produce a purely neural satiation, as indicated by the pronounced slowing in telencephalic self-stimulation rates after 4- to 8-hr. periods of rapid responding.

The possibility should not be overlooked, however, that an organism with positive moti-

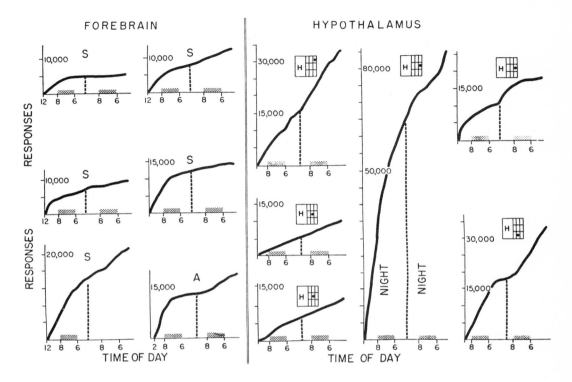

FOREBRAIN

HYPOTHALAMUS

RESPONSES

RESPONSES

TIME OF DAY

TIME OF DAY

Fig. 3. (See text for explanation.) The boxes marked *H* on the right indicate electrode position in hypothalamus as medial to lateral (left to right) and anterior to posterior (top to bottom).

vational mechanisms is under some danger of having these mechanisms run away on the positive feedback principle, as evidenced by the hypothalamic self-stimulators, which go to sheer exhaustion.

summary

In these experiments self-stimulation rates via hypothalamic and telencephalic electrodes were measured for 1 hr. a day for a month, and then for 48 consecutive hours. All Ss gave stable rates throughout the hour and from day to day in 1-hr.-a-day tests. In the 48-hr. satiation tests, animals with hypothalamic

electrodes self-stimulated to exhaustion and showed no intrinsic satiation tendencies. The Ss with telencephalic electrodes, however, showed radical slowing of self-stimulation after 4 to 8 hr. of continuous responding. This indicates some intrinsic satiation effect in self-stimulation via telencephalic electrodes.

references

1. Olds, J. A preliminary mapping of electrical reinforcing effects in the rat brain. *J. comp. physiol. Psychol.*, 1956, **49**, 281–285.
2. Olds, J. Runway and maze behavior con-

trolled by basomedial forebrain stimulation in the rat. *J. comp. physiol. Psychol.,* 1956, **49**, 507–512.

3. Olds, J., & Milner, P. Positive reinforcement produced by electrical stimulation of septal area and other regions of rat brain. *J. comp. physiol. Psychol.,* 1954, **47**, 419–427.

chapter 6

motivation 2

In Chapter 1 the nervous system was presented as the primary system responsible for the coordination of behavior. In this chapter on motivation, the stress is on the interaction of the neural and chemical systems in the coordination and regulation of behavior.

The first article by Frank Beach (Reading 20) gives a review of the literature on the regulatory mechanisms in a comparative study of organisms. After establishing the individual importance of neural and chemical factors, Beach proceeds to examine their coaction in the regulation of sexual behavior. Since the study of the physiological psychology of sex is Beach's special area of research, his discussion of coaction is authoritative for sexual behavior and, at the same time, gives the general approach to the interrelation of the two sets of factors.

Sexual behavior in most higher organisms (mammals and birds) depends on innate neural structures that are sensitized by sex hormones. In general, the higher the creature is phylogenetically, the less is the importance of immediate hormone stimulation and the more the importance of brain control. Even in the primates, however, hormone sensitization is vital, as illustrated by the differences between pre-pubertal castrates (no hormonal sensitization) and post-pubertal castrates (hormonal sensitization). The post-pubertal castrates show arousal and other sexual behavior, whereas the pre-pubertal castrates do not. Also, the lower the animal stands in his phylum, the greater is the difference between males and females. In general, males depend more on cortical factors, and females depend more on hormones. In the human species, however, both sexes depend more heavily on cortical than on hormonal factors.

In the second selection in this chapter (Reading 21), Beach and his collaborators show the importance of the cortex in mating behavior of male cats. *Unilateral* decortication in male rats stops mating behavior—in cats it does not. In both species *bilateral* decortication causes a cessation of mating behavior. This study corroborates the previous findings on species differences and on the importance of the cortex in male mammals.

In the third article (Reading 22, by Allan Mirsky), the importance to the social behavior of monkeys of the administration of sex hormones is reported. Previous studies had indicated that in lower animals and chimpanzees the injection of male hormones (androgens) tends to enhance dominance of both males and females, whereas the injection of estrogens "reduce aggressiveness or are without effect." Mirsky shows that with the rhesus macaque monkeys hormone administration does not change dominance and aggressiveness. Such findings as these are important in reminding the scientist to be wary of too broad a generalization of experimental findings.

In Reading 23, Daniel Lehrman demonstrates that in birds "the stimuli provided by the bird's activity and that of its mate affect the pattern of hormone secretion, which in its turn influences the behavior." The importance of this paper lies in the demonstration that chemical factors interact with neural factors arising from the overt behavior in another organism. Not only do neural and chemical factors influence behavior, but behavior in turn influences these factors.

In the last article in this chapter (Reading 24), Charles Lyman gives a full and interesting account of the phenomenon of hibernation. Although a wide variety of warm-blooded birds and mammals hibernate (body temperature falls from around 100°F to about 40°F), Lyman points out that nobody knows why animals hibernate—or why animals that are similar do not hibernate. His account has heuristic value in that it suggests a wide variety of needed research dealing with vitamin, hormone, and other physiological factors.

20   neural and chemical regulation of behavior *

Frank A. Beach

1. What is the relationship between the maturation of reflexes and the development of the nervous system in mammal fetuses and infants?

2. How do chemical factors affect the development of the nervous system?

3. How do hormones affect the behavior of adults?

4. What are the differences in the contribution of the neocortex between male and female mammals?

5. What are the differential effects in male and female infra-primate mammals of pre-pubertal and post-pubertal castration?

* F. A. Beach, "Neural and Chemical Regulation of Behavior," *Biological and Biochemical Bases of Behavior*" H. F. Harlow and C. N. Woolsey (eds.) (University of Wisconsin Press, 1958), 263–284. Reprinted with permission.

The first aim of this paper is to survey interdisciplinary research dealing with the neural and chemical regulators of behavior. Such a survey, of course, cannot be complete. Recent progress in the development of biochemical techniques and increases in our knowledge of neurophysiological function have produced a remarkable advance in the understanding of the neurochemical bases for behavior. In this area of interdisciplinary research a major break-through in the near future seems almost inevitable.

A second objective of the present discussion is to present a detailed analysis of one type of behavior in terms of its neural and chemical correlates. My purpose is to illustrate the interdisciplinary nature of current research; to show how the neural, chemical, and experiential influences which regulate behavior are being studied; and to examine the way in which all three act together to control one particular type of response.

Longitudinal or epigenetic studies of physiological mechanisms controlling behavior have proven their worth time and again. Relationships between a particular physical system and the organism's behavior are often most clearly seen at the time that the relationship develops. Study of the way such relationships evolve often throws light upon their nature in adult forms. Accordingly, various types of physiology-behavior correlations will be considered here from two points of view: the developmental aspect and the aspect of their nature in the adult organism.

relationships between behavior and the nervous system

developmental schedules

The intimate and fundamental nature of relationships between the nervous system and behavior is strikingly revealed by correlations between the appearance of new forms of behavior and the completion of growth changes in associated neural structures. This was convincingly demonstrated by Coghill in his classic studies of swimming behavior in amphibian larva (23). Coghill was able to analyze the development of this complex form of behavior into a sequence of reflexive responses, beginning with lateral flexion of the anterior end of the embryo and resulting eventually in the rapid, undulating movements necessary to true swimming. At the same time, he showed that the progression from one behavioral stage to the next is closely related to the laying-down of new pathways in the central nervous system. Coghill's work provided a sound basis for the theory that reflexogenic development in embryonic and neonatal organisms depends heavily upon maturational changes within the nervous system.

This generalization also applies to the human fetus, as shown by the investigations of Hooker (33) and Humphrey (34). These workers report that the earliest reflexogenic response of the human infant occurs at approximately seven and one-half weeks of menstrual age. Stimulation of the nose-mouth area evokes contralateral axial flexion which is limited to the cervical region. The appearance of this response to external stimulation is closely correlated with the penetration of the first cervical segments by the descending root of V.

It has long been known that some reflexes which are present in the newborn infant change at a predictable time after birth, and such maturational changes in reflexive response are related to concomitant developments in the nervous system. For example, the waning of the Babinski reflex is usually regarded as a product of maturational changes in the pyramidal tract. Hines's meticulous studies of postural reflexes and progression in the young macaque provide convincing proof that the gradual maturation of locomotory behavior in primates depends upon growth changes within the nervous system (32).

That changes in various bodily adjustments of anthropoid apes and human beings reflect parallel changes in the nervous system is also indicated by the existence of regular "timetables of development." This has been amply demonstrated by Gesell's work on human children (28) and by the more recent studies of Riesen and Kinder on the young chimpanzee (44).

As individuals grow older it becomes more difficult to discern relationships between further developmental changes in physiological systems and behavioral maturation. Nevertheless, it is exceedingly likely that some of the changes which occur in humans during adolescence are related to changes in brain function, such as those that affect the EEG.

behavior during maturity

To summarize the evidence concerning relations between the nervous system and adult behavior would be a monumental task and quite out of place in the present discussion. The results of clinical medicine, human brain surgery, and experimental studies of infrahuman animals place beyond question the conclusion that complex behavior and brain function are closely interrelated. Longitudinal studies suggest that the brain may undergo deteriorative changes with advancing age, and there are many psychological investigations which suggest a parallel alteration in certain intellectual capacities and perhaps in emotional behavior as well.

relations between body chemistry and behavior

developmental aspects

Chemical factors in neural maturation. From the ontogenetic point of view one of the first and most important aspects of the relationship between body chemistry and behavior pertains to biochemical factors which control the laying down of basic neural circuits during embryonic development. This evidence has been reviewed by Sperry (49), whose own experimental work brilliantly illustrates the importance to psychology of such interdisciplinary attacks upon central problems.

During the development of the visual system fibers arising in the ganglion layer of the retina extend their axons through the optic stalk to terminate eventually in the optic tectum. The final establishment of midbrain connections is not a chance affair. Instead, axons associated with a particular quadrant of the retina invariably establish contact with cells in a particular tectal region. It is hypothesized that this "homing behavior" of the growing axone depends upon biochemical affinities between different separate parts of the retina and corresponding areas in the optic tectum. Experimental interference with the establishment of normal connections between the visual end-organ and its central projection area results in permanent disturbance of visually directed behavior.

Enzyme systems and behavioral maturation. Another example of biochemical factors influencing behavioral growth has been revealed by investigations of the development of enzyme systems in amphibian embryos. Following the original studies of Coghill, Sawyer (46) measured the concentrations of acetylcholine and cholinesterase in salamander embryos at different stages of development. His principal finding was that cholinesterase, which is thought to be essential for the rapid transmission of nerve impulses, is present in relatively small amounts in the very young embryo and increases in concentration as the organism develops. Most significant is the fact that a sudden rise in cholinesterase level is closely correlated with the appearance of the fully developed swimming reaction.

The findings of Coghill and Sawyer underscore the fact that the development of swimming behavior depends upon maturational changes in both the nervous system and the enzymes which influence neural function. That neural maturation alone is not sufficient to produce the behavior was demonstrated by Sawyer when he raised salamanders in a solution of esserin, which does not interfere with neural growth but does inactivate cholinesterase. The experimental larvae grew normally, but they showed no swimming activity. Individuals that had been kept in esserin well past the time at which swimming would have appeared were transferred to pure water, and within a very short time, as the esserin effects wore off, fully developed swimming behavior appeared.

Hormonal factors in ontogenesis. Many changes take place in the endocrine system in the course of development, and some of these are closely associated with changes in behavior. Some of the relationships, although correlated in time, are obviously remote as far as mediating effects are concerned. For example, amphibian behavior changes in several ways as a result of metamorphosis, and the metamorphic change is known to depend upon secretion of thyroxin. The behavioral alterations are thus an indirect product of endocrine activity.

In a few instances fairly direct relationships have been discovered. One example is revealed by Kollros' study of the development of the eye blink reflex in the tadpole (40). Appear-

ance of this response awaits the attainment of a functional condition in certain crucial centers in the midbrain. Kollros implanted minute fragments of agar impregnated with thyroxin in the locality of this reflex center. In this fashion he was able to stimulate precocious appearance of the ocular response well in advance of the expected metamorphic modifications of the total organism.

The striking changes which occur in many species at the time of puberty can often be traced directly to the secretion of hormones by the reproductive glands. Morphologic changes such as growth of the copulatory organ in the male rat or of the comb in the rooster are known to depend upon testicular secretions; and in the absence of these chemical stimulators the normal structural changes do not occur. In addition the testis hormone appears to affect the central nervous system. Thus the young chick injected with testosterone propionate not only grows a large comb but also is stimulated to crow in the fashion of an adult cock. Similarly, androgen treatment of prepuberal male rats produces growth and secretory activity in the seminal vesicles and at the same time induces fully developed copulatory reactions.

biochemical factors in adulthood

Hormones. Secretions of several endocrine glands affect behavior throughout adult life. More detailed evidence on this point will be presented later, but at the present juncture it is pertinent to note that endocrine pathology is often reflected in abnormal behavior. For example, extreme hypothyroidism has a lasting effect upon behavior, as does hypogonadism, or deterioration of the adrenal cortex, or malfunction of the pituitary.

Roughly speaking, hormonal influences upon behavior can be divided into two categories. There are those effects which are exerted through the central nervous system directly, and those which involve nonnervous structures. The testis hormone influences sexual behavior of some male animals in part by virtue of its capacity to modify the epithelium of the glans penis in such a way as to increase its sensitivity to tactile stimulation (14). Similarly, part of the effect of ovarian hormones upon feminine sexual behavior undoubtedly is due to estrin-induced local changes in the vagina and associated structures.

The parental feeding responses of the ring dove and other members of the pigeon family are stimulated by treatment with prolactin. This hypophyseal secretion undoubtedly has many effects upon the bird, but its influence upon this particular response has been traced to changes which it produces in the crop sac. The engorged crop serves as a source of local stimulation which is important if not essential to the initial feeding responses directed by inexperienced parents toward their first squabs (41).

Of course, it would be a mistake to conclude that all hormonal effects upon behavior must involve changes in receptor or effector structures. It is, for example, quite clear that the sexual responsiveness of male rats remains high despite experimental interference with genital sensation (11). Furthermore, there are some kinds of hormonally conditioned behavior which do not appear to depend upon peripheral changes. For example, the aggressive behavior of the female hamster toward the male is eliminated or greatly reduced by the presence of ovarian hormones, and this appears to be primarily, if not exclusively, a central nervous change (38).

The ingenious experiments of Richter (43) have shown very clearly that the food preferences of some animals are affected by endocrinological factors. In the presence of various hormonal insufficiencies homeostatic shifts in food intake often occur spontaneously. Although it was at one time supposed that changes in peripheral receptors might be responsible, more recent experiments implicate the central nervous system (3).

Other endogenous chemical factors. Biochemical factors affecting behavior in adulthood involve many effects of enzyme systems. In particular, cholinesterase and acetylcholine appear to play an important role in the functioning of the nervous system. Rosenzweig and Krech have measured the relative concentration of these enzymes in different parts of the cerebral cortex of the rat. They find differences in the cholinesterase activity of different brain regions, and some of these differences are in turn correlated with behavior. The pattern of enzyme activity in the brains of rats whose behavior is dominated by visual cues is different from that found in animals that react primarily to spatial stimuli.

Clinical medicine provides us with numerous examples of behavioral abnormalities which are associated with defects in body chemistry. Thus, the intellectual deficit associated with phenylketonuria is correlated with an abnormally high level of phenylpyruvic acid resulting from inability to metabolize phenylalanine, although the relationship probably is not a direct one (35). The hallucinations and delusions which often accompany pellagra have been shown to be results of the primary vitamin deficiency (50).

coaction of neural, hormonal, and experiential factors in the regulation of sexual behavior

To shift now from a discussion of generalities to the consideration of more detailed findings, I propose to examine the ways in which neural and hormonal factors function in the regulation of sexual behavior.

neural components

A few scattered experiments have dealt with the neural factors involved in mating behavior of fish, amphibia, reptiles, and birds, but most of the available evidence comes from studies on mammals.

Contribution of noncortical mechanisms. These investigations suggest first of all that many of the simpler, reflexive responses which are normally incorporated into the total sexual pattern are mediated by centers situated below the cortex and even in the spinal cord. For instance, male mammals are capable of genital erection and ejaculation after complete section of the spinal cord in the lumbar region (1). Decerebrate female cats and guinea pigs display the postural reflexes of coition (1). A series of experiments by Bard and others (2, 24) indicate that the fundamental mating reactions of infraprimate females are mediated by thalamic mechanisms. Other studies implicate the hypothalamus as well (26).

Investigations of subcortical function in masculine sexual performance are not numerous. According to Clark (21), hypothalamic injury involving the medial half of the anterior hypothalamus reduces sexual performance in the male rat. A more extensive and systematic investigation by Rogers (45) showed that male rats sustaining damage to the ventromedial premammillary areas eventually cease mating but can be restored to normal sexual performance by the administration of androgen. Apparently the loss of potency in such cases reflects decrease in androgen output by the testis, which in turn is due to interference with pituitary gonadotropic function. In a different category are those rats with com-

plete or nearly complete destruction of the tuberal regions. Animals in this category rarely mate after operation and are unresponsive to androgen therapy. In this instance crucial neural circuits appear to have been disrupted.

It appears that the amygdala and perhaps the pyriform and temporal cortex may contribute to masculine sexual behavior. In any event, Klüver and Bucy (39) reported "hypersexuality" in male monkeys following temporal injury. More recently, Schreiner and Kling (47) have described changes in the sexual behavior of male cats following destruction of the pyriform cortex and extensive invasion of the amygdala. These changes consisted of the appearance of copulatory attempts directed toward a variety of biologically inadequate stimulus partners including chickens, dogs, monkeys, and other male cats.

An unpublished exploratory study conducted in my laboratory suggests that lesions to the amygdala produce a temporary rise in the sexual responsiveness of male dogs, but this change is reversible, and the increased reactivity disappears within a few months. Removal of a large part of the limbic cortex in males of this species is followed by a reduction in sexual activity, but this change also is dissipated several months after operation.

Contribution of the neocortex in male mammals. The neocortex plays an important role in the mediation of copulatory behavior in males of several species and is less important in others. According to Stone (51), extensive invasion of the neopallium does not eliminate copulatory activity in male rabbits. Brooks (20) found that complete decortication does not abolish the sexual act in males of this species provided the olfactory bulbs are intact. Subsequent loss of the bulbs eliminates coital performance in decorticated males.

Male rats may continue to copulate after

loss of large portions of the neocortex, but complete decortication eliminates all responsiveness to the receptive female (4). Furthermore, partial operations which fail to eliminate sexual behavior have nevertheless been shown to reduce the male's susceptibility to sexual arousal.

Partially decorticated males that continue to copulate do so in normal fashion. Apparently at this level of the evolutionary scale the cortex is not essential for coordination of the separate reactions involved in pursuit of the female and execution of the coital response. However, cortical tissue is not without sexual function. Its primary contribution has to do with maintaining the male's sexual excitability at such a level that lower executive centers are stimulated and thrown into action in response to the appropriate external cues.

More recent investigations of cortical function in the sexual activity of male cats tell a different story (17, 18, 54). It is clear that the carnivore cortex is more intimately involved than that of the rodent in the management of mating responses. In the cat, as in the male rat, total decortication abolishes all responses to the estrous female. However, removal of a sufficient amount of cortex from the occipital lobe can interfere with mating without producing any recognizable decrease in the male's sexual excitability. Cats suffering this type of brain injury will copulate normally if they are placed in contact with the receptive female. Cortical blindness prevents their locating the distant female and approaching her, and hence indirectly interferes with sexual activity. It does not reduce sexual excitability or interfere with the ability to execute the coital pattern.

Males of this species which have been deprived of the frontal lobes show no decline in sexual responsiveness. They follow the receptive female continuously and repeatedly attempt to mate with her. However, because of motor abnormalities produced by the frontal lesion, such cats are almost totally incapable of completing the mating. They grip the female, mount her (usually in an abnormal position), and execute copulatory attempts; but they are unable to carry the pattern through to its normal end point.

Comparison of rodents and carnivores makes it apparent that evolutionary changes resulting in the increased corticalization of sensorimotor control over all complex behavior has had its effects upon sexual activity. By virtue of its assumption of a greater degree of authority over a wide variety of behavioral responses, the neopallium in the cat has become more heavily involved in the male's mating performance. It is possible that the neocortex plays a dual role, contributing not only to the organization of the reproductive performance, but also to the general level of excitability of the male.

Contribution of the neocortex in female mammals. The neural mediators of sexual behavior in female mammals differ from those in males. To begin with, the cerebral cortex seems to be much less heavily involved in feminine sexuality. Decorticated female rabbits (20), guinea pigs (24), and rats (7) continue to show sexually receptive behavior under the appropriate forms of hormonal stimulation. Furthermore, decerebrate female cats (1) and dogs (29) are said to mate with sexually active males. Careful observations of the mating pattern in decorticated rats reveal that it is somewhat disorganized, but the response is sufficiently integrated to permit fertile copulation by a normal male.

It is of considerable interest to note that the differential effects of neocortical injury upon masculine and feminine sexual behavior in the rat can be demonstrated in one and the same individual. Female rats of many different strains will show masculine sexual behavior when placed with a second female that is in estrus. It has been demonstrated that this type of response is totally eliminated by complete decortication despite the fact that the same females continue to show receptive behavior when they are treated with the necessary ovarian hormones and tested with active males (7).

These sex differences are of particular significance because they can be meaningfully related to other differences which will be considered in detail later. The latter pertain to the differential effects of previous experience in males and females and to the degree to which gonadal hormones are essential for mating performance in the two sexes.

With the exception of the study by Klüver and Bucy, there is no evidence concerning the neural control of sexual behavior in primates. If we extrapolate from the studies of rodents and carnivores, it seems reasonable to assume that the mating behavior of primates would be even more seriously affected by extensive cortical injury, since in the higher mammals the brain has become increasingly important as an arbiter of all kinds of voluntary activity.

hormonal components

A few experiments have been concerned with the effects of hormones on the sexual behavior of submammalian vertebrates, but most of the evidence pertains to mammals and it is with this class that the following summary deals.

Several endocrine glands including the anterior pituitary, the thyroid, and the adrenals play a role in the maintenance of normal sexual behavior. However, the most direct effects upon sexuality are exerted by the reproductive glands.

Gonadal hormones in female mammals. In females of most lower mammalian species sexual behavior is heavily dependent upon ovarian hormones. For some animals estrin is the only hormone involved in mating, but for others both estrin and progesterone are important. In either case, sexual behavior is typically exhibited only when the related hormone or hormones are present in sufficient concentration. Mating responses are lacking in prepuberal individuals, and the first display of sexually receptive behavior usually coincides with the first full estrous cycle.

The sudden appearance of adult mating reactions is a direct result of increased secretory activity by the ovaries. Identical behavior can be produced precociously by treating prepuberal females with the appropriate ovarian substances (6). It is clear, therefore, that the neural and muscular components of the sexual response are integrated and capable of action before they are normally thrown into play by the sensitizing effects of ovarian hormone.

Adult infraprimate females normally display sexual activity only at those times when the ovaries are producing relatively large amounts of estrin. This is, of course, the time that the female is fertile and capable of conception as a result of copulation. For most mammals the breeding period is annual or semiannual and lasts a relatively short time. In the case of some domesticated species the female is polyestrous and exhibits a regular cycle of alternating phases of receptivity and nonreceptivity. This cycle is timed by the secretory cycle of the reproductive glands. When a female is not physiologically in estrus, she is not exciting to the male and will not permit coitus. During the estrous period the female appears to be a very stimulating partner and readily permits coition.

In species of this type removal of the

ovaries in adulthood produces prompt and permanent loss of the female's sexual receptivity. Replacement therapy involving administration of estrogen or estrogen plus progesterone occasions a temporary resurgence of erotic responsiveness and mating behavior (8).

One point omitted in the foregoing generalizations is of primary importance. This is that they do not apply to every female in every species. There are some females that never come into behavioral estrus. Although the ovaries produce mature follicles which are obviously secreting estrin, and although they show signs of vaginal response to ovarian hormones, there are always a few individuals who fail to display the expected behavioral change. Animals of this type can sometimes be brought into heat after ovariectomy if they are treated with very large amounts of estrogen and progesterone. Less marked differences in sensitivity to hormonal stimulation are found even among females that regularly come into heat. Some can be stimulated to show sexual behavior with minimal amounts of the appropriate hormones, whereas others react positively only after two or three times as much hormone has been injected (53).

Like infraprimate mammals, female primates are also clearly influenced by hormonal secretions of the reproductive glands. Immature female monkeys and apes rarely if ever exhibit the complete coital pattern although they sometimes engage in sex play with young males. In adulthood female monkeys and chimpanzees display cycles of sexual responsiveness which are closely correlated with the menstrual cycle, and maximal receptivity occurs during that time when the estrogen level is high and ovulation is imminent. During the rest of the cycle the female is not easily aroused sexually and appears to offer little erotic attraction for the male. It is nonetheless noteworthy that some females will permit copulation when the ovaries are relatively quiescent and when estrogen concentrations are low. This is practically never seen in infraprimate animals and probably marks a significant evolutionary change.

The effects of ovariectomy and replacement therapy on the sexual behavior of female primates are about what might be expected from the foregoing description. The majority of females become sexually inactive after ovariectomy and remain so indefinitely. A few individuals occasionally engage in sporadic sexual contacts, but their behavior is sluggish and is not marked by the characteristic signs of excitement which are shown by the estrous female. Treatment of ovariectomized monkeys or apes with estrogen is followed by the physical signs of estrus, such as swelling of the sex skin, and usually by the appearance of marked behavioral receptivity to the male.

Individual differences in the response to ovarian hormones are more marked than among lower mammals. Some intact primate females are totally unreceptive at all times regardless of the ovarian condition. As suggested earlier, other individuals may be partially receptive despite the complete absence of ovarian secretions. Reactions to the male are affected, not only by the physiological condition of the female, but also by more subtle psychological factors, with the result that distinct individual preferences exist, so that a given female may mate readily with one male and at the same time completely refuse the sexual attentions of a second potential partner.

Gonadal hormones in male mammals. Turning now to a consideration of the hormonal components of masculine sexual behavior, we may first consider males of the lower mammalian species.

Whereas female rodents, carnivores, and

ungulates practically never exhibit the adult mating pattern prior to the first physiological estrus, young males frequently display various portions of the masculine sexual response well before the onset of puberty. They frequently pursue other individuals, and sometimes such pursuit ends with one animal mounting the other, clasping him or her in the sexual position, and executing a few weak pelvic movements. This adumbrated display of masculine coition by prepuberal male mammals is not dependent upon the small amounts of androgen which are known to be secreted by the prepuberal testis, because the prepuberal sexual play of male rats is not prevented by castration on the day of birth (11). Apparently some slight degree of sexual responsiveness is possible without the support of gonadal hormones. In this respect males and females are dissimilar.

That testicular hormones are exceedingly important for masculine sexual performance has been shown in experiments involving injection of androgen into prepuberal males. Immature males treated in this fashion begin to display complete mating reactions including erection and ejaculation (6). Thus, in the male as in the female, the neuromuscular components of copulatory behavior are organized and capable of adult functioning before they are normally called into action.

In the normal course of development the sexual activity of young male rodents undergoes a striking change when the testes start to secrete adult levels of testosterone. It is at this point that mating responses become more frequent, vigorous, and complete and that the terminal reaction of ejaculation puts in its appearance.

Males of many mammalian species are similar to females in that they are inactive sexually save during the annual or semiannual breeding season. Such species are represented by the common ground squirrel, the Alaskan fur seal, and various species of American and Old World deer. In contrast, males of other species remain constantly active throughout the year. The gonads of seasonally breeding males regress and are quiescent except during the time of rut. The testes of constantly breeding species produce sperm throughout the year, and the interstitial tissue secretes androgen at a fairly steady rate.

The sexual inactivity of males out of breeding season is directly related to the absence of gonadal secretions. This has been demonstrated by administering exogenous androgen to animals of this type. Such treatment evokes the prompt appearance of mating responses out of season. The same result can be obtained by stimulating the quiescent testis to secretory activity through appropriate gonadotrophic stimulation (9).

The role of testosterone in males of the constantly breeding type is revealed by the results of castration. Castration of male rodents and lagomorphs is followed by fairly rapid decline in potency. There are differences among species and among individuals within the same species, but in the main, sexual activity declines to a prepuberal level within a few weeks after operation. This is true for the male rabbit (52), guinea pig (9), hamster (15), mouse (9), and domestic rat (12). In every species which has been investigated, the post-castrational loss of sexual responsiveness and ability can be reversed by the administration of androgenic hormone. It is clear that in these animals the susceptibility to sexual arousal and the capacity to mate are heavily dependent upon secretory activity of the reproductive glands. At the same time it should be remembered that individual differences exist and that they have some theoretical significance.

The rate of decline in sexual responsiveness

varies from one castrated rat to another, and the amount of hormone necessary to restore preoperational vigor is subject to similar inter-individual differences (12). Male guinea pigs also vary in the intensity of their sexual drive. Following castration, males fall off to approximately the same low level of sexual responsiveness. But when such castrates are treated with a constant amount of testosterone propionate, they react differently. Those males that showed high sexual drive prior to castration return to this level under the influence of the exogeneous hormone. Other individuals which had been low-drive males preoperatively respond to the same amount of androgen with the exhibition of mating activity at a low drive level (30). Apparently the precastrational differences in sexual drive are due, not to differences in the amount of hormone secreted by the testis, but to individual differences in the sensitivity of the target tissues which react to testicular secretions.

In mammals above the level of a rodent or lagomorph, the effects of castration are somewhat different. Male dogs and cats that have had sexual experience tend to retain potency and responsiveness for some time after castration. Here, again, individual differences are apparent. Some males exhibit a partial loss of responsiveness within a few months after operation while others show no such change for more than two years postoperatively (48).

Those males that decline in sexual capacity following castration can be restored to normal levels of responsiveness by androgen administration. Apparently the phylogenetic differences between carnivores and rodents include a partial reduction in the degree to which masculine sexual behavior depends upon testicular hormone. This may be indirectly related to a fact mentioned earlier, namely, that concomitant changes appear to have taken place in the neural control of such behavior.

It will be recalled that female primates are somewhat less dependent upon ovarian hormones than are females of infraprimate mammalian types. This difference is accentuated in the male. The prepuberal sexual play of young monkeys and apes is more frequent and varied than that of immature males of lower mammalian species. Erection, masturbation, and attempts at copulation have been observed in prepubescent primates (19). Castration does not eliminate sexual activity in adult males (37), nor does it prevent the development of copulatory patterns when the operation is performed before puberty (22). The only element in the sexual repertoire which seems to necessitate androgenic support is the ejaculatory reflex.

This is not to say that the sexual capacity of castrated primates is equal to that of normal animals. Sexual excitability may remain high for an indefinite period, and copulation may continue, but mating performance is often perfunctory and lethargic, and administration of androgen usually produces recognizable increases in erotic responsiveness and coital capacity.

experiential components

The sexual behavior of animals or human beings cannot be understood exclusively in terms of the hormonal condition of the individual or the species organization of the nervous system. A third important factor in sexuality is the individual's previous experience. This component presumably reflects functional changes produced in the nervous system by experience, but present knowledge does not permit us to deal with experiential effects in physiological terms. For the time being, therefore, the behavioral factors must be considered separately.

Effects of experience in the male. There is

ample evidence to support the conclusion that the sexual performance of male mammals can be altered by individual experience. Male rats which have been reared in individual cages and exposed to receptive females periodically during prepuberal life, when complete copulation is impossible, are less likely to show normal copulatory behavior in adulthood than are control males that have never had this type of infant conditioning (36). On the other hand, adult males of this species which have been reared in isolation from the age of weaning are capable of completely normal coital reactions the first time they are placed with a receptive female (5). This is also true of some dogs and cats. In other words, for these animals the achievement of normal sexual goals does not depend upon practice and learning although it may be affected by certain types of experience.

It is clear that experience can exert pronounced effects upon the sexual behavior of males of many mammalian species (27). There are numerous observations to the effect that males tend to become sexually inhibited if their contact with receptive females is rendered painful or frightening. One experiment carried out in my laboratory showed that male rats which were subjected to a punishing electric shock each time they attempted to copulate eventually ceased responding to receptive females. The experimentally induced sexual inhibition persisted for two weeks to a month after the last punishment and was then dissipated in most individuals. A few males remained permanently unresponsive to the female after having been inhibited by electric shock. These individuals were restored to normal sexual performance by a series of electrically induced convulsions (10).

The converse of inhibition has also been demonstrated. Stimuli which are initially neutral become sexually exciting if they have been repeatedly associated with complete sexual expression. An environment in which copulation has occurred tends to evoke premonitory signs of sexual arousal as soon as the male enters it. Male cats and dogs which appear reluctant to mate under laboratory conditions can be induced to do so by appropriate conditioning procedures (16). When this has been effected, the inhibition of sexual responsiveness disappears, and in subsequent contacts with the receptive female the males mate promptly and frequently.

In harmony with the observation that the sexual excitability of male mammals is "conditionable," is the additional evidence that sexual reward can be used to produce the learning of instrumental responses. For example, male rats will learn to turn a wheel when the reward is opportunity for copulation with the receptive female (25). In a comparable study it has been shown that the speed with which male rats will traverse a straight alley to reach a receptive female is directly related to the degree of sexual excitement and intensity of behavior displayed when contact with the female is established. Castration produces a decrease in running speed, and subsequent androgen therapy occasions a gradual increase in alley performance and re-establishment of normal sexual functions (13). It is significant that copulatory behavior and running speed covary even when hormonal conditions are constant. Castrates occasionally show sexual behavior despite the absence of hormone, and upon such occasions they traverse the alley at high speed. Other castrates, having a similar hormonal condition but failing to copulate with the female do not run as rapidly in the alley.

Effects of experience in the female. In the case of lower mammals the experiential component seems to be less important to the female than to the male. There is no indication that the conditions under which female rats, cats, or dogs are reared have any effect upon their sexual receptivity in adulthood. The first time that a female comes into heat she is normally receptive, and when placed with an experienced male, she will promptly mate. Her initial performance is indistinguishable from that of females that have mated many times.

Preliminary results obtained in the Yale laboratories indicate that receptive females will traverse a straight alley when the goal box contains a male rat. However, the female's speed in the alley is unrelated to her sexual behavior. For animals in one group the goal box contained a sexually active male that copulated promptly as soon as the female emerged from the end of the alley. For a second group the goal box contained a sexually inactive male that never copulated. Opportunity to copulate with the male did not produce faster running to the goal box. In fact, females that received the inactive male as an incentive object tended to show faster running in the alley than did those females with which the male copulated in the goal box. These results are distinctly different from those obtained with male rats. The male's running speed is positively related to sexual reinforcement (13).

I noted earlier that some male cats and dogs fail to copulate when they are first tested under laboratory conditions, although they can be induced to do so and may eventually become very active sexually. Comparable inhibition of sexual performance has never been noted in females of either species. The first time that a female dog or cat is brought into heat and put with a male under laboratory conditions, she exhibits completely normal sexual receptivity and will mate without delay.

The apparent difference in the importance of experience for sexual behavior in male and female rodents and carnivores may be directly related to another sex difference mentioned earlier, namely, the difference in the degree to which the cerebral cortex is involved in masculine and feminine behavior. It will be recalled that decortication eliminates sexual responsiveness in male rats, dogs, and cats but does not have this effect upon females of the same species. Also to be considered in this connection is the difference in the degree to which sexual behavior is dependent upon gonadal hormones. The female's performance seems to be somewhat more rigidly controlled by such secretions than does that of the male.

Phylogenetic differences. The importance of experience in shaping the individual's sexual habits is much more pronounced in primates than in lower mammals. Nissen's findings suggest that male and female chimpanzees are incapable of successful coitus until they have learned to copulate by trial-and-error experimentation or have been sexually trained by an experienced partner (42). To this observation should be added the facts that autoeroticism and homosexual behavior are much more frequent in primates than in lower mammals (31).

It is reasonable to assume that the evolutionary increase in experiential control of sexual activities is an outcome of the increasing importance of the neocortex as a mediating agent. In addition, the partial relaxation of hormonal dominance over sexual responsiveness makes possible greater latitude in individual sexual adjustments.

Evolutionary shifts in the physiological control of sexuality are most evident in our own species. Here one sees the greatest degree of diversity. Exclusive homosexuality, complete reversal of sex roles, sexual responsiveness to immature individuals, to animals, or even to inanimate objects, total sublimation of sex drive—these and many other uniquely human manifestations are possible only because the experiential component plays a dominant role in shaping human sexual behavior. The primary importance of individual experience is in turn due to reduced reliance upon gonadal hormones and increased intervention of the cerebral cortex.

theoretical analysis

The factors involved in sexual behavior include neural mechanisms which mediate erotic arousal, other mechanisms responsible for execution of the coital act, gonadal hormones, and special forms of external stimulation resulting in arousal.

Mechanisms for arousal. The arousal mechanism (AM) appears to be organized and functional in sexually inexperienced animals. Male and female rats, cats, ·or chimpanzees demonstrate signs of sexual excitement when stimulated by an active partner of the opposite sex even though they have never copulated.

The reactivity of the AM varies from individual to individual in the absence of previous sexual experience. The majority of naive male rats can be induced to copulate only if they are stimulated by a female in full heat. But there are a few inexperienced males which attempt to copulate with nonreceptive females or with other males. These are individuals in which the AM is very easily stimulated. The differences must be attributed to some inherent quality of the neural mechanism. It cannot be interpreted as a consequence of hormonal variations because similar individual differences are seen in males which have been castrated on the day of birth.

In sexually inexperienced males the AM is primarily reactive to stimuli associated with a biologically appropriate partner, i.e., a receptive female of the same species. However, the reactivity of the AM may be altered by experience. Stimuli which were originally ineffective may later become sexually exciting as a result of their association with biologically adequate sexual stimuli. The AM, in other words, can be "conditioned" to a variety of nonsexual external cues. Such conditioning need not be of a positive nature. Animals and human beings may learn not to respond sexually to stimulus objects which originally were effective evokers of the copulatory reaction.

The susceptibility of the AM to modification by experience varies with the sex and the species of the individual. In male rats, cats, and dogs sexual arousal can be conditioned to new cues, but there is no evidence that females are similarly affected by experience. The sexual responsiveness of male primates is more labile and modifiable than that of male rodents and carnivores, and female primates differ from the females of lower species in that the AM probably can be affected by experience.

Mechanisms for copulation. When sexual arousal reaches a threshold level, the executive or consummatory mechanism (CM) is thrown into action. The functional organization of the CM is probably complete in inexperienced male and female rats, rabbits, dogs, and cats. The motor pattern of copulation is stereotyped and invariable and is not materially altered by experience.

In contrast, organization of the CM is incomplete in male and female chimpanzees. The separate elements in the copulatory pattern can be elicited, but the naive primate cannot execute them in the proper sequence with the requisite degree of precision to effect successful copulation. Integration of the various responses into a smooth-flowing pattern depends upon practice. Because learning is involved, individual differences in the method of copulation are discernible in this species.

Neural components of the AM and CM. We cannot as yet describe these mechanisms in precise neurological terms, but it is possible to indicate something about their composition. The CM in males and females of all mammalian species includes spinal components which regulate genital reflexes and some of the gross postural adjustments involved in coitus. The CM of primates embraces centers and systems extending all the way to the neocortex. The cortex and various subcortical tracts and nuclei are also involved in the CM of male carnivores, but this is not true of females. The highest essential centers in the CM of the female carnivore lie in the diencephalon.

It is clear that the CM of female rodents is like that of female carnivores, and it is probable that the same is true of the male. Male rats cease copulating after extensive cortical injury, but this need not reflect interference with the CM. The fact that some brain-operated males can be induced to copulate after administration of large amounts of androgen suggests that the original loss was due to lowered activity of the AM.

As far as the AM is concerned, it appears that this mechanism does not depend upon the cortex in female rodents or carnivores, for decorticated rats, cats, and dogs display full sexual receptivity. Crucial portions of the AM seem to be located within the diencephalon. Males of these same species exhibit a reduction in sexual excitability following extensive cortical injury, hence the masculine AM must include cortical elements. The AM of male and female primates almost certainly involves a large cortical component.

Relations to experience and hormone effects. Sexual behavior is dependent upon or affected by learning and experience to the extent that the neocortex participates in the functions of the AM or CM.

The neocortex is not involved in the CM of

the male or female rat; hence, the coital act can be performed by both sexes without practice. It is involved in the AM of the male but not of the female; therefore, the male's susceptibility to arousal is modifiable by experience, and that of the female is not. The neocortex is involved in both the AM and the CM of male and female primates with the result that they must learn to copulate, and their sexual excitability is modifiable as a result of experience.

The influence of gonadal hormones upon sexual behavior is probably restricted to the subcortical level and lower portions of the brain and cord. The nature of the effect is a reduction in the threshold to stimulation. Cortical portions of the AM serve to supplement or augment the action of sex hormones upon lower centers. In certain instances the cortical component of the AM may assume so dominant a role over the entire arousal mechanism that gonadal hormones are not necessary for the occurrence of sexual behavior. For example, the persistence of copulatory behavior in male dogs and cats castrated after a great deal of sexual experience may be due to the effect of that experience upon the cortical portion of the AM.

If the cortical component is lacking, sexual behavior will not occur in the absence of the appropriate gonadal hormones. This is why female mammals below the level of primates are asexual when not in estrus. A relatively small cortical factor, as in the male rodent, permits modification of arousal through experience but cannot support normal copulatory behavior in the absence of sex hormones.

It is clear that in males of many species the CM does not depend upon androgen. Castrated carnivores and primates can copulate provided the requisite degree of arousal is attained. Whether the same is true of female mammals has not yet been determined.

references

1. Bard, P. Central nervous mechanisms for emotional behavior patterns in animals. *Res. Publ. Ass. nerv. ment. Dis.*, 1939, **19**: 190–218.
2. Bard, P., and D. McK. Rioch. A study of four cats deprived of neocortex and additional portions of the forebrain. *John Hopk. Hosp. Bull.*, 1937, **60**: 73–147.
3. Bare, J. K. The specific hunger for sodium chloride in normal and adrenal-ectomized white rats. *J. comp. physiol. Psychol.*, 1949, **42**: 242–53.
4. Beach, F. A. Effects of cortical lesions upon copulatory behavior of male rats. *J. comp. Psychol.*, 1940, **29**: 193–244.
5. ———. Analysis of the stimuli adequate to elicit mating behavior in the sexually inexperienced male rat. *J. comp. Psychol.*, 1942, **33**: 163–207.
6. ———. Sexual behavior of prepuberal male and female rats treated with gonadal hormones. *J. comp. Psychol.*, 1924, **34**: 285–92.
7. ———. Effects of injury to the cerebral cortex upon the display of masculine and feminine mating behavior by female rats. *J. comp. Psychol.*, 1943, **36**: 169–98.
8. ———. A review of physiological and psychological studies of sexual behavior in mammals. *Physiol. Rev.*, 1947, **27**: 240–307.
9. ———. *Hormones and behavior.* New York: Hoeber, 1948.
10. Beach, F. A., M. W. Conovitz, F. Steinberg, and A. C. Goldstein. Experimental inhibition and restoration of mating behavior in male rats. J. genet. Psychol., 1956, **89**: 165–81.
11. Beach, F. A., and A. M. Holz. Mating behavior in male rats castrated at various ages and injected with androgen. *J. exp. Zool.*, 1946, **101**: 91–142.
12. ———. Effects of different concentrations of androgen upon sexual behavior in cas-

trated male rats. *J. comp. physiol. Psychol.*, 1949, **42**: 433–53.
13. Beach, F. A., and L. Jordan. Effects of sexual reinforcement upon the performance of male rats in a straight runway. *J. comp. physiol. Psychol.*, 1956, **49**: 105–10.
14. Beach, F. A., and G. Levinson. Effects of androgen on the glans penis and mating behavior of castrated male rats. *J. exp. Zool.*, 1950, **114**: 159–71.
15. Beach, F. A., and R. S. Fauker. Effects of castration and subsequent androgen administration upon mating behavior in the male hamster (Cricetus auratus). *Endocrinology*, 1949, **45**: 211–21.
16. Beach, F. A., and A. Zitrin. Induction of mating activity in male cats. *Ann. N.Y. acad. Sci.*, 1945, **46**: 42–44.
17. Beach, F. A., A. Zitrin, and J. Jaynes. Neural mediation of mating in male cats. II. Contributions of the frontal cortex. *J. exp. Zool.*, 1955, **130**: 381–401.
18. ———. Neural mediation of mating in male cats. I. Effects of unilateral and bilateral removal of the neocortex. *J. comp. physiol. Psychol.*, 1956, **49**: 321–27.
19. Bingham, H. C. Sex development in apes. *Comp. Psychol. Monogr.*, 1928, **5**: No. 1 (Whole No. 23).
20. Brooks, C. McC. The role of the cerebral cortex and of various sense organs in the exictation and execution of mating activity in the rabbit. *Amer. J. Physiol.*, 1937, **120**: 544–53.
21. Clark, G. Sexual behavior in rats with lesions in the anterior hypothalamus. *Amer. J. Physiol.*, 1942, **137**: 746–49.
22. ———. Prepubertal castration in the male chimpanzee, with some effects of replacement therapy. *Growth*, 1945, **9**: 327–39.
23. Coghill, G. E. *Anatomy and the problem of behaviour.* New York: Macmillan, 1929.
24. Dempsey, E. W., and D. McK. Rioch. The localization in the brain stem of the

oestrous responses of the female guinea pig. *J. Neurophysiol.*, 1939. **2**: 9–18.

25. Denniston, R. H., II. Quantification and comparison of sex drives under various conditions in terms of a learned response. *J. comp. physiol. Psychol.*, 1954, **47**: 437–40.

26. Fisher, C., H. W. Magoun, and S. W. Ranson. Dystocia in diabetes insipidus: The relation of pituitary oxytocin to parturition. *Amer. J. Obstet. Gynec.*, 1938, **36**: 1–9.

27. Ford, C. S., and F. A. Beach. *Patterns of sexual behavior.* New York: Harper, 1951.

28. Gesell, A. Behavior patterns of fetal-infant and child. *Proc. Ass. Res. nerv. Dis.*, 1954, **33**: 114–26.

29. Goltz, F. Der Hund ohne Grosshirn. *Pflüg. Arch. ges. Physiol.*, 1892, **51**: 570–614.

30. Grunt, J. A., and W. C. Young. Consistency of sexual behavior patterns in individual male guinea pigs following castration and androgen therapy. *J. comp. physiol Psychol.*, 1953, **46**: 138–44.

31. Hamilton, G. V. A study of sexual tendencies in monkeys and baboons. *J. Anim. Behav.*, 1914, **4**: 295–318.

32. Hines, M. The development and regression of reflexes, postures, and progression in the young macaque. *Contr. Embryol. Carneg. Instn.*, 1942, **30**: 153–210 (Whole No. 196).

33. Hooker, D. Early human fetal behavior, with a preliminary note on double simultaneous fetal stimulation. *Proc. Ass. Res. nerv. Dis.*, 1954, **33**: 98–113.

34. Humphrey, T. The trigeminal nerve in relation to early human fetal activity. *Proc. Ass. Res. nerv. Dis.*, 1954, **33**: 127–54.

35. Jervis, G. A. The genetics of phenylpyruvic oligophrenia. *J. ment. Sci.*, 1939, **85**: 719–62.

36. Kagan, J., and F. A. Beach. Effects of early experience on mating behavior in male rats. *J. comp. physiol. Psychol.*, 1953, **46**: 204–8.

37. Kempf, E. J. The social and sexual behavior of infrahuman primates with some comparable facts in human behavior. *Psychoanal. Rev.*, 1917, **4**: 127–54.

38. Kislak, J. W., and F. A. Beach. Inhibition of aggressiveness by ovarian hormones. *Endocrinology*, 1955, **56**: 684–92.

39. Klüver, H., and P. C. Bucy. Preliminary analysis of functions of the temporal lobes in monkeys. *Arch. Neurol. Psychiat.*, Chicago, 1939, **42**: 979–1000.

40. Kollros, J. J. Localized maturation of lid-closure reflex mechanism by thyroid implants in tadpole hindbrain. *Proc. Soc. exp. Biol., N.Y.*, 1942, **49**: 204–6.

41. Lehrman, D. S. The physiological basis of parental feeding behavior in the ring dove. *Behaviour*, 1955, **7**: 241–86.

42. Nissen, H. Instinct as seen by a psychologist. In W. C. Allee, H. W. Nissen, and M. F. Nimkoff, A re-examination of the concept of instinct. *Psychol. Rev.*, 1953, **60**: 287–97.

43. Richter, G. P. Biology of drives. *J. comp. physiol. Psychol.*, 1947, **40**: 129–34.

44. Riesen, A. H., and E. F. Kinder. *Postural development of infant chimpanzees.* New Haven: Yale Univer. Press, 1952.

45. Rogers, C. M. Hypothalamic mediation of sex behavior in the male rat. Unpublished doctor's dissertation, Yale Univer., 1954.

46. Sawyer, C. H. Cholinesterase and the behavior problem in Amblystoma. *J. exp. Zool.*, 1943, **92**: 1–29.

47. Schreiner, L., and A. Kling. Behavioral changes following rhinencephalic injury in cat. *J. Neurophysiol.*, 1953, **16**: 643–59.

48. Schwartz, M., and F. A. Beach. Effects of adrenalectomy upon mating behavior in castrated male dogs. *Amer. Psychologist*, 1954, **9**: 467–8.

49. Sperry, R. W. Mechanisms of neural maturation. In S. S. Stevens (Ed.), *Handbook of experimental psychology.* New York: Wiley, 1951, pp. 236–80.

50. Spies, T. D., C. D. Aring, J. Gelperin, and W. B. Bean. The mental symptoms of pellagra: Their relief with nicotinic acid. *Amer. J. med. Sci.*, 1938, **196**: 461–75.

51. Stone, C. P. The effects of cerebral destruction on the sexual behavior of male rabbits. III. The frontal, parietal and occipital regions. *J. comp. Psychol.*, 1926, **6**: 435–48.

52. ———. The retention of copulatory ability in male rabbits following castration. *J. genet. Psychol.*, 1932, **40**: 296–305.

53. Young, W. C., E. W. Dempsey, H. I. Myers, and C. W. Hagquist. The ovarian condition and sexual behavior in the female guinea pig. *Amer. J. Anat.*, 1938, **63**: 457–87.

54. Zitrin, A., J. Jaynes, and F. A. Beach. Neural mediation of mating in male cats. III. Contributions of occipital, parietal and temporal cortex. *J. comp. Neurol.*, 1956, **105**: 111–26.

21 neural mediation of mating in male cats *

Frank A. Beach, Arthur Zitrin, and Julian Jaynes

1. Were the results of this experiment on cats predictable from the findings of earlier studies on rats and rabbits?

2. How can the great differences in behavior between unilateral and bilateral decorticates be accounted for?

3. What effects did androgen administration have on unilateral and bilateral decorticates?

* F. A. Beach, A. Zitrin, and J. Jaynes, "Neural Mediation of Mating in Male Cats," *J. comp. physiol. Psychol.*, 49 (1956), 321–327. This selection, Part I of the study, is entitled "Effects of Unilateral and Bilateral Removal of the Neocortex." Reprinted with permission.

Extensive cerebral injury interferes with copulatory behavior in male rabbits (14, 15, 16) and rats (2, 3). In cortically operated rats there is a decrease in the proportion of males continuing to copulate when the lesions involve more than 20 per cent of the neopallium, and the magnitude of the decrease becomes progressively greater as lesion size increases. If the total invasion exceeds 60 to 75 per cent of the neocortex, sexual reactions are eliminated. The behavioral change does not appear to depend upon the locus of the lesion within the cortex, a finding which argues against the existence of any specific, cortical "sex center." The most parsimonious interpretation of this evidence assigns to the neocortex a general, facilitative role. It has been suggested that in the male rat the cortex, acting as a whole, contributes to the arousal and maintenance of sexual excitement but does not mediate any sensorimotor adjustments essential to coition.

In contrast to the smooth-brained rodents, the carnivores possess a convoluted and more highly differentiated cerebral cortex. It is possible, therefore, that the neopallium plays a more complex role in the control of mating behavior in this order than in rodents. Cortical localization of sensory and motor functions is more marked in carnivores than in rodents, and therefore it may be that the locus of neocortical injury in cats is a far more important variable than it is in rats.

Previous studies of the effects of cortical lesions on the mating behavior of carnivores have been reported, but the sexual pattern has not been systematically analyzed, and results have not been presented quantitatively. In one study, coital responses survived in 6 out of 7 male cats following bilateral removal of the frontal and prefrontal cortex, but sensory and motor abnormalities produced by the operation resulted in a high incidence of disorientated reactions to the female (11). In a more recent experiment it was found that 12 of 15 male cats suffering injury to the pyriform cortex and amygdala attempted to copulate with a wide variety of stimulus animals including other male cats, dogs, monkeys, and chickens (13). Other observers found that decerebrate cats display no mating reactions (1) and that decerebrate male dogs "show no interest in the rutting bitch" (9).

The present paper, the first of a series, describes the general procedures, methods of testing, data on the normal copulatory pattern of the cat, and its changes following unilateral and bilateral removal of the cerebral cortex. Subsequent reports will deal with the effects of lesions restricted to specific cortical areas.

method

maintenance and preparation of animals

The female cats used as stimulus animals in the mating tests were ovariectomized adults.

Approximately three days before they were to serve as stimulus animals, the females were given an intramuscular injection containing 0.55 mg. of estradiol benzoate.[1] This treatment produced full sexual receptivity within three days, and semiweekly injections of 0.2 mg. of estrogen maintained the condition indefinitely. If a female lost weight and became emaciated after a prolonged period of treatment, injections were discontinued and she was not used again until she had regained good condition.

The 12 male subjects in which the normal

mating pattern was studied were selected from an original group of 17 on the basis of their proven sexual vigor.

None of the males mated spontaneously when first tested in the laboratory, and eventually it was found necessary to "condition" each animal in the manner described by Zitrin and Beach (17). After the conditioning or training procedures had elicited copulation, the cats began to mate spontaneously, and thereafter their sexual performance proved to be highly reliable.

During all but the preliminary phases of the experiment, the males were kept in individual living cages in an indoor laboratory room. The regular diet consisted of horse meat, beef heart, and canned fish.

testing techniques and items recorded

Tests for sexual behavior were conducted in a room 8 ft. by 8 ft. with one wall of wire mesh through which the animals could be observed. Before each test, the female's receptivity was made certain by demonstrating that she would show lordosis and treading of the hind legs in response to stimulation of the perineum.

In the first few tests males were allowed at least 15 min. to explore the observation room before the female was brought in, but they soon became so familiar with the surroundings that no adaptation period was necessary. In all tests for which results are reported, the male was placed in the observation room and the receptive female was promptly introduced. During the following 60 min. records were made of eight standard behavioral items as well as additional observations of any unusual responses.

The items regularly scored included the number of times the male gripped the scruff

---

[1] Estradiol benzoate (Progynon-B) was generously supplied by Dr. Edward Henderson of the Schering Corporation, Bloomfield, New Jersey, who also provided the testosterone propionate (Oretone) used in this experiment.

of the female's neck in his teeth and then failed to mount (*extra grips*), the number of times he mounted the female, and the number of times intromission occurred. In addition to these frequency scores, records were made of the time elapsing between the introduction of the receptive female and the first mounting response by the male (*mount latency*), the time from each mount to the achievement of intromission (*intromission delay*), and the time from the beginning of intromission to the male's dismounting (*intromission duration*).

spacing of tests, operations, and hormone injections

Periodic mating tests were conducted until the frequency scores and time scores for each cat had become fairly constant. The median intervals between preoperative tests ranged from three to five days. Data collected in the last four tests before operation serve as the measure of preoperative behavior in our analysis of results.

Following preoperative testing five males were subjected to unilateral decortication, and tests were resumed when the animals appeared to have recovered. One male received four tests beginning 13 days after operation, and a second cat was tested four times starting on the seventeenth postoperative day. Both animals copulated successfully in all tests, but their mating reactions were less frequent and consistent than they had been before operation, and these males were therefore retested several months later. If this second series is considered the formal postoperative tests for these two animals, the resumption of testing for all males occurred from 42 to 202 days after operation. From two to seven tests were given each animal, and the interest interval was usually 3 to 5 days. As far as our tests could indicate, any alterations that unilateral

decortication produces in sexual activity remain unchanged in the period between 42 and 252 days after operation.

Two hemidecorticated males were subjected to a second operation in which the neocortex was removed from the other hemisphere. These operations occurred within 2 days after the last sex test following hemidecortication, and 72 and 158 days, respectively, after the first operation. One animal was given five mating tests during the seven months following complete decortication, and the other male was observed in eight tests conducted over a period of 11 months after the second operation.

To control for the possibility that extensive brain injury might lead to reduced secretion of testicular androgen, one decorticate was injected with testosterone propionate approximately every other day for three months, starting seven months after the second operation. The initial dosage was 10 mg. per injection, and this amount was doubled for the final five treatments. During the period of hormone treatment the animal was observed in seven mating tests.

operative techniques, postoperative care, and reconstruction of lesions

Operations were performed with aseptic precautions while the animals were anesthetized with Nembutal administered intraperitoneally. The skull was opened by trephine, and sufficient bone was removed to provide an adequate field. Cortical tissue was removed by aspiration, and the wound was closed.

In the first operation the left cortex was removed in three cats and the right in the other two animals. Unilateral operations caused no serious interference with the animals' ability to feed and care for themselves.

Following bilateral decortication, the cats did not eat spontaneously and had to be hand-fed for some time. Spontaneous eating was gradually re-established, but the decorticated animals never groomed themselves and had to be brushed and combed at frequent intervals.

When postoperative testing was completed, the animals were sacrificed, the brains were fixed in formalin, embedded in paraffin, sectioned at 50 micra, and every fifth section was stained with thionin.

results

quantitative measures of mating behavior in unoperated cats

A brief qualitative account of the sequence of events comprising the cat's sexual pattern will render the statistical treatment of results more intelligible.

When exposed to an estrous female, the sexually active male cat utters a specialized "sex call," not heard at other times.[2] The male grips the loose skin of the female's neck between his teeth, and she assumes the mating position. Occasionally a male may release his grip without mounting, but more commonly he assumes a position astride the female and maintains the neck grip until dismounting. Once mounted, the male begins to execute alternate stepping movements of the rear legs, moving his hind quarters backward until the genitalia are slightly posterior to the base of the female's tail. Then the hind quarters are lowered and brought forward in such a manner that the erect penis is directed toward the perineal region of the female, and the male

[2] This call has been described by Moelk (12) as a modified "demand cry," composed of voiced inhalation followed by a heavily stressed exhaled vowel sound trailing off to a murmur.

executes thrusting movements of the hind quarters.

In some instances difficulty is encountered in achieving intromission, and a male may release the female, dismount, and begin again. More often, intromission is effected, and when this occurs the male stops thrusting and maintains full penetration for several seconds, after which he releases the neck grip and dismounts. After a variable delay the entire pattern is repeated, and a vigorous and experienced male may mate ten times in an hour.

The following quantitative description of normal mating is based upon the performance of 12 males in 48, 1-hr. tests.

Frequency, timing, reliability, and intercorrelations of sexual responses. Group averages for all measures of sexual behavior are presented in Table 1. The average number of

Table 1. Average Measures of Sexual Behavior of 12 Male Cats in 48 One-Hour Tests

Measure	Average Frequency	Measure	Average No. Seconds
Mounts	8.9	Mount latency	5.8
Intromissions	5.3	Intromission delay	77.0
Extra grips	0.8	Intromission duration	4.3

total mounts (with and without intromission) per preoperative test ranged from 5.0 to 12.8, the mean number for all 48 tests being 8.9. Group means for frequency scores are calculated as the average of the individual means of the group. For time scores they are the average of individual medians. On the average, 63 per cent of the mounts led to intromission. The average frequency of intromissions per hour test showed considerable individual variation, ranging from 1.8 in the least active male, to 8.3 in the most vigorous copulator. Combination of the individual means yields an average group score of 5.3 intromissions per hour.

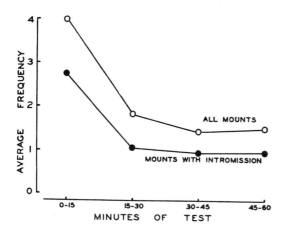

Fig. 1. Distribution of copulatory reactions throughout the 1-hr. test.

Figure 1 shows the temporal distribution of mounts and intromissions throughout the 60 min. of exposure to the female. Mating activity was more frequent in the first quarter of the test than in succeeding quarters. A drop after the first 15 min. occurred in all 12 cats, both for total mounts and the frequency of intromission, and is therefore statistically significant beyond the .01 level of confidence by the sign test. It will be noted that the proportion of mounts culminating in intromission did not change appreciably throughout the test.

Normal males rarely failed to mount after gripping the female, the average frequency of this behavior ranging from 0 in some cats to 1.3 per test in one individual. For the group as a whole, the mean frequency per test of extra grips was 0.8.

Latency and duration of sexual responses. In general, male cats that are thoroughly accustomed to copulating in a given environmental setting tend to initiate sexual behavior with a minimum of delay. In preoperative tests the median *mount latency* was 5.8 sec. Again there was considerable individual variability,

and the median score for different cats ranged from 1 to 278 sec.

Intromission occurred almost invariably on the first mount. The average *intromission delay* for all preoperative tests was 77 sec., individual medians ranging from 48 to 145 sec. The median duration of intromission for various individuals varied from 1.9 to 7.7 sec., and the mean of the 12 individual medians was 4.3 sec.

Reliability coefficients for the several measures of sexual activity were calculated, using the rank-difference method, correlating scores from tests 1 and 3 with those from tests 2 and 4. The results are presented in Table 2.

Table 2. Odd-Even Reliability Coefficients for Six Measures of Sexual Behavior of 12 Unoperated Male Cats

Behavioral Measure	Reliability (rho)
Frequency of intromissions	.98
Mount latency	.92
Intromission duration	.90
Intromission delay	.84
Frequency of extra grips	.59
Frequency of mount	.32

With the exception of the frequency of mounts and of extra grips, the measures of sexual activity used in this study were very consistent.

Intercorrelations. Correlations between the various measures were calculated by the rank-difference method. The correlation between intromission frequency and intromission delay was −.81, which, according to Kendall (10), is significant at the .01 level. The percentage of mounts with intromission and the frequency of intromission were positively correlated at +.70 ($p < .05$). Percentage of mounts with intromission and intromission delay correlated to the extent of −.58 ($p < .05$). The remaining intercorrelations were not statistically significant.

effects of unilateral decortication

Examination of the sectioned brains revealed that in all animals all the cortex above the rhinal fissure had been removed. In no case was there more than minor invasion of the archipallium, and the basal ganglia, thalamus, and other subcortical structures were spared completely.

All five operated males had achieved intromission in each of the four preoperative tests. Following hemidecortication two cats were tested four times (no. 21 and 22), one was tested three times (no. 24), and one was tested twice (no. 23). Intromission occurred in all postoperative tests. The interval between operation and the resumption of testing for these four cases ranged from 42 to 95 days. The fifth operate (no. 25) was observed in seven tests, beginning 202 days after surgery, and achieved intromission in only three tests.

Frequency and timing of behavior. Postoperative changes in the frequency of the various behavioral measures are summarized in Table 3. There was some reduction of the frequency of mounting and of intromission in four of the five animals. All hemidecorticates

Table 3. Average Frequency of Mating Responses Before and After Unilateral Decortication*

| | Mounts | | Intro-missions | | Extra Grips | |
Cat No.	Be-fore	After	Be-fore	After	Be-fore	After
21	9.3	7.5	8.3	6.3	3.0	11.0
22	12.8	5.0	7.3	3.1	1.3	6.3
23	6.5	5.5	4.8	5.0	0.0	6.5
24	6.3	4.0	3.3	2.7	0.3	6.0
25	7.0	12.0	4.8	1.1	0.8	2.5
Mean of Group	8.4	6.8	5.7	3.6	1.1	6.5

* All preoperative means are based on four tests for each cat. The number of tests on which postoperative means are based is given in the text.

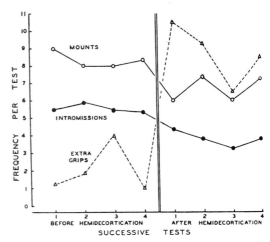

Fig. 2. Average frequency of different sexual responses before and after removal of the neocortex from one hemisphere.

exhibited an increase in the average number of grips that did not lead to mounting. These results are presented graphically in Figure 2.

There was no change in the spacing of sexual responses throughout the hour's test. The percentage of mounts leading to intromission was not altered by hemidecortication. Intromission delay was not affected, but there was an increase in the mount latency in all animals as shown in Table 4.

The fact that all unilaterally operated males took longer to achieve the first mount was not due to any reduction of their interest in the receptive female. Instead, it reflected interference with normal mating resulting from the "forced circling" responses which were common in four of the five hemidecorticates. As is well known (8), unilateral injury to the frontal cortex is characteristically followed by a tendency to move in circles toward the side of the lesion. In the present experiment hemidecorticated males often approached the female as soon as she entered the testing room and then circled several times before gripping and mounting.

Table 4. Timing of Mating Responses Before and After Unilateral Decortication*

Cat No.	Median Mount Latency in Seconds		Median Intromission Delay in Seconds		Median Duration of Intromission in Seconds	
	Be-fore	After	Be-fore	After	Be-fore	After
21	4	11	51	89	4.2	3.6
22	1	86	64	45	7.1	5.5
23	9	22	93	155	4.3	3.2
24	3	121	56	72	2.3	4.5
25	1	3	93	70	5.2	7.0
Median of Group	3	22	64	72	4.3	4.5

* All preoperative medians are based on four tests for each cat. For the number of tests on which postoperative medians are based, see text.

Following unilateral operation the intercorrelations of measures described for normal animals were still evident, and in addition several new relationships appeared. The correlation between mount latency and mount frequency was −1.00. That between intromission duration and percentage of mounts with intromission was −1.00. The frequencies of extra grips and intromissions correlated at +1.00.

effects of bilateral decortication and androgen treatment

Shortly after their final test as hemidecorticates, males 21 and 24 were deprived of the remaining neocortex. This description of the operation was confirmed by examination of the brain sections. During the ensuing 12 months No. 21 was given eight mating tests while No. 24 was observed with receptive females on five occasions. Neither cat showed any mating behavior at any time.

They reacted similarly to the testing situation. In all tests they uttered long and loud calls which sometimes increased in frequency when they were touched or when placed on the female's back. The latter procedure produced no sexual behavior or any signs of an erection, although penile erections could be elicited by direct stimulation of the genitals. These decorticate cats occasionally reacted violently to tactile stimulation, a slight touch eliciting a mass reaction including vocalization and increased restlessness. At other times they showed little responsiveness.

In an attempt to determine whether the loss of sexual activity could be due to indirect interference with the pituitary-gonad system and consequent reduction in testicular androgen, the testes of male 21 were studied histologically. No abnormality of interstitial tissue could be detected, and the tubules showed normal spermatogenesis.

A second check on the possibility of endocrine disturbance involved treating male 24 with testosterone propionate which has been shown to revive mating behavior in castrated cats.[3] Between seven and ten months after the second operation, this animal was subjected to regular, periodic injections of androgen. The hormone produced no recognizable changes in behavior in the eight tests conducted during the period of treatment.

discussion

The major findings of this study are as follows. (a) After appropriate "conditioning," the mating performance of intact male cats becomes highly consistent and reliable. (b) The number of intromissions per hour is the most stable measure of mating, having an odd-even reliability of +.98. (c) Unilateral decortication does not eliminate mating, although it slightly reduces the frequency of mounting and intromission, increases extra

[3] L. R. Aronson. Personal communication, 1955.

grips, and increases the delay preceding the first mount. (*d*) Bilateral decortication eliminates all mating responses.

The finding that cats continue to copulate after unilateral decortication was unexpected. An earlier study of male rats showed that mating responses were eliminated in two out of six unilaterally decorticated animals (4). In this connection, it should be noted that although hemidecortication has no adverse effects upon testicular function, androgen injections revived copulatory responses in rats which ceased mating following unilateral decortication (4). This indicates that the absence of copulatory ability after cortical injury is probably due to lowered sexual excitability, and that the loss may be compensated by raising the androgen level above normal. Since sexual responsiveness was not impaired in male cats following destruction of one cortex, a marked species difference in the cerebral mechanisms for sexual behavior is indicated.

It is likely that decrease in the frequency of some mating responses after unilateral decortication in male cats was due to sensory and motor defects. For example, circling to the side of the lesion was common. In three hemidecorticates, grips appeared to be unusually strong and were often maintained for an abnormal length of time. Some incoordination of the forelimbs during mounting was observed in two operates. We suggest that unilateral decortication does not impair the responsiveness of the male cat to sexual stimuli, but that motor and perhaps sensory abnormalities consequent to the operation may interrupt sexual performance, thus decreasing the number of successful copulations during the hour's test.

It has previously been reported that decerebrate male dogs "show no interest in the rutting bitch" (9), and that decerebrate male cats exhibit no mating reactions (1). The present findings permit the additional conclusion that these effects of decerebration are duplicated by removal of the neocortex. Brooks (6) described the survival of coital behavior in "decorticate" male rabbits. Davis (7) reported comparable findings for the male rat, but the extent of the lesion was not checked by histological study, and the completeness of the operation in Davis' study has been questioned (2). Lagomorphs are apparently an exception, but for those rodents and carnivores that have been examined, the male's mating pattern is abolished following decortication. This finding is of particular interest, since comparable operations fail to eliminate mating responses in any female mammal studied to date (5).

summary

Twelve male cats were observed in a series of 60-min. mating tests with receptive females. When their sexual performance had become stable, five males were subjected to unilateral removal of the neocortex. Following postoperative recovery and an additional series of mating tests, two males of this group were deprived of the remaining neocortex. After further testing, one bilateral decorticate was treated with androgen and observed in a final series of tests. The results were as follows:

1. Adult male cats brought into the laboratory did not mate readily in initial tests, but following a "conditioning" procedure they copulated consistently and reliably.

2. The number of intromissions per 60-min. test was the most reliable indicator of mating performance (odd-even reliability = +.98). Normal male cats mounted on the average 8.9 times, and achieved intromission 5.3 times per hour test.

3. More matings occurred in the first part of the test period than in the latter parts.

4. Unilateral removal of the neocortex had the following effects upon coital activity: (*a*) increase in the latency of mating, (b) decrease in the frequency of mounting and intromission responses, (*c*) marked increase in the frequency of grips not followed by mounting, (*d*) no change in the percentage of mounts resulting in intromission, (*e*) occasional motor abnormalities such as forced circling, and (*f*) no detectable diminution of responsiveness to sexual stimuli.

5. Bilateral removal of the neocortex in male cats abolished all sexual behavior except for some vocalization. This result probably was not due to androgenic deficiency, since the testes appeared histologically normal and since androgen administration has no effect upon decorticated males.

references

1. Bard, P. The hypothalamus and sexual behavior. In *The hypothalamus and central levels of autonomic function.* Res. Publ. Ass. Nerv. Ment. Dis., 1940, **20**, 551–594.
2. Beach, F. A. Effects of cortical lesions upon the copulatory behavior of male rats. *J. comp. Psychol.,* 1940, **29**, 193–244.
3. Beach, F. A. Copulatory behavior of male rats raised in isolation and subjected to partial decortication prior to the acquisition of sexual experience. *J. comp. Psychol.,* 1941, **31**, 457–470.
4. Beach, F. A. Relative effects of androgen upon the mating behavior of male rats subjected to forebrain injury or castration. *J. exp. Zool.,* 1944, **97**, 249–285.
5. Beach, F. A. A review of physiological and psychological studies of sexual behavior in mammals. *Physiol. Rev.,* 1947, **27**, 240–307.
6. Brooks, C. McC. The role of the cerebral cortex and of various sense organs in the excitation and execution of mating activity in the rabbit. *Amer. J. Physiol.,* 1937, **120**, 544–553.
7. Davis, C. The effect of ablation of neocortex on mating, maternal behavior and the production of pseudopregnancy in the female rat and of the copulatory activity in the male. *Amer. J. Physiol.,* 1939, **127**, 374–380.
8. Fulton, J. F. *Physiology of the nervous system.* (2nd Ed.) New York: Oxford Univer. Press, 1943.
9. Goltz, F. Der Hund ohne Grosshirn. *Pflüg. Arch.,* 1892, **51**, 570–604.
10. Kendall, M. G. *Rank correlation methods.* London: Chas. Griffin, 1948.
11. Langworthy, O. R. Behavior disturbances related to decomposition of reflex activity caused by cerebral injury. An experimental study of the cat. *J. Neuropath. exp. Neurol,* 1943, **3**, 87–99.
12. Moelk, M. Vocalizing in the house-cat: a phonetic and functional study. *Amer. J. Psychol.,* 1944, **57**, 184–205.
13. Schreiner, L., & Kling, A. Behavioral changes following rhinencephalic injury in cat. *J. Neurophysiol.,* 1953, **16**, 643–659.
14. Stone, C. P. The effects of cerebral destruction on the sexual behavior of male rabbits. I. The olfactory bulbs. *Amer. J. Physiol.,* 1925, **71**, 430–435.
15. Stone, C. P. The effects of cerebral destruction on the sexual behavior of male rabbits. II. The frontal and parietal regions. *Amer. J. Physiol.,* 1925, **72**, 372–385.
16. Stone, C. P. The effects of cerebral destruction on the sexual behavior of male rabbits. III. The frontal, parietal, and occipital regions. *J. comp. Psychol.,* 1926, **6**, 435–448.
17. Zitrin, A., & Beach, F. A. Induction of mating activity in male cats. *Ann. N.Y. Acad. Sci.,* 1945, **46**, 42–44.

22   influence of sex hormones on social behavior in monkeys *

Allan F. Mirsky

1. How well did similar studies using other species predict the results of this experiment? Why?
2. Why did the experimenter use castrated (gonadectomized) animals in this experiment?
3. What implications for human beings exist in the comparison of differences between chimpanzees and macaque monkeys?

Studies conducted on such widely different infraprimate animals as fish (12), reptiles (13), birds (1), and mammals (2) have shown that androgens generally enhance the dominance of both male and female animals, while estrogens either reduce aggressiveness or are without effect. The few investigations of the behavioral effects of gonadal hormones in primates have been confined to the chimpanzee. Yerkes (16), Nowlis (14), and Crawford (9), who studied male-female and female-female pairs in a competitive feeding situation, reported that subordinate females often obtained more food while in estrus than at other times. Birch and Clark (5, 6, 7, 8), working chiefly with castrate chimpanzees, reported the effects of administering sex hormones to one or another member of like-sexed pairs. After androgen treatment, a subordinate female obtained most or all the peanuts in a competitive feeding situation; prior to this

* A. F. Mirsky, "The Influence of Sex Hormones on Social Behavior in Monkeys," *J. comp. physiol. Psychol.*, 48 (1955), 327–335. Reprinted with permission.

treatment she had obtained few, if any, of the nuts. Estrogen had the same effect on this female. After androgen treatment, a dominant male whose peanut-getting priority was not complete, obtained nearly all the nuts; estrogen had the effect of making him subordinate to his cage mate. Nowlis (14) reported estrous enhancement of the food scores of females in eight of the ten like-sexed and different-sexed pairs he studied.

Other studies suggest that these effects do not invariably occur in chimpanzees. In Yerkes' (16) study describing the relationship between priority of response and the sexual status of the female, more than half the male-female combinations (23 of 45) were discarded because the "typical" effect (i.e., the male dominates the feeding situation except when the female is in estrus) was not obtained. Crawford (9) found a reliable increase in food scores of subordinate members of female pairs during their maximum estrus phase in only 6 of the 16 pairs he studied.

Since it is questionable whether the phenomena described by Birch and Clark may be generalized to include all chimpanzees, it is also questionable whether they apply to all primates. The present study was designed to investigate the effects of gonadal hormones on dominance behavior in another primate, the rhesus macaque (*Macaca mulatta*).

part 1

In Part 1 of this experiment two groups of five animals were studied; in Part 2, four groups of two.

subjects

Two groups of young macaques were used; one consisted of five females, Miriam, Esther,

Naomi, Ruth, Olga; the other, of five males, Al, Les, Hal, Frank, Gene. All animals had been gonadectomized at least two months prior to the experiment. The animals in each group were housed either together in a large group cage of dimensions 8 ft. by 4½ ft. by 7 ft., or separately in individual cages of dimensions 2 ft. by 2½ ft. by 2½ ft. The periods of group- and individual-cage living are reported in Table 1.

procedure

Testing. When housed in the group cages, each group was observed daily at a regular time. The E sat in front of the group cage and introduced 75 peanuts, one at a time, through the wire mesh of the cage front by means of a feeding device which consisted of a length of 1½-in. pipe mounted obliquely on a stand so as to extend 1 ft. into the large cage. The E recorded which animal got each peanut and the dominant-subordinate interaction that occurred. At the end of the observation session, Rockland monkey pellets were thrown into the cage in amounts sufficient to make up the daily total ration of 80 cal/kg body weight per animal (exclusive of peanuts). This diet was supplemented three times a week with one-half orange per animal. The animals were fed the same diet when housed individually.

Establishing the hierarchy. The characteristic "straight-line" hierarchy found in groups of macaque monkeys has been frequently described (11). In this social arrangement, the direction of all aggressive or dominant interaction is invariant, and always unidirectional. Thus, if X engages in dominant interaction against Y, he is said to be dominant over Y. Once the hierarchy is established (and this usually takes place very rapidly), Y never engages in dominant interaction against X. If Y is in turn dominant over Z in the group,

Table 1. Experimental Plan of Part 1

Period	Length (days)	Description
1	10	Group cage base line measures
2	2	Control separation
3	10	Group cage postcontrol separation measures
4	2	Separation to implant No. 5 animal with androgen
5	25	Group cage measures of hormone effect
6	2	Separation to remove pellet from No. 5 animal
7	25	Group cage posthormone measures
8	2	Separation to implant No. 2 animal with androgen
9	25	Group cage measures of hormone effect
10	2	Separation to remove pellet from No. 2 animal, and to implant No. 5 animal with estrogen
11	25	Group cage measures of hormone effect
12	2	Separation to remove pellet from No. 5 animal
13	15	Group cage posthormone measures
14	2	Separation to implant No. 2 animal with estrogen
15	25	Group cage measures of hormone effect
16	2	Separation to remove pellet from No. 2 animal
17	25 (females) 15 (males)	Group cage posthormone measures

then X will also invariably be dominant over Z. This kind of group relationship will be summarized by the notation X→ Y→ Z.

In terms of one of the five-animal groups used in this study, i.e., Al, Les, Hal, Frank, Gene, the hierarchy was considered established once the four bits of dominant interaction Al→ Les, Les→ Hal, Hal→ Frank, and Frank → Gene were observed. After these four acts were observed, it could have been confidently predicted that all dominant interaction between Al and Hal would have the direction Al→ Hal, all dominant interaction between Les and Gene, the direction Les →

Gene, etc. These four acts occurred on the first day of observation. This nonquantitative unidirectional nature of dominant interaction in the group defines the term hierarchy as it is used in this study.

Recording of behavior. Three categories of behavior were recorded during the daily session: dominant acts, peanut-getting acts, and subordinate acts. A dominant act was recorded for an animal engaging in one of the following kinds of behavior:

1. Mild attack. The animal (A) assigned the dominant act chases, pushes, strikes or pulls the tail or hair of another animal (B).

2. Severe attack. A bites B.

3. Displace. A displaces B from a position the latter was occupying.

4. Other moves. As A approaches or turns around, B moves away although no aggressive intent is discernible on the part of A toward B.

5. Other fails to initiate action toward peanut. Although a peanut has fallen farther from A than B, B makes no attempt to reach for the peanut for at least 5 sec. During this time, B watches A's movements closely.

6. Threatening gesture. A growls, glowers threateningly, adopts an "all fours" stance, wags his head aggressively in the direction of B, or crouches as if to spring after B (but does not actually attack B). One, or several of these behaviors in combination, constitutes a threatening gesture.

7. Sniffs mouth. A smells at the mouth of B. This action, like that described in number 8, was often followed by an attempt to steal food.

8. Passive manipulation. A lifts one of B's limbs or opens B's mouth, while B passively submits to A's handling.

9. Head stand. A stands on B's head, shoulders, or back as A gets a nut or prepares to catch one.

10. Mounts feeding pipe. A sits on or supports his weight by the feeding pipe, using his front paws, for at least 5 sec. As is thus in a position to catch the peanuts as they fall from the pipe.

11. Steals peanut. A takes a nut from B's paw or from the ground where B had placed it.

12. Attempts to steal peanut. A tries to take a nut from B but does not succeed.

A peanut-getting act was recorded for an animal engaging in one of the following kinds of behavior:

1. Gets peanut. A gets a peanut without competition from any other animal, or before another animal gets close to the nut.

2. Attempts peanut—successful. A and B contest or try actively for a nut and A gets the nut.

3. Attempts peanut—unsuccessful (see 2). B is credited for his attempt.

A subordinate act was recorded for an animal engaging in one of the following kinds of behavior:

1. Cringe or short withdrawal. B grimaces coweringly, or runs from A a distance less than the length of the cage, without changing his plane of motion (i.e., does not move from the floor to the wall or vice versa).

2. Long withdrawal. B changes his plane of motion or jumps from one side of the cage to another.

3. Flight. B runs or leaps rapidly away from A, placing as much distance as is physically possible between himself and A.

4. Stops action toward peanut. See B's role in dominant act 5.

5. Has mouth sniffed. See B's role in dominant act 7.

6. Passively permits manipulation. See B's role in dominant act 8.

7. Is stood upon. See B's role in dominant act 9.

Dominant acts 1 to 9 are interanimal dominant acts for which both a dominant and a subordinate act were scored; dominant acts 10 to 12 are single-animal dominant acts for which only a dominant act was scored.

Although not used in dominance scoring, all instances of mounting, grooming, and presenting were recorded.

Each animal received a tally of 1 for each dominant, subordinate, and peanut act in which he engaged. The daily total peanut acts for an animal, not including unsuccessful attempts, constituted his *Peanut Score* (P Score). The daily total of all dominant acts and unsuccessful peanut attempts constituted his *Other Dominance Score* (O Score). The sum of these two scores made up his *Total Dominance Score* (D Score), and the sum of all subordinate acts made up an animal's *Subordination Score* (S Score).

In the groups studied, all but the least dominant animal (No. 5 in the hierarchy) engaged in interanimal dominant acts, single-animal dominant acts, and in peanut-getting acts. Animal No. 5 was never observed to initiate interanimal dominant acts. All animals except the Number 1 animal in the hierarchy of each group engaged in subordinate acts. Changes in P, O, D, and S Scores and/or changes in the hierarchy were taken to be evidence of an effect of the hormone on dominance behavior.

Reliability. In order to determine the inter-rater reliability of this system of recording behavior, two observers trained in this method made separate tallies of the behavior occurring during three observation sessions of the male colony. The two observers agreed as to the hierarchy-ranks of the five animals (i.e., Al → Les → Hal → Frank → Gene). In no instance did one observer score as dominant an act that the other observer scored as subordinate. Ten per cent of the dominant and subordinate acts

on the scoring sheets of the two observers were scored as not seen by both observers. Of the remaining acts, there was 95 per cent agreement on the scoring. Of the peanut acts (including unsuccessful attempts), 99.6 per cent were seen by both observers, and they agreed on the scoring of 98.3 per cent. The three-day D-Score and S-Score totals of the five animals according to Observer 1 correlated .99 with the corresponding totals of Observer 2.

Validity. In order to determine the validity of this system of recording behavior, the rank of the animals in each group according to their position in the hierarchy was compared with their rank according to mean D Score and S Score during the first two control periods of the experiment (per. 1 and 3, Table 1). The hierarchy of the female colony, ranked from most to least dominant, was Miriam, Esther, Naomi, Ruth, Olga; in order of mean D Score, from highest to lowest, the animals ranked Miriam, Esther, Ruth, Naomi, Olga. The rho correlation between the two sets of ranks was .90, $p < .05$. The hierarchy-ranks of the male colony were identical with the mean D-Score ranks: (from most to least dominant) Al, Les, Hal, Frank, Gene (rho = 1.00). In contrast with the high correlations between hierarchy ranks and D-Score ranks, the correlations between hierarchy ranks and S-Score ranks were low and not significant. Ranked by S Scores, from highest to lowest, the females were: Esther, Ruth, Naomi, Olga, Miriam; the males were: Les, Frank, Hal, Gene, Al. The rho correlation of these rankings with hierarchy-ranks (from most to least dominant) was −.10, $p > .05$ in each case.

The D and S Scores provide a more sensitive measure of the group structure and interaction than just the hierarchy-ranks. It is for this reason that changes in P, O, D, and S

Scores, as well as changes in hierarchy-rank, were used to evaluate the effects of the hormones. In addition, changes in score-rank were taken to be evidence of an effect of the hormone on dominance behavior.

Hormone administration. Pure crystalline pellets of hormone were implanted by aseptic technique in the back of the anesthetized animal. A small incision was made in the infrascapular portion of the back, the pellet placed on top of the fascia several inches away from the site of the incision, and the wound closed with interrupted sutures. The estrogen pellets consisted of 25 mg. of Progynon (estradiol); the androgen pellets were 75 mg. of Oreton-F (testosterone propionate).[1] All pellets were removed 28 days after implantation. In addition, the tissue surrounding the pellet was excised to insure removal of all the hormone.

Pellet implantation was used in preference to frequent injection of hormone because it necessitated only one breaking-up of the colony. Moreover, this method of administration has been described as tending to simulate natural secretion of the hormone and as providing regular absorption rates (15).

design

Base line measures of the group structure and interaction were obtained. Then, the animal lowest in the hierarchy (i.e., No. 5) was treated with androgen. After suitable measures had been obtained, the pellet was removed and posthormone measures obtained. Next, the Number 2 animal in the hierarchy was treated with androgen. This treatment sequence was then repeated with estrogen. The plan of the experiment is presented in

[1] The hormones used in this study were supplied by the Schering Corporation of Bloomfield, New Jersey.

Table 1. The procedure was identical for the two colonies except that period 17 was 25 days for the female colony as compared with 15 days for the male colony.

part 2

In Part 2, groups of two instead of five monkeys were studied. The observation procedure, method of recording behavior, and means of administering hormones were identical with those described in Part 1.

subjects

Eight young gonadectomized monkeys, four of each sex, were divided into four like-sexed pairs. The pair members were as follows: Teddy and Ike, Jake and Abie, Naomi and Viola, Ruth and Sally. Although Ruth and Naomi had been used in Part 1 of this study, neither had been subjected previously to hormone administration. The members of each pair were housed either together in a large cage of dimensions 3¾ ft. by 4½ ft. by 6½ ft., or separately in individual cages of dimensions 2 ft. by 2½ ft. by 2½ ft.

design

The procedure was identical for all pairs: after obtaining base line measures, the subordinate member of each pair was treated with hormone. One subordinate male received androgen, the other subordinate male, estrogen. Similarly, one subordinate female received estrogen, the other subordinate female, androgen. The experimental plan is summarized in Table 2. Since no hierarchy-rank or score-rank was changed by hormone treatment, no posthormone measures have been included.

Table 2. Experimental Plan of Part 2

Period	Length (days)	Description
1	10	Pair cage base line measures
2	2	Control separation
3	10	Pair cage postcontrol separation measures
4	2	Separation to implant subordinate animals with hormone (Viola and Ike with androgen, Ruth and Abie with estrogen)
5	25*	Pair cage measures of hormone effect

* 20 days in the case of Sally and Ruth.

results

physiological effects of hormones

Implantation of estrogen invariably produced marked swelling and reddening of the sex skin in the females and the scrotal sac in the males. In addition, both sexes displayed swollen nipples and faces, as well as pronounced wrinkling and folding of the skin on the back and legs. These changes are the typical result of estrogen treatment of macaques (18). The swelling and reddening usually disappeared within ten to fifteen days after removal of the estrogen; the wrinkling and folding occasionally persisted in mild form for a somewhat longer time.

Except for one male (Ike), which showed slight reddening of the skin around the penis, and one female (Viola), whose sex skin reddened slightly, no animal showed external physical effects of androgen.

behavioral effects of hormones

Part 1. Dominance and subordination. In no case was any hormone treatment accompanied by a change in the dominance-subordination relationship existing between two animals

prior to such treatment. There were no observed instances of dominant interaction contrary to the direction implicit in the straight-line hierarchies of the two colonies, which persisted as originally established throughout the duration of the study. The hierarchy of the male colony was Al → Les → Hal → Frank → Gene; the hierarchy of the female colony was Miriam → Esther → Naomi → Ruth → Olga. The other behavioral results are illustrated in Figures 1 and 2. These figures illustrate the means of the various scores (P, O, D, and S) for the two colonies in each of the experimental periods. The ranking of the animals according to each of these scores in any experimental period can be determined by noting the ordinate values of the scores at that period, i.e., the animal with the highest mean score in any period ranks highest, and the animal with the lowest mean score ranks lowest. The ranking of the animals of each colony according to the hierarchy was usually consistent with the ranking according to P Scores, O Scores, and D Scores (Fig. 1 and 2). The animals that ranked first in the hierarchy (Al and Miriam) usually ranked first on these measures; the animals that ranked second in the hierarchy (Les and Esther) usually ranked second on these measures. The scores of the three remaining animals in each group were usually rather close, and there was more variation among their score-ranks than in the ranks of the animals first and second in the hierarchy. With regard to S Scores (Fig. 1 and 2) Les and Esther (the animals second in the hierarchy) usually ranked highest, whereas Al and Miriam (first in the hierarchy) with zero scores invariably ranked lowest.

It is apparent from these figures that there was only one change in score-rank of more than one position associated with hormone treatment. Esther's S Score (Fig. 2) fell from

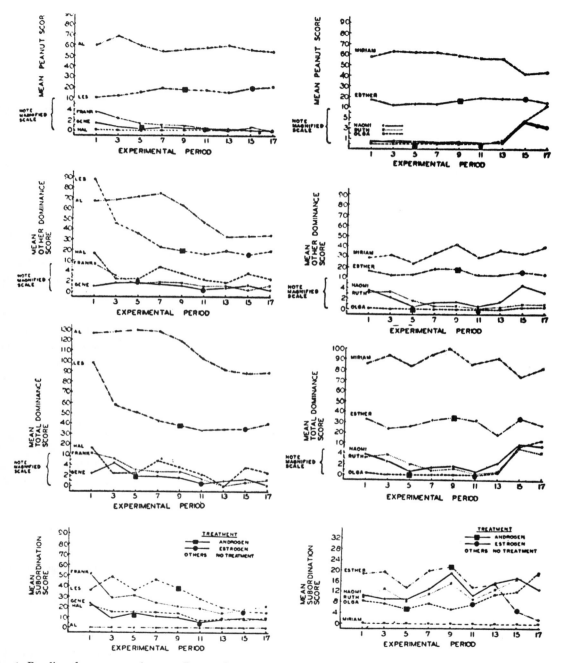

Fig. 1. Reading from top to bottom, Peanut Scores, Other Dominance Scores, Total Dominance Scores, and Subordination Scores, 5-male colony.

Fig. 2. Reading from top to bottom, Peanut Scores, Other Dominance Scores, Total Dominance Scores, and Subordination Scores, 5-female colony.

rank 2 in the pre-estrogen period (per. 13) to rank 4 in the estrogen period (per. 15). Although the change in S Score was significant ($p < .01$), neither the absolute score value nor the score-rank reverted to the pre-estrogen level after the withdrawal of the hormone. A return to the pre-hormone level would be expected in view of Birch and Clark's (5, 6) results with estrogen treatment of chimpanzees. Significance levels were computed by means of Fisher's t test, using a pooled estimate of day-to-day variance.

There were only four other scores out of the total of 32 (8 treatments × 4 scores) that changed significantly with hormones. One of these score changes, Les' S Score, although decreasing significantly ($p < .02$) during androgen, does not appear to be attributable to the effects of the hormone. Although his S Score fell one rank at this time, there was a more significant score decrease ($p < .01$) from the androgen period' (per. 9, Fig. 1) to the post-androgen period (period 11); moreover, both decreases appear to be a reflection of a gradual reduction in Les' S Score extending from period 3 to period 17. Les' O Score and D Score (Fig. 1) also decreased steadily during the experiment.

Two of the changes accompanied Gene's treatment with androgen in period 5. Gene's (and Olga's) score changes in period 5 were evaluated against the combined control data from periods 1 and 3. There were significant decreases in Gene's P Score ($p < .01$, Fig. 1) and D Score ($p < .05$, Fig. 1). The D-Score change was accompanied by a fall in rank of one position, and was not reversed following the withdrawal of hormone. The remaining change was a reduction in Gene's S Score during estrogen treatment ($p < .02$, Fig. 1). The S-Score change was not accompanied by a change in rank, nor did the score increase significantly after the hormone was withdrawn.

Mounting, grooming, and presenting. The only significant change in the frequency of mounting, grooming, and presenting accompanied the estrogen treatment of Esther. Her daily mean of all such acts combined increased from 0.33 in the pre-estrogen period to 3.56 during estrogen treatment ($p < .01$).

Part 2. Dominance and subordination. The data from the four pairs studied, i.e., Teddy and Ike, Jake and Abie, Naomi and Viola, and Sally and Ruth, are summarized in Figure 3. As can be seen from this figure, the priority of peanut-getting established by the dominant member of the pair in period 1 was not

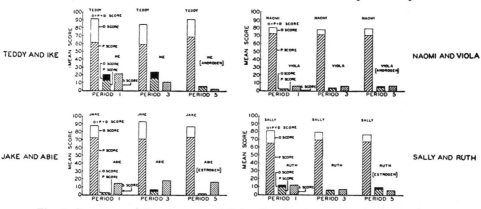

Fig. 3. Summary of Dominance and Subordination Scores, 2-animal colonies.

changed by any hormone treatment. More-over, the direction of dominant-subordinate interaction was always Teddy → Ike, Jake → Abie, Naomi → Viola, Sally → Ruth through-out the study.

Although there were seven significant score changes in Part 2, none of them was large; the dominant animal of the pair invariably achieved a higher P, O, and D Score than the subordinate animal. The only significant change accompanying hormone treatment in the two females was a decrease in Ruth's S Score ($p < .05$). With the males, on the other hand, there were significant reductions in Abie's P Score ($p < .05$) and D Score ($p < .01$), and in Ike's P, O, D and S Scores ($p < .01$ in each case). These comparisons are based on the combined data of control periods 1 and 3 versus period 5. The highly significant reduction in all Ike's scores results from a change in the technique of peanut-getting employed by his dominant pair-mate Teddy, rather than from any hormonal effect on Ike. During periods 1 and 3, Teddy typically remained on the floor of the cage and chased each peanut as it fell from the feeding pipe. Although Teddy was clearly dominant in peanut-getting (mean P Score = 60.75), Ike managed to garner about 20 per cent of the nuts (mean P Score = 14.25), usually being attacked in connection with every peanut he got (mean S Score = 16.6). During period 5, however, Teddy adopted the technique of sitting on the pipe and catching the nuts as they fell. This had the effect not only of increasing his mean P Score to 69.56, and increasing the number of his mountings of the feeding pipe from a mean of 0.7 during periods 1 and 3 to a mean of 13.9 during period 5, it also decreased the interaction between the two animals. Thus, Ike's reduced P Score reflects Teddy's increase, Ike's low-ered O Score reflects the fewer opportunities

he had to attempt to get peanuts so long as *Teddy* sat on the pipe, and Ike's lowered D Score *reflects* the decrease in P and O. The decrease in *Ike's* S Score to a mean of 3.20 results not only *from the* increase in physical distance between the *two animals* during the sessions, but also from the *fewer* occasions (fewer peanuts and peanut *attempts*) on which Ike could provoke attacks *from* Teddy.

Mounting, grooming, and presenting. Mounting, grooming, and presenting were rarely seen in these pairs during the observation sessions, and there was no significant differ-ence accompanying the treatment of any ani-mal.

discussion

The results of this study emphasize how ineffective hormones may be in inducing changes in the social behavior of macaques. The straight-line hierarchies in the six groups that were studied remained unchanged during the course of the study. Moreover, no hor-mone treatment was accompanied by a score increase; the seven significant score decreases in Parts 1 and 2 that are not explainable in terms of nonhormonal factors reveal little or no consistent pattern. Two changes accompa-nied androgen treatment of a low-status male (Gene's P and D scores); three other changes accompanied estrogen treatment of a low-status male (Abie's P and D scores, Gene's S score); one change accompanied estrogen treatment of a high-status female in the group of five (Esther's S Score); the remaining change accompanied estrogen treatment of the subordinate member of a pair of females (Ruth's S Score). These changes are not related to changes in the frequency of ob-served mounting, grooming, and presenting behavior, for only one animal (Esther) showed a significant change in such behavior. Since these changes show little or no consistency and since the hierarchies remained intact, the most reasonable interpretation of the results is that gonadal hormones have no effect on dominance in unisexed macaque social groups; the changes observed in dominance and subordination scores are the result of other factors in the relationships of the animals. One of those other factors is apparently identified in the case of Ike's changes with androgen, and another is illustrated in Figure 1 in the case of Les's change with androgen.

These results are in striking contrast with those of Birch and Clark (5, 6, 7, 8). The difference does not appear to lie in differences in experimental design: both studies used castrate animals (this is true for three of the four Birch and Clark investigations) and both studies employed daily observation of the animals in a competitive feeding situation. It is not likely that the difference in age between Birch and Clark's mature chimpanzees and the young animals of the present study accounts for the difference in results. In his survey of the interrelationships between endocrine secretions and patterns of overt response, Beach concluded:

Neuromuscular elements responsible for such hormonally conditioned behavior patterns as courtship, mating and care of the young are fully organized and ready to function relatively early in life, well in advance of the time that they will normally be activated . . . their organization is complete prior to the time that the hormones which will sensitize them to stimulation are secreted in sufficient quantities to become effective (3, p. 211).

If dominance behavior in the macaque is a "hormonally conditioned behavior pattern," it probably would have been manifested in the animals of the present study. Although these results differ markedly from those of Birch and Clark, they differ less from the results of Yerkes (16), who found no estrous enhancement of dominance in at least half the male-female combinations he studied, and the results of Crawford (9), who found no such effect in 10 of the 16 pairs he studied.

A difference between the species which may account for the difference in results relates to the character of the social relationships generally observed in the macaque and the chimpanzee. Yerkes and Yerkes (17) and Maslow (10) have noted that dominance in the chimpanzee is usually expressed in a relatively nonviolent and noncontactual manner, especially when compared with the expression of dominance in certain catarrhine monkeys, such as the macaque. One chimpanzee may dominate another completely without any observed instances of attacking or biting. This kind of social relationship has been described by Maslow as "friendly" and "protective." In the macaque, on the other hand, aggressive chasing and biting is apparently an invariable concomitant of social dominance, prompting Maslow to describe it as "brutal" and "sadistic." Yerkes' (16) and Crawford's (9) data suggest that temperamental differences may be the cause of the frequent obscuring of estrous enhancement of dominance in the female chimpanzee. Some of the reasons offered by Yerkes for atypical cases (i.e., male-female pairs in which the female dominated the feeding situation only while she was in estrus) included "unassertiveness," "timidity," and "exceptional aggressiveness or dominance" of the female. Crawford concluded, "a variety of reactive patterns built up during the life of the animal . . . may determine the outcome of any test of dominance" (9, p. 508).

Since temperamental differences may obscure hormonal effects in the relatively unaggressive chimpanzee, individual differences in aggressiveness may always act to obscure hormonal effects on dominance in unisexed macaque groups because of the greater role of aggression in the social behavior of the macaque. Hormonally induced dominance would therefore appear to be relatively weaker than the dominance resulting from other factors if the latter is pronounced among members of a species. Thus, the hormonal effects on dominance in the chimpanzee in a competitive feeding situation as described by Birch and Clark may not be demonstrated when individual members of a species are capable of wide variations in aggressiveness.

This research has emphasized that aggression and dominance are not invariably influenced by sex hormones; the social behavior of the macaque in a competitive feeding situation is markedly refractory to such treatment. Beach (4) has urged the necessity for studying many kinds of animals to avoid the error of overgeneralizing from a few; the results of the present study reiterate his point. Despite the fact that the response of several species to gonadal hormones has been investigated, it would seem to be impossible to describe the response of any other species without actually conducting the research.

summary

1. Unisexed social groups of male and female castrate *Macaca mulatta* were observed daily in a competitive feeding situation, and instances of dominant, subordinate, and other interanimal behavior were recorded.

2. After control measures of the group hierarchy and behavior had been obtained, various members of the groups were implanted with pellets of androgen or estrogen.

3. In no case was hormone administration accompanied by changes in the hierarchy or by an increase in the number of instances of dominant behavior.

4. Although 7 of the 12 treatments were accompanied by a significant decrease in either dominant or subordinate behavior scores, the change in 2 cases could not reasonably be attributed to hormone administration, and the changes in the other 5 show little or no consistency. This suggested that gonadal hormones were without effect on unisexed groups of castrate macaques, and that the observed changes resulted from other factors.

5. It is suggested that the difference between these results and those derived from the chimpanzee is related to the greater degree of aggressiveness characterizing the social behavior of the macaque as compared with the chimpanzee.

references

1. Allee, W. C., & Collias, N. E.. The influence of estradiol on the social organization of flocks of hens. *Endocrinol.*, 1940, **27**, 87–94.

2. Ball, J. The effect of testosterone on the sex behavior of female rats. *J. comp. Psychol.*, 1940, **29**, 151–165.

3. Beach, F. A. *Hormones and behavior.* New York: Hoeber, 1948.

4. Beach, F. A. The snark was a boojum. *Amer. Psychologist*, 1950, **5**, 115–124.

5. Birch, H. G., & Clark, G. Hormonal modification of social behavior: II. The effects of sex-hormone administration on the social dominance status of the female-castrate chimpanzee. *Psychosom. Med.*, 1946, **8**, 320–331.

6. Birch, H. G., & Clark, G. Hormonal modification of social behavior: IV. The mechanism of estrogen-induced dominance in chimpanzees. *J. comp. physiol. Psychol.*, 1950, **43**, 181–193.

7. Clark, G., & Birch, H. G. Hormonal modifications of social behavior: I. The effect of sex-hormone administration on the social behavior of a male-castrate chimpanzee. *Psychosom. Med.*, 1945, **7**, 321–329.

8. Clark, G., & Birch, H. G. Hormonal modifications of social behavior: III. The effects of stilbesterol therapy on social dominance in the female-castrate chimpanzee. *Bull. Canad. psychol. Ass.*, 1946, **6**, 15–18.

9. Crawford, M. P. The relation between social dominance and the menstrual cycle in female chimpanzees. *J. comp. Psychol.*, 1940, **30**, 483–513.

10. Maslow, A. H. Dominance quality and social behavior in infrahuman primates. *J. soc. Psychol.*, 1940, **11**, 313–324.

11. Maslow, A. H., & Flanzbaum, S. The role of dominance in social and sexual behavior of infrahuman primates: II. An experimental determination of the behavior syndrome of dominance. *J. genet. Psychol.*, 1936, **48**, 278–309.

12. Noble, G. K., & Borne, R. The effect of sex hormones on the social hierarchy of *Xiphorus helleri*. *Anat. Rec.*, 1940, **78**, Suppl. 147.

13. Noble, G. K., & Greenberg, B. Induction of female behavior in male *Anolis carolinensis* with testosterone propionate. *Proc. Soc. exp. Biol. Med.*, 1941, **47**, 32–37.

14. Nowlis, V. Sexual status and degree of hunger in chimpanzee competitive interaction. *J. comp. Psychol.*, 1942, **34**, 184–194.

15. Vest, S. A., Drew, J. E., & Langworthy, O. R. Implantation of crystalline testosterone in the monkey. *Endocrinol.*, 1940, **27**, 455–460.

16. Yerkes, R. M. Social behavior of chimpanzees: Dominance between mates in relation to sexual status. *J. comp. Psychol.*, 1940, **30**, 147–186.

17. Yerkes, R. M., & Yerkes, A. W. Social behavior in infrahuman primates. In C. A. Murchison (Ed.), *A handbook of social psychology*. Worcester, Mass.: Clark Univer. Press, 1935, pp. 973–1033.

18. Zuckerman, S., Van Wagenen, G., & Gardiner, R. H. The sexual skin of the rhesus monkey. *Proc. Zool. Soc. London*, 1938, **108**, 385–401.

23 effects of female sex hormones on incubation behavior in the ring dove*

Daniel S. Lehrman

1. Why did Lehrman consider inconclusive the previous research on prolactin as a factor in incubation?

2. How did he design his experiment in order to be certain of the sequence of events leading to incubation?

3. What is the sequence leading to incubation in the ring dove?

4. What is the most important finding presented in this study?

If a pair of ring doves is placed in a cage with a nest and eggs, they will begin to sit on the eggs four to seven days later. In a previous paper, it was shown that the readiness to incubate was brought about in part by association of the mates, and in part by participation in nest-building activity (8). This suggests that exteroceptive factors associated with the mate and with nest-building bring about phys-

* D. S. Lehrman, "Effects of Female Sex Hormones on Incubation Behavior in the Ring Dove (*Streptopelia Risoria*)," *J. comp. physiol. Psychol.*, 51 (1958), 142–145. Reprinted with permission.

iological changes which underlie the onset of incubation behavior. It is well known that external stimuli are influential in the control of hormonal cycles in birds (1, 7, 10), and it has been reported that various steroid hormones induce broodiness in doves (16). It therefore seems desirable to determine more directly what hormonal changes might be involved in the onset of incubation behavior.

Riddle and Lahr (16) showed that progesterone, implanted into unisexual pairs of ring doves kept together in the test cage, induced incubation behavior after three to nine days. They also found that the crops of such doves were enlarged after several days of incubation induced in this manner. Since prolactin had previously been found to induce broodiness in laying hens (15), and since prolactin is the hormone responsible for crop growth (14), these authors concluded that the progesterone had induced incubation by stimulating the release of prolactin from the birds' own pituitary glands.

Two points about this experiment seem to warrant further investigation. Patel (13) showed that participation in incubation itself stimulates prolactin secretion. The present author (8) showed that association between the mates helps induce incubation. We may therefore ask: (a) Is there any evidence of prolactin secretion at the *beginning* of progesterone-induced incubation, and (b) does progesterone administration bring about readiness to incubate when it is not concurrent with association between members of the pair? In addition, the role of estrogen needs to be investigated, since estrogen and progesterone sometimes seem to have additive or synergistic effects (11).

The purpose of the present study is to examine the effect of certain hormones on the occurrence of incubation behavior. The specific questions under investigation are: (a) Do progesterone and estrogen induce readiness to incubate, and (b) is there any evidence of prolactin secretion at the commencement of such incubation?

method

subjects

The Ss were 69 adult male and 69 adult female ring doves (*Streptopelia risoria*), all of a laboratory colony derived from stock obtained from J. W. Steinbeck, Concord, California.

Cages and maintenance. Details of experimental cages, housing, feeding, and rearing procedures were described in a previous paper (8).

Experience prior to testing. All Ss were birds with previous breeding experience consisting of two successful breeding cycles, and had been in isolation for three to five weeks prior to testing. During the tests Ss were never paired with birds with which they had previously mated.

Further details may be found in the earlier paper (8).

procedure

Birds which had been in isolation for from two to four weeks were given seven daily hormone (or control) injections. Each injection consisted of 0.1 ml. of sesame oil. Injections were made alternately into the right and left pectoral muscles.

On the day following the last injection, the birds of the first three groups were placed in pairs in the experimental cages. Each such cage was equipped with a bowl containing a nest with two eggs, placed in the standard position, and a handful of nesting material (pine needles) on the floor.[1] The nests and eggs were obtained from pairs in the breeding colony. The birds were observed from two to five times daily, and the day on which they began to incubate the eggs noted. The criterion for incubation was that the bird should allow O to lift it slightly off the eggs and replace it, without abandoning the nest even momentarily. With one exception, when a sitting bird was removed, its mate immediately took its place.

All introductions of birds into the experimental cages took place between 9 A.M. and 9:30 A.M.

Some birds from each group were killed for autopsy within 8 hr. after first being observed sitting on the eggs. The crops were immediately excised and weighed.

Group 1: Standard. This group of 16 pairs consisted of 8 pairs injected daily with 0.1 ml. of sesame oil, combined with 8 pairs (from a previous study) which received no injections. Eight pairs were killed for autopsy.

Group 2: Progesterone. Each S of 14 pairs received daily 0.1 mg. of progesterone.[2] Eight pairs were killed for autopsy.

Group 3: Estrogen-incubation. Each S of 23 pairs received daily 0.4 mg. of diethylstilbestrol.[3] Thirteen pairs of "reactors" (see below) were killed for autopsy.

The remaining two groups were not tested for incubation behavior, but were kept in isolation and killed for autopsy on the day following the last injection.

Group 4: Estrogen. Each S of eight pairs received daily 0.4 mg. of diethylstilbestrol.

Group 5: Control. Each S of eight pairs

[1] Pine needles were provided through the courtesy of E. M. Hargrave of Acme, N. C.

[2] Progesterone ("Lutocylin," CIBA) was supplied through the courtesy of Robert Gaunt of Ciba Pharmaceutical Co.

[3] Diethylstilbestrol was supplied through the courtesy of Aleck Borman of E. R. Squibb & Sons.

received daily injections of 0.1 ml. of sesame oil.

results

qualitative observations

Observation of the birds immediately after they were introduced into the experimental cages revealed striking and consistent differences in their behavior.

Standard. When pairs were introduced into the cage without prior hormone treatment, the males immediately began the typical courtship behavior, consisting of cooing and bowing at the female (3). After a few minutes, the females characteristically stood on the rim of the nest bowl and performed the cooing, accompanied by a slight quivering of the tips of the wings, which is the usual behavior of a female in a potential nest site. This behavior is similar to that of experienced pairs introduced into a cage without a nest and eggs.

Progesterone. Progesterone-injected birds immediately went to the nest and stood in it, crouching over the eggs with the feathers of the abdomen erected so as to expose the incubation path. Usually it was possible, within 5 min. or so, for O to place his hand under the bird without causing it to leave the nest. All these birds were settled on the eggs within 20 min. of their introduction into the cage.

Estrogen-incubation. Estrogen-injected birds soon picked up pine needles and carried them to the nest. Active nest-building behavior was observed in birds of this group all during the first day in the cage.

incubation

The results from Groups 1, 2, and 3 are presented for comparison in Figure 1. These

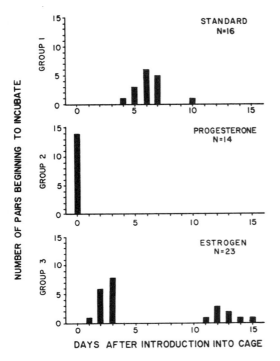

Fig. 1. Distribution of latencies of incubation behavior in groups of ring doves subjected to different hormone pretreatments. Birds introduced into experimental cages between 9:00 A.M. and 9:30 A.M. on Day 0. N = number of pairs.

groups differed with respect to the type of hormone treatment they received during the seven days preceding their introduction into the cage containing a nest bowl with nest and eggs.

It is apparent that progesterone brought about complete readiness to incubate in all birds of Group 2. The estrogen-injected birds of Group 3 fall into two dichotomous groups: *reactors*, which were not fully ready to incubate, but which the latency of incubation behavior was shorter than in the nontreated standard group; and *nonreactors*, in which the latency of incubation behavior was longer than in the standard birds. The differences among all four of these groups are statistically

significant ($p < .01$) when tested by Fisher's exact method (17). It is assumed that, in the nonreactors, the exogenous estrogen merely disrupted the normal development of broodiness until its effects were dissipated. Our analysis at present will be concerned with the facilitation of incubation behavior by estrogen in the reactors.

crop weights

Since crop weights are affected by prolactin secretion in doves (14), analysis of them should indicate whether the occurrence of prolactin is necessarily associated with incubation behavior. The crop weights of all groups are presented in Table 1, where the data for

Table 1. Crop Weights of Ring Doves (mg.)

Group	N	Mean	SD
1. Standard	16	849.4	128.30
2. Progesterone	16	817.6	96.55
3. Estrogen-incubation[a]	21	790.4	90.43
4. Estrogen	16	782.1	71.02
5. Control	16	872.7	99.53

[a] Reactors only.

males and females are combined. Crop weights of males and females within each group were compared by both Fisher's t test and the Mann-Whitney U test (17), and no significant differences were found (all $ps > .05$).

The Mann-Whitney U test was used to test the differences in crop weights between various groups. The results indicate that when birds were subjected to a treatment which resulted in incubation only after an appreciable latency period, the crops were no heavier at the end than at the beginning of the latency period (Control vs. Standard, $p > .10$; Estrogen-incubation [reactors only] vs. Estrogen, $p > .10$). Birds subjected to a treatment which induced immediate incubation had crops no heavier than birds whose treatment left them ready to incubate only after an appreciable latency period (Progesterone vs. Estrogen, $p > .10$; Control vs. Progesterone, $p > .10$). Estrogen, which shortened the latency period, actually resulted in significantly *decreased* crop weights (Control vs. Estrogen-incubation, $p < .05$; Control vs. Estrogen, $p < .02$).

In summary, there is no indication in the data that readiness to incubate is associated with increased crop weight.

discussion

Since progesterone brings about readiness to incubate without increased crop weights, the finding of Riddle and Lahr (16) that crop weights were increased after several days of progesterone-induced incubation does not show that the progesterone stimulated prolactin secretion. Rather, it confirms Patel's (13) report that prolactin secretion is stimulated by participation in incubation. Meites and Turner (12) found that progesterone administration would not induce prolactin secretion in pigeons (their birds had no opportunity to sit on eggs).

Although in the light of the facts presented here, previous data on crop weights do not demonstrate prolactin secretion at the beginning of incubation, the presence of such secretion is not necessarily excluded. Lahr and Riddle (6), using a very sensitive method of detecting cell divisions in the crop wall, found suggestive indications of prolactin secretion at the beginning of incubation in a normal breeding cycle. Further research should therefore determine (*a*) whether progesterone induces prolactin secretion which can be detected by methods more sensitive than that of

crop weights, and (*b*) whether incubation can be induced by injection of prolactin in amounts too small to cause changes in crop weight. Both these questions are now being studied in this laboratory.

It was previously reported that participation in courtship for seven days results in a shortened latency period for incubation upon subsequent introduction of nest and eggs into the cage (8). This effect is similar to that of estrogen injection for seven days in the present experiment. It was further reported that participation in courtship and in nest-building for a similar period resulted in readiness to incubate immediately, an effect identical with that of progesterone injection in the present experiment. It may also be noted that the estrogen-injected birds in the present experiment, unlike the untreated birds, engaged in intensive nest-building upon being introduced into the cage. In explanation of these facts, we may tentatively suggest that participation in courtship (at least in the female) stimulates estrogen secretion, undoubtedly via an effect upon the pituitary gland (5). The estrogen stimulates nest-building activity, and it appears probable that, under these conditions, participation in nest-building activity stimulates the release of progesterone, which in turn induces incubation behavior. The impression that progesterone is secreted at this time is strengthened by the fact that this hormone, in addition to eliciting incubation behavior, may trigger the release of an egg from the ovary (4) and stimulate the growth of the estrogen-primed oviduct (2, 9), both of these being events that normally occur just before the onset of incubation.

Further research is required to demonstrate the exact nature of the stimuli responsible for the successive changes in hormone secretion which appear to underlie the succession of nest-building and incubation behavior. It is clear, however, that in this species, and possibly in other birds, the influence of hormones on the behavior cycle is paralleled by influences exerted on the pattern of hormone secretion by stimuli coming from the behavior of the bird and of its mate.

summary

Sixty-nine pairs of ring doves with previous breeding experience were treated, while in isolation cages, with estrogen or progesterone, or left untreated. Some of the birds in each treatment were then killed for autopsy, others were placed in pairs in cages containing nests and eggs, and autopsied when they began to sit on the eggs. Untreated birds sat after 4–10 days. Progesterone-injected birds sat immediately. Estrogen-treated birds sat after 1 to 3 days (15 pairs) or after more than 11 days (8 pairs).

Analysis of crop weights of the various groups showed that there was no increase in crop weight associated with the onset of incubation behavior or with hormone treatment that induced such behavior. There is thus no evidence that prolactin secretion was involved in the induction of incubation behavior by progesterone or estrogen.

Comparison of the effects of progesterone and estrogen on incubation behavior with the effects of participation in courtship and in nest-building suggests that courtship stimulates estrogen secretion and that estrogen stimulates nest-building behavior, which in turn encourages progesterone secretion, leading to incubation.

The results indicate that stimuli provided by the bird's activity and that of its mate affect the pattern of hormone secretion, which in its turn influences the behavior.

references

1. Benoit, J. Etats physiologiques et instinct de reproduction chez les oiseaux. In P.-P. Grassé (Ed.), *L'Instinct dans le comportement des animaux et de l'homme*. Paris: Masson, 1956. Pp. 177–260.

2. Brant, J. W. A., & Nalbandov, A. V. Role of sex hormones in albumen secretion by the oviduct of chickens. *Poultry Sci.*, 1956, **35**, 365–373.

3. Craig, W. The expressions of emotion in the pigeons. I. The blond ring-dove (*Turtur risorius*). *J. comp. Neurol.*, 1909, **19**, 29–82.

4. Fraps, R. M. The varying effects of sex hormones in birds. *Mem. Soc. Endocrinol.*, 1955, No. 4, 205–219.

5. Harris, G. W. *Neural control of the pituitary gland*. London: Edward Arnold, 1955.

6. Lahr, E. S., & Riddle, O. Proliferation of crop-sac epithelium in incubating and prolactin-injected pigeons studied with the colchicine method. *Amer. J. Physiol.*, 1938, **123**, 614–619.

7. Lehrman, D. S. On the organization of maternal behavior and the problem of instinct. In P.-P. Grassé (Ed.), *L'Instinct dans le comportement des animaux et de l'homme*. Paris: Masson, 1956. Pp. 475–520.

8. Lehrman, D. S. Induction of broodiness by participation in courtship and nest-building in the ring dove (*Streptopelia risoria*). *J. comp. physiol. Psychol.*, 1958, **51**, 32–36.

9. Lehrman, D. S., & Brody, P. Oviduct response to estrogen and progesterone in the ring dove (*Streptopelia risoria*). *Proc. Soc. exper. Biol. & Med.*, 1957, **95**, 373–375.

10. Marshall, F. H. A. Exteroceptive factors in sexual periodicity. *Biol. Rev.*, 1942, **17**, 68–90.

11. Mason, R. C. Synergistic and antagonistic effects of progesterone in combination

with estrogens on oviduct weight. *Endocrinology*, 1952, **51**, 570–572.

12. Meites, J., & Turner, C. W. Effect of sex hormones on pituitary lactogen and crop glands of common pigeons. *Proc. Soc. exper. Biol., N.Y.*, 1947, **64**, 465–468.

13. Patel, M. D. The physiology of the formation of "pigeon's milk." *Physiol. Zool.*, 1936, **9**, 129–152.

14. Riddle, O. Physiological responses to prolactin. *Cold Spring Habor Sympos. quant. Biol.*, 1937, **5**, 218–228.

15. Riddle, O., Bates, R. W., & Lahr, E. L. Prolactin induces broodiness in fowl. *Amer. J. Physiol.*, 1935, **111**, 352–360.

16. Riddle, O., & Lahr, E. L. On broodiness of ring doves following implants of certain steroid hormones. *Endocrinology*, 1944, **35**, 255–260.

17. Siegel, S. *Nonparametric statistics*. New York: McGraw-Hill, 1956.

24 hibernation in mammals and birds*

Charles P. Lyman

1. What characteristics must a bird or mammal possess in order to evolve into a hibernator?

2. What environmental conditions are ideal for a hibernator?

3. What role is played by the endocrine glands during hibernation?

4. What happens to a hibernating animal if its body temperature approaches freezing (32°F)?

5. What lines of research need to be explored in order to understand hibernation better?

* C. P. Lyman, "Hibernation in Mammals and Birds," *Amer. Scient.*, 51, No. 2 (June 1963). Copyright the Society of the Sigma Xi. Reprinted by permission.

Warm-bloodedness or homeothermism is as much a characteristic of mammals as is the ability to suckle their young. It is believed to have started as much as 150 million years ago when mammals first developed from reptilian stock, though direct evidence, such as the imprint of fossilized hair, has never been found. Whatever may be the precise date of the appearance of primitive temperature regulation, it is certain that mammals have lived in their own warm internal environment for many millions of years. If the duck-billed platypus and the spiny anteater give any clue, the original control of body temperature was far from precise. These most primitive of living mammals, which lay soft-shelled eggs and suckle their young, have considerable variation in body temperature, depending on the temperature of the environment. The marsupials and placental mammals probably originated at about the same time, perhaps one hundred million years after the duck-billed platypus and spiny anteater, and both groups, generally speaking, maintain an even body temperature throughout their adult life.

The precision of the control of the deep body temperature in many mammals is remarkable, particularly in larger animals whose ratio of body mass to surface area is high. In many such mammals, including man, the body temperature often does not vary more than ½°F. over a twenty-four hour period, and a small rise in body temperature may indicate a serious illness. The mechanisms which control the body temperature with such accuracy are not completely understood. Cold and heat receptors in the skin and the temperature of the blood reaching the hypothalamic region of the brain both must combine to regulate the amount of cutaneous vasodilation, sweating and panting for cooling the body, or the amount of shivering, vasoconstriction and piloerection for keeping it warm.

It is a peculiarity of both mammals and birds that the body temperature is remarkably high, averaging a little less than 100°F. in mammals and three or four degrees higher in birds. Physiologists have speculated that this temperature setting may be the result of the high environmental temperatures which can occur on the earth. If a mammal maintains its body temperature precisely, it must be able to cool itself in a warm environment as well as warm itself in a cool one. Cooling can only be produced by evaporative water loss. In many parts of the world, even in temperate latitudes, the air temperature can be near 100°F. with a high humidity. If a mammal's body temperature was set at 85°F. instead of 98°F. it would be physically impossible for it to cool itself by evaporative water loss at an air temperature of 100°F., and the body temperature would rise. According to this concept, the mammalian body temperature is set high because it is easier to remain hot than to keep cool. Even with their high body temperature, mammals can be exposed to natural environmental temperatures which are so hot that no amount of evaporative water loss will keep the body temperature down, and the animals suffer an explosive heat rise which is often fatal.

Although it may be physically more practical to maintain a high body temperature, it is, nevertheless, metabolically expensive. With a core temperature fixed at 100°F. an arctic mammal must find enough food to hold this temperature when the environmental temperature is as much as 150 degrees lower. Mammals often reduce this metabolic effort by allowing peripheral parts of the body such as legs and ears to cool while maintaining the core temperature, but they do not allow their deep body temperature and their brain temperature to drop and still continue an active life. It may be true that coordination is impos-

sible if the temperature of the brain varies. Each purposeful muscular movement, each thought, involves the interaction of untold numbers of nerve cells, and each cell and synapse may have its own temperature characteristics. If the temperature fluctuates, the precise synchronization between nerve cell and nerve cell may be lost, and coordination vanish. The same thing would occur if half the operators in a complex long distance phone call were unexpectedly exposed to low temperatures. They might get used to handling the switchboard using arctic mittens, but it would take some adaptation, and if the temperature was always changing they could not be as efficient as they would be under constant conditions.

The mammals which have the most variable body temperatures and still remain active are the primitive Prototheria (duck bills and spiny anteaters) and the Edentates, an order which comprises the tree sloths and the armadillos. The tree sloths in particular have a very unsteady body temperature, and they are proverbial as the slowest moving and least coordinated of mammals. Thus the concept that a steady brain temperature is necessary for the ultimate in mammalian performance is strengthened by the stupidity of the thermolabile sloth.

Scattered among the various orders of mammals are animals which abandon the warmblooded state in an almost purposeful manner, and sink into a torpor in which the body temperature approaches that of the protective cave or burrow. Under these conditions, the body temperature may drop to a few degrees above the freezing point of water and the metabolic rate may be reduced more than fifty-fold. This condition is usually called "hibernation," but we are in need of a better word. "Hibernation" may apply equally well to reptiles, amphibians, invertebrates, or even plants which pass the winter in a state of dormancy, yet none of these give up a heritage of homeothermy to reach the hibernating state. Furthermore, a state which is physiologically equivalent to hibernation may occur in mammals during the summer so that the Latin "hiber" or "winter" can be particularly inappropriate. However, it may be too soon to settle on a precise word for this phenomenon in mammals, and perhaps we should wait until we know more about it before we give it a descriptive word of its own.

At least five of the eighteen living orders of mammals contain species which hibernate. Small opposum-like marsupials, both from South America and Australia, have recently been shown to be hibernators. Among the Insectivora the European hedgehog is the best known hibernator, but the tenrec of Madagascar also hibernates. In the Primates there are at least two lemurs which are reported to hibernate, and most of the bats (Chiroptera) of temperate regions hibernate throughout the winter. It is among the rodents that the largest number of hibernators is found. Dormice, ground squirrels, birchmice, chipmunks, and woodchucks are among the best known hibernators from this group. Notable among the non-hibernators are the ungulates and the carnivores. Folklore to the contrary, bears do not enter the deeply hibernating state. They often retire to dens during the winter and remain curled in a ball for long periods, but Hock and others have shown that their body temperature does not drop below 91°F., and they are ready to wake up at once and amble drowsily away (4).

Although Samuel Johnson claimed that swallows "conglobulate together" and hibernate in rivers during the winter, it has not been recognized until recently that some birds enter a state which is very similar to hibernation in mammals. Swifts, poorwills and hum-

mingbirds all possess the ability to lower their body temperature in an unfavorable thermal environment, though swifts apparently can not survive body temperatures below about 65°F. Some hummingbirds permit their temperature to decline every night and rewarm each morning, thus effecting considerable saving of metabolic energy. During the incubation period, when the eggs must be kept constantly warm, the female maintains a high body temperature day and night (9). It is remarkable that hibernation occurs in any birds, for their ability to migrate is so well developed that hibernation to avoid an unfavorable environment would seem superfluous. However, many bats may migrate long distances and hibernate at the end of migration.

As far as physiological research on hibernation is concerned, most of the studies have been confined to bats, hedgehogs, and to rodents, particularly ground squirrels, woodchucks or marmots, dormice and hamsters. Although there are some differences between the various species, the general pattern is quite similar among all the mammalian hibernators. The bulk of more recent investigation is concerned with rodents, principally because of the availability of these animals, and most of our discussion will be confined to this group.

Many rodents, such as the various species of ground squirrels, hibernate during a definite season even in an artificially illuminated, air-conditioned laboratory where they can obtain no obvious cues concerning the time of year. During the spring, breeding takes place and the young are born. As fall approaches, the animals become lethargic and lay on large quantities of fat, so that they may actually double their body weight in little more than a month. If exposed to cold during the spring and summer, they increase their food consumption and metabolic rate and maintain their warm-blooded body temperature. If exposed to cold during the autumn or winter, they enter the hibernating state, usually within twenty-four hours. On the other hand, the semipopular Syrian hamster of pet stores shows very little seasonal influence and will enter hibernation at any time of year if exposed to cold for a sufficiently long period. Some of the very small rodents, such as our western pocket mouse, will enter hibernation if denied food and water (1). The tiny birchmouse of Scandinavia hibernates each night and rewarms each day during the summer and hibernates for longer periods during the winter (5). In this it resembles the insect-eating bats of our temperate region, for they cool during the day and warm again before their evening hunt for insects. Small mammals have a very low body mass to surface ratio, so they lose heat very quickly, and this is notably true of bats with their vascular wing membranes. Hibernation for them in particular would seem to be an excellent economy.

No one knows why animals should enter hibernation during one period and remain stubbornly warm-blooded during another. It is true that many of the endocrine glands undergo a histological involution after the breeding season is over, and this may form suitable background for hibernation to occur, but there is no compelling evidence to suggest that any single endocrine gland controls the onset of hibernation and hibernation has not been notably hastened by the removal of endocrine glands. Certainly the autumnal fattening seems to be related to the onset of hibernation, for fat animals tend to start hibernating sooner than thin ones. In spite of this, fattening is not a necessity, for thin animals of the same species may hibernate though the onset may be delayed. Some species of hibernators do not lay on fat in the fall but store quantities of food. The golden hamster is a food storer, and the onset of hibernation is delayed if this animal is given only as much food as it can eat (7).

It seems probable that mammals enter hibernation from a condition of normal sleep, but it is difficult to decide when sleep stops and hibernation begins. Animals in hibernation thus usually maintain their normal sleeping position. Bats hang suspended from the roofs of caves, or cluster together on the damp walls, often with beads of moisture clinging to their fur. Other animals curl in a tight ball with their heads under their tails and their tails often wrapped around their bodies. In their well-formed nests, only the top of the back is visible—a position which must afford the maximum conservation of heat. Actually heat conservation is usually not a problem for animals in hibernation, but circumstances may arise when it is a matter of life or death.

Until recently the physiological changes which take place during a bout of hibernation had not been measured because of the lack of instrumentation. Unlike most physiological studies where the experimenter can produce the condition he wishes to study at will, there is no known way of producing hibernation. The investigator must design his apparatus so that the animal is in natural comfort, and then hope that the recording machines do not break down until the necessary information has been obtained. Chronically implanted thermocouples and skin electrodes for recording heart rate and electromyograms are now routine. More sophisticated approaches such as indwelling brain electrodes and blood vessel cannulae have yielded much interesting information. Always the investigator is faced with the problems of dealing with a small, wild animal which may object so strenuously to a piece of apparatus that it will never hibernate. Some species are temperamentally unfit for laboratory experiments, and have to be abandoned after many frustrations. Thus it is no wonder that the information accumulates but slowly, and that comparative data for various species are far from complete.

When the ground squirrel or woodchuck starts to enter hibernation, the heart rate, and probably also the metabolic rate, decline before the body temperature starts to drop. This would indicate that entering hibernation may be an active process, in which these vital functions and others such as thermogenesis are actually suppressed, with the resulting decline in body temperature. This is in contrast to the situation in a reptile or amphibian when exposed to cold. In this case the animal cools because he has no way of remaining warm, and the heart rate and metabolic rate decline because the whole system becomes colder. The decline of the mammalian hibernator into hibernation is rarely a smooth affair, however, for periodically the heart accelerates and the animal may move or actually shiver as if resisting the whole process. If cardioacceleration and shivering continue for long enough, the body temperature may rise briefly and occasionally the animal may arouse completely from the hibernating state. Usually, however, the resistance is short-lived, the heart rate slows, shivering stops and the animal once again starts sinking into hibernation.

Using the California ground squirrel, Strumwasser (10), has shown that this animal does not reach the depths of hibernation on its first try of the season, but only allows its temperature to drop a certain distance, remain there for a time, and then warm again to the homeothermic body temperature. On the next day at the same time, the animal again starts to enter hibernation, and this time allows its body temperature to go lower, and so on each day until the body temperature is only one or two degrees above that of the environment. These "test drops" suggest that the animal is preparing itself for lower and lower temperatures, like a timid bather dipping in a cold ocean (Figure 1). Although it has not been shown that "test drops" occur in every species of hibernator, still the observation suggests

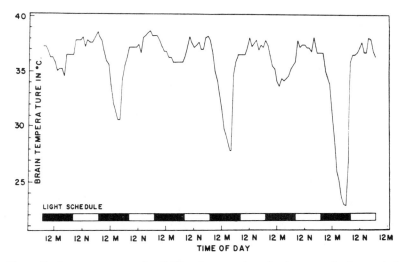

Fig. 1. Brain temperature of a California ground squirrel over a six day period. Note how temperature drops at about the same time each day and declines further every other day. M = Midnight, N = Noon. (10.)

that the animal will not allow its body temperature to drop below a critical point until the body and brain have become adapted to a lower temperature.

Whether the hibernator enters hibernation in one bold sweep or in a series of steps, eventually the animal arrives at the deeply hibernating state. The optimum environmental temperature for hibernation in most mammals is about 40°F., and the hibernator's temperature is very close to this. In bats, with their almost complete lack of insulation, the body and environmental temperature are virtually the same; hamsters may be a degree warmer, and ground squirrels two or three degrees. The respiratory rate, which is ordinarily rapid in small animals, is reduced to less than one a minute, usually ˌoccurring in a series of two or three quick gasps followed by long periods of rest. Heart rate may be reduced to as low as two or three beats a minute but the mean blood pressure remains much higher than would be expected for such a low rate. Undoubtedly there is a generalized constriction of the peripheral blood vessels as the animal enters hibernation, which becomes more profound as hibernation deepens, and this serves to maintain the blood pressure. Since the body temperature is the same in all parts of the body, there is no indication that the vasoconstriction is occurring in one particular area.

In spite of the low body temperature, the hibernating mammal still maintains its mammalian heritage of a fixed internal environment, or homeostasis, within surprisingly fine physiological limits. The respiratory centers are remarkably sensitive to carbon dioxide, and the arterial blood is thoroughly oxygenated. Acid-base balance stays within normal range and serum electrolytes undergo no great changes, though serum magnesium is high. The blood sugar is low in some species during hibernation, but it never reaches hypoglycemic levels and it remains normal in other species.

Perhaps the most interesting evidence for homeostasis in the hibernating animal concerns the residuum of control over body temperature. In all hibernators, body temperature passively follows fluctuations in environmental temperature between about 38 and 55°F. If, however, the environmental temperature approaches the freezing point of water, the hibernating animal increases its metabolic rate and often is able to keep its body temperature above freezing without waking from hibernation. This reaction gives some insight into limitations of hibernation as a way of life. While it is true that the tissues and organs of animals which hibernate will function at lower temperatures than non-hibernating mammals, still the hibernating animal cannot tolerate freezing. In spite of the well-insulated position the hibernator adopts, more metabolic energy must be utilized as the temperature of the hibernaculum sinks below 32°F., and hibernation begins to lose its advantage as an economical way to spend the winter. Actually, we find that most hibernators live in temperate climates, and that hibernation is not a way of life in the arctic and antarctic. The most northern dwelling hibernator, the Arctic ground squirrel, has a range which extends just beyond the Arctic Circle, and its hibernating quarters are in places which afford the maximum protection against the rigors of winter.

For an animal to maintain its internal environment during hibernation, it is obvious that at least parts of its central nervous system must continue to function, and some indication of this can be obtained by recording the electrical activity with fine electrodes implanted in the brain. The technique is difficult and there is much to be learned, but it seems clear that the amount of electrical activity varies from species to species. In the golden hamster, for example, the cerebral cortex is electrically quiet during hibernation. On the other hand, in the California ground squirrel several patterns of electrical activity can be recorded at brain temperatures of 45°F., and other hibernators show gradations between these extremes (8). There seems to be a good correlation between the cortical electrical activity and the behavior of the species while it is hibernating. During hibernation the hamster is completely inert, and even the experienced investigator often cannot determine if it is alive without the help of an electrocardiograph. The California ground squirrel can move its legs in an uncoordinated manner, cock its ears, and even utter a squeal while hibernating. If all animals showed the same patterns of electrical activity in the brain during hibernation and if changes in this activity could be correlated with changes in the physiological condition of the animals, then it should be relatively easy to implicate definite areas of the brain as controlling centers during hibernation. Because hibernators do not fit into a standard pattern, the problem is complicated even further and much more work is needed in this promising approach to the study of hibernation.

It is typical of all mammalian hibernators that they do not remain in this state throughout the winter, but awake from time to time. Some species such as the golden hamster hibernate usually for less than a week at a time. They then awake, void, eat a little and return to hibernation usually within twenty-four hours. In contrast, bats may stay in hibernation continuously for a month or more, and other species fall between these extremes. The reason for these periodic arousals is unknown, and from the aspect of metabolic economy the animal would be bet-

ter off without them, for it has been calculated that one arousal uses as much energy as ten days in hibernation. Arousal from hibernation does not imply an increase in environmental temperature and the animal warms using only heat which it generates itself.

Arousal from hibernation will also occur if the animal is poked or otherwise physically disturbed, and this can be studied with relatively little difficulty. Disturbing the hibernating animal causes an almost immediate cardioacceleration which continues throughout the arousal period so that the heart rate at the peak of the waking may be one hundred times as fast as the slow rate of deep hibernation. Immediately after the initial disturbance, muscle action potentials can be recorded which soon develop into gross muscular shivering, occurring first in the anterior part of the body. The rise in body temperature is initially confined to the anterior so that midway through arousal the temperature near the heart may be as much as 40°F. warmer than the rectal temperature, even in an animal as small as a hamster (Figure 2). This uneven distribution of heat is accomplished by a differential vasoconstriction which reduces the blood flow to the posterior to a trickle and shunts it to the anterior. Midway through arousal, blood flow in the forelegs can be thirteen times as great as in the hind legs. Interestingly enough, the blood flow to the interscapular brown fat pad is also rapid at this time (6, 2). This type of adipose tissue is abundant in all hibernators and, because of its histological appearance, has long been known as the "hibernating gland." It is known to be a source of quickly available energy, and it may well be that it is an important source of heat during arousal.

Arousal from hibernation is a stupendous physiological effort, and is certainly the most dramatic phase of the hibernating cycle.

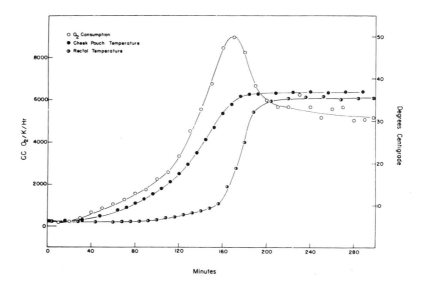

Fig. 2. Plot of oxygen consumption and cheek pouch and rectal temperature of a hamster arousing from hibernation in an environmental temperature of 42°F. Note the difference in temperature between the anterior and posterior and the large rise in metabolic rate as the animal warms.

When the temperature of the anterior has reached nearly 98°F. and the temperature of the posterior is rising rapidly due to sudden vasodilation, the metabolic rate is higher than in an animal undergoing the most violent exercise. The hair is erect and the animal shakes as if it had the ague, while the respiratory rate is extremely rapid and uneven. The whole process seems designed to allow the hibernator to warm in the least possible time, yet it takes two or three hours before the animal is fully awake and rewarmed throughout the whole body (Figure 2).

All the evidence indicates that hibernation, from its initiation through the long dormancy to the violent arousal, is a controlled process, developed through evolution to permit the animal to escape from an unfavorable environment. The same type of hibernation, using the same basic physiological modifications, occurs in mammals which are so remotely related phylogenetically that one must conclude that hibernation developed separately in several groups as the environmental stress arose. It is not a primitive return to the cold-blooded state indicating a vestigial reptilian type of temperature control, but rather a specialized temperature regulation with precise refinements of its own.

How successful, then, is hibernation as a way of life? It seems to be the only way in which well-coordinated, "modern" mammals have been able to rid themselves of the metabolic burden of a high body temperature. To do this they reach a condition in which they are virtually helpless. This condition of helplessness cannot be terminated at once, as in waking from natural sleep, but takes minutes or even hours to cast off in spite of beautifully coordinated physiological effort. Furthermore, the active yearly life of the hibernator is compressed into a few short months, for most animals hibernate for at least half of the year. During the active period the adults must breed, raise young and prepare themselves for the next season of hibernation. Very little, if any, cell growth or multiplication takes place during hibernation, so that the development of the reproductive organs must occur after hibernation has ceased, perhaps abetted by brief periods of growth during the periodic arousals. With the active life thus crammed into a brief period, there is usually but time for one litter a year. The life of a species depends on its power to raise young to the reproductive age, and the hibernator is certainly at a disadvantage here when compared to a mammal which can bear litters throughout the year. Finally, if growth cannot occur during hibernation, animals with long gestation periods would have obvious troubles if they were to hibernate.

The rodents may give us the clearest picture of the advantages and disadvantages of hibernation as a way of life. This order of mammals, with its high reproductive rate and rapid rate of evolutionary change, has repeatedly produced convergent species from remotely related groups to fit into definite ecological niches. Hibernation is one of these convergent developments. Cade (3) points out that hibernation has developed in at least five different lineages of rodents, but in double that number of lineages hibernation is not known to occur at all. Although we are a long way from knowing the life history of most of the rodents, still we know of only fifty-odd species of rodents which hibernate out of a total of more than one thousand species. Thus we must conclude that for certain precise conditions hibernation is an advantage, but that the great majority of mammals do better forever fastened to the millstone of a high metabolic rate.

references

1. Bartholomew, G. A. and T. J. Cade. 1957. Temperature regulation, hibernation, and aestivation in the little pocket mouse, *Perognathus longimembris*. *J. Mammal.*, **38**, 60–72.
2. Bullard, R. W. and G. E. Funkhouser. 1962. Estimated regional blood flow by rubidium 86 distribution during arousal from hibernation. *Am. J. Physiol.*, **203**, 266–270.
3. Cade, T. J. 1963. The evolution of torpidity in rodents. Second International Symposium on Nature Mammalian Hibernation (in press).
4. Hock, R. J. 1957. Metabolic rates and rectal temperatures of active and "hibernating" black bears. *Fed. Proc.*, **16**, 440.
5. Johansen, K. and J. Krog. 1959. Diurnal body temperature variations and hibernation in the birchmouse, *Sicista betulina*. *Am. J. Physiol.*, **196**, 1200–1204.
6. Johansen, K. 1961. Distribution of blood in the arousing hibernator. *Acta physiol. scand.*, **52**, 379–386.
7. Lyman, C. P. 1954. Activity, food consumption and hoarding in hibernators. *J. Mammal.*, **35**, 545–552.
8. Lyman, C. P. and P. O. Chatfield. 1955. Physiology of hibernation in mammals. *Physiol. Rev.*, **35**, 403–425.
9. Pearson, O. P. 1960. Torpidity in birds. In: *Mammalian Hibernation. Bull. Mus. Comp. Zool.*, **124**, 93–104.
10. Strumwasser, F. 1960. Some physiological principles governing hibernation in *Citellus beecheyi*. In: *Mammalian Hibernation. Bull. Mus. Comp. Zool.*, **124**, 285–320.

chapter 7

learning

Some degree of learning ability is essential for an organism to adapt to its environment. Of all creatures, the species *Homo sapiens* is most dependent on learning for the transmission of its culture from generation to generation. For these reasons, the study of learning is vital to an understanding of human behavior.

In other branches of psychology, the overt aspects of the process of learning are studied, whereas physiological psychologists, biophysicists, and biochemists study what happens in the nervous system and in nerve cells. One logical way for the nervous system to handle a learned change in behavior would be to store it in some neural trace or engram. Other psychologists assume the engram, whereas physiological psychologists search for its actual structure and functioning.

In the first article in this chapter (Reading 25), Roger Sperry discusses some of the theoretical attempts to explain the neural basis of the conditioned response. If the neural trace set up in this simple type of learning could be understood, the door would be opened to a full comprehension of all learning. Although Sperry gives several interesting possibilities, the fact remains that at the present time the nature of the engram is a mystery.

One productive way to study the correlation between the nervous system and learned behavior is to make lesions in specific areas of the brain and note the effect of these lesions on learning. Robert Thompson (Reading 26) uses the lesion method to determine which thalamic nuclei and adjacent midbrain structures are involved in maintaining an avoidance conditioning response. In addition to the experimental results, of special interest to the student are the "other behavioral observations" presented by Thompson. A good experimenter learns a great deal about his results by being alert to behavior changes and variables not incorporated into his original research design.

Ronald Racine and Daniel Kimble (Reading 27) also use the lesion method to correlate brain function and behavior. They find that in rats hippocampal lesions prevented the performance of a delayed alternation task. Of importance is the fact that this experiment extends a finding already established for monkeys to another species (rats).

A chemical approach is another effective way to search for an understanding of the physiology of learning. In the article by W. J. Richards and J. C. Stockburger (Reading 28), the chemical approach takes the form of a study of the effects of hormones on learning. Since thyroid hormones affect the metabolism and general activity of an animal, Richards and Stockburger verified the expectation that rate of learning would be a function of thyroid hormone level. They found that hypothyroid, normal, and hyperthyroid animals "differ significantly in rate of learning and extinction."

Another chemical approach is to study directly the chemical changes that occur in the brain during learning. J. Trevor Peirce (Reading 29) substantiates an earlier finding that "normally occurring differences in cortical cholinesterase activity are related to behavioral differences."

25 neural basis of the conditioned response*

R. W. Sperry

1. What does Sperry mean by "anticipatory set" or "expectancy?"
2. What theoretical importance is given to the concept of "central facilitory set"?
3. What types of experiments can be designed to test Sperry's conclusions?

A bell sounds and the conditioned dog lifts its forepaw. Although the physiological explanation of this seemingly simple sequence of events has been sought intensively ever since conditioned responses were first discovered more than a half century ago (7), we still lack today a satisfactory picture of the underlying neural mechanism. Even the broadest outlines of the neural events remain obscure.

It was first thought that the repeated association of bell and paw movement opened new pathways between the auditory and response centres of the brain. The repeated firing of the two brain centres in association was presumed to leave some kind of residual effect on the interconnecting nerve pathways making it easier for future impulses to travel these same routes. Although now regarded as being much too simple in its original form, this explanation continues to survive with various modifications (5). In particular it is now agreed that the new cerebral associations

* R. W. Sperry, "On the Neural Basis of the Conditioned Response," *Brit. J. Animal Behav.*, 3 (1955), 41–44. Reprinted with permission.

are more than the direct transcortical linkages earlier supposed, and must involve devious and highly complex pathways.

The physical nature of the residual effects or lasting traces left in the brain remains a matter of pure speculation. Among the wide range of possibilities that continue to receive consideration are the following: growth of new fibre connections, i.e. of axonal and dendritic collaterals and new synaptic endfeet, alteration of transmission resistance at synapses as by expansion and contraction of endfeet or by changes in synaptic membrane permeability, adjustments of excitation threshold within nerve cells or in local portions of their dendritic expansions, specific chemical sensitization of neurons to qualitatively distinct modes of excitation, chemical changes in the neurofibrils and in the neuronal proteins, selective sensitization of neurons to specific spatial patterns of activation, and even structural and chemical changes within the glia.

As an alternative to the notion of the brain traces or engrams as static changes in brain tissue, it has been suggested that the traces might take the form of perseverating eddies of active discharge maintained in self-reexciting circuits (4, 8). However, the fact that conditioned responses ordinarily survive deep anesthesia, electro-convulsive shock, epileptic seizures and other disruptions of functional continuity has seemed to rule out any explanation expressed entirely in these dynamic terms.

There remain, nevertheless, certain explanatory advantages in the dynamic form of brain trace, and in a recent advance in learning theory a dual form hypothesis has been proposed (3) that incorporates the benefits of both the older static and the newer dynamic type of memory trace. In this dual scheme, self-maintained reverberatory excitation is held responsible for the rapid short-term

effects in learning and conditioning. In time the continued reverberatory activity is presumed to lead to permanent micro changes in brain morphology that make possible long-term retention of conditioned responses and their survival through states of deep coma, electro-convulsive shock, and the like.

In general the physiological theories have thus far tended to neglect a factor that long has been recognized in psychological studies to be an important element in conditioning, namely, the so-called "anticipatory set" or "expectancy."[1] The incorporation of this factor into the physiological picture leads directly to significant revisions in our thinking about the underlying neural mechanism and to a modified hypothesis which, though somewhat increased in complexity, appears nevertheless to fit better the whole complex of the conditioned response including some of its more paradoxical features.

Following this approach we are lead to postulate as an important aspect of the conditioning process the intermediation of complex high level patterns of central nervous facilitation, i.e. the neural counterparts and derivatives of the psychological expectancies and anticipatory sets. The pattern of central excitation aroused in the brain by the conditioned stimulus can then be assumed to be governed by an intermediate pattern of transient facilitation, rather than being channelled directly by neural engrams or traces as traditionally conceived. Unlike the dynamic traces of earlier theory, the central facilitory pattern or "set" is not a simple vestige or trace of cerebral excitation involved in an earlier pairing of conditioned stimulus and response. It represents, rather, a novel and relatively independent organization arising out of high level

[1] For a recent discussion of the expectancy factor in conditioning see L. E. Cole (1) *Human Behavior*, pp. 257–304.

cerebral activity such as insight, expectancy and the like. In this hypothesis, the permanent structural changes for long-term retention do not help directly to form new associations between sensory and motor centres. Instead they reinforce the intermediary expectancy or facilitory set.

The concept of the central facilitory set and its role in conditioning is best illustrated perhaps with reference to a simple voluntary reaction in man. Let us suppose that electrodes have been taped to the hand of a human subject and that the person has been instructed to lift the hand promptly when a bell sounds, on the penalty of receiving otherwise a severe electric shock. At the sound of the bell, his hand jerks upward instantly, just as quickly as does the paw of the conditioned dog. In the human subject this withdrawal response at the sound of the bell involves a novel pattern of central excitation, which is not the product of any long training, or repeated pairing of bell and shock stimuli. There is no grooving of the fibre pathways between receptor and effector centres of the cortex. In fact, the particular train of central excitation set off by the bell may never have occurred previously in the person's lifetime.

Under these circumstances we say that the human subject gets himself physiologically set to make the proper response at the sound of the bell. The brain pathways for arm flexion become temporarily opened while those for innumerable other possible reactions are temporarily closed. In other words, the prevailing distribution of excitation and inhibition in the brain circuits opens the way for the bell stimulus to release instantly that specific response for which the circuits are adjusted. Once the circuits are properly set, extraneous sensory excitation tends to be absorbed without effect and incompatible reactions are excluded. The novel motor effect of the bell stimulus derives in this case, not from any new pattern of structural pathways but, rather, from a new pattern of central excitation and facilitation.

We note that the human subject could just as easily set himself to make the reverse response (i.e. to depress the hand instead of lifting it), in which case the excitatory sequence initiated by the bell discharges with equal rapidity into the antagonist muscles. The transient brain set could be patterned likewise for a reaction with the foot, or with the opposite hand. In each case, the specific and immediate motor effect of the incoming auditory impulse is determined by the particular facilitory set that dominates or prevails in the brain at the time the sensory excitations enter.

These governing facilitory sets may be generalized or specific in their organization on both sensory and motor side. For example, a person could set himself to respond only to a bell of low pitch and not to one of high pitch. Or, his set might be quite nonspecific such that any loud noise would set off the reaction; even a sudden tactile stimulus might suffice. Similarly on the motor side, a single response may be rigidly predetermined, or a choice of two responses made possible, or any of a given category.

The main point to be emphasized is that a purely transient, dynamic setting of the brain circuits, in terms of active facilitation and inhibition, is quite capable by itself of causing the bell stimulus to set off a particular limb movement. There is no need here for any new fibre pathways, chemical traces in the neuroplasm, or new synaptic associations. It is evident, furthermore, that *the same response, or other responses, could be coupled functionally in a similar manner to any neural stimulus (of the type employed in conditioning) simply by an appropriate adjustment in the cerebral facilitory set.* (In referring to these transient adjustments of the brain mechanism as *facilitory* sets, it should be recognized that the central *inhibitory* phase of the process may be fully as important as the facilitory.)

There is much to suggest that the coupling of bell and forepaw response in the dog during conditioning is achieved through the development of a comparable cerebral facilitory set. The bell-shock expectancy that it takes only a moment to convey to the brain of man with the aid of language, may require hours or days to develop in the brain of the dog by the more roundabout method of example and experience. Eventually as a result of training, the dog comes to expect the shock at the sound of the bell. More than this the dog comes to anticipate both the bell and shock so that by the time the bell sounds, the dog already is actively prepared in advance (like the human subject) to make the correct forelimb response.

We may thus suppose that in the brain of the conditioned animal a well-organized facilitory set appears prior to the incidence of the conditioned stimulus. It is this special pattern of central facilitation—absent before training and developed through training—that is directly responsible for channelling the sensory impulses into the proper motor response.

The activity of these cerebral facilitory sets is not confined to conditioning and voluntary reaction. They operate continually in behaviour and constitute a prime factor in the control of all brain function. Thinking, perceiving, recognizing, imagining, reasoning, reflex activity, learning, and remembering, as well as conditioning and voluntary activity, have all been found in the laboratory to be profoundly affected by the so-called "mental set" (2). It is by means of differential facilitory sets that the brain is able to function as many machines in one, setting and resetting itself dozens of times in the course of a day,

now for one type of operation, now for another. In short, a great deal of the plasticity in vertebrate behaviour, including that of conditioning, is made possible, not through structural remodelling of the fibre pathways but through dynamic readjustments in the background of central facilitation.

To account for the long-term retention of conditioned responses, one must infer further that the facilitory sets and associated dynamic readjustments become reinforced by some permanent type of neural trace, or engram. In considering the problem of the patterning of the brain engrams, it is all-important that one does not lose sight of the primary role played by the above dynamic factors. Even after a long rest interval, or electroshock treatment, the conditioned response is still dependent upon a preliminary rearousal of the anticipatory set. If the proper pattern of central facilitation has not been established by the time the bell sounds, the conditioned forepaw response fails to occur (1).

A number of implications regarding the nature of the static engram are incorporated in this approach to conditioning, some of which may be stated briefly as follows: (*a*) The engrams for a conditioned response do not take the form merely of new associations between the receptor and effector centres of the brain, however complex. A different type of engram pattern is implied, namely, a pattern so designed as to facilitate, at the proper time and place, the establishment of the correct expectancy and facilitory set. (*b*) With much of the burden of the detailed patterning of the conditioned response relegated to the dynamics of cerebral facilitation, the engrams themselves need be much less extensive and complete than is otherwise necessary. Relatively small changes at critical points may be sufficient to reactivate a given anticipatory set in the proper dynamic background. (*c*) The static engrams on the one hand and the dynamic facilitory patterns on the other are regarded as co-functions, i.e. the operation of the two factors in long-term retention becomes mutually dependent with the conditioned response being a product of the combined action. (*d*) Since the engrams reinforce higher level cerebral activity, they are believed to be complex and diffused rather than localized in nature even in the very simplest conditioned responses. (*e*) The engram patterning is further complicated by the fact that the engrams must function in large part to support the transitions between the expectancies and sets as well as the facilitory patterns per se.

There are definite advantages from the engineering standpoint in having the permanent alterations of the brain designed to reinforce the higher level intermediary facilitation, instead of having them affect the sensory-motor associations directly. This makes it possible, to mention just one advantage, for different (even antagonistic) motor responses to be linked simultaneously to the same sensory stimulus, something that may be desirable to suit different circumstances. This scheme also provides much more readily for that class of phenomena included under the terms "sensory and motor equivalence." In general, with this kind of arrangement, the sensory and response mechanisms of the brain do not become tied down nor selectively modified for specific habits, but remain free to be used in various ways and in various combinations in all categories of behaviour.

This description of the neural events also accounts more readily than earlier theories for findings like those of Lashley (6) and others on the effects of brain extirpation. Consider the difficulty, on this basis, of trying to ablate even so simple a habit as the conditioned paw movement mentioned above for illustration. One might eliminate the conditioned response by extirpating enough of the auditory centres

of the brain to prevent the stimulus from reaching the anticipatory set. However, if the facilitory set is strongly organized, very little stimulus is needed to trigger off the response. In fact, it is known that the response may occur spontaneously under certain conditions without any outside stimulus. Any small remnant of the primary sensory area that would permit the impulses from the bell to filter through to the central facilitory set would be enough to trigger off the conditioned response.

Similarly on the motor side, any undamaged motor mechanisms by which the animal can achieve the desired effect will be sufficient. The ability to switch quickly from one motor pattern to another to accomplish an end (motor equivalence) is already an intrinsic property of the brain. Once the dog learns that contact with the shock electrode must be broken immediately after the bell sounds, any remaining means available is automatically called into play to accomplish this end. Consequently extensive and widely paralyzing lesions in the motor cortex are required to prevent an animal from making a conditioned response in one way or another. For some learning situations any residual ability to move at all may be enough to carry out the learned performance.

To effectively destroy by surgery the engrams themselves or the expectancies, insights, and sets which they reinforce is equally difficult. According to the foregoing, the constellation of engrams for even the simplest conditioned response tends to be complex in design and diffused through the brain, and thus highly resistant to local ablation. Further, the intermediary central facilitation is reinforced from all sides by a great mass of stimuli, associated not only with the conditioning chamber, but also with the situations leading to it, with the experimenter's person, even with the home cage and with various related events in the diurnal cycle. To eliminate by brain damage the channels for all these reminders of the conditioning experience would be prohibitive.

references

1. Cole, L. E. (1953). *Human behavior*. New York: World Book Co.
2. Gibson, J. J. (1941). A critical review of the concept of set in contemporary experimental psychology. *Psychol. Bull.*, **38**, 781–817.
3. Hebb, D. O. (1949). *The organisation of behaviour*. New York: Wiley.
4. Hilgard, E. R., & Marquis, D. G. (1940). *Conditioning and Learning*. New York: Appleton-Century.
5. Konorski, J. (1948). *Conditioned reflexes and neuron organization*. Cambridge University Press.
6. Lashley, K. S. (1950). In search of the engram. *Symp. Soc. exp. Biol.*, **4**, 454–482.
7. Pavlov, I. P. (1927). *Conditioned reflexes*. Oxford University Press.
8. Young, J. Z. (1938). *In de Beer: Evolution*, Oxford University Press, 179–205.

26   thalamic structures and conditioned response in rats*

Robert Thompson

1. What surgical techniques were used in studying the thalamus?

* R. Thompson, "Thalamic Structures Critical for Retention of an Avoidance Conditioned Response in Rats," *J. comp. physiol. Psychol.*, 56 (1963), 261–267. Reprinted with permission.

2. What are the three thalamic areas that serve in maintaining the CR?
3. What are the "exceptional cases" described by Thompson? How should these cases be studied?

The aim of the present study is to identify by the lesion method those thalamic nuclei and adjacent midbrain structures which are critically involved in the maintenance of an avoidance conditioned response. In an effort to determine whether any differential effects are operative as a function of the sense modality studied, different groups of rats were trained either with a visual or an auditory signal.

Previous reports have revealed that the conditioned response is particularly susceptible to interference by subcortical brain damage. Structures such as the hippocampus (5, 15), cingulate (13), amygdala (6), thalamic nuclei (12), caudate nucleus (23), lateral hypothalamic area (18), pretectal region (16), and the midbrain reticular formation (3) all seem to share in the function of maintaining the CR. These results coupled with those showing the deleterious effects of neocortical lesions (14) suggest that most of the thalamic and midbrain nuclei may participate in the performance of an avoidance conditioned response. Such a conclusion would have considerable theoretical implications in view of the high degree of localization demonstrated for an approach-avoidance brightness discrimination habit (8, 20).

method

subjects

A total of 75 adult albino rats of the Harlan strain were used. Approximately half were trained with the visual signal, while the remaining Ss were trained with the auditory signal.

apparatus

The conditioning box consisted of a grid floor and Plexiglas walls. A space of ½ in. which existed between the top of the walls and the lid allowed S to escape or avoid the charged grid by gripping onto the edge of the walls with its forefeet. The box was positioned between two 100-w. frosted light bulbs. Mounted on top of the perforated lid was a 5-in. speaker which could be actuated by a Hewlett-Packard oscillator. Further details of the apparatus have already been reported (17).

surgery and histology

Operations were carried out under chloral hydrate anesthesia and semiasceptic conditions. Bilateral thalamic lesions were produced by applying a direct current of 1 or 2 ma. for a duration of 15 sec. through an implanted needle insulated except for the tip. (A comparatively small number of Ss were subjected to frontal neocortical lesions by the aspiration method.) At the conclusion of the experiment, each operated S was sacrificed, the brain removed, frozen and sectioned at 50 μ. Every third unstained section showing the lesion was photographed at 10X with a Leitz enlarger. Estimates of the percentage of bilateral damage to certain thalamic regions were computed in a manner which has been fully described elsewhere (21).

procedure

Conditioning trials took place in a darkened, sound-attenuated room. Thirty-seven Ss were conditioned to make a jumping response to the onset of the two 100-w. lights, whereas 38 additional Ss were trained to make the same response to the onset of a 1,000 cps pure tone having an intensity of 96 db. (standard reference: 0.0002 microbars at 1,000 cps). A trial consisted of a 5-sec. presentation of the CS followed by a combination of the signal and shock until the appropriate response was made. If S succeeded in making a CR (jumping and gripping onto the edge of the walls with its forefeet during the initial 5-sec. presentation of the signal), the signal was immediately turned off and the shock postponed. Sixteen to 20 trials were given daily with an intertrial interval of 15–90 sec. Training was terminated when S made at least 9 CRs within a series of 10 trials in 1 day.

Approximately 4 hr. after learning, the majority of Ss were subjected to bilateral thalamic lesions. An attempt was made to secure six discrete thalamic operated groups differentiated on the basis of the anterior-posterior, dorsal-ventral, and medial-lateral location of the lesions. A few Ss received bilateral midbrain or frontal cortical lesions. After a recovery period of 2–3 weeks, all operated and control Ss were required to relearn the task that was learned preoperatively. The postoperative training procedure was identical to that used in original learning. Relearning trials were administered daily until S reached the criterion of 9 CRs within a series of 10 trials or until S received approximately twice the number of trials that was required in original learning.

results

postoperative retention

Table 1 presents the mean learning and retention scores (percentage of trial savings) for both the visual and auditory habits, Ss

Table 1. Mean Learning and Retention Scores for Each Conditioning Habit

	Visual				Auditory			
	Learning		Retention		Learning		Retention	
Location of lesion	N	Trials	Savings (%)	Range (%)	N	Trials	Savings (%)	Range (%)
Control	6	26.2	93.3	80–100	7	45.4	94.0	80–100
Medial pretectal diencephalon	5	45.0	−62.0	−100–90	7	46.4	53.1	−25–98
Lateral pretectal diencephalon	4	47.5	80.0	70–90	2	58.0	99.0	98–100
Parafascicular nucleus	4	34.0	−100.0	—	6	38.2	−47.7	−100–25
Midline thalamic nuclei	4	35.5	−63.0	−100–48	1	49	−100	—
Dorsomedial nucleus	4	43.5	−58.0	−100–68	5	51.5	−64.0	−100–80
Lateral thalamic nuclei	4	34.0	88.9	80–95	1	36	89	—
Superior colliculus	2	58.5	89.5	84–95				
Medial geniculate nucleus					2	34.5	57.5	40–75
Frontal cortex	1	49	−100	—	3	45.3	−100	—

being grouped in terms of the locus of damage. Instead of using total trials to criterion in the computation of the learning and retention scores, we counted only those trials in which a CR failed to appear. The postoperative data will be discussed separately in terms of the site of damage.

Medial pretectal diencephalon. The thalamic structure particularly damaged in this group was the anterior portion of Gurdjian's nucleus posterior. However, there was also partial involvement of the *pretectal nucleus, parafascicular nucleus, habenulopeduncular tract,* posterior commissure, and the posterior extension of the dorsomedial nucleus. In Table 1, it can be seen that destruction of this area severely impaired retention of the visual task. Of the five Ss involved, four were unable to relearn the avoidance response even after receiving approximately twice the number of trials that was required in original learning. With the use of a nonparametric test (1), the difference in savings scores between this operated group and the control group was significant at the .05 level.

In contrast, lesions of equal magnitude to this pretectal area did not seriously disturb the retention of the auditory task. Although the

mean savings score was somewhat inferior to the controls, the difference failed to reach significance. Furthermore, a comparison of the two operated groups revealed that the auditory Ss were significantly superior to the visual Ss in retention scores ($p = .05$).

Lateral pretectal diencephalon. The structures damaged in this group include the pretectal nucleus, the nucleus lateralis posterior and the posterior part of the nucleus ventralis. It is to be noted in Table 1 that the six Ss suffering injury to this area exhibited retention scores comparable to those of the controls for both the visual and auditory tasks.

Parafascicular nucleus. Those Ss subjected to lesions in the ventromedial region of the caudal thalamus were severely retarded in relearning both the auditory and visual habits. Of the ten Ss involved, five failed to relearn and only one earned a positive savings score. The differences in retention between the operated and the respective control groups were significant at the .01 level.

Dorsomedial nucleus. The lesions of this group completely destroyed the *n. medialis dorsalis* along with small portions of the habenular, parataenial and midline nuclei. All Ss, except two, displayed considerable difficulty in reacquiring the avoidance response to either visual or auditory stimuli. The differences between the control and operated groups were significant at the .01 level for the visual task and at the .05 level for the auditory task.

Midline thalamic nuclei. This group of five *S*s received lesions destroying large portions of the *n. reuniens, centralis, paracentralis, medialis ventralis* and *rhomboidalis.* Four exhibited a severe impairment in relearning the visual habit ($p = .01$), while the only *S* involved in the auditory habit failed to reach the criterion.

Lateral thalamic nuclei. This group consisted of five *S*s having lesions destroying large portions of the *n. lateralis* and *ventralis.* As noted in Table 1, these lesions had no appreciable effect on the postoperative performance of either habit.

Other brain stem structures. Table 1 shows that two *S*s sustaining injury to the superior colliculus displayed virtually perfect memory of the visual habit. The performances of these *S*s are especially interesting because of the completeness of the destruction. Inspection of the sections revealed that each *S* suffered total loss of all layers of the tectum extending from its anterior margin to the rostral border of the inferior colliculus. It is also of interest to note that the two *S*s sustaining large lesions in the medial geniculate nucleus earned retention scores on the auditory habit which were only slightly inferior to the controls. Finally, four *S*s having lesions in the dorsolateral tegmentum at the level of the medial geniculate bodies earned savings scores on the auditory task which were comparable to those of the controls. Similarly placed lesions likewise produced no detrimental effect on the retention of the visual habit.

Frontal cortex. A total of four *S*s were subjected to bilateral neocortical lesions primarily involving the region delineated as Area 10 by Krieg (7). Although these lesions did not destroy more than 15% of the total neocortical surface (Figure 1), no *S* succeeded in relearning the avoidance response to either the visual or auditory signal.

other behavioral observations

As noted in a previous study (16), certain subcortical lesions may obliterate the avoidance response, but may spare the fear-producing properties of the conditioned stimulus. All of the operated *S*s of this study which failed to relearn the jumping response did, in the course of training, show frequent responses of the anticipatory type (squeaking, sudden muscular movements, abrupt changes in respiration, general body orientation toward the top of the box) at the onset of either the light or sound. Table 2 gives the percentage of these

Table 2. Mean Percentage of Conditioned, Anticipatory and Spontaneous Responses Appearing During the Course of Relearning for Those Animals Failing to Reach the Criterion

Location of Lesion	N	Conditioned Responses (%)	Anticipatory Responses (%)	Spontaneous Responses (%)
Dorsomedial nucleus	9	3.0	54.0	1.4
Midline thalamic nuclei	4	3.5	40.0	10.8
Parafascicular nucleus	5	5.0	56.8	12.0
Posterior nucleus	4	5.0	54.8	22.8
Frontal cortex	4	4.3	55.3	17.0

emotional components of behavior over the course of relearning. On the average, these operated *S*s exhibited an emotional response on half of the relearning trials. Thus, these data indicate that the fundamental deficit lies in the execution of the avoidance response to the signal and not in the incapacity to associate the signal with the forthcoming shock.

The possibility that the operated *S*s were

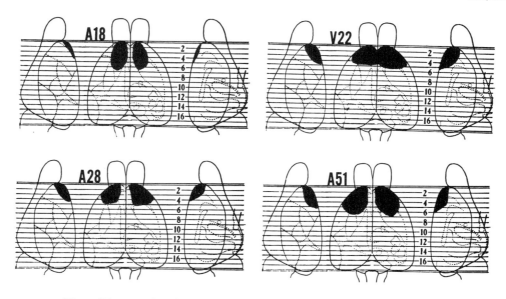

Fig. 1. Diagrams showing the cortical lesions in four rats. (Rat V22 was trained on the visual habit, while the remaining three were trained on the auditory habit.)

suffering from some peripheral motor deficit preventing the execution of the jumping response is refuted by the following observations. Of the 26 operated Ss which failed to reacquire the habit, only four (two with dorsomedial thalamic lesions, one with a midline thalamic lesion, and one with a cortical lesion) displayed a consistent reluctance to jump in response to the electrified grid. The remaining Ss performed the UR with approximately the same agility and vigor as that shown by the controls. Furthermore, the majority of the Ss which failed to relearn the habit exhibited numerous "spontaneous responses" during the course of postoperative training, a spontaneous response being defined as the appearance of the CR during the intertrial interval. However, differential effects were obtained as a function of the locus of subcortical damage. Although no significant differences were noted preoperatively, Table 2 shows that those Ss suffering

dorsomedial thalamic lesions displayed relatively few spontaneous responses. Only 5 Ss out of the entire 26 which failed to relearn the avoidance response also failed to show a single spontaneous response during the course of retraining. These five Ss had lesions involving the *n. medialis dorsalis*.

discussion

The preceding results suggest that three functionally and anatomically distinct thalmic systems serve in maintaining the avoidance CR examined in the present experiment. Two of these systems appear to be nonspecific in function in that they critically participate in mediating both the visual and auditory habits. One of these coincides with the diffuse thalamic system which includes the *n. parafascicularis, reuniens, centralis, paracentralis, medialis ventralis*, and *rhomboidalis*. The second nonspecific system is mainly represented by the *n. medialis dorsalis*. The third system, apparently more specific in function, has been crucial for vision only. It consists of the thalamic area occupied by the anterior portion of the nucleus posterior. Whether or not a comparable thalamic region exists for audition cannot be unequivocally answered by the present data.

Behaviorally, lesions destroying portions of the diffuse thalamic nuclei profoundly disturb the retention of the avoidance response, but do not grossly interfere with the performance of either the unconditioned, spontaneous or emotional components of the conditioning process. It is probably more than coincidence that this system of thalamic nuclei which mediates the electrographic arousal response (10) should also assist in mediating an avoidance CR. Further implication of the ascending brain stem reticular formation in conditioning behavior derives from the finding that posterior hypothalamic damage likewise impairs the performance of an avoidance habit (18). To what extent these diffuse thalamic nuclei maintain the CR by either conveying reticular impulses to the cortex, serving as intrathalamic association areas, or providing important pathways to the limbic system cannot be answered at the present time. Parenthetically, it must be pointed out that the effects of lesions in the diffuse thalamic system on the avoidance response are practically identical with those produced by injections of reserpine (24). It is not improbable, therefore, that the behavioral consequences of drugs of this type may arise from their depressing action on this thalamic system.

Because a somewhat different behavioral and anatomical picture emerges in connection with the *n. medialis dorsalis*, we have designated this thalamic region to be a part of a second nonspecific system subserving the CR. Injury to this nucleus not only abolishes the avoidance response, but virtually eliminates the occurrence of spontaneous responses during the intertrial interval. (Although evaluation procedures were crude, the UR appeared to remain essentially unaffected in the majority of the *S*s.) It is interesting to note that a similar deficit in conditioning behavior following large dorsomedial thalamic lesions occurs when food is used as a reward (12). It would seem that the distinct projection of the dorsomedial nucleus to the frontal cortex (Area 10 in the rat, Krieg, [7]) is not entirely responsible for the relative infrequency of spontaneous responses. As shown in Table 2, the four *S*s suffering almost complete damage to Area 10 exhibited a considerable number of these responses during the course of relearning. Presumably, the dorsomedial nucleus in the rat must have other significant connections, a conclusion previously reached by Krieg (7) on anatomical grounds. The fact that this nucleus is linked anatomically with the diffuse thalamic system (4, 11) and the limbic system (2, 9) would also suggest the possibility that the region of the dorsomedial nucleus is a major integrating center for "anticipatory" conditioning behavior.

It must be emphasized that the retention loss of the avoidance response arising from lesions in the mesial thalamic nuclei or the frontal cortex is not readily attributable to a generalized intellectual impairment. Previous work (17, 20, 21) has demonstrated that similarly placed lesions do not significantly disturb the performance of an approach-avoidance brightness discrimination habit. The apparatus employed in these discrimination studies utilized escape from shock as a motive. While other explanations are available, these findings are interpreted as indicating that the diffuse thalamic system, dorsomedial nucleus and the frontal cortex, although not critically involved in the mediation of relatively simple learned differential responses based upon escape from noxious stimulation, are of special importance in situations requiring the initiation or arousal of learned anticipatory response complexes.

The finding that damage to the nucleus posterior produced a selective impairment on the visual conditioning habit is in agreement with previous investigations concerned with approach-avoidance discrimination learning (19, 21). Since extirpation of the visual cortical areas similarly interferes selectively with habits based upon visual cues (8, 19), the existence of some functional connection between the visual cortex and the nucleus posterior would seem likely. Both corticofugal and corticopetal projections (7) are available to effect this proposed association. The present findings suggest that the region of the nucleus posterior constitutes an important subcortical correlative center through which optic impulses eventually reach the response mechanism responsible for the evocation of either approach or avoidance behavior.

Finally, it is noteworthy to mention the considerable variability of the individual savings scores shown in Table 1. While lesions in the dorsomedial, midline, or posterior thalamic nuclei significantly disrupted the avoidance response, there were several "exceptional" cases in which almost perfect retention scores were obtained. For example, one S in the medial pretectal group exhibited excellent retention of the visual task, while the remaining four Ss failed to relearn the identical habit. Attempts to correlate these exceptional cases with such variables as the length of the recovery period, size or location of the lesion, speed of original learning, or age of S have proved fruitless. A similar series of exceptional cases

have recently been reported in connection with visual discrimination tasks (22).

references

1. Festinger, L. The significance of differences between means without reference to frequency distribution function. *Psychometrika*, 1946, **11**, 97–105.
2. Guillery, R. W. Afferent fibers to the dorsomedial thalamic nucleus in the cat. *J. Anat., London*, 1959, **93**, 403–419.
3. Hernández-Peón, R., & Brust-Carmoma, H. Functional role of subcortial structures in habituation and conditioning. In J. F. Delafresnaye (Ed.), *Brain mechanisms and learning: A symposium*. Oxford: Blackwell. 1961. Pp. 393–408.
4. Johnson. T. N. Finer connections between the dorsal thalamus and corpus striatum in the cat. *Exp. Neurol.*, 1961, **3**, 556–569.
5. Kimura, D. Effects of selective hippocampal damage on avoidance behavior in the rat. *Canad. J. Psychol.*, 1958, **12**, 213–218.
6. King, F. A. Effects of septal and amygdaloid lesions on emotional behavior and conditioned avoidance responses in the rat. *J. nerv. ment. Dis.*, 1958, **126**, 57–63.
7. Krieg, W. J. S. Connections of the cerebral cortex: I. The albino rat. C. Extrinsic connections. *J. comp. Neurol.*, 1947, **86**, 267–394.
8. Lashley, K. S. *Brain mechanisms and intelligence*, Chicago: Univer. Chicago Press, 1929.
9. Massopust, L. C., & Thompson, R. A new interpedunculodiencephalic pathway in rats and cats. *J. comp. Neurol.*, 1962, **118**, 97–105.
10. Moruzzi, G., & Magoun, H. W. Brain stem reticular formation and activation of the EEG. *EEG. clin. Neurol.*, 1949, **1**, 455–473.
11. Nauta, W. J. H., & Whitlock, D. G. An anatomical analysis of the non-specific

thalamic projection system. In J. F. Dela-fresnaye (Ed.), *Brain mechanisms and consciousness: A symposium*. Springfield, Ill.: Charles C. Thomas, 1954. Pp. 81–104.

12. Pechtel, C., Masserman, J. H., Schreiner, L., & Levitt, M. Differential effects of lesions of the mediodorsal nucleus of the thalamus on normal and neurotic behavior in the cat. *J. nerv. ment. Dis.*, 1955, **121**, 26–33.

13. Peretz, E. The effects of lesions on the anterior cingulate cortex on the behavior of the rat. *J. comp. physiol. Psychol.*, 1960, **53**, 540–548.

14. Pinto-Hamuy, T. Role of the cerebral cortex in the learning of an instrumental conditioned response. In J. F. Delafresnaye (Ed.), *Brain mechanisms and learning: A symposium*. Oxford: Blackwell, 1961. Pp. 589–600.

15. Thomas, G. J., & Otis, L. S. Effects of rhinencephalic lesions of conditioning of avoidance responses in the rat. *J. comp. physiol. Psychol.*, 1958, **51**, 130–134.

16. Thompson, R. The interpeduncular nucleus and avoidance conditioning in the rat. *Science*, 1960, **132**, 1551–1553. (a)

17. Thompson, R. Retention of a brightness discrimination following neocortical damage in the rat. *J. comp. physiol. Psychol.*, 1960, **53**, 212–215. (b)

18. Thompson, R., & Hawkins, W. F. Memory unaffected by mamillary body lesions in the rat. *Exp. Neurol.*, 1961, **3**, 189–196.

19. Thompson, R., Malin, C. F., & Hawkins, W. F. Effect of subcortical lesions on retention of a kinesthetic discrimination habit. *Exp. Neurol.*, 1961, **3**, 367–374.

20. Thompson, R., & Massopust, L. C. The effect of subcortical lesions on retention of a brightness discrimination in rats. *J. comp. physiol. Psychol.*, 1960, **53**, 488–496.

21. Thompson, R., & Rich, I. A discrete diencephalic pretectal area critical for retention of visual habits in the rat. *Exp. Neurol.*, 1961, **4**, 436–443.

22. Thompson, R., & Rich, I. Differential effects of posterior thalamic lesions on retention of various visual habits. *J. comp. physiol. Psychol.*, 1963, **56**, 64–69.

23. Thompson, R. L. Effects of lesions in the caudate nuclei and dorsofrontal cortex on conditioned avoidance behavior in cats. *J. comp. physiol. Psychol.*, 1959, **52**, 650–659.

24. Wenzel, B. M. Relative resistance to reserpine of responses based on positive, as compared with negative, reinforcement. *J. comp. physiol. Psychol.*, 1959, **52**, 673–681.

27 hippocampal lesions and delayed alternation in the rat *

Ronald J. Racine and Daniel P. Kimble

1. What was the necessity of Phase 1 in the experimental procedure?

2. What was the purpose of having a group with cortical lesions? Why were there not other groups with lesions in other parts of the brain?

3. What are the several possible interpretations of the results of this experiment?

problem

The hypothesis that the hippocampus is involved in "recent memory" (7) has not received consistent support from laboratory studies with animals (2, 5, 4).

* R. J. Racine and D. P. Kimble, "Hippocampal Lesions and Delayed Alternation in the Rat," *Psychonomic Sci.*, 3 (1965), 285–286. Reprinted by permission.

On the other hand, laboratory studies of monkeys with medial temporal lobe-hippocampal removals (6, 5, 10, 9) have pointed to delayed alternation deficits as particularly conspicuous postoperative results.

The present study investigated the effects of hippocampal lesions on the temporal limits of retention of a delayed alternation task in rats, using Petrinovich & Bolles' method (1961). If the hippocampus is involved in recent memory, the lesion effect should become increasingly apparent as the delay period is extended.

method

The Ss were 30 experimentally naive, 60-day-old, male Sprague-Dawley rats. The apparatus consisted of a T-maze with a $48 \times 4\frac{1}{2} \times 6$ in. stem, $24 \times 4\frac{1}{2} \times 6$ in. arms, and two detachable $12 \times 6 \times 6$ in. goal boxes. Ss were placed on a 23 hr. water deprivation schedule and gentled for two days. They were then given four trials/day for two days in a straight alley alternately attached to each goal box. S was allowed 1 min. of drinking on each trial. Ss were then given two free and two forced trials each day for three more days to insure that they would have entered each goal arm 50% of the time prior to the beginning of alternation training.

Maze training—Phase 1. Ss were run three trials/day using a noncorrection method. They were allowed 20 sec. drinking following each correct response and were detained for 20 sec. in the goal box after each incorrect response. The first choice of each day was rewarded regardless of the side chosen. The second and third choices were rewarded only if S alternated its last response. This training was continued for 28 days with an intertrial interval of 10 min.

Phase 2. The 10 Ss which alternated most consistently continued into Phase 2. The same procedure was followed except that the intertrial interval was extended, first to 20 min., then to 40 min., then to 1 hr., and then in $\frac{1}{2}$ hr. intervals. If S alternated without error for two consecutive days, it was advanced to the next longer delay interval. When an animal accumulated four errors at an interval, it was considered to have failed and surgery was then performed on that S. The surgical procedure was similar to that reported previously (Kimble, 1963).

Phase 3. Phase 3 was initiated 10 days following surgery. The procedure was identical to that of Phase 1. Each S was tested with a 10 min. intertrial interval until its performance in 10 consecutive trials was equal to its performance of the last 10 trials of Phase 1. When this criterion was reached, S advanced to Phase 4, which was identical to Phase 2.

An examination of the sectioned brains revealed extensive (50–90%) and bilateral hippocampal lesions in all the hippocampectomized Ss.

The brains of the cortically lesioned Ss revealed bilateral damage to neocortex, and no hippocampal damage except for a slight surface invasion in one S (Fig. 1).

results

The 10 Ss with the highest alternation scores during Phase 1 were chosen to continue training. Table 1 shows the pre- and postoperative performance of each animal. Postoperatively, all of the cortically lesioned Ss immediately reached their preoperative performance level of Phase 2 within the minimum number of trials necessary. However, none of the hippocampectomized Ss ever approached their preoperative level, during 20 days (60

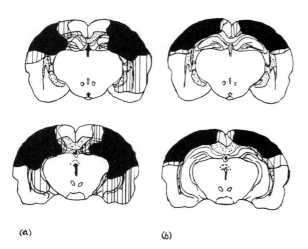

(a)   (b)

Fig. 1. Reconstruction of hippocampal (a) and cortical (b) lesions. Black area indicates minimal lesion extent, lined area indicates maximal lesion extent.

Table 1. Delayed Alternation Temporal Limits and Total % Correct

Rat No.	Temporal Limit in min. and (total % correct)	
	Preoperative	Postoperative
Cortical Lesion Ss		
3	90 (73.5)	150 (82.3)
5	120 (76.3)	180 (85.4)
7	120 (75.0)	*
8	180 (91.6)	*
9	210 (82.1)	240 (82.1)
Hippocampal Lesion Ss		
1	40 (68.7)	fail (30.2)
2	60 (77.2)	fail (30.0)
4	120 (83.3)	fail (6.2)
6	120 (76.4)	fail (25.0)
10	330 (88.7)**	fail (46.2)

* died during surgery
** did not fail, testing discontinued at 5½ hr. interval

trials) at delay intervals of 10 min. The delay interval was then lowered to approximately 5–10 sec. (excluding drinking time, Ss being replaced in the start box immediately after each trial) in order to determine if alternation behavior could be obtained under these conditions. It could not. Ss were run an additional 20 days (60 trials) with this short delay. The level of alternation behavior ranged from 5–37% at the 10 min. delay, and 0–55% at the 10 sec. delay among the hippocampectomized Ss. The number of days of 100% alternation behavior, i.e., two consecutive alternations, did not increase for any of these Ss, remaining at less than 5% for ⅘ Ss even at the 10 sec. delay. This result indicates that even at < 10 sec. delays, the hippocampectomized Ss were incapable of performing the alternation task. For example, S No. 10, who had never failed preoperatively, failed postoperatively, even at the 10 sec. interval. Each cortically lesioned S extended its preoperative temporal limit following surgery.

discussion

The complete failure of the hippocampectomized Ss to perform the delayed alternation task contrasts with the total lack of effect seen in the cortically lesioned Ss. The present study thus confirms for the rat the results of Mahut & Cordeau (5), Orbach, Milner & Rasmussen (6), Pribram et al (9) and Rosvold & Szwarcbart (10) with monkeys, that medial temporal lobe-hippocampal ablations impair delayed alternation behavior. The exact reason for this result, however, is not completely clear. While "recent memory loss" cannot be dismissed as a possible interpretation, the hippocampectomized animals showed no consistent improvement at even very short delay periods, as might be predicted from this hypothesis.

Another possible interpretation is that of "response perseveration" (1, 5). Evidence for this effect was seen at the 10 min. delay; three of the five temporal lobe-hippocampal Ss fixating on a position habit. However, only one S remained fixated at the shorter delay period, while the other Ss displayed a random response pattern.

Kimble & Pribram (3) have shown that hippocampal lesions in the monkey interfere with "sequential responding," and that response perseveration may only be one manifestation of such a deficit. Since the delayed alternation task constitutes a simple behavior sequence, our results are compatible with this interpretation, although conclusions regarding the functional role of the hippocampus must remain tentative.

references

1. Ellen, P., & Wilson, A. S. Perseveration in the rat following hippocampal lesions *Exp. Neurol.*, 1963, **8**, 310–317.
2. Kimble, D. P. The effects of bilateral hippocampal lesions in rats. *J. comp. physiol. Psychol.*, 1963, **56**, 273–283.
3. Kimble, D. P., & Pribram, K. H. Hippocampectomy and behavior sequences, *Science*, 1963, **139**, 824–825.
4. Madsen, M. C., & Kimble, D. P. The maze behavior of hippocampectomized rats under massed and distributed trials. *Psychon. Sci.*, 1965, **3**.
5. Mahut, Helen, & Cordeau, J. P. Spatial reversal deficit in monkeys with amygdalohippocampal ablations. *Exp. Neurol.*, 1963, **7**, 426–434.
6. Orbach, J., Milner, Brenda, & Rasmussen, T. Learning and retention in monkeys after amygdala-hippocampus resection. *Arch. Neurol.*, 1960, **3**, 230–251.
7. Penfield, W., & Milner, Brenda. Memory deficit produced by bilateral lesions in the hippocampal zone. *Arch. Neurol. Psychiat.*, 1958, **79**, 475–497.
8. Petrinovich, L., & Bolles, R. Delayed alternation: evidence for symbolic processes in the rat. *J. comp. physiol. Psychol.*, 1957, **50**, 363–365.
9. Pribram, K. H., Wilson, W. A., & Conners, Jane. Effects of lesions of the medial forebrain on alternation behavior of rhesus monkeys. *Exp. Neurol.*, 1962, **6**, 36–47.
10. Rosvold, H. E., & Szwarcbart, Maria K. Neural structures involved in delayed-response performance. In J. M. Warren, and K. Akert, (Eds.). *The frontal granular cortex and behavior.* New York: McGraw-Hill, 1964. Pp. 1–15.

28 thyroid hormone and conditioning*

W. J. Richards and J. C. Stockburger

1. From a knowledge of the general effects of the thyroid hormone on behavior, the specific effects on conditioning and extinction could be logically predicted. Why was this experiment necessary?

2. How does thiouracil work to produce a hyperthyroid state?

3. What generalizations can be drawn from these findings? Why is caution necessary?

Several investigators have studied the effects of an excess or a deficiency of thyroid hormone on learning in various situations. A few of these studies (e.g., 1, 3) have employed the conditioned response, but most of them were based upon such a small number of cases that statistical evaluation of the findings would be difficult.

It has been shown (4) that interference with normal thyroid function disturbs both metabolic processes and activity level of the

* W. J. Richards and J. C. Stockburger, "Thyroid Hormone and Conditioning," *J. comp. physiol. Psychol.*, 51 (1958), 445–447. Reprinted with permission.

animal. The use of a complex learning situation makes it difficult to separate behavioral changes due to these factors from those changes which indicate learning. A simple avoidance-conditioning situation would allow a more precise study of the effects of the thyroid hormone on learning, since this technique would minimize differences in metabolic and activity levels between groups with different thyroid states.

The present study tests the hypothesis that hyperthyroid, hypothyroid, and normal white rats will differ significantly in their rate of learning and extinction of a simple conditioned response. Further, it is hypothesized that the order of mean trials to learn and to extinguish (from low to high) will be hyperthyroid, normal, and hypothyroid.

method

subjects

The Ss were 36 experimentally naive male white rats, 60 to 90 days of age at the beginning of the study. Individual animals were matched on the basis of litter and weight and placed in one of three groups—a hyperthyroid group, a hypothyroid group, or a normal control group.

apparatus

The apparatus was a box 7 by 18 by 10 in. with a grid floor through which shock could be administered, and with a glass front through which responses of the animal could be observed. A masonite partition 1 in. high and 7 in. wide was placed in the center of the box. A 7½-w. frosted bulb was located at each end of the box. The grid floor was constructed so it could be activated one-half at a time. A selector switch allowed E to set

the combination of light and the half of the grid to be used on each trial. The light and grid were connected through an interval timer so that 2 sec. after the appearance of the light, the shock was given. The E timed each trial by means of a stop clock.

procedure

The hyper- or hypothyroid state was induced by feeding desiccated thyroid or thiouracil, respectively. The Ss were placed on an initial dosage of the appropriate drug of .02% by weight per gram of body weight per day for 14 days prior to the beginning of learning. A maintaining dosage of .01% by weight per gram of body weight per day was given throughout the remainder of the experiment. The Ss were kept in individual cages with water available at all times. The daily ration of ground, moistened dog chow, with which the appropriate drug was mixed, was given to them immediately after the experimental session. A preliminary study in which the basal metabolic rate was measured periodically indicated the effectiveness of this method of administration and these dosages of drugs.

Each S was given ten trials per day in the apparatus until a criterion of ten successive "correct" trials was attained. A trial consisted of the following sequence: S was placed in the apparatus and allowed a few seconds to explore. The light at the opposite end of the apparatus was turned on. If S crossed the partition and approached the light within 2 sec. of its onset, S avoided the shock. If S failed to respond within this time limit, shock was administered, and it continued until the response was made. Records were maintained of trials to learn, time per trial, proportion of anticipatory responses, and the trial on which the first anticipatory response occurred.

Extinction trials were conducted in the

same manner except that the shock was never used. The criterion was ten successive trials, on each of which the response occurred with a latency greater than 2 sec. Twelve of the 36 animals were used in a preliminary study in which learning only was measured. Since the data on learning for this group did not differ significantly from the data for the other 24 animals, they were included in the analysis. Thus, extinction data are presented for only 24 animals.

results and discussion

Table 1 shows the data for trials to learn and to extinguish. Groups I, II, and III in the

Table 1. Mean Trials to Learn and to Extinguish

Group	M	σ	Groups	t	p
			Learning[a]		
I	140.8	70.99	I vs. II	3.07	<.05
II	200.0	95.20	I vs. III	4.89	<.01
III	240.8	95.90	II vs. III	2.22	<.05
			Extinction[b]		
I	96.25	64.98	I vs. II	2.58	<.05
II	133.75	42.41	I vs. III	3.31	<.05
III	168.75	73.56	II vs. III	2.28	>.05

[a] n for each group = 12
[b] n for each group = 8

table represent the hyperthyroid, normal, and hypothyroid groups, respectively. It will be noted that the differences in learning for all comparisons are significant at the .05 level or better. These data show that when a simple learning situation is employed, thereby minimizing differences among groups in metabolic and activity levels, the thyroid condition does influence the process of learning in the manner hypothesized. In this situation the hyperthyroid animals learned at the fastest rate,

followed by the normals, then the hypothyroid animals.

The order of mean trials to extinguish for the three groups was as hypothesized, but only two of the three comparisons reached the .05 level of significance. These data appear to show that the hyperthyroid condition has a greater effect on both learning and extinction than does the hypothyroid state. It will be noted that the groups in which thyroid function was disturbed (I and III) showed greater variability of response during extinction than did the normal animals. These differences are not statistically significant.

Data on the proportion of conditioned responses made during the learning showed no significant differences among the three groups, nor did the time per trial. The latter finding was expected, since the animals were shocked into response. Further, there were no significant differences in the mean trial number on which the first conditioned response occurred.

It might be argued that this test situation does not really minimize the differences among the groups in activity level. If it could be shown that the extinction scores were independent of acquisition scores and the differences between groups were still significant, this finding would tend to support the belief that a reduction in the effects of differences in activity level for the three groups was achieved. An analysis of covariance was performed. It showed the differences in extinction scores to be significant above the .01 level.

The inhibitory effect of a thyroid deficiency on learning has been known for a long time. Previous studies of the effect of an excess of the hormone have given contradictory results. Some studies (1, 2) have reported results which indicate a slight facilitory effect of an excess, and others (5) have reported no such effects or have reported effects similar to those obtained with a thyroid deficiency. One possible explanation for the latter finding is given by Richter's (4) study. He showed that a large overdose of desiccated thyroid produced the same decline in activity as did a deficiency of the hormone. This finding indicates that the dosage of desiccated thyroid or thyroxin may be a critical factor in determining whether any differences in learning rates are found in studies of this problem.

The present study, using a very simple learning situation, has demonstrated that a slight excess of the thyroid hormone led to faster learning and extinction than was obtained with the normal animal, and that a deficiency produced the opposite effect. One cannot draw broad generalizations from these findings; if it is assumed, however, that the process of learning is governed by essentially the same principles for all kinds of learning situations, these results are suggestive.

summary and conclusions

Differences in rate of learning and extinction of a CR were determined for three matched groups of white rats—a normal, a hyperthyroid, and a hypothyroid group. The data justify the following conclusion: The groups differ significantly in rate of learning and extinction. The order of mean trials to learn and to extinguish from high to low is: hypothyroid, normal, hyperthyroid. The only comparison failing to reach significance at the .05 level was between the hypothyroid and normal groups on extinction trials.

references

1. Kleitman, N., & Titelbaum, S. The effect of thyroid administration upon the differen-tiating ability of dogs. *Am. J. Physiol.*, 1936, **115**, 162–167.
2. Mann, C. W. Learning in relation to hyper-thyroidism in the white rat. *J. comp. Psychol.*, 1942, **34**, 251–261.
3. Morrison, G. W., & Cunningham, B. Characteristics of the conditioned response in cretinous rats. *J. comp. Psychol.*, 1941, **31**, 413–425.
4. Richter, C. P. The role played by the thyroid gland in the production of gross bodily activity. *Endocrinology*, 1933, **17**, 73–87.
5. Thompson, R., & Kenshalo, D. R. Dis-crimination learning and habit reversal as affected by thyroid hormone. *J. comp. physiol. Psychol.*, 1954, **47**, 36–40.

29 cerebral cholinesterase activity and "hypothesis" behavior

J. Trevor Peirce

1. What is the purpose of the Krech Hypothesis Apparatus? How was it used in this experiment?
2. Why should there be a relation between differences in cortical cholinesterase activity and differences in behavior?
3. How can the differences between the results of this experiment and the previous results of Krech and others be explained?
4. What were the limitations of this study?

The California experiments relating the cerebral-cortical activity of the brain enzyme,

[29] J. T. Peirce, "Cerebral Cholinesterase Activity and 'Hypothesis' Behavior in a Problemless Maze," *J. comp. physiol. Psychol.*, 52 (1959), 168–171. Reprinted with permission.

cholinesterase (ChE), and behavior in rats (1, 2, 6) have demonstrated that individual differences in ChE activity exist among normal rats. More importantly, these normally occurring differences were shown to be linked to differences in behavior.

Behavioral testing was done in the Krech Hypothesis Apparatus, a four-choice-point, linear, alley maze wherein one alley at each choice point is illuminated, the other dark; one alley is correct, the other is blocked at its far end. Both the left-right position of the light and of the correct side vary independently and irregularly in a pattern such that no behavior systematically oriented to the maze stimuli will result in more than chance choice of the correct side: the maze is unsolvable.

In this unsolvable-problem situation, rats do show systematic orientation of their behavior, or "hypothesis behavior," to use Krechevsky's (3) terms.

In previous California experiments, run under the above conditions, animals showing high cortical ChE activity tended to behave more in terms of the spatial features of the maze, while animals with low ChE activity showed relatively more visual orientation. The correlation between ChE and degree of predominance of spatial over visual orientation was $+.28$ with an N of 125.

The present experiment was run in the Krech Hypothesis Apparatus under conditions closely simulating those of earlier experiments. The major difference was that, in the present experiment, all the blocking doors were removed: there were no wrong alleys, and, from this point of view, the situation was a problemless one.

By removing the blocking doors, it was sought to answer three questions. (*a*) Is the relationship between ChE and behavior specific to a problem situation? That is, is the presence of objectively different consequences of choice at each choice point of importance for the correlation? Is ChE linked to a problem-solving factor? (*b*) On the assumption that the absence of blocking doors removes one incentive for animals to vary their behavior (every choice is correct), one might expect a "purer" expression of sensory preferences. So we may ask: What is the relation between this "purer" measure of sensory preference and ChE? (*c*) Do animals show systematic, or "hypothesis," behavior in the Krech Hypothesis Apparatus if there are no differential consequences of choice? Witkin (8), using a different apparatus, has found hypothesis behavior in a problemless situation, but no data have been available for the Krech apparatus.

method

subjects

A total of 28 male rats, 110 to 135 days old, were run. A first group comprised 14 rats of the S_{13} strain, descendants of the Tryon (7) cross between maze-bright and maze-dull rats. A second group consisted of 14 S_3 rats, descendants of the Tryon maze-dulls.

apparatus

Krech Hypothesis Apparatus. This maze is shown in Figure 1. The maze was painted black throughout. In the ceilings of the choice-alleys, at all four choice points, a 15-w. bulb was set above opal glass. At each choice point, one choice alley was illuminated, the other dark. Black curtains hung at the far ends

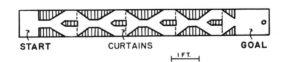

Fig. 1. Floor plan of the Krech Hypothesis Apparatus.

of all choice alleys. The room was darkened during maze runs, the only illumination coming from the lights at the choice points, from a small, low-intensity light above the food dish in the goal box, and from a dim light at *E*'s station at the starting end of the maze.

Pretraining for the Krech apparatus was performed in a pretraining unit with the same external dimensions as the maze itself. The interior of the pretraining box was divided into four rectangular sections, in addition to starting and goal boxes. Curtains hung in the centrally located doors that led from one compartment to the next. Dim light from the room windows was present.

Automatic titrator. This was a product of the International Instrument Company, Canyon, California. For details of construction and procedure see Krech et al. (1) and Rosenzweig et al. (6).

procedures

Pretraining. All animals were placed on a 24-hr. feeding schedule 15 days before the start of regular testing.

Since these animals were run as part of a large research project, they received a "generalized" pretraining designed to acclimate them to a small, gray alley maze, an elevated maze, and the Krech Hypothesis Apparatus. On ten days of the pretraining period, 5-min., daily exploratory tests were given in another room on an elevated Y maze.

During the 15 days of pretraining, 6 days were devoted to practice in the pretraining unit. On the last of these days, immediately before testing began, each animal received ten runs through the pretraining unit.

Behavioral testing. Five days of testing were given, each animal making 12 runs per day. The right-left position of the lighted alleys varied irregularly from choice point to choice

point and from trial to trial in the standard pattern previously used in this apparatus. The light appeared equally often on the left and on the right.

Chemical testing. ChE assays were performed more than thirty days after the end of behavioral testing, at which time all animals were over 200 days old. This age falls well within the range wherein it has been shown (6) that ChE differences correlate with behavioral indices.

Two samples of cerebral cortical tissue were taken from each animal. A bilateral sample was taken from an area in the somesthetic region, a region previously shown to be necessary for spatial hypothesis behavior (5). A second bilateral sample was taken from the visual cortex, an area necessary for visual hypothesis behavior.

Samples were weighed immediately upon excision and then frozen until assay. One to two days after excision, samples were homogenized in physiological saline and aliquots containing approximately 12 mg. of tissue were pipetted off and put in the reaction chamber of the automatic titrator. There, acetylcholine was added, and the rate of addition of base required to hold the pH constant at 7.95 gave a measure of the rate of release of acetate as the ChE of the sample broke down the acetylcholine.

results

cholinesterase assays

The ChE activity of each sample was computed as moles acetylcholine 10^{10} hydrolized per milligram of tissue per minute. The mean value of ChE activity for somesthetic (S) cortex was 70.9 ($SD = 5.12$); for visual cortex (V), it was 59.0 ($SD = 6.37$). Averaging these gives the $(V + S)/2$ score previously used in the California experiments. For the entire group, the mean $(V + S)/2$ was equal to 65.0 with an SD of 4.9. These figures were comparable to those of earlier experiments that employed this apparatus. Differences between the strains of rats were insignificant.

Running duplicate aliquots from the same tissue homogenate permitted computation of a reliability coefficient for the titration procedure. In current experimental series, r_μ was equal to $+.91$. This is identical to the figure obtained by Krech et al. (1).

behavioral testing

As in previous California experiments, two types of behavioral analysis were made. *"Hypothesis"* *Measures:* When an animal's behavior, on a given day, was significantly systematic (i.e., deviated from chance at the .01 level of confidence) in terms of the left-right aspects of the maze, the animal was said to show a spatial hypothesis; when significantly systematic in terms of the light-dark cues, the animal was said to show a visual hypothesis. *Spatial-minus-Visual Preference Score:* For each day, the animal's deviations from chance visual behavior were subtracted from his deviations from chance spatial behavior. These daily Spatial-minus-Visual Preference Scores $(S - V)$ were then algebraically summed over the test period. A plus score indicates that the animal is relatively more oriented to the spatial cues, a negative score indicates predominantly visual orientation.

Table 1 shows that there is a strong general tendency for the animals of both groups to show visually oriented behavior during the early phases of testing. Of the 28 animals, 22 showed statistically significant light-going behavior on the first day (i.e., 33 or more

Table 1. Mean Spatial-Visual Preference Scores

Day	Group I	Group II	Both Groups	SD Both Groups
1	−7.4	−8.3	−7.8	10.1
2	−4.8	−8.6	−6.7	11.7
3	+1.2	−4.1	−1.4	9.9
4	+2.4	−3.7	−0.7	11.9
5	+4.7	−2.1	+1.3	12.0
5-Day Total	−3.9	−26.7	−15.3	46.2

Note.—Minus scores indicate visual preference; positive scores, spatial preference.

choices of light out of 48 choices), while only five animals showed significant spatial behavior. During the course of testing, the behavior became more spatially oriented: on the fifth and final day, there were only 11 significant visual hypotheses, but 16 spatial hypotheses. In the five days of training, the animals averaged 1.68 different *types* of hypotheses. Ten animals showed only one type of hypothesis, 14 showed two, and four showed three different types. Multiplying each hypothesis adopted by each animal by the number of days on which S showed that hypothesis reveals that the average animal showed 4.6 hypothesis-days; 2.8 of these were visual, and 1.8 were spatial. Eight animals had at least one day on which they showed both a visual *and* a spatial hypothesis.

correlations between ChE and behavior

Neither number of types of hypotheses nor number of hypothesis-days were significantly related to ChE activity. However, the Pearson r between ChE $(V + S)/2$ and Spatial-visual Preference $(S - V)$ was $-.44$, significantly different from zero at the .02 level of confidence. This negative relationship also holds within each group. For the S_{13} (bright-by-dull) rats, $r = -.51$; for the S_3 (dull) rats, $r = -.33$.

discussion

The answers to the questions posed earlier in this paper are clear.

1. Normally occurring levels of cortical ChE activity are related to behavior in the Krech Hypothesis Apparatus, even in the absence of differential consequences of choice. However, the obtained negative correlation of $-.44$ was not only in the opposite direction from the positive correlation of $+.28$ found by the California group (6), but differs from their correlation at better than the .001 level of confidence.

This finding of a discrepancy between correlations raises an important question of interpretation. The California group (1, 6) has held that the systematic orientation of behavior to given cues reflects attempts at (or "hypotheses" about) the solution of the maze. Since almost all animals display light-going tendencies on their initial runs, light has been considered the dominant stimulus, and the correlation between ChE and behavior has been interpreted to mean that high ChE animals are less stimulus-bound to this dominant light cue. Thus, they are able to vary their behavior and attempt solution of the problem in terms of the nondominant, spatial stimuli. Low ChE animals, on the other hand, are less able, by this interpretation, to break away from the dominant stimulus.

This interpretation would suggest that, in the present problemless situation, the reversed correlation between ChE and S−V scores might be due to a reversal of the dominance relationship between visual and spatial cues such that vision is no longer dominant. Such a reversed dominance relationship would still enable us to say that high cortical ChE goes with "broad attention" or non-stimulus-boundedness. However, three facts make such an interpretation difficult. First, the data reflect the same high initial visual orientation and subsequent decline that have defined the dominance of visual cues. Secondly, the S_{13} animals showed more spatial orientation than the S_3 rats. This corresponds to previous findings (4, 6). Finally, on the first test day, when light-going and (presumably) visual dominance were maximal, both groups showed negative correlations between ChE activity and S − V scores ($r = -.29$ and $-.31$).

2. To the extent that the problemless situation leads to a less contaminated measure of the rat's tendency systematically to behave in terms of visual or spatial cues, it is seen that high ChE activity goes with visually oriented behavior. By this, it is not meant that high ChE activity does, necessarily, reflect or affect sensory preferences; if it does, the present data suggest that it leads to visual orientation.

Any association between cortical ChE activity and visual preference means, of course, that the correlations found in previous problem situations were obtained despite the preference factor.

3. In the absence of differential consequences of choice in the Krech Hypothesis Apparatus, rats do show statistically significant hypotheses. They also show shifts of hypotheses, both between and within sensory modes.

Finally, it should be emphasized that the most important finding of the present experiment is that of a relationship between *normally* occurring differences of cortical ChE activity and behavior. This substantiates the basic conclusion of the California group that

ChE activity is of significance for organismic behavior, and extends this conclusion to an altered behavioral situation.

summary

Twenty-eight rats were run in a Krech Hypothesis Apparatus from which all blocking doors were removed. Following behavioral testing, assays were made of cerebral cortical cholinesterase activity. A correlation of −.44 was found between cholinesterase activity and the tendency to prefer spatial, as against visual, orientation in the maze. This correlation is opposite in sign, and differs significantly, from the positive correlation previous experimenters (1, 2, 6) found between these variables when, in the same maze, blocking doors were present and the maze was unsolvable.

It is emphasized that the most important finding of the present experiment is that normally occurring differences in cortical cholinesterase activity are related to behavioral differences.

references

1. Krech, D., Rosenzweig, M. R., & Bennett, E. L. Dimensions of discrimination and level of ChE activity in the cerebral cortex of the rat. *J. comp. physiol. Psychol.*, 1956, **49**, 261–268.

2. Krech, D., Rosenzweig, M. R., Bennett, E. L., & Krueckel, B. Enzyme concentrations in the brain and adjustive behavior patterns. *Science*, 1954, **120**, 994–996.

3. Krechevsky, I. The genesis of "hypotheses" in rats. *Univer. Calif. Publ. Psychol.*, 1932, **6**, 45–64.

4. Krechevsky, I. Hereditary nature of "hypotheses." *J. comp. Psychol.*, 1933, **16**, 99–116.

5. Krechevsky, I. Brain mechanisms and "hypotheses." *J. comp. Psychol.*, 1935, **19**, 425–462.

6. Rosenzweig, M. R., Krech, D., & Bennett, E. L. Brain chemistry and adaptive behavior. In H. F. Harlow & C. L. Woolsey (Eds.), *Biological and biochemical bases of behavior.* Madison, Wis.: Univer. Wisconsin Press, 1958. Pp. 367–400.

7. Tryon, R. C. Genetic differences in maze-learning ability in rats. *Yearb. Nat. Soc. Stud. Educ.*, 1940, **39** (I), 111–119.

8. Witkin, H. A. "Hypotheses" in rats: An experimental evaluation of the hypothesis concept. III. Summary evaluation of the hypothesis concept. *Psychol. Rev.*, 1942, **49**, 541–568.

brain lesions

The brain is of such importance in the initiation and control of behavior that nearly any injury to the brain can be expected to affect behavior. The total effect of a brain lesion on behavior, however, is a function of many factors. For example, rats that run a maze poorly are affected more by a given brain lesion than are rats that learn a maze easily. In human beings, not only does intelligence play a role, but also such factors as motivation and other individual personality variables.

In the first two articles (Reading 30 by Malcolm Piercy, et al. and Reading 31 by J. McFie and O.L. Zangwill) a detailed analysis is given of two conditions that follow unilateral injury to the cerebrum. Constructional apraxia is an inability to construct (for example, copy a drawing) under visual control. Spatial agnosia is the inability to comprehend spatial relations visually. Since the patient with spatial agnosia also has trouble with construction or copying, the two conditions can be confused. The constructional apraxia patient need not have spatial agnosia, but the spatial agnosia patient will appear to have constructional apraxia.

Piercy and his co-workers indicate that lesions in the right cerebral lobe cause most of

315

the cases of constructional apraxia. They admit that lesions in the left hemisphere may also cause this condition. McFie and Zangwill conclude that the right-sided lesions produce spatial agnosia, whereas the left-sided lesions produce pure constructional apraxia. These two papers illustrate the difficulty of making a precise differentiation in this area.

The understanding of the effects of brain lesions on the behavior of humans depends on the better-controlled studies of animals with experimentally produced brain lesions. In Reading 32, Robert McCleary shows the effects of limbic system lesions in the cat. He demonstrates the interesting fact that "cats with bilateral lesions in the subcallosal area are deficient in *passive* avoidance behavior but are normal or quicker than normal in the acquisition of an *active* avoidance response. Conversely, cats with bilateral cingulate lesions are deficient in the acquisition of an *active* avoidance response but show normal *passive* avoidance behavior."

The last article in this chapter (Reading 33) is by Daniel Kimble, one of McCleary's students. This is a clear-cut experiment; yet, Kimble warns, "monolithic hypotheses concerning behavioral significance of the hippocampus are likely to be oversimplifications." This admonition by Kimble is a good one to close this or any other section of articles on physiological psychology. In no other field is the next decade likely to show more changes in what today are called "the facts."

30 constructional apraxia and unilateral cerebral lesions *

Malcolm Piercy, H. Hécaen, and J. de Ajuriaguerra

1. In the history of the study of constructional apraxia, what trends in etiology appear?
2. Are the difficulties involved in deciding whether or not to call a case "constructional apraxia" merely a matter of semantics?
3. What design changes might be made by these experimenters?

I. introduction

Defective execution of constructional tasks under visual control is generally recognized as a disability which may result from a posterior cerebral lesion. On two points, however, there is no general agreement. There is disagreement as to whether the syndrome is more particularly associated with one cerebral hemisphere than the other and there is no generally accepted theory of the nature of the disability.

Following the earlier descriptions (25, 24, 14, 10), this disability rapidly came to be considered as the product of a left hemisphere lesion. This resulted partly from the anatomical evidence associated with earlier cases, partly from the occasional association with

* M. Piercy, H. Hécaen, and J. de Ajuriaguerra, "Constructional Apraxia Associated with Unilateral Cerebral Lesions: Left- and Right-Sided Cases Compared," *Brain*, 83 (1960), 225–242. Reprinted with permission.

Gerstmann's syndrome, and partly no doubt as a result of a ready presumption that any agnosic or apraxic disability must be associated with damage to the "dominant" hemisphere.

Certain authors (17, 4, 26) pointed out that the disability may be associated with right hemisphere lesions and even claimed that the right hemisphere had an exclusive role in this respect. Similarly, Poetzl, who was one of the first to describe the disability as a left hemisphere syndrome, nevertheless took the view that the right hemisphere was specially involved in the maintenance of a temporo-spatial framework in terms of which information from the environment is interpreted.

These views attributing a special role to the right hemisphere did not, however, gain general acceptance and the notion that, except in anomalous cases, the right hemisphere is "subordinate" to the left hemisphere in respect of all forms of gnosis and praxis is still fairly general.

From the outset there has been much speculation concerning the nature of the constructional disability and this is reflected in the terminology employed by different authors. The terms visual-spatial agnosia (26), visual-spatial syndrome (15), temporo-spatial disorientation (4), clearly assume an agnosic defect. Perhaps the most common view was that there is a disturbance of the organization of motor activity *in relation* to the perception of spatial properties of the environment. This is illustrated by the terms "apractognosia for spatial articulation" (17) and "planotopokinesia" (20). Kleist, to whom with Strauss (27) we owe the most commonly used term, "constructional apraxia," took a similar view. For him, constructional apraxia was a disturbance of "a cerebral mechanism concerned with visuo-kinesthetic associations."

More recently there have been a number of communications emphasizing the frequency with which the syndrome occurs as a result of a right hemisphere lesion and suggesting that differences exist between the constructional apraxia produced by left and right hemisphere lesions. Paterson and Zangwill (22, 23) described 3 cases of visual-spatial agnosia associated with lesions of the right cerebral hemisphere and drew attention to the similar patterns of disability reported in earlier cases with left hemisphere lesions. McFie, Piercy and Zangwill (19) presented 8 cases with visual-spatial and constructional disabilities in whom the lesion was exclusively (6 cases) or predominantly (2 cases) right-sided. These authors felt unable to claim an exclusive role for the right hemisphere and maintained that any such conclusion should be based, not on a few selected cases but on "the outcome of controlled clinical and experimental observation." They did, however, tentatively suggest that the pattern of visual-spatial and constructional disability in their right-sided cases differed in subtle respects from that found in left-sided cases.

Almost simultaneously Hécaen, Ajuriaguerra and Massonnet (11) independently reported the same syndrome in cases with right hemisphere lesions but emphasized that vestibular disturbances were present in their cases and pointed to the possible role of these disturbances in the production of the visual-spatial and constructional disability. They also suggested that certain features of their patients' performance set them apart from the comparable left hemisphere syndrome: neglect of the left side of a model in copying; diagonal orientation of drawings; inability to represent perspective in drawings of three-dimensional objects; inability to articulate different parts of a two-dimensional drawing.

Critchley (3) extensively discussed the

problem of constructional apraxia on the basis of a large number of cases and came to the conclusion that the syndrome was most flagrant in bilateral cases and that the disability was possibly less severe in left hemisphere cases than in right hemisphere cases.

Duensing (5) made a radical distinction between visual-spatial agnosia, which he associated with the right hemisphere, and the corresponding left hemisphere disability, which he regarded as a defect of execution. For him the distinction between the two syndromes was analogous to that between receptive and expressive aphasia. The drawings of left hemisphere cases were said to be marked by more hesitations, greater simplification of outline, and to be facilitated by the presentation of a model for copying. The drawings of patients with visual-spatial agnosia on the other hand were less hesitant, were characterized by "piecemeal" representation (as described by Paterson and Zangwill) and were not facilitated by the representation of a model for copying. It must be noted, however, that Duensing's formulation was based on differences observed between a group of 4 cases with predominantly, but not exclusively, left parietal lesions and a group of 2 cases showing visual-spatial agnosia, one of these having a right parieto-occipital lesion and the other bilateral occipital lesions. It is thus somewhat dubious whether the difference between his two groups may justifiably be attributed to the laterality of the lesions.

Denny-Brown, Meyer and Horenstein (6) have put forward a quite different interpretation. According to these authors truly agnosic defects occur only with major hemisphere lesions but non-agnosic unilateral defects of perception may occur in association with a lesion of the parietal lobe of either side. They maintain that one of the functions of the parietal lobes is the integration of the spatial attributes of sensory impulses from the contralateral side of the body (and in the case of vision impulses corresponding to the contralateral visual field). A unilateral parietal lesion it is claimed may thus result in a unilateral defect of "spatial summation" (the term "amorphosynthesis" is also used). They suggest that unilateral neglect of space, which has frequently been reported with right hemisphere lesions, is equally common with left parietal lesions but tends to be obscured by the presence of dysphasia and agnosic defects. Their findings, based on a single case, make it "inconceivable to us that the right parietal region has some special unique significance in regard to visual space-perception."

Ettlinger, Warrington and Zangwill (9) reported 10 carefully studied cases with right-sided posterior cerebral lesions exhibiting disturbances of spatial perception and constructional performance and concluded that the disabilities which they observed could not wholly be accounted for either by impairment of differential visual sensitivity (1), unilateral imperception (6) or central vestibular derangement (11, 13) or a combination of these. They suggest retaining the term visual spatial agnosia for this syndrome and put forward a tentative explanation in terms of restriction of the field of visual attention and disorganization of spatial orientation at a conceptual level.

The greatest single difficulty in evaluating published evidence on this problem arises from the fact that the basis upon which cases are selected varies from one report to another. In particular, there has been no study reporting a series of relevant cases with unilateral lesions, with a basis of case selection that is strictly comparable for both right and left hemisphere lesions. The present paper communicates a series of cases exhibiting constructional apraxia in association with unilateral cerebral lesions, and the effort has been made to ensure that identical criteria should be used for the selection of right- and left-sided cases. The details which it is possible to present in respect of any individual patient are by no means as full here as in some previous reports. Nevertheless, it is hoped that an investigation which is carefully controlled as to the selection of cases will make some contribution to an understanding of the comparative importance of the left and right cerebral hemispheres for visual-spatial and constructional performance.

II. results

incidence of constructional apraxia

Punch card records had been kept of all patients seen in the neurosurgical service of l'Hôpital Ste. Anne between 1947 and 1955. All these patients had been examined by one of the authors and all the cards had been punched by the examiner. The cards recorded the principal neurological findings in over 3,000 cases. All cards punched for constructional apraxia were selected and reference was then made to the detailed case notes for further information.

A total of 80 cards had been punched for constructional apraxia but, of these, 13 had bilateral lesions. We were left therefore with 67 patients with unilateral lesions exhibiting constructional apraxia. Forty-two of these had right-sided lesions and 25 had left-sided lesions. In order to compare the incidence of constructional apraxia in left- and right-sided cases it was necessary to know the total number of cases with unilateral left- and right-sided cerebral lesions covered by the punch card system. Accordingly, all cards punched for unilateral lesion involving the

cerebral cortex or subcortical white matter were selected and these were divided into two groups according to the side of the lesion. Each of these groups was then divided into two further groups according to whether or not constructional apraxia was exhibited. The result is shown in Table 1, where the contin-

Table 1. Relationship between Side of Unilateral Lesion and Incidence of Constructional Apraxia

			Constructional Apraxia		
			Present	Absent	Total
Side of	Left		25	190	215
Lesion	Right		42	146	188
		Total	67	336	403

$$X^2 = 7 \cdot 55; \ p < 0 \cdot 01$$

Constructional apraxia occurs significantly more frequently with right hemisphere lesions than with left hemisphere lesions.

gency of incidence of constructional apraxia upon the side of the responsible lesion is found to be statistically significant ($x^2 = 7 \cdot 55$; $p < \cdot 01$). The 42 right-sided cases with constructional apraxia constitute 22.3 per cent of all strictly unilateral right-sided cases recorded in the service, whereas the 25 left-sided cases constitute only 11.6 per cent of all unilateral left-sided cases recorded. Constructional apraxia was thus observed twice as frequently in cases with right hemisphere lesions as in cases with left hemisphere lesions.

A more detailed analysis of the data is shown in Table 2. Here only unilateral post-Rolandic lesions have been considered. 37.8 per cent of all such right hemisphere lesions resulted in a constructional apraxia, as against 16.7 per cent of all such left hemisphere lesions. Analysis in terms of the distribution of lesions within each hemisphere suggests that lesions giving rise to constructional apraxia are considerably more restricted in their site in the case of the right hemisphere than in the case of the left hemisphere. The right tem-

Table 2. Relationship between Incidence of Constructional Apraxia and Locus of Lesion (Based on all Cases with Unilateral Post-Rolandic Lesions)

| | Side of Lesion | | | |
| | Left Constructional apraxia | | Right Constructional apraxia | |
	Present	Absent	Present	Absent
Temporal	5	40	1	19
Temp-occip.	1	6	0	2
Occipital	2	20	1	10
Par-temp.	6	12	3	9
Parietal	4	34	11	20
Par-occip.	5	11	18	9
Temp-par-occip.	2	2	8	0
	25	125	42	69
		150		111

poro-parieto-occipital region and, to a lesser extent, the right parieto-occipital and parietal regions appear especially vulnerable. In contrast to this, lesions of the temporal, temporo-occipital, occipital and parieto-temporal regions more frequently result in constructional apraxia when the lesion is left-sided than when it is right-sided. In other words, given the side of the lesion in a case of constructional apraxia, the site of the lesion within the hemisphere could more confidently be predicted in a right hemisphere case than in a left hemisphere case. The functions impaired in constructional apraxia thus appear to be more focally organized in the right hemisphere than in the left. Considered in conjunction with the over-all higher incidence of the disability with right-sided lesions, this anatomical evidence lends significant support to the hypothesis of right hemisphere dominance for the functions in question.

The results so far described are based on all unilateral cases exhibiting constructional apraxia, irrespective of other symptoms present and irrespective of the handedness of the patient. It was felt, however, that, in comparing the quality of the performance of the two groups of patients, it was important to exclude those in whom there was a general disturbance of consciousness to which the failure in constructional tasks might conceivably be regarded as secondary. Those patients in whom there had been evidence of general confusion were therefore excluded for the purpose of qualitative comparisons. It was also decided to exclude all left-handed patients since, in their case, it can be argued that the effects of cerebral lesions are atypical. The analysis which follows is therefore based on all right-handed cases with constructional apraxia who were free from general confusion and in whom the cerebral lesion was strictly unilateral. Forty-two cases conformed to these criteria: 24 with right-sided lesions; 18 with left-sided lesions.

other disabilities

Details of the lesions present in the 42 cases whose constructional performances are described are shown in Table 3. This table also shows the incidence of hemianopia, paresis of the contralateral upper limb, dysphasia, apraxia (other than constructional), Gerstmann's syndrome, and topographical disorientation.

The relevance of dysphasia and paresis of the upper limb are discussed in detail below but brief comment on the other disabilities shown in the Table is also called for. Six left-sided cases exhibited a general apraxia and in these cases the constructional defect could be regarded as secondary to the more general executive disability. If these 6 were excluded from consideration, the difference in the incidence of constructional apraxia in left- and right-sided cases would be even more striking. Seven right-sided cases showed an apraxia for dressing. The incidence of hemianopia is roughly equal in both groups of patients (about 50 per cent) and may therefore be

Table 3A. Left-sided Cases

Case	Lesion Left hemisphere	Paresis of upper limb	Hemianopia	Gerstmann's syndrome	Dysphasia	General apraxia	Topographical disorientation
1	Par.-occ. meningioblastoma	0	0	0	+	+	0
2	Vascular accident	0	+	0	0	0	0
3	Vascular accident	0	0	0	0	0	0
4	Temp. neoplasm (angiogram)	+	0	0	+	0	0
5	Temp. glioma	0	0	0	0	+	0
6	Parietal trauma	+	+	+ Fing. agn.	0	0	0
7	Par.-temp. angioma	0	+	+ Fing. agn.	0	0	± With maps
8	Parietal glioblastoma	+	0	0	+	+	0
9	Front.-temp. glioma	0	+	0	+	0	0
10	Par.-temp. vasc. accident	0	0	+ L.R. dis.	+	0	0
11	Par.-occ. vasc. accident	0	+	0	+	0	0
12	Par.-temp. (EEG, motor and sensory evidence)	+	0	+ Fing. agn.	± (Parox.)	0	0
13	Temp.-par.-occ. porencephaly	0	+	0	0	0	0
14	Parietal arachnoiditis	0	0	+ Fing. agn.	0	0	+ In house
15	Temp. glioma	+	+	0	+	+	0
16	Middle cerebr. thrombosis	0	0	0	+	+	0
17	Temp. glioma	0	0	0	+	0	0
18	Temp.-par.-occip. glioma	0	0	0	+	+	0

regarded as not contributing to the difference between the two groups in the severity and incidence of constructional apraxia. Finger-agnosia was present in 4 left-sided cases and some degree of left/right disorientation in 1 more. Definite disturbance of topographical orientation was observed in 1 left-sided and 2 right-sided cases. The left-sided case tended to get lost in his own house but apparently had no special difficulty with route-finding in streets. Both right-sided cases had general route-finding difficulties. Three further cases (1 left-sided, 2 right-sided) had difficulty in understanding a map of their own country.

Unfortunately the patients under consideration were not tested for general intellectual impairment but, as mentioned above, patients showing confusion or other disturbances of consciousness were excluded.

severity of constructional apraxia

Thirty-two paitents (15 with right-sided lesions and 17 with left-sided lesions) were tested for their ability to draw simple geometrical figures such as a square, a diamond, a cross, a circle or a triangle. Nine of the 15 patients with right-sided lesions produced failures on this simple test but only 3 of the 17 patients with left-sided lesions.

It is of considerable interest that in the case

Table 3B. Right-sided Cases

Case	Lesion Right Hemisphere	Paresis of upper limb	Hemianopia	Apraxia for dressing	Topographical disorientation
19	Temp.-parieto-occipital glioma	+	+	0	± With maps
20	Vasc. accident	0	+	0	0
21	Temp.-par.-occip. necrosis	0	+	+	0
22	Par.-occ. astrocytoma	+	+	+	0
23	Temp.-par.-occip. astrocytoma	+	+	0	+
24	Metastases (R. hemisphere only)	+	± Inf. quad.	0	0
25	Int. carotid thrombosis	+	± Partial	0	0
26	Occip.-temp. gliosis	0	± Inf. quad.	+	+
27	Occip. lobectomy	0	+	0	0
28	Occip. trauma	0	+	0	0
29	Int. carotid thrombosis	0	0	0	0
30	Temp.-par. glioma	+	0	0	0
31	Parietal trauma	0	0	0	0
32	Par.-occip. astrocytoma	+	0	0	± with maps
33	Occip.-par. glioma	0	+	0	0
34	Par.-temp. glioma	+	0	+	0
35	Post-Rolandic (EEG and motor evidence)	0	0	0	0
36	Parietal glioma	+	+	0	0
37	Temp.-par.-occip. meningioma	+	0	+	0
38	Parietal glioma	+	0	0	0
39	Par.-occip. glioblastoma	+	+	+	0
40	Par.-temp. glioblastoma	+	+	0	0
41	Post. cerebr. thrombosis	+	+	0	0
42	Par.-occip. glioma	0	+	+	0

of patients with left-sided lesions all 3 patients who showed incapacity in the simplest drawing tests also showed clinically obvious apraxia not limited to constructional performances. There is thus not one patient in the left-sided group whose failure on very simple drawing tests could not be attributed to a more general apraxia; whereas in the right-sided group there are 9 out of 15 patients (or 6 out of 12, if patients with apraxia for dressing are excluded) showing these gross constructional failures without any general apraxia.

It is evident therefore that the impairment of drawing tends to be more severe in the right hemisphere cases than in the left hemisphere cases.

Five left-sided cases and 10 right-sided cases were tested for their ability to copy matchstick models. These models varied in complexity from simple geometrical figures such as a triangle or a square to two-dimensional representations of a house and a cube (made with 11 and 9 matchsticks respectively). The results are shown in Table 4. A total of 14 out of 15 failures were made by the right hemisphere cases, as against 5 out of 9 by the left hemisphere cases. Here, as in the drawings, the right hemisphere cases are distinctly more impaired than the other group.

Table 4. Matchstick Copying Test

Left Hemisphere Cases

	House	Cube	Simple forms	Total
Tested	3	4	2	9
Correct	2	1	1	4
Failure	1	3	1	5

Right Hemisphere Cases

	House	Cube	Simple forms	Total
Tested	7	4	4	15
Correct	1	0	0	1
Failure	6	4	4	14

comparative performance in copying and spontaneous drawing

Figs. 1 and 2 show spontaneous drawings of a house and copies of a drawing of a house for all patients who were tested for both performances. In 7 of the relevant 10 cases with left-sided lesions, the copy was unequivocally superior in construction to the free drawing (Cases 3, 6, 7, 10, 11, 15 and 16). In the remaining 3 cases the two performances were of approximately equal quality. Seven right-sided cases were tested both for free drawing and for copying a drawing of a house and, of these, only 2 produced copies which might fairly be judged superior to the corresponding free drawings (Cases 19 and 28).

If Figs. 1 and 2 are compared, it is evident that the two groups of patients can be distinguished far more readily by their copies than by their free drawings. The copies executed by left-sided cases are far more recognizable as drawings of a house than are the corresponding drawings of right-sided cases. The same cannot be said of the spontaneous drawings of a house executed by the two groups. The left hemisphere group are perhaps somewhat superior in this task but the difference is by no means as strikingly obvious as that to be observed between the copies.

It appears therefore that the provision of a model to copy considerably facilitates the drawing ability of patients with left hemisphere lesions but has little effect in right hemisphere cases. This is in conformity with Duensing's suggestion.

Fig. 3 shows attempts at copying a drawing of a house made by those right hemisphere cases who did not attempt a corresponding free drawing. Attempts at copying a drawing of a cube are shown for both groups in Fig. 4. These results are referred to on the left.

complexity of structure

Although in many cases the drawings produced by right- and left-sided cases are not individually distinguishable, there appears to be one type of drawing which is typical of the right hemisphere syndrome. This is the attempt at a copy which, although unrecognizable as a picture, is comparatively complicated in structure. This can be seen in the copies of a house by Cases 30 and 39 and the copies of a cube by Cases 25, 30 and 37. Left-sided cases producing unrecognizable copies tended to produce more simply structured drawings.

This tendency for the unrecognizable copies produced by the two groups to differ in complexity can be quantified. Six of the attempts by left-sided cases to copy a drawing of a cube and 10 of those by right-sided cases could fairly be judged as unrecognizable (in Fig. 4: Cases 1, 3, 5, 9, 11, 15, 19, 22, 23, 25, 26, 30, 37, 38, 39, 42). The copies of a cube have been selected for this analysis in preference to copies of a house since all but one of the left hemisphere copies of a house were fully recognizable. A count was made of the number of lines constituting each copy of a cube made by our patients. In making this count, over-scorings of the same line were not counted

Copies   Spontaneous

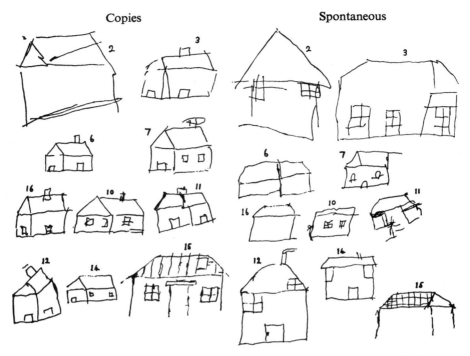

Fig. 1. Drawings of a house by left hemisphere cases. The numbers refer to the cases listed in Table 3.

Copies   Spontaneous

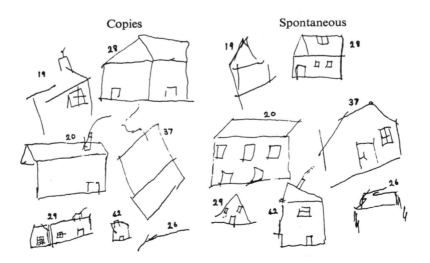

Fig. 2. Drawings of a house by right hemisphere cases. The numbers refer to the cases listed in Table 3.

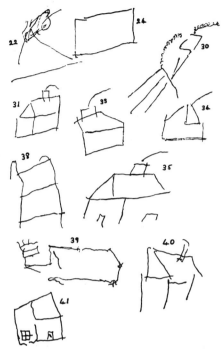

Fig. 3. Further copies of a house by right hemisphere cases. The numbers refer to the cases listed in Table 3.

but continuously drawn lines which abruptly changed direction were counted as two lines. Continuous curves were counted as single lines, as were interrupted straight lines. The mean number of lines for the left hemisphere group of unrecognizable drawings was 4.83 and for the corresponding right hemisphere group 8.9. A "t" test showed this difference to be statistically significant (p < .05).

Among the *recognizable* copies of a cube there was no significant difference between the mean number of lines used by the right- and left-sided groups (9.44 and 8.86 respectively). It is instructive to note that, within the group of right hemisphere cases, the mean number of lines used in unrecognizable drawings (8.9) is not significantly different from the number used in recognizable drawings (9.44). But within the left hemisphere group

the mean number of lines used in unrecognizable drawings (4.83) is about half the number used in recognizable drawings (8.86). This suggests that severe incapacity in left-sided cases tends to result in a more simplified drawing, whereas in right-sided cases severe incapacity tends to result in a drawing which, although disorganized, is comparable in complexity to the drawing which serves as a model.

orientation of drawings

A further difference between the two groups which may be tentatively suggested concerns the orientation of the drawings on the paper. In copying drawings of a cube and of a house, certain right hemisphere cases oriented their drawings diagonally on the paper. This is obvious in some of the productions of Cases 25, 30 and 37, and questionably apparent in Cases 19 and 42. In Case 37 the tendency is apparent in all three of the available drawings. The only left-sided case in whom this tendency is even questionably apparent is Case 11.

It is of some interest that, although this tendency can be seen in drawings both of a house and of a cube, it is not obtrusive in drawings of a bicycle (not shown here). The tendency is perhaps encouraged by the diagonal lines which are conventionally necessary to represent a 3-dimensional object on a 2-dimensional surface: that is to say that the orientation of particular lines may determine the orientation of the drawing as a whole. This finding is related to Hécaen, Ajuriaguerra and Massonnet's suggestion that right hemisphere cases find special difficulty in representing perspective.

Broadly similar spatial confusion may be seen in the intimate structure of the drawings of both groups of cases. The simplest example is perhaps in the copy of a house by Case 12

Left hemisphere cases   Right hemisphere cases.

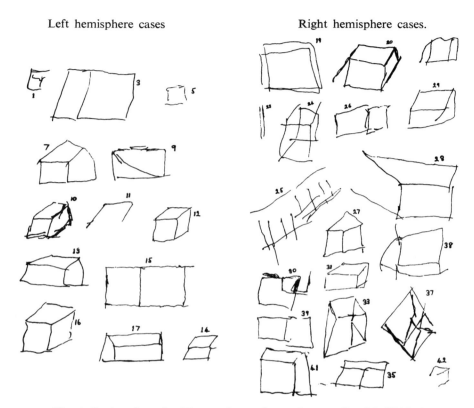

Fig. 4. Copies of a cube. The numbers refer to the cases listed in Table 3.

and the spontaneous drawing of a house by Case 42. In both of these drawings the chimney has been drawn at right angles to the diagonal line representing the top of the roof. An inappropriate "frame of reference" has evidently been used for the perpendicular orientation of the chimney. It would appear, however, that confusion of this type affecting the orientation of the *drawing as a whole* occurs more frequently in right hemisphere cases than in left hemisphere cases.

"closing-in" effect

Ideomotor or ideational apraxia occurred in 6 of our 18 constructional apraxia cases with left-sided lesions. All of these 6 showed in their constructional performances a marked tendency either to superimpose the constructed copy upon the model or to overlap the model with the copy ["closing-in" effect of Mayer-Gross, (21)]. These were the only left-sided cases to show the "closing-in" effect. Two of the 24 right-sided cases also showed the "closing-in" effect and both of these exhibited apraxia for dressing. Five other right-sided cases exhibited apraxia for dressing without a "closing-in" effect. It can thus be said that all of our patients with a "closing-in" effect in their constructional performances also exhibited some other kind of apraxia and that, in the case of left-sided lesions, "closing-in" was always accompanied by frank apraxia for other than constructional performances. We do not wish to claim special significance for this finding but feel that it should be put on record.

unilateral neglect

Neglect of the left side was an identifiable factor in the impaired constructional performances of 7 of the right-sided cases. In the left-sided cases neglect of the right side could be identified in the drawings of 2 cases. This observation is based on all available drawings executed by our two groups of patients, including drawings of bicycles, drawings of a man and simple geometrical forms, as well as the drawings shown in Figs. 1 to 4. Unilateral neglect was also apparent in the behaviour (reading, counting, ignoring the left side of the body) of 7 right-sided cases who did not show this deficit in their constructional performances. Comparable behavioural evidence was not observed in any left-sided cases. Fourteen of the 24 right-sided cases therefore exhibited some kind of neglect for the left side of space, as against 2 of the 18 left-sided cases who exhibited some kind of neglect for the right side of space.

III. discussion

It is clear from these results that the term "constructional apraxia" may be applied descriptively to disabilities occurring in association with unilateral lesions of either cerebral hemisphere. Our results suggest that this type of disability occurs twice as frequently with right-sided as with left-sided lesions and that the defect as more severe in the former group. This is in accordance with Critchley's suggestion (3) that constructional apraxia is more

readily demonstrated in cases of disease of the subordinate hemisphere.

We must now consider possible explanations of the higher incidence and greater severity of constructional apraxia in right-sided cases.

One possibility is that in left hemisphere cases constructional apraxia may be masked by other defects such as aphasia and paresis of the dominant hand. This must be considered carefully since the present study was carried out *post hoc* and was restricted to patients already diagnosed as exhibiting constructional apraxia. Ten of our 18 left-sided cases were dysphasic and the dysphasia included a comprehension defect in all 10 cases. It is thus clear that dysphasia does not preclude the identification of a constructional apraxia. However, the possibility remains that, in some cases, constructional apraxia was masked by an unusually severe dysphasia and so did not appear in our records. Nevertheless, although it is conceivable that the incidence of constructional apraxia might be artificially lowered in left-sided cases, it would be difficult to account in this way for the reduced severity of constructional apraxia in this group. On the contrary, if dysphasia tends to mask the constructional disability, the milder cases in particular would tend to be obscured, thus artificially increasing the average severity of constructional apraxia in left-sided cases.

A similar argument applies to the possibility that constructional apraxia was masked by paresis of the preferred hand in some cases of left hemisphere lesion. Although the incidence could be reduced if the disability of milder cases were mistakenly attributed to the paresis, this should not reduce the apparent severity of the defect. Indeed the selective factor might be expected to increase the apparent severity of the constructional disability. Moreover, all cases that had incapacitating paresis of the preferred hand were also tested with the non-preferred hand.

A further possible selective factor is the failure to test for constructional apraxia in patients with paresis of the preferred hand or with aphasia. Since all patients entered on the punch cards were examined by one of the authors, it can be said with some confidence that this is an unlikely explanation. However, in order to exclude this possibility as objectively as possible, the following control procedure was carried out. All cards punched for both aphasia and hemiplegia but not punched for constructional apraxia were selected. There were 20 such cards. Reference was then made to the detailed case notes of these 20 patients. It was found that 12 of these had been carefully examined for constructional apraxia with negative results. All 8 that had not been so examined had gross clouding of consciousness and the aphasia had been either severe and obvious or else (more frequently) inferred from the history given by relatives. Against this indirect evidence suggesting that the differences between our left- and right-sided cases are not adequately accounted for by artifacts of case selection, must be set the observation that the incidence of paresis of the upper limb is higher in our right hemisphere cases (14 out of 24) than in our left hemisphere cases (5 out of 18). Accordingly, our conclusions as to the relative incidence of constructional apraxia with left- and right-sided lesions are provisional only. The difference in the severity of the disability is, however, less equivocal.

Denny-Brown, Meyer and Horenstein (6) have suggested that disabilities of the type reported here may be attributed to "amorphosynthesis." We do not propose to discuss these authors' distinction between amorphosynthesis and agnosic defects but we must point out that their interpretation can be applied to our results only if it is assumed that the differences

between our two groups are attributable either to selective factors or to the presence of agnosia plus amorphosynthesis in left-sided cases but amorphosynthesis only in right-sided cases. The first of these alternatives has already been discussed and the second is improbable in view of the greater severity of the disability in right-sided cases.

Two further possibilities remain to be considered. Constructional apraxia may result from impairment of a function which is bilaterally although unequally represented. Alternatively, constructional apraxia may be a disturbance which is functionally different according to the hemisphere involved.

It is clear that some of our findings are quite consistent with the first of these two alternatives. Constructional apraxia occurs more frequently and with greater severity in right-sided cases and we also have evidence suggesting that functions impaired in constructional apraxia are more focally organized within the right hemisphere than within the left. This is what would be expected if the right hemisphere were dominant for the functions in question.

Nevertheless, despite this evidence, such an interpretation presents difficulties. Other focal "intellectual" signs of cerebral dysfunction are generally regarded as having strictly unilateral significance, except in rare and anomalous cases. Thus aphasia, ideomotor apraxia, finger agnosia, object agnosia, acalculia and left-right disorientation are rarely attributed to a right hemisphere lesion, and it is by virtue of this fact that the right hemisphere in right-handed people has come to be designated the minor or subordinate hemisphere. It has been argued that language may be represented bilaterally in left-handed people (2, 28, 12) but this is by no means generally accepted (7, 8) and also those who claim bilateral representation of language in left-handed people also suggest that dysphasia in these cases is mild and transient. Bilateral focal but unequal representation of a special group of perceptuomotor skills would therefore be a little surprising, although not theoretically unacceptable.

The hypothesis that constructional apraxia may result from a disturbance of one of two different functions, and that these two functions are represented respectively in the right and left hemisphere demands for its support evidence of differences between the two syndromes other than differences in severity and frequency. The differences which we have been able to show are comparatively subtle. They have been educed from the groups as a whole and, although certain types of performance appear more typical of right hemisphere dysfunction than left, it would not usually be possible to infer the side of the responsible lesion from constructional performance alone. Two of the differences described above could not readily be equated with differences in severity. Thus the observation that the presentation of a model to copy facilitates the drawings of left hemisphere cases but not those of right hemisphere cases suggests that different or additional functions are impaired in the right hemisphere group. Similarly, an increase in the severity of the constructional disability has different consequences in the two groups. In the left hemisphere group the more impaired patients tend in their copies of drawings towards gross simplification of outline, whereas in the right hemisphere group the more impaired patients tend towards erroneous elaboration of detail. This observation is frankly inconsistent with the hypothesis of a difference in severity alone.

Both of these findings are consistent with the hypothesis that, in general, constructional apraxia associated with right hemisphere lesions involves greater impairment of perceptual functions than is the case in the left hemisphere syndrome. A corollary hypothesis is that, when left hemisphere cases show severe constructional apraxia, this results from comparatively greater impairment of executive functions than is usual in right hemisphere cases. Among our patients, the only 3 left-sided cases to fail on the very simplest drawing tests also had a clinically obvious apraxia which extended beyond constructional performances, and in these cases it may be that the constructional defect was secondary to the general apraxia. It seems right to enquire therefore whether constructional disability resulting from a left hemisphere lesion may not frequently be a minor or special form of general apraxia. Unfortunately we lack information as to how frequently ideomotor apraxia as described by Liepmann is unaccompanied by constructional disability in cases of unilateral left hemisphere lesions. If this were never or hardly ever the case, then the hypothesis would receive further support. We may add that, if this evidence were forthcoming, it would be a reasonable presumption that, at least in some cases, a lesion might just fail to produce an ideomotor apraxia but might nevertheless be sufficient to produce impairment at a higher level of intellectual organisation, i.e. on constructional tasks. Analogous "subclinical" disability may frequently be observed in the sphere of language. A progressive cerebral lesion may at first produce definite impairment in language-intelligence tests and only at a later stage result in a dysphasia as ordinarily understood (18).

These considerations, however, await further enquiry and it is important not to oversimplify the problem. Thus it would be naïve to suppose that perceptual processes are in no respect impaired in the constructional apraxia of left hemisphere origin since, for example, it may reasonably be argued that ideomotor apraxia in some sense involves faulty perception. Nor can one afford to ignore the fairly frequent association of left hemisphere constructional apraxia with left-right disorientation, finger-agnosia or disturbance of topo-graphical orientation. We believe cognitive impairment contributing to constructional apraxia to be greater in the right hemisphere syndrome, but we would not attribute an exclusive role to the right hemisphere in this regard. The most that we wish to claim for this study is that it is based on all appropriate cases admitted to a particular neurosurgical unit over a period of eight years, and that the results strongly suggest that the right cerebral hemisphere has a special, non-subordinate role in the cognitive functions necessary for normal constructional performance.

summary

1. Studies of constructional apraxia are briefly reviewed in relation to the respective roles of the two cerebral hemispheres.

2. On the basis of records kept in a particular neurosurgical unit over a period of eight years, an analysis is presented of the incidence, severity and nature of constructional apraxia resulting from unilateral cerebral lesions.

It is observed that the disability is more frequent and more severe in right hemisphere cases and that the localization of responsible lesions tends to be more restricted in right hemisphere cases. Qualitative differences between the constructional performances of left and right hemisphere cases are analysed and discussed.

3. It is concluded: (a) that the differences between the two groups in the severity and frequency of the disability cannot be accounted for by the masking effect of paresis and dysphasia or by unilateral imperception; (b) that the qualitative differences observed cannot be attributed to differences in severity alone; (c) that the right cerebral hemisphere in right-handed people has a special non-sub-ordinate role in the cognitive functions involved in normal constructional performance.

acknowledgment

Malcolm Piercy was supported in this work by a grant from the Centre National de la Recherche Scientifique, by arrangement with the Medical Research Council. This assistance is gratefully acknowledged.

references

1. Bay, E. (1950) "Agnosie und Funktions-wandel: Eine hirnpathologische Studie." Berlin.
2. Chesher, E. C. (1936) *Bull. Neurol. Inst. N.Y.*, **4**, 556.
3. Critchley, M. (1953) "The Parietal Lobes." London.
4. Dide, M. (1938) *Encéphale*, **33**, (ii), 276.
5. Duensing, F. (1953) *Dtsch. Z. Nerven-heilk*, **170**, 72.
6. Denny-Brown, D., Meyer, J., and Horenstein, S. (1952) *Brain*, **75**, 433.
7. Ettlinger, G., Jackson, C. V., and Zangwill, O. L. (1955) *J. Neurol. Neurosurg. Psychiat.*, **18**, 214.
8. ———, ———, ——— (1956) *Brain*, **79**, 569.
9. ———, Warrington, E., and Zangwill, O. L. (1957) *Brain*, **80**, 335.
10. Head, H. (1926) "Aphasia and Kindred Disorders of Speech." Cambridge.
11. Hécaen, H., de Ajuriaguerra, J., and Massonnet, J. (1951) *Encéphale*, **40**, 122.
12. ———, and Piercy, M. (1956) *J. Neurol. Neurosurg. Psychiat.*, **19**, 194.
13. Hoff, H. (1953) *Proc. Vth Int. Neurol. Congr.*, **1**, 195.
14. Kleist, K. (1934) Gehirnpathologie vornehmlich auf Grund der Kriegserfahrungen. Handbuch der ärztlichen Erfahrungen im Weltkriege, 4, 2. 343. Leipzig.
15. Krapf, E., and Courtis, B. (1937) *Rev. neurol. B. Aires*, **1**, 280.

16. Krol, M. B., and Stolbun, D. (1933) *Z. ges. Neurol. Psychiat.*, **148**, 142.

17. Lange, J. (1936) *In Handbuch der Neurologie* edited by O. Bumke and O. Foerster, **6**, 807.

18. Mcfie, J., and Piercy, M. F. (1952) *Brain*, **75**, 292.

19. ——, ——, and Zangwill, O. L. (1950) *Brain*, **73**, 167.

20. Marie, P., Bouttier, H., and Bailey, P. (1922) *Rev. Neurol.*, **29**, 505.

21. Mayer-Gross, W. (1935) *Proc. R. Soc. Med.*, **28**, 1203.

22. Paterson, A., and Zangwill, O. L. (1944) *Brain*, **67**, 331.

23. ——, —— (1945) *Brain*, **68**, 188.

24. Poetzl, O. (1928) "Die Aphasielehre vom Standpunkte der klinischen Psychiatrie. I. Die optisch-agnostischen Störungen." Leipzig.

25. Poppelreuter, W. (1917) "Die psychischen Schädigungen durch Kopfschuss im Kriege 1914–1917. IV: Die optische Apraxie." Leipzig.

26. Scheller, H., and Seidemann, H. (1931) *Mschr. Psychiat. Neurol.*, **81**, 97.

27. Strauss, H. (1924) *Mschr. Psychiat. Neurol.*, **56**, 65.

28. Subirana, A. (1952) *Schweiz. Arch. Neurol. Psychiat.*, **69**, 321.

31 visual-constructive disabilities and lesions of left cerebral hemisphere*

J. McFie and O. Ł. Zangwill

1. What differences are there between this study and the previous one by Piercy et al. in approach and conclusions? Were these experimenters aware of the other study?

2. Can the hypothesis about the differences between constructional apraxia and spatial agnosia be applied to Piercy's study?

3. Why is it so difficult to do this type of study?

* J. McFie and O. L. Zangwill, "Visual-Constructive Disabilities Associated with Lesions of the Left Cerebral Hemisphere," *Brain*, 83 (1960), 243–259. Reprinted with permission.

I. introduction

In a series of papers (24, 25, 23, 8) we have presented an analysis of the disabilities of construction associated with lesions of the right cerebral hemisphere. In brief, the syndrome described consists of disorganization of construction, drawing, etc., in a characteristic way; failure on tasks involving spatial analysis, frequent failure on tasks requiring an even simpler maintenance of orientation, e.g. counting scattered dots; and in many cases "apraxia for dressing" and topographical memory loss. We have also noted that this syndrome is characteristically associated with lesions of the parieto-occipito-temporal region of the right (minor) hemisphere. While many of the patients have also had visual field defects, neglect of the left half of the body, or vestibular disturbances of central type (cf. "Funktionswandel" of Bay (2); amorphosynthesis of Denny-Brown et al., (5); vestibular derangement of Hécaen et al., (10) we have argued that none of these is invariably related to the syndrome, which appears rather to demand an appreciable element of conceptual spatial loss. As this is commonly manifested in performances under visual control, we have hitherto retained the term "visual-spatial agnosia" to describe the deficit. Essentially the same syndrome has been described under the term "apractognosia" by Hécaen et al. (12, 13) following excision of the supramarginal and angular gyri and the posterior portion of the superior temporal gyrus on the right.

At the same time, we have been aware that disabilities of construction, manipulation, drawing, etc., have commonly been held to be symptoms of parietal lobe dysfunction, without distinction as to the side affected. Thus in Critchley's (4) monumental survey of the parietal lobes, the table (p. 392) which summarizes the disabilities associated with *unilateral* (regardless of side) lesions includes "constructional apraxia (?)": the mark of interrogation is sustained by omission of the disorder from those associated with dominant hemisphere lesions (p. 394), while it reappears in association with minor hemisphere lesions (p. 396). In his description of constructional apraxia (Ch. VI) Critchley makes it clear that, since Kleist's first use of the term, there has been continued discussion concerning the precise nature of the disability, revolving chiefly round the question whether it was primarily an executive or a perceptual deficit. On the other hand, since Kleist's (15) description of constructional apraxia as "a disturbance which appears in formative activities (arranging, building, drawing) and in which the spatial part of the task is missed, although there is no apraxia of single movements," most authors have accepted a *spatial* derangement as an integral feature of the disability. Mayer-Gross (20), however, has doubted whether it plays a significant part: "in most cases, the patients are able to recognize or imagine direction, localization and extension in space: they have no disturbance in perception of visual, tactile or vestibular space." This is evidently a very dissimilar condition from the syndrome of visual-spatial agnosia, and suggests that constructional apraxia may have an altogether different basis. Mayer-Gross considered the disturbance to be fundamentally in "activity space" (Wirkraum), adding that "one has

however to realize that it implies a specific visual factor inseparable . . . from the motor element."

The significance of the site of the lesion responsible for the disability was not generally considered relevant to the discussion: many of the cases described (17, 18, 19) were evidently suffering from a generalized dementia, and, in the few post-mortem examinations reported, lesions were generally bilateral. Nevertheless, the common association of the disability with acalculia, alexia, finger agnosia and receptive language disorders resulted in agreement that it frequently occurred with left parietal lesions.

There have been few comparisons between the disabilities resulting from comparable lesions of left and right hemispheres. Hécaen *et al.* (11) have reported a series of 50 cases of parietal lobe tumours, 22 of the left side and 28 of the right. They noted with surprise that while 12 of the cases with right-sided lesions showed visual-constructive disabilities (described by them as "constructional apraxia"), only 3 of the left-sided group did so. Although they found lasting disturbances of body-scheme and "apraxia for dressing" only in association with right-sided lesions, they felt they were not in a position to distinguish between the types of constructional disability arising from lesions on different sides. In a series of 17 posterior cerebral excisions, Hécaen *et al.* (12) found that the 2 cases of left-sided excision, though both in left handers, showed no disturbance of spatial perception. In a further analysis of the disabilities of these patients, Hécaen *et al.* (13) observed that "there is a strange difference, which is not easily understood, between the functions of the two parietal lobes. . . . Ideational and ideomotor apraxias form part of the clinical picture due to left-sided lesions. The apraxia for dressing is met with only in right-sided lesions. The visuo-constructive disabilities are integral parts of both the right and the left syndrome, and the exact difference between these two types of constructional apraxia is not yet clearly established." Arseni *et al.* (1) have reported a purely statistical survey of 32 patients with parietal tumours: excluding the left handers, of 9 with left-sided lesions 6 showed "constructional apraxia," of whom 4 showed "spatial agnosia," one showed "spatial disorientation" and one loss of topographical memory, but none showed "apraxia for dressing." Of the 20 with right-sided lesions, all showed "constructional apraxia," 18 showed "spatial agnosia," 2 showed "spatial disorientation," 12 "loss of topographical memory," and 15 "apraxia for dressing." The authors do not make any statements of the criteria used to establish these categories, but the differences in grouping of the signs are of interest. Reitan (26), reviewing the results of psychological testing of some 2,000 neurological patients, states that "the frequency of constructional dyspraxia (as shown in difficulty in copying accurately common spatial configuration) is much greater in patients with damage of the right cerebral hemisphere than in patients with damage of the left cerebral hemisphere."

The present communication describes a series of patients with lesions in the left cerebral hemisphere, in whom constructional disability was a predominant psychological manifestation. All of the patients were right-handed.

II. cases

Case 1 (N.H. 1874). A commercial artist, aged 57, was admitted complaining of speech difficulty, numbness of the right hand, and general mental deterioration.

For about a year before admission his wife had noticed a slight falling-off in his powers of concentration and retention, reaching proportions which were quite unusual for him. Three months ago, he was for a few moments unable to speak; a month later he had the first of a number of attacks of burning pain in the right hand, following which it had remained numb and slightly clumsy. At the same time a persistent language defect became evident, and his spelling and mental arithmetic also began to deteriorate. He had also some difficulty in dressing himself correctly; and occasionally a generalized morning headache.

On neurological examination his fields of vision were full, and visual acuity 6/12 on the right and 6/9 on the left (corrected). There was slight marginal blurring of the optic discs. There was hypalgesia on the right side of the face, and some weakness on voluntary movement. There was slight increase in tone and tendon reflexes in the right limbs, and absence of abdominal reflexes on this side, but both plantars were extensor. The whole right side of the body was hypæsthetic to touch, and in the right hand and foot, vibration and position sense were diminished.

On psychological examination his premorbid intelligence was placed in the superior range (Terman-Merrill Vocabulary score: 35). He showed a mild, but clear-cut receptive dysphasia and slight difficulty in reading and writing. He was unable to sort on Weigl's test, and showed some impairment on Wechsler's Similarities test (score: 11).

Performance on *visual-constructive tasks* was considerably impaired. His score on Kohs' block designs (53) was below the level expected. His copying of geometrical figures was poor; and his freehand drawing was surprisingly poor, considering his profession as an artist. There was no evidence of topographical disability, and his drawing of a map of England, though over-simplified, was correct in general proportion.

There was no evidence of apraxia of a "lower" type; but he showed certain perceptual disabilities. Thus, his Matrices score was only 44 (average adult), and he found the problems very difficult, taking one hour ten minutes over the test. He had difficulty in mentally reversing the position of clock hands; counted hours anti-clockwise (e.g. from 9 to 5 as five hours); and had difficulty in distinguishing his own right and left.

He was exceedingly aware of his disabilities, and was prone to "catastrophic" reaction to failures on tests.

Air encephalography demonstrated the presence of a left parietal expanding lesion, and a right temporal decompression was made. The patient died a month later.

At post-mortem examination a cystic-glioma, measuring about 4 cm. in either direction, was found in the cortex of the left inferior parietal lobule (Fig. 1, Case 1).

Case 2 (N.H. 12055). A maintenance engineer, aged 56, was admitted with complaints of attacks of dizziness, with loss of consciousness, and episodes of mental confusion and speech disorder.

While at work two weeks before admission, he suddenly "came over dizzy," and found himself unable to understand speech or to express his own thoughts. Returning from his doctor's house, he felt uncertain as to his whereabouts; "everything looked strange and unfamiliar"; but he arrived home safely, and lost consciousness for about a quarter of an hour. These episodes of confusion had recurred; and with them he had noticed that in the right half of his fields of vision a rainbow of colours appeared, superimposed upon but not obscuring the objects seen. Between these episodes, he had still a slight difficulty in speaking, and occasional headaches, but otherwise no complaints.

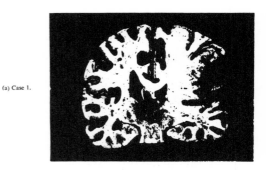

(a) Case 1.

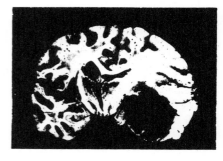

(b) Case 2.

Fig. 1. Photographs of sections of cerebral hemispheres.

On neurological examination he had a right upper quadrantic hemianopia, and an equivocal right plantar response, but otherwise no abnormality. V.A.R. 6/6: V.A.L. 6/9.

On psychological examination he showed a moderate degree of general impairment, from a previously bright normal level: his digit span was reduced to 5, he failed Weigl's sorting test, and he had some difficulty in interpreting complex pictures; arithmetical ability was not markedly impaired. His dysphasia was moderately severe: he was able to understand and carry on a normal conversation, but verbal learning, reading, and writing were very poor.

His disabilities were also marked on *visual-constructive tasks*. He was able to produce only four block designs within the prescribed time; and his freehand drawing was poor. In his drawing of the road junction at Shepherd's

Bush (near his home) he made a conspicuous error in representing the Uxbridge Road as actually running on to the Green; but the relationships of all the roads were correctly represented, as were the features in a plan of his ward, and even the indication of perspective in drawing a chair.

There was no evidence of dyspraxia, either in concrete actions or in pantomime, nor of dressing disability. He represented horizontal and vertical correctly, and made no errors in counting scattered objects or grouped cubes, nor in problems involving direction and points of the compass.

He was well aware of the main features of his impairment, and was able to judge whether or not his performance was correct.

Air encephalography showed a slight shift to the right of the interventricular septum, and compression of the left lateral ventricle; but a biopsy revealed no abnormality, and the patient was discharged.

He was readmitted, six months after his first admission, drowsy, double incontinent, aphasic, and with a right hemiplegia; and died a month later.

At post-mortem examination a glioma was found in the left temporal lobe, extending from near the temporal pole to within 5 cm. of the occipital pole (Fig. 1, Case 2).

Case 3 (N.H. 37018). A housewife, aged 47, admitted on account of attacks of vertigo, weakness of the right hand, and speech difficulty.

Three years before admission she had a severe attack of vertigo, diplopia and vomiting which lasted nearly all day. During the next year, she had a number of similar, though less severe, attacks, involved gross nystagmus to the right. Six weeks before admission, while shopping, her right hand became suddenly unable to hold the basket, and she became unable to speak. She returned home without difficulty, but had great trouble in getting the key into the lock, and in turning it. Later she had clonic spasms in the right arm, and lost consciousness for half an hour. She continued to have slight difficulty in expressing herself, and had frequent headaches.

On neurological examination she showed no reduction of visual acuity or field defect. The right corneal reflex was reduced, as was sensation over the arc of the third division of the fifth nerve. There was weakness of the right side of the face, and of the right limbs. Tendon reflexes on the right side were exaggerated, with brief ankle-clonus, and equivocal right plantar response. There was a marked degree of cortical sensory loss over the right side of the body.

On psychological examination her premorbid intelligence was placed in the bright normal range (Bellevue Vocabulary score: 30). Besides a moderate receptive dysphasia, dyslexia and dysgraphia, she showed evidence of a moderate degree of general intellectual impairment: digit span was reduced to 5; she was unable to do Weigl's sorting test; and her arithmetical ability was impaired, though she was not frankly dyscalculic.

On visual-constructive tasks her impairment was also marked. She was able to copy only the first of the block designs; she copied matchstick patterns poorly; and took more than the normal maximum time to assemble the Bellevue Manikin. Her freehand bicycle and copies of drawings were also of poor quality. On being required to indicate different sides of her body, she showed a moderate degree of right-left disorientation; but she was able to hold a stick accurately in horizontal and vertical positions. Her account of topography in the neighborhood of her home (Brighton) was accurate, although she made some "left-right" errors in assigning compass directions (e.g. said Black Rock was west of Palace Pier), though it was evident from her descriptions that she knew where these were.

On the *executive* side, she had some finger dyspraxia, but had no difficulty in demonstrating the use of objects, in fact or in pantomime. On the *perceptual* side, she showed no evidence of visual-spatial disability: she counted cubes and scattered objects correctly, and reproduced the chief spatial relationships in designs she was required to copy.

At operation a fairly well-demarcated gliomatous mass was found in the convexity of the left parietal cortex, stretching from the central sulcus about 5 cm. posteriorly, and measuring about 7 cm. from its upper to its lower borders. It was dissected out and found to merge with brain substance to a depth of about 5 cm.

Case 4 (N.H. 26057). A retired public assistance officer, aged 62, who complained of disturbance of vision and mental deterioration.

Six months previously he had first noticed difficulty in reading and writing, and he began to make errors in spelling: this progressed, so that he had to read word by word. At the same time calculation deteriorated, so that he became unable to do the simplest sums. On one occasion, about a month before admission, he was unable to say what he wanted to, "he talked scribble," as he put it; but generally had little trouble with speech. Recently he had found placing knives and forks on the table difficult; but had no difficulty in finding his way about or in getting dressed.

On neurological examination he showed a macula-splitting right homonymous hemianopia, but visual acuity was 6/9 in the remaining half-fields, and there was no papilloedema. Motor and sensory systems, and reflexes, showed no abnormality.

On psychological examination his vocabulary level (Wechsler-Bellevue score: 40) indicated a superior premorbid intelligence. He showed a mild nominal dysphasia, but his flow of speech, and his comprehension, were good. He showed also a mild alexia and agraphia of receptive type, and marked dyscalculia.

He showed marked impairment on *visual-constructive tasks*, particularly in freehand drawing. He was able to do only the first four block designs, and was quite unable to cut a star-shape out of a piece of paper. At the same time, he was able adequately to represent the plan of the ground floor of his house, and to hold a stick accurately in horizontal and vertical positions. He did not show any difficulty in right-left discrimination.

He showed evidence occasionally of a mild dyspraxia, having some difficulty in knotting his tie or dressing gown cord. On the perceptual side, he was able to count scattered objects, but failed to count piles of cubes correctly *largely on account of his dyscalculia:* he also showed some difficulty in interpreting pictures.

He was aware of the main features of his disability, and was able to judge the correctness or otherwise of his solutions.

Ventriculography demonstrated a shift to the right of the left lateral ventricle, while the left temporal horn showed a filling defect in its proximal portion: appearance of a space-occupying lesion in the left temporo-parietal region, which was also seen to be slightly calcified. Biopsy showed this to be a grade III astrocytoma, and the patient died three weeks later: post-mortem examination was not made.

Case 5 (N.H. 29536). A farm labourer, aged 47, was admitted complaining of severe frontal headaches for a month.

He admitted that his vision had deteriorated, and his wife observed that his memory had deteriorated over the past few months.

On neurological examination he showed a right homonymous hemianopia, with visual acuity 6/24 and 6/36 in the remaining left half-fields. There was bilateral papillœdema, with several small hæmorrhages on the right. There was some fine nystagmus on looking to the right, but no other defect of external ocular movements. The right corneal response was diminished, and on Weber's test the sound referred to the right ear. The right limbs showed slight spastic weakness, and reflexes on that side were brisker: there was unsustained ankle clonus on the left, sustained on the right. Pain and touch were apparently perceived equally on both sides, but there was suppression on the right to bilateral simultaneous stimulation.

On psychological examination he was inclined to be drowsy, and at times confused, but was able to respond to questions quite well. He showed no dysphasia, but was practically acalculic, alexic and agraphic. His vocabulary score (Bellevue scale: 20) placed his premorbid intelligence in the average normal range, but he failed Weigl's sorting test.

He showed also marked disabilities in the *visual-constructive* sphere. He could do only the first two block designs, and had difficulty in constructing a star out of match sticks. Freehand drawing was of very poor quality, but he was able to represent very well the road junction near his home, and to indicate the positions and directions of the half-dozen roads concerned. He showed right-left disorientation both on himself and on the examiner, and some finger agnosia: but he was able to represent horizontal and vertical co-ordinates adequately with a stick. He also did the Stanford-Binet paper cutting item very well.

On the *executive* side, he showed no disabil-

ity; on the *perceptual* side, he counted scattered objects and piles of cubes very well, but had considerable difficulty in interpreting pictures and scored only 15 on Raven's Matrices.

Biopsy in the left parieto-occipital region demonstrated the presence of a grade II oligodendroglioma. This responded to deep X-ray therapy, and the patient was well and working a year later.

Case 6 (N.H. 53466). A business manager, aged 50, complaining of attacks of giddiness, deteriorating vision, and memory impairment.

For two years he had had attacks of unsteadiness, particularly when standing, which lasted only a few moments and then passed off leaving a slight frontal headache. Gradually the headaches became more severe. About six months before admission he noticed "difficulty with eyesight": this proved to be essentially difficulty in reading and writing. For the same period, his memory for recent events had become worse, his ability to do mental arithmetic deteriorated, and he had occasional feelings of "clumsiness" in his right leg. He had not had any difficulty in dressing or performing other tasks, nor had he suffered any topographical disturbance. His wife stated that in conversation he tended to "say the last part of the sentence first."

Neurological examination revealed a right homonymous hemianopia, with visual acuity 6/36 corrected in the remaining half-field on the right: in the left eye there was a lens opacity, and objects could only be perceived at one foot. There was slight inco-ordination of rapid movements in the right limbs, and occasional inattention on the right to bilateral simultaneous stimuli, but otherwise no somatic disability.

Psychological testing placed his premorbid intelligence in the superior range (Bellevue vocabulary: 33). He was mildly dysphasic, but understood and responded adequately to questions; his verbal reasoning was moderately impaired (Bellevue similarities: 7) and his arithmetical ability was practically non-existent. He passed Weigl's sorting test, though with difficulty: digit span was 5.

He showed marked impairment on *visual-constructive tasks:* he was unable to copy any of the block designs from the cards, and only one from a model; he was unable to reproduce matchstick patterns from memory, and copied them poorly; and his drawing of a bicycle was over-simplified and fragmentary.

There was no evidence of dyspraxia, nor of finger agnosia: his right-left discrimination was occasionally at fault. There was a suggestion of neglect of his right hand, and of the right side of drawings and designs. Spatial perception, on the other hand, appeared to be unimpaired: he counted scattered dots correctly: he represented horizontal and vertical co-ordinates correctly; and the orientation of writing, and of the framework of his drawings, etc., was satisfactory.

At operation a large vascular meningioma was found on the left side, originating from the dura over the occipital lobe and extending forward through cerebral tissue into the left lateral ventricle, compressing the posterior part of the parietal lobe against the dura. It was removed and a course of irradiation given, following which his psychological disabilities had almost disappeared. Ten months after admission he returned to his administrative work.

Case 7 (N.H. 69228). A housewife, aged 59, with six months' history of difficulty in using her right hand, and deterioration of memory, concentration, reading and writing.

Eighteen months earlier she had two focal attacks involving the right hand: she did not lose consciousness but was amnesic for the episodes. She was admitted but investigations were not conclusive. Since then she became more easily fatigued, and during the last six months had frequently dropped things from her right hand, and would lean to the right when walking. Her reading, writing and memory deteriorated over this time.

On neurological examination vision was J.1 (corrected) in both eyes, with a right homonymous attention defect but no hemianopia. There was ataxia of movement in all limbs, but more so on the right side. Tendon reflexes were hyperactive on both sides, and abdominal reflexes absent on the right. Joint-position sense, two point discrimination and stereognosis were impaired on the right side, as well as attention to pin-prick.

Psychological examination placed her premorbid intelligence in the average normal range (Bellevue vocabulary: 20), with no evidence of verbal intellectual impairment (Similarities score: 11). Her arithmetic was moderately impaired (raw score: 4) and digit span only 5 forwards and 3 reversed. She was mildly dysphasic, making a number of paraphasic errors, but comprehension and expression were not significantly impaired: in reading and writing she made a number of errors even with easy words. She was able to explain a single complex picture (Terman-Merrill "Telegraph Boy") but was unable to deal with series (Picture Arrangement score: 4).

Visual-constructive tasks showed the most severe impairment: she was able to copy only the first block design, being unable to do the second from the card or from a model (the difficulty was always in placing the last, the top right hand, block); she could copy only the simplest drawings and matchstick patterns, and in the more complex ones showed gross over-simplification.

Otherwise she showed no executive disability, her right-left discrimination, on herself, was unsure, but otherwise she showed no evidence of spatial disability. The orientation of her writing and drawings was good; and on the Terman-Merrill cube counting test (M, X, 1) she made only two errors, both of which she corrected on recounting.

At operation a meningioma was found overlying the left parietal lobe, extending from the central sulcus to the posterior border of the angular gyrus. Following its removal there was a transient right hemiplegia, but she recovered from this and from her psychological disabilities.

Case 8 (N.H. 51896). A 37-year-old woman, an aircraft instrument inspector, complaining of seizures for five years.

A *grand mal* seizure occurred, without warning, while she was at work five years previously, and since then she had others at irregular intervals, approximately one a month. She also had minor attacks in which speech was arrested, the right hand moved involuntarily, and she might perform a few purposeless actions. On one occasion she experienced a distinct sensation of her surroundings being unreal and unfamiliar. Following these attacks she was confused for a few minutes, but gradually recovered her orientation.

She had never noticed any difficulty in her work, in finding her way about, or in dressing. As the seizures were increasing in frequency, she was admitted for investigation.

Neurological examination revealed no abnormality, apart from an equivocal right plantar response noted shortly after a minor seizure. Vision was 6/20 on the right and 6/12 on the left, with no field defect. Left carotid arteriography and air encephalography showed no evidence of any abnormality. EEG records showed evidence of a progressive

abnormality: the first, six months after her first seizure, was flat and featureless; the second, seven months before admission showed episodes of generalized abnormal activity with higher voltages on the left, and also isolated sharp waves suggesting a focus in the left frontal region; in the third, four months before admission, the record "again shows a fairly severe left-sided abnormality, which on this occasion is temporal rather than frontal"; while the fourth, made after admission, showed an increase in the generalized disturbance, again of greater amplitude in the left temporal region, together with occasional independent discharges of sharp waves in the left temporo-parietal and temporo-occipital regions. She was discharged to be followed in the outpatient department.

Psychological testing showed a considerable degree of deterioration, from a previously bright normal level. While pictorial and verbal test scores (Bellevue equivalent scores) ranged from 9 to 14, her score on Block Designs was 5 and on Arithmetic 3. She had a mild degree of nominal and receptive dysphasia, made a number of spelling errors when writing, and had difficulty in sorting on Weigl's test.

On *visual-constructive tasks* she showed the most striking impairment: she was able to make only the first two block designs, and on subsequent ones generally started off well but had great difficulty in placing the last one or two blocks correctly. She was unable to construct a 4-pointed star with matchsticks unless the model was left before her, and even then had difficulty placing the matches; and she was unable to construct a swastika with eight matches even with the model before her. Her drawing of a bicycle was simplified and inaccurate.

On the other hand, she passed the cube-counting test (using the card); she passed

Table 1. Associated Disabilities

Case No.	1	2	3	4	5	6	7	8
Visual field defect	—	+	—	+	+	+	—	—
Unilateral neglect	—	—	—	—	—	+	—	—
Counting scattered objects	NT	—	—	—	—	—	—	—
Dressing disability	+	—	—	—	—	—	—	—
Deformation of co-ordinates	NT	—	—	—	—	—	NT	NT
Right-left disorientation	+	—	+	—	+	+	+	—
Topographical disorientation	—	+	—	—	—	—	—	—
Cube counting*	NT	—	—	(+)	—	NT	—	—
Paper cutting†	NT	NT	—	—	—	NT	NT	—
Abstraction deficit‡	+	+	+	NT	+	—	NT	+
General impairment	+	++	+	++	++	+	+	+

* Terman-Merrill Form L, *IX*, 1.   +disability.
† Terman-Merrill Form M, *X*, 1.   —no disability.
‡ Weigl's sorting test.   NT not tested.

both parts of the paper-cutting test; she made no errors in identifying her own or the examiner's right and left; and described correctly a complex picture.

III. analysis of disabilities

Associated disabilities are considered under the same headings as in our earlier papers: they are summarized in Table 1.

Visual field defects. Four of the patients showed field defects, ranging from hemianopia and defective vision in one eye (Case 6) to quadrantic loss (Case 2): in the remaining 4 patients perimetry showed no restriction of the fields.

Unilateral neglect. In only 1 patient (Case 6) was there a suggestion of neglect of one side of space, and this was by no means marked: he tended not to use his right hand on tasks usually done with both hands, and he commenced writing and drawing on the left side of the paper, not making use of the right side.

Counting scattered objects. This was done accurately by all patients given the task.

Dressing disability. There was evidence of difficulty in dressing himself in only 1 patient (Case 1).

Deformation of co-ordinates. The 5 patients tested were all able to represent correctly the horizontal and vertical co-ordinates of space with a stick held in one hand, with the eyes open and closed (16).

Right-left disorientation. 5 of the 8 patients made errors in distinguishing the right and left sides of their own bodies: these errors also extended to sides of the examiner's body. The remaining 3 patients made no errors, on themselves or on the examiner.

Topographical disorientation. Only 1 patient (Case 2) gave a history of loss of topographical memory, although this was more episodic than the disability noted in right-sided cases. He also made a considerable error of orientation in drawing a map.

Cube counting. Of the 6 patients asked to count irregular piles of cubes, either drawn on a card or as solid models, only 1 (Case 4) made conspicuous errors, and this was largely on account of dyscalculic errors in adding columns of 2 and 3 cubes.

Paper cutting. All of the 4 patients tested passed at least one part of this test.

Non-verbal abstraction. On Weigl's sorting test, 5 of the 6 patients tested were unable to shift from one principle to another.

General impairment. As estimated by com-

Table 2. Comparison between Left- and Right-Sided Lesions

	Left		Right	
	No. examined	No. with disability	No. examined	No. with disability
Unilateral neglect	8	1	21	14
Dressing disability	8	1	15	10
Cube counting	6	(1)	7	6
Paper cutting	4	0	10	9
Topographical loss	8	1	18	9
Right-left discrimination	8	5	21	0
Weigl's sorting	6	5	16	1

parison of their present test scores with their vocabulary scores, or with the level expected from their occupations, all patients showed a significant degree of deterioration and in three (Cases 2, 4 and 5) this was considered to be to a marked degree.

Comparison between the disabilities found in these patients and the disabilities found in association with right-sided lesions (24, 25, 23, 8) shows a strikingly different distribution (Table 2). Of the cases with right-sided lesions, the majority showed unilateral neglect and dressing disability, and also failed tests which call for spatial analysis; nearly half had trouble with topographical orientation; but none showed right-left disorientation on their own bodies, and only one was unable to sort both ways on Weigl's test. Examination of the

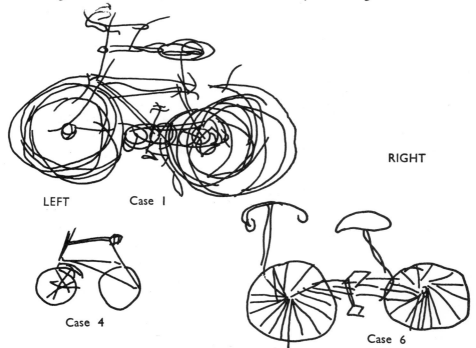

LEFT   Case I

Case 4

RIGHT

Case 6

Fig. 2. Drawings of a bicycle. Cases with right-sided lesions from McFie *et al.* (23).

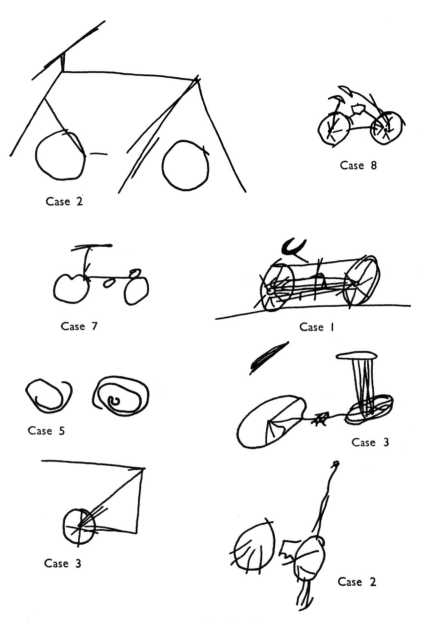

Case 2

Case 8

Case 7

Case 1

Case 5

Case 3

Case 3

Case 2

Fig. 2. (*Continued.*)

reports shows that general intellectual impairment in these cases was on the whole absent or slight. In the patients with left-sided lesions, on the other hand, few show unilateral neglect, dressing disability, failure on spatial tests or topographical disorientation, while the majority show right-left disorientation on themselves and are unable to do the abstraction test; and there is in all cases a moderate or marked degree of general impairment.

There are also clear differences between the performances of the two groups on drawing and construction tests. Fig. 2 shows the efforts of patients from each group at drawing a bicycle from memory. While the drawings of the right-sided group represent many of the parts of the machine, they tend to be placed inaccurately in spatial relationship to other parts, the ultimate dissolution being a kind of exploded diagram (cf. the "piecemeal approach" of Paterson and Zangwill, (24). The drawings of the left-sided group tend to preserve an accurate spatial relationship, but show a reduction in the parts represented, and ultimately a grossly over-simplified machine (an exception to this is seen in the bicycle

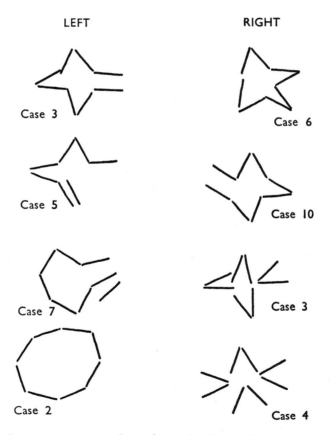

LEFT   RIGHT

Case 3

Case 5

Case 7

Case 2

Case 6

Case 10

Case 3

Case 4

Fig. 3. Attempts at constructing a four-pointed star with matchsticks. Cases with right-sided lesions from Ettlinger *et al.* (8).

drawn by Case 1: by occupation an artist, he was bewildered at his inability to make a correct drawing, and drew repeated lines in an effort to improve his production). In their behaviour too these patients show differences, the right-sided cases drawing fairly energetically and often adding more strokes in an effort to make the picture correct, while the left-sided cases draw slowly, putting the few parts in with apparent difficulty.

Similar differences are found in other constructional tasks. Reproducing a four-pointed star with matchsticks (Fig. 3) the right-sided patients move the matches about a great deal, but have difficulty in representing any coherent structure; while left-sided patients place the matches slowly and carefully, and often arrive at a simplified figure which is coherent but is no longer a star. In copying Kohs' block designs, the right-sided patients may fail to orient any of the blocks correctly, and may even lose the simple square outline of the design (an excellent example is reproduced by Critchley, 1953, p. 183, Fig. 91), while the left-sided patients may be able to reproduce the design all except for the last block, which seems to cause great difficulty, and at least they preserve the square outline of the group of blocks.

In conclusion, the analysis indicates that the visual-constructive disabilities found in our cases with left-sided lesions are qualitatively different from those found with right-sided lesions, and are associated with a different pattern of deficits. Evidence of disturbance of spatial perception is absent or slight, and associated disabilities dependent upon a large spatial element, such as dressing disability and topographical disorientation, are rare. On the other hand, evidence of intellectual impairment in other fields is more common, and the constructional disability appears to involve a difficulty in copying some other aspect of a design than its purely spatial relationships, as well as some difficulty in actual manipulation of the components.

IV. discussion

As in our series of patients with right-sided lesions, the occurrence of visual field defect is not invariable (it was found in only half the present group) and cannot be held responsible for the disturbances of construction. Unilateral neglect, whether of the patient's limbs or of extrapersonal space, was found in only one of the present series, in contrast with the majority of our right-sided cases: a similar distribution, in favour of cases with right-sided lesions, was found in the groups presented by Hécaen et al. (11) and by Arseni et al. (1). Even in the series with right-sided lesions, however, we argued (Ettlinger et al., 8) that our "findings disprove the contention that visual-constructive disorder is wholly referable to unilateral neglect—or to a defect of 'morphosynthesis' presumed to underlie it"; and in the present series, it is even more apparent that the constructional disability cannot be attributed to "amorphosynthesis" as described by Denny-Brown et al. (6, 5).

Apart from the different types of breakdown on constructional tasks, the outstanding difference between the groups with left- and right-sided lesions is in the associated manifestations of *conceptual spatial* impairment and of other forms of *intellectual* impairment. Failure on tests requiring a relatively small amount of manipulation, in contrast to considerable understanding of spatial properties, was almost invariable in the right-sided series, but rarely encountered in the left-sided group. The paper-cutting test requires a minimum amount of drawing ability, and was passed by all those tested in the present series, but was failed by all except one of those with right-sided lesions. The cube-counting test calls for no manipulation on the part of the patient: in the present series, one patient was unable to produce the correct answers, a failure attributable largely to acalculia, which made it impossible for him to add up the numbers of cubes correctly. The occurrence of topographical disorientation, in the sense of getting lost in a familiar environment, parallels the occurrence of other conceptual spatial deficits: it was noted in half the patients with right-sided lesions, but in only one of the left-sided group.

Dressing disability showed a similar distribution, being in evidence in half of the right-sided group, but in only one of the left-sided group. We should emphasize that by "dressing disability" we imply the same disturbance as that described in patients with right cerebral lesions by Brain (3) as "apraxia for dressing." These patients made mistakes of orientation in putting on their clothes, e.g. trying to put them on upside-down or back-to-front: this is not the same disability as that described as "apraxia for dressing" by Denny-Brown *et al.* (6, 5), which was essentially a failure to dress the neglected half of the body.

The one disability which might, *a priori*, be thought to be related to disintegration of spatial concepts, but does not in fact appear to be so, is the failure of right-left discrimination on the patient himself. This was found in none of the earlier series, but was present in 5 of the present group. Its occurrence with left parietal lesions is of course well known, and constitutes an integral feature of Gerstmann's syndrome; but it may be of some theoretical interest to note that this evident disorder of personal body-scheme is not related to disturbance of appreciation of extrapersonal space.

In fields of intellectual function other than those involving spatial concepts, the patients with left-sided lesions showed consistently greater deficits than those with right-sided lesions. Some degree of language impairment was invariable; dyscalculia was common; and failure on a nonverbal abstraction test was seen in all but one of the present group, as opposed to one only of the right-sided series. Two of the present group showed some dyspraxia of "lower" type; 2 were unable to interpret a complex picture ("Simultanagnosie"); and the 2 tested on Raven's Matrices did poorly. This constellation of deficits is not uncommon with left parietal lesions: in Schiller's (27) series of 46 cases with left hemisphere gunshot wounds, intellectual deficits were most frequently associated with post-central lesions; of 58 cases with localized lesions, McFie and Piercy (22) found a significant degree of impairment on a number of intellectual tests in the left parietal group; and the same authors (21) found a significantly greater incidence of failure on Weigl's sorting test with left-sided lesions, of which the majority were in the parietal lobe. In the series of parietal cases analysed by Arseni *et al.* (1) there are fewer patients with left-sided lesions: the authors state that a number of left-sided cases had to be excluded on account of massive aphasia or general impairment which made precise examination impossible. There is no suggestion, from any comparative series, that the degree of constructional disability parallels the extent of intellectual impairment.

The common feature, by intention, of our series with left- and with right-sided lesions is failure on visual-constructive tasks, but even in this narrow field differences in performances are evident (Figs. 2 and 3). The disintegration of constructions and drawings in cases of spatial agnosia has already been amply described: in contrast, the performances of the left-sided group show difficulty, restriction, and retardation of a kind which corresponds closely to the description of constructional apraxia (18, 19, 20). These disabilities parallel the disturbances in drawing noted by Head (9) in some of his aphasic patients: "capacity to draw from a simple model . . . may be profoundly reduced if as with semantic aphasia the main defects depend on inability to appreciate the general meaning of a situation" (p. 360); and drawing a ground plan, drawing spontaneously, and drawing from memory were also impaired in patients with semantic aphasia, all of whom had sustained parietal or parieto-occipital injuries. Three of the aphasics described by Weisenburg and McBride (28) manifested gross disturbances of constructive performance; and of one in particular they observed that the disability "does not involve the simple reproduction of spatial figures but the production of these, and in the more complex language processes where the difficulty is evidently similar in nature, it is clear that the essential disorder is not spatial but constructive." A distinction between types of breakdown in construction has been noted by Duensing (7), who did not ascribe the differences to side of lesion, but rather to consequences of bilateral lesions (spatial disintegration) or unilateral ("apraxic" type). Most authors, however (11) have not drawn attention to these differences in the nature of the constructional disability; although Critchley (4, p. 194) distinguishes between right and left parietal *agraphia*, the former being characterized by defects of arrangement, while the latter involves defects of language.

It has not been our purpose to attempt an analysis of constructional apraxia: the efficiency of different aspects of perception and execution was not examined in sufficient detail in our patients, nor were intellectual functions studied in sufficient detail to enable the relative influence of general impairment and of circumscribed disability to be assessed. Our final observation is on the subject of localization of the lesion, which in our patients has been consistently in the posterior parietal region. While the majority were tumours, in one patient (Case 8), in whom the syndrome was no less marked than in the others, the only abnormality found was a focal disturbance of electrical function. As we have noted, the majority of examples of constructional apraxia described have been in cases of generalized dementia, in whom the lesion must be presumed to be widespread: the disability has been ascribed to the left parietal region largely on account of its coexistence with other dominant parietal symptoms such as those of Gerstmann's syndrome. From the point of view of detailed analysis, however, such cases are unsatisfactory, since on the one hand patients with dementia often show bizarre features which may not be confirmed in a series, and on the other, the extent of impairment due to degeneration of other parts of the cerebrum cannot be assessed. Confirmation of differences between left- and right-sided lesions, and fuller analysis of the nature of constructional apraxia, will therefore depend upon studies of patients with localized lesions, on the one hand (cf. Hécaen and Piercy) of unselected cases showing the disability, and on the other of cases selected to emphasize the common features of the syndrome.

v. summary

A group of 8 patients is described in whom a lesion in the left hemisphere was accompanied by a prominent degree of visual-constructive impairment. In contrast to previously described groups with right-sided lesions, the disability in this group was rarely associated with unilateral neglect, apraxia for dressing, or failure on tests involving spatial analysis, including topographical memory; but was frequently associated with right-left disorientation and general intellectual impairment, including failure on a sorting test, with which the groups with right-sided lesions had little difficulty. There are also qualitative differences in the nature of the visual-constructive breakdown between the groups with left-sided and right-sided lesions, the former showing more difficulty in manipulation and restriction of response.

It is suggested that the disability shown by the present group of patients corresponds to the classical description of *constructional apraxia*, and is essentially different from the disability associated with *spatial agnosia* found with right-sided lesions.

It is noted that the lesion in all the cases was in the posterior parietal region, and it is suggested that fuller analysis of the disability will depend upon examination of series with adequately localized lesions.

acknowledgment

We are grateful to members of the staff of the National Hospital for referring patients to us for examination, and for allowing us to make use of their findings in this paper. We are particularly grateful to Dr. Eliot Slater for his encouragement and support, and to Dr. George Ettlinger for his assistance and advice.

references

1. Arseni, C., Voinesco, I., and Goldenberg, M. (1958) *Rev. neurol.*, **99**, 623.
2. Bay, E. (1954) *Dtsch. Z. Nervenheilk.*, **171**, 454.
3. Brain, W. R. (1941) *Brain*, **64**, 244.
4. Critchley, M. (1953) "The Parietal Lobes." London.
5. Denny-Brown, D., and Banker, B. Q. (1954) *Arch. Neurol. Psychiat., Chicago*, **71**, 302.
6. ———, Meyer, J. S., and Horenstein, S. (1952) *Brain*, **75**, 433.
7. Duensing, F. (1953) *Dtsch. Z. Nervenheilk.*, **170**, 72.
8. Ettlinger, G., Warrington, E., and Zangwill, O. L. (1957) *Brain*, **80**, 335.
9. Head, H. (1926) "Aphasia and Kindred Disorders of Speech." Cambridge.
10. Hécaen, H., de Ajuriaguerra, J., and Massonnet, J. (1951) *L'Encéphale*, **40**, 122.
11. ———, David, M., van Reeth, P., and Clément, J. (1953) *Wien. Z. Nervenheilk.*, **8**, 1.
12. ———, Penfield, W., Bertrand, C., and Malmo, R. (1954) *Proc. V. int. Congr. Neurol.*, **3**, 335.
13. ———, ———, ———, ——— (1956) *Arch. Neurol. Psychiat., Chicago*, **75**, 400.
14. ———, and Piercy, M. F. (In press.)
15. Kleist, K. (1954) "Kriegsverletzungen des Gehirns." *In* "Handbuch der ärztlichen Erfahrungen im Weltkriege 1914–1918" edited by O. von Schjerning. Leipzig. Vol. 4, 343.
16. Lenz, H. (1944) *Dtsch. Z. Nervenheilk.*, **157**, 22.
17. Lhermitte, J., and Trelles, J. O. (1933) *L'Encéphale*, **28**, 413.
18. Mayer-Gross, W. (1935) *Proc. R. Soc. Med.*, **28**, 1203.
19. ——— (1936a) *J. ment. Sci.*, **82**, 744.
20. ——— (1936b) *Proc. R. Soc. Med.*, **29**, 1396.
21. McFie, J., and Piercy, M. F. (1952a) *J. ment. Sci.*, **98**, 299.
22. ———, ——— (1952b) *Brain*, **75**, 292.
23. ———, ———, and Zangwill, O. L. (1950) *Brain*, **73**, 167.
24. Paterson, A., and Zangwill, O. L. (1944) *Brain*, **67**, 331.
25. ———, ——— (1945) *Brain*, **68**, 188.

26. Reitan, R. (1959) "The Effects of Brain Lesions . . . on Human Beings." Indiana University Medical Center.
27. Schiller, F. (1947) *J. Neurol. Neurosurg. Psychiat.*, **10**, 183.
28. Weisenburg, T. H., and McBride, K. E. (1935) "Aphasia." New York.

32 limbic-system lesions in the cat *

Robert A. McCleary

1. Do the findings in this study follow predictably from the knowledge of the limbic system obtained from MacLean (Reading 3) and Magoun (Reading 16)?
2. What innovations in procedure does McCleary introduce in this article?
3. What, briefly, are McCleary's findings?
4. What follow-up experiments suggest themselves?

Behavioral scientists, particularly in America, tend to regard the response as nothing but a convenient dependent variable. However, psychological and neural considerations alike suggest that the development, selection, and emission of responses are processes worth study in their own right (8, 10, 13). The present series of experiments is concerned with evaluating, at the behavioral level, the electrophysiological findings of Kaada (4) that clearly demonstrated contrasting response effects resulting from stimulation in two different parts of the limbic system. Along with many other observations in cat, monkey, and man, Kaada reported that stimulation in the area surrounding and below the genu of

* R. A. McCleary, "Response Specificity in the Behavioral Effects of Limbic System Lesions in the Cat," *J. comp. physiol. Psychol.*, 54 (1961), 605–613. Reprinted with permission.

the corpus callosum (so-called subcallosal cortex) produced motor *inhibitory* effects in the cat while, conversely, stimulation in the medial and anterior cingulate gyrus resulted in motor *facilitation*. The two areas in question are shown in Figure 1. These modulating effects on motor activity were apparent with cortically induced movements, peripherally induced reflexes, and with various ongoing autonomic responses. Limited portions of these findings had already been reported prior to Kaada's exhaustive study of these areas (5).

In view of the demonstrated role of limbic system structures in avoidance behavior, experimental interest in the behavioral effects of lesions in these two forebrain areas centered on some form of fear-motivated behavior. Accordingly, the following working hypothesis was developed:

Bilateral lesions in subcallosal cortex (motor inhibitory area) should disrupt normal performance under circumstances requiring a frightened animal to *inhibit* responding, as is most dramatically seen when an animal "freezes" or "plays possum." Conversely, bilateral lesions in the cingulate gyrus (motor

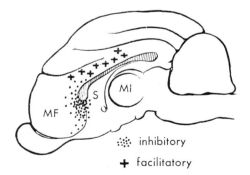

Fig. 1. Midsagittal drawing of the cat brain, showing two areas on the mesial cortex from which Kaada (4) obtained, respectively, inhibitory and facilitatory motor effects. (The hatched area is the corpus callosum. Abbreviations: *MF*, mesial frontal cortex; *S*, septal area; *MI*, *massa intermedia* of the thalamus.)

facilitatory area) should interfere with a frightened animal's performance when the situation requires the making of an *active* response, as when an animal takes flight in the face of a fear provoking stimulus.

These two categories of behavior can be economically described, using the nomenclature of Mowrer (11, p. 28), as examples of passive avoidance behavior and active avoidance behavior, respectively. It was further hypothesized that neither type of lesion should have a disruptive effect on the opposite type of response. In short, the hypothesis involved what has come to be known as a double dissociation.

With the exception of three animals with subcallosal lesions, all experimental animals contribute to the behavioral data in both sections of the present work. For ease of cross-checking, all experimental and normal animals retain the same number designation wherever they appear in the present data.

general method

subjects

All the animals in both experiments were either young adult or full-grown adult male cats. For the 28 cats that compose the Ss for the total study, the body weight ranged from 6 to 9½ lb. All animals were maintained in separate living cages and fed on commercial cat food.

procedure

Surgery. The first three subcallosal lesions (S1, S2, and S3) were made stereotaxically with multiple, bilateral electrode placements. Electrocoagulation was accomplished with direct current. Bilateral placements (2 mm. either side of the midline) were made every 2

mm. between +15 and +23, and coagulation was attempted at each of these settings from a depth of 15 to 19 mm. beneath the surface of the cortex. Aside from these three cases, the remaining five subcallosal lesions and eight cingulate lesions were done by open surgery.[1]

The general surgical procedure was the same for both types of experimental lesion. Under pentobarbital anesthesia (45 mg/kg) and following the administration of a parenteral coagulant (Koagamin) and penicillin, a large unilateral opening was made in the dorsolateral aspect of the skull. The defect extended from the posterior limit of the frontal sinuses back to the cerebellar tentorium and extended several millimeters beyond the midline to permit visualization of the longitudinal sinus. A dural flap was turned back and the exposed hemisphere gently retracted. In the case of the cingulate lesion, the dorsal surface of the callosum was first cleanly exposed and then portions of the cingulate gyrus removed bilaterally by suction. For the subcallosal lesions it was necessary to further retract the hemisphere and visualize the dorsal aspect of the genu of the corpus callosum. The suction pipette was then inserted ventral of the genu and cortex aspirated bilaterally without complete visual monitoring. In some instances it was necessary to remove the posterior portion of one frontal sinus in order to get satisfactory exposure of the genu. The muscle and skin layers were closed in the customary manner and the animal was kept on parenteral penicillin for three days post-operatively.

Histology. Upon completion of behavioral

[1] The author is indebted to B. R. Kaada (University of Oslo) for his help in making the stereotaxic lesions in S1, S2, and S3. Thanks are also due R. Y. Moore (University of Chicago) for demonstrating the general surgical approach used in the open surgery in the present study.

testing, the experimental animals were sacrificed and their brains placed in formalin. When hardened, the brains of the cingulate group were halved at the midline through the use of a thread loop that was easily centered by using the longitudinal fissure as a guide. This permitted the cingulate lesions to be promptly examined, grossly, with binocular dissecting glasses. With the exception of the last three cingulate Ss (mC6, mC7, and mC8), the brains were then embedded in paraffin and serially sectioned at 20μ. Every twentieth section was mounted and stained with thionin to permit microscopic examination of the extent of the lesion. All brains from the subcallosal group were embedded intact, in the customary manner, and treated histologically as described above.

experiment 1: passive avoidance behavior

method

Apparatus. The apparatus for the passive avoidance test consisted of a specialized feeding box, measuring 3 ft. by 2½ ft. by 2 ft. A hinged door on the front allowed the cat to be introduced into the box and also contained a one-way viewing mirror. The interior of the box was partitioned into a larger "waiting room" and a smaller feeding cubicle. These two compartments were separated by a sliding door that could be lifted manually by E from outside the apparatus. The feeding cubicle (10 in. by 8 in. and 10 in. high) was designed to permit only the front half of the Ss to be introduced as they ate from a small metal food trough attached at the rear of the cubicle. The metal floor of this feeding area was covered with a porous cloth that could be dampened to assure adequate electrical contact of the Ss' front feet as they were eating. The metal floor

and the metal food trough were separated by an air gap in the floor of the cubicle. These two metal components were connected to the two poles of a 20-v., 3-ma. ac transformer that delivered a shock across the trough and floor when E depressed a telegraph key. In the rear wall of the feeding cubicle, a second, smaller sliding door was located through which E could place food into the feeding trough between trials.

Behavioral procedure. Feeding experience was started from 4 to 10 days postoperatively. The procedure consisted of training the animals to eat exclusively in the test apparatus. The Ss were eventually shocked while they ate, and E observed how long it took for them to return to feeding in the absence of any other source of food. In the interests of quantification, however, the following regimentation was imposed on the Ss: Only one small serving (approximately a heaping tablespoon) of commercial cat food was placed in the trough at any one time. To assure electrical contact of the mouth parts, the food was soaked with milk. The S was required to eat this serving and then back out of the cubicle, at which time the connecting door was shut. Following a 1-min. interval, the connecting door was again opened and S was allowed to eat another serving. One trial followed another in this way until S was satiated, at which time it was returned to its home cage, with only water available, until the following day. An animal was judged satiated when it did not approach the food for two successive 1-min. trials or when appreciable food was left in the trough for several successive trials. In general, the Ss ate one-half can of cat food during each day's series of trials. The approach latency (from the time the connecting door was opened until S contacted the food) was measured for each trial. After 5 to 8 days of such feeding experience (varying from S to S) the animals were anxious to get into the feeding box each day, were running with consistent short latencies, ate promptly, and exited promptly from the cubicle upon completion of eating. At this point an animal was judged ready for the shock procedure.

On "shock day," the first 4 feeding trials were the same as usual. On the fifth trial, however, electric shock was applied to the cat when its mouth was well immersed in the wet food mixture. After S had withdrawn from the cubicle, the door was shut in the usual manner. One-minute trials (i.e., a 1-min. opportunity to approach the food) were then alternated with 1-min. intertrial intervals until 15 trials were completed for the day. In the event that an S returned to the food within 5 trials after the first shock trial, it was given a second and final shock and the 15 test trials were counted as starting after the last shock. If an S did not return to the food during the first 5 trials following the initial shock, no further shock was given when it did eventually return to eat. At any rate, no more than two shocks were ever given to any S. All Ss were returned to the feeding box for 10 additional test trials on the following day, without any additional shock being employed. This completed the passive avoidance test. The experimental Ss that participated in both this testing procedure as well as the active avoidance test (Experiment 2) were always first exposed to the present experimental procedure.

results

Normal controls. The highly consistent behavior of normal animals in the passive avoidance test is shown in Figure 2. Following two shocks at the food trough, normal animals without exception refuse to approach the trough again in the 60 sec. permitted for each

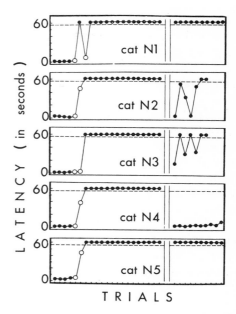

Fig. 2. Approach latencies of normal control cats in passive avoidance test. (Open circles represent trials on which a shock was received at the food trough. Since the animals were allowed only 60 sec. on each trial, points above the dashed line represent trials during which an S did not enter the feeding cubicle. The performance on shock day is shown to the left of the two, parallel vertical lines; to the right are shown the first 10 trials of the following day.)

of the remaining 15 trials of the day. On the following day, some return to eating and some do not. The two animals that did not eat at all on the second day (N1 and N5) were maintained on daily testing (without any other food available) until they first returned to the food trough. For these two animals, this occurred on Day 3 and 5, respectively. This simple behavioral situation seems to fulfill the experimental requirements of a passive avoidance test: Normal cats avoid further punishment by temporarily suppressing or inhibiting their usual approach response to the food.

One unexpected outcome in these results deserves brief additional mention. Except for one trial in the case of N1, no passive avoidance occurred until *two* shocks were received. It was as though the cats did not have the proper set to be able to profit completely from the first shock experience. This might be described as an example of two-trial learning.

The general behavior of the normal animals was also quite consistent during the avoidance trials. For the first few trials following the second shock, there were clear signs of disturbance: abortive approach responses, mewing or howling, and attempts to escape from the enclosure. By the end of the day's 15 trials, however, the animals would be sitting almost motionlessly as far from the food cubicle as possible—frequently not even looking when the connecting door was lifted to signal the start of a trial.

Effect of bilateral subcallosal lesions. In contrast with normal cats, the animals with bilateral lesions encroaching on subcallosal cortex (Kaada's inhibitory area) appeared almost totally incapable of inhibiting their approach response following the two shock-trials. The individual records for each of the eight animals in this subcallosal group are shown in Figure 3, together with a diagram of each animal's lesion. Although a more detailed discussion of the lesions will follow below, it should be pointed out promptly that no successful lesion avoided some degree of invasion of the anterior septal region. In fact, S8 (planned to be a septal lesion) has widespread bilateral damage of the septal area. As will be discussed later, there is probably little reason to distinguish between septal and subcallosal lesions as far as the present behavioral phenomenon is concerned. Finally, it should be noticed that in two cases (S2 and S6) an adequate bilateral lesion was not achieved. These two animals, however, afford useful control cases since their passive avoidance behavior was entirely normal.

Most of the *S*s in the subcallosal group showed a moderate amount of periodic hyperactivity while in their home cages. It was not persistent pacing nor obstinate progression but simply appeared to be increased reactivity to environmental change (in the sense that kittens are more hyperactive than cats). In two cases (S5 and S7), hyperactivity was not apparent. Presumably, such hyperactivity can be regarded as another manifestation of the loss of inhibitory cortex.

Effect of bilateral cingulate lesion. The effect of bilateral cingulate lesions on passive avoidance behavior can be easily described: there is no effect at all. The response of all eight of these experimental animals to being shocked in the feeding cubicle was indistinguishable from the performance of the normal animals already shown in Figure 2. It is clear that the loss of cingulate cortex in no way interferes with the animals' ability to inhibit a response in the interests of avoiding punishment.

Since cingulate lesions can be made with direct visual monitoring, there is very little accidental variation in the lesions of this experimental group. Therefore, only the two cingulate lesions having, respectively, the greatest and the least AP dimension are shown in Figure 4. As will be discussed in Experiment 2, this degree of variation in the length of the cingulate lesions was a planned experimental variable. For the present purposes, however, it is only necessary to note that none of the bilateral cingulate lesions had any influence on passive avoidance behavior.

experiment 2: active avoidance behavior

method

Apparatus. The behavioral apparatus was one form of the common double-grill shuttle

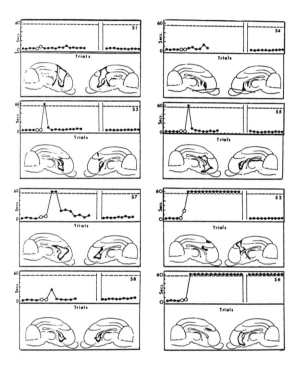

Fig. 3. Approach latencies for operated animals of the subcallosal group in the passive avoidance test. (Symbols have the same meaning as in Figure 2. The bilateral lesions for each S are shown as projections on the midsagittal surface of the cat brain. Although the anterior part of the callosum was variously involved in all the lesions, it is shown intact to serve as a landmark. Location of lesions should be compared with functional areas shown in Figure 1. In S4, the lower portion of the forebrain, as indicated, was not available for histological study.)

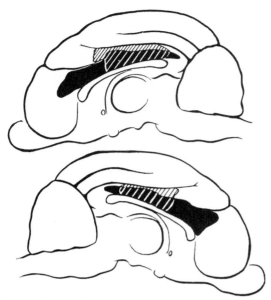

Fig. 4. The two lesions in the cingulate group having, respectively, the greatest and the least AP dimension. (The lesion shown in solid black is that of C3. The hatched area shows the lesion of mC7. The darker hatched area is common to both lesions.)

box. Two compartments (24 in. by 12 in. and 18 in. high), in which *E* could view *S* from outside, were separated by a sliding door which *E* could manually raise from his position in front of the avoidance box. The grill floors of the compartments were connected through a telegraph key to an 80-v., 3-ma. ac transformer. A switch allowed the grill floor of either compartment to be electrified selectively. An electric buzzer, mounted on top of the box immediately above the connecting door, served as the CS. Although no attempt was made to supply striking visual cues that would differentiate the two compartments, the construction and interior painting of the two compartments provided a number of discernible differences between the two sides of the shuttle box.

Procedure. A trial was started by activating the buzzer and simultaneously raising the connecting door. After 5 sec. of the CS, intermittent shock at a rate of about two per second was paired with the buzzer until *S* escaped through the connecting door to the non-electrified compartment. At this point, the buzzer was stopped and the door quietly dropped to the closed position. When good escape responses were occurring, the attempt was made to supply only as many intermittent shocks as were necessary to produce a clear escape response. Except for two days' sessions with one animal and one day with a second animal, all training sessions were handled by the same *E*. The *S*s were given 45 trials on the first training day and 40 trials on each day thereafter until a criterion of 9 out of 10 avoidance trials was reached. If this criterion was not reached in 300 trials, training was terminated. In two cases, described in the results section, training was terminated earlier than this because of persisting absence of the escape response.

results

All the results for Experiment 2 are presented in Figure 5. Trials to criterion in the double-grill shuttle box are shown individually for the normal animals as well as for animals in the two lesioned groups. Disregarding the one deviant case (N10), the results with the normal animals are within the limits to be expected with this type of behavioral test. No explanation can be offered for the prolonged acquisition period required by N10.

Effect of bilateral subcallosal lesion. It is clear from Figure 5 that animals subjected to bilateral subcallosal lesions are *at least* as efficient as normal animals in the acquisition of an active avoidance response. This, it will be recalled, was the only requirement of the hypothesis underlying the present series of

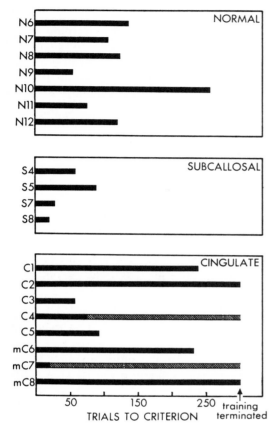

Fig. 5. Trials to criterion on the active avoidance test for normal controls and both types of operated animals. (See text for an explanation of the cross-hatched bars in the cases of C4 and mC7.)

experiments. Whether such animals are actually capable of *prompter* acquisition of an active avoidance response cannot be said with certainty from the present data although the present results strongly suggest that this is the case.

Only four of the eight subcallosal animals reported in Experiment 1 are included in Figure 5. This is because the first three experimental animals of the subcallosal group (S1, S2, and S3) had been sacrificed prior to the beginning of the work that contributed to

Experiment 2. Cat S6 is not included in Figure 5 because (as will be seen in Fig. 3) this animal did not have a successful bilateral subcallosal lesion.

Animals S4, S5, S7, and S8, which did contribute to the present data, all had lesions that involved the subcallosal area bilaterally and they had previously demonstrated a clear deficiency in *passive* avoidance behavior. Yet they are normal—or better than normal—in the acquisition of an *active* avoidance response.

Effect of bilateral cingulate lesion. Before discussing the over-all data for the cingulecto-mized animals in Figure 5, the behavior of animals C4 and mC7 must be described separately. Contrary to any of the other 17 cats observed in the shuttle box, these two animals (after 75 and 11 trials, respectively) refused to escape to the opposite compartment upon presentation of the intermittent shock. Neither animal had made a single avoidance response prior to this disruption in normal escape behavior. In a very obvious way, these two animals simply "froze" onto the electrified grill. From this position, they soon learned that turning their foot pads up beneath them, as they crouched, supplied some partial insulation. From then on, despite shaving their legs and increasing the shock, no further active escape responses were made. Although these animals frustrated the original experimental aims, their behavior made it dramatically clear that they would not learn an active avoidance response in 300 trials—or, for that matter, in 3,000 trials. The cross-hatched portion of the bars in Figure 5 are indicative of this interpretation.

Turning now to the over-all consideration of the cingulate group, first attention should be directed to Animals C1 through C5. Only three (C1, C2, and C4) of these five animals showed the hypothesized deficiency in the acquisition of an active avoidance response. Animals C3 and C5 were well within the normal range. When the histology on these animals was reviewed, one possible explanation presented itself: The lesions for the two negative cases extended somewhat more anteriorly than in the remaining animals (e.g., see the lesion for C3 in Fig. 4). It was felt possible that the forward extension of such lesions, through invasion of inhibitory area, might balance out some of the behavioral effect of the primary cingulate lesion. Accordingly, three additional animals (mC6, mC7 and mC8) were given lesions that were restricted to approximately the middle half of the cingulate gyrus (e.g., see the lesion for mC7 in Fig. 4). As can be seen in Figure 5, the three animals with midcingulate lesions were all acceptable positive cases.

It should be remembered that none of these cingulate animals showed any abnormality in *passive* avoidance behavior. Their deficiency only became apparent when they were required to make an *active* avoidance response.

discussion

The original hypothesis is compatible with the present results. However, there are some alternative interpretations which also should receive consideration.

If the positive effect of either of the two lesions is considered separately, a number of possible mechanisms come to mind that might underlie the observed behavioral abnormality. At the simplest level of consideration, the animals might simply be deteriorated in some nonspecific way (e.g., less alert, or, for that matter, too alert and thus distractible); they might be insensitive to shock or lacking in the affective component that is usually associated with noxious stimulation; finally, at a more complex level of consideration, there could be some form of central deficit in learning ability —either, e.g., in the ability to acquire a learned fear or in the ability to discriminate the various external cues involved in either of the two behavioral situations. Such a list of logical possibilities could almost be expanded at will. This type of explanation of the present results, however, can be rejected since it would apply with equal weight to both types of avoidance test. Yet, no experimental animal was abnormal in both tests.

Attempts at interpretation must necessarily focus on the differences that exist between the two test situations. In this context, there are two alternative possibilities aside from the planned difference in the response requirements involved in the two types of avoidance behavior. For one thing, the passive avoidance test seems to involve a more obvious, approach-avoidance conflict situation than does the active avoidance test. In actual fact, however, there is also a conflict situation in the shuttle-box test. On any given trial, an active avoidance response requires the animal to return to the precise place where it was most recently shocked.

There is a second alternative difference between the passive avoidance situation and the shuttle box: Hunger motivation is involved in the former but not in the latter. It might be supposed that subcallosal lesions increased hunger drive and thus forced the animals in that group to return more promptly to the food trough despite the threat of shock. However, in the passive avoidance situation where the animals of all groups were observed while eating for a number of days prior to receiving shock, no consistent group differences in voraciousness or amount eaten were noted.

Finally, it might be argued that the active avoidance test presents a more difficult problem than the passive avoidance test and that it is on this basis that the cingulate lesion had its effect on the shuttle-box performance. However, it has already been shown that bilateral cingulate lesions have no effect on food-reinforced T-maze performance, which is at least as difficult as the active avoidance test (12). For the time being, then, the response-specific hypothesis that gave rise to the present work seems to contain the most believable explanation of the results. It should be noted, however, that nothing in the present data makes it mandatory to believe that the response-modulating function of cingulate and subcallosal areas is necessarily limited exclusively to the case of fear-motivated behavior. Whether or not these forebrain areas have a more general influence on response emission is, of course, open to straightforward experimental examination.

Keeping in mind that there is probably no valid reason in the present type of behavioral study to differentiate between subcallosal and septal lesions (see below), one recalls several other studies which point in the same direction as the present work. For example, Brady and Nauta (1), Thomas, Moore, Harvey, and Hunt (14), and King (6) have described a behavioral syndrome following septal lesions in rats which the latter author describes as "hyperemotionality." The important point is that these animals had exaggerated startle reflexes and acquired avoidance responses in a shuttle box more rapidly than normal controls. Both characteristics are perfectly compatible with the idea that the so-called septal syndrome basically represents the loss of response inhibition. Brady and Nauta also report that such rats are deficient in the performance of a CER—the response in question being the *inhibition* of a lever response. If the behavioral effects of the present subcallosal lesions really represent the same thing that is observed in

the septal rats, King's use of the term "hyperemotionality" now seems inappropriate. An animal that returns promptly to the source of a punishing shock (see Experiment 1) would not ordinarily be regarded as hyperemotional.

On the cingulate side of the present hypothesis, there are also some experimental studies that fit in well with the current findings. Following bilateral lesions that involved the cingulate area in rats, both Peretz (12) and Thomas and Otis (15) reported a deficiency in the acquisition of avoidance responses in a shuttle box. Although the workers in both studies suggested that the lesions might have interfered with the motivational status of the animals, their results are equally compatible with the present hypothesis. There is no doubt that the present cingulectomized cats, in the active avoidance test, developed a very clear-cut fear response to the CS (crouching, howling, and defecating). Such an observation casts serious doubt on the idea that the Papez circuit is involved in "emotional arousal."

anatomical considerations

Since the present work took origin from Kaada's (4) electrophysiological findings concerned with the effect of stimulation in two different areas on the surface of the mesial cortex, primary anatomical interest was directed to the location of the lesions relative to the mesial surface. Other characteristics of the lesions, however, require some brief description.

Except as noted below, the consistent characteristic of the subcallosal lesions amounted to shallow ablations, involving the cortical cell layer and immediately underlying white matter. This does not, of course, apply to the three stereotaxic lesions in which the electrodes were introduced 2 mm. off the midline. In these three cases (S1, S2, and S3) the path of the lesion passed through the white matter immediately beneath (i.e., lateral) to the cortical layer except at those several supracallosal points where the splenial and coronal sulci invaginated the cell layers across the vertical electrode paths.

With regard to the subcallosal group, one additional specific point deserves mention: While the continuity of the corpus callosum (in its genual portion) was routinely disrupted, this was also the case in the two negative cases (S3 and S6). Further, a control animal, subjected only to callosal section, performed normally in both avoidance tests. All things considered, the important area (for the subcallosal effect) seems to be the cell and fiber layers lying medially of the mesial wall of the anterior horn of the lateral ventricles (in the subcallosal and mesial frontal regions) and/or the extension of the lesions back into the anterior septal region.

The depth of the cingulate lesions varied from very superficial ablation of the cortical layer to involvement of the underlying white matter to the full depth of the gyrus. In the animals with deeper lesions, the callosum was interrupted at various points along the extent of the lesion. However, the depth of the lesions did not differentiate between the six positive and two negative cases.

On both electrophysiological and behavioral grounds, there is some reason to believe that the inhibitory function which is disrupted by subcallosal (and presumably septal) lesions might be mediated by a pathway that takes origin diffusely in mesial frontal cortex, converges caudally (near the midline) through subcallosal cortex, and continues on down the brain stem by way of ventral hypothalamus. Such a pathway is particularly suggested by the electrophysiological work of Kabat (5) on respiratory inhibition in the cat. Possibly related fronto-hypothalamic path-

ways have been reviewed by Clark et al. (3). At the behavioral level, Brutkowski (2) has already reported disinhibition in dogs resulting from lesions that involve mesial frontal cortex, and Maher and McIntire (9) have reported loss of a CER, involving crouching, in rats subjected to frontal ablation. Further, Levine and Soliday (7) have demonstrated prompter acquisition of active avoidance responses in rats following ventral hypothalamic lesions.

There is nothing to say about the efferent pathway of the motor facilitatory effect except that the relevant outflow from cingulate cortex apparently does not involve either the hippocampal-fornix system or the pyramidal tract (4).

summary

Based on electrophysiological data which demonstrated an opposing motor effect of stimulation in subcallosal cortex and cingulate gyrus, a behavioral hypothesis was developed that predicted a response-specific effect of lesions in these two parts of the limbic system.

The hypothesis was confirmed by the following findings:

1. Cats with bilateral lesions in the subcallosal area are deficient in *passive* avoidance behavior but are normal or quicker than normal in the acquisition of an *active* avoidance response.

2. Conversely, cats with bilateral cingulate lesions are deficient in the acquisition of an *active* avoidance response but show normal *passive* avoidance behavior.

Physiological and behavioral considerations suggest that the subcallosal effect results from the disruption of a pathway (mediating response inhibition) that passes caudally from mesial frontal cortex through subcallosal cortex and continues on down the brain stem through the ventral hypothalamus.

references

1. Brady, J. V., & Nauta, W. J. H. Subcortical mechanisms in emotional behavior: Affective changes following sepal forebrain lesions in the albino rat. *J. comp. physiol. Psychol.*, 1953, **46**, 339–346.
2. Brutkowski, S. Comparison of classical and instrumental alimentary conditioned reflexes following bilateral prefrontal lobectomies in dogs. *Acta biol. exp.*, 1959, **14**, 291–299.
3. Clark, W. E., LeGros, & Meyer, M. Anatomical relationships between cerebral cortex and the hypothalamus. *Brit. med. J.*, 1950, **6**, 341–345.
4. Kaada, B. R. Somato-motor, autonomic and electrocorticographic responses to electrical stimulation of 'rhinencephalic' and other structures in primate, cat and dog. *Acta physiol. Scand.*, 1951, **24**, Suppl. 83.
5. Kabat, H. Electrical stimulation of points in the forebrain and mid-brain: The resultant alterations in respiration. *J. comp. Neurol.*, 1936, **64**, 187–208.
6. King, F. A. Effects of septal and amygdaloid lesions on emotional behavior and conditioned avoidance responses in the rat. *J. nerv. ment. Dis.*, 1958, **126**, 57–63.
7. Levine, S., & Soliday, S. The effects of hypothalamic lesions on conditioned avoidance learning. *J. comp. physiol. Psychol.*, 1960, **53**, 497–501.
8. McCleary, R. A. Type of response as a factor in interocular transfer in the fish. *J. comp. physiol. Psychol.*, 1960, **53**, 311–321.
9. Maher, B. A., & McIntire, R. W. The extinction of the CER following frontal ablation. *J. comp. physiol. Psychol.*, 1960, **53**, 549–552.
10. Maier, N. R. F. Selector-integrator mechanisms in behavior. In B. Kaplan & S. Wapner (Eds.), *Perspectives in psychological theory*. New York: International Univer. Press, 1960. Pp. 135–172.
11. Mowrer, O. H. *Learning theory and behavior*. New York: Wiley, 1960.
12 Peretz, E. The effects of lesions of the anterior cingulate cortex on the behavior of the rat. *J. comp. physiol. Psychol.*, 1960, **53**, 540–548.
13. Sperry, R. W. Neurology and the mind-brain problem. *Amer. Scientist*, 1952, **40**, 291–312.
14. Thomas, G. J., Moore, R. Y., Harvey, J. A., & Hunt, H. F. Relations between the behavioral syndrome produced by lesions in the septal region of the forebrain and maze learning of the rat. *J. comp. physiol. Psychol.*, 1959, **52**, 527–532.
15. Thomas, G. J., & Otis, L. S. Effects of rhinencephalic lesions on conditioning of avoidance responses in the rat. *J. comp. physiol. Psychol.*, 1958, **51**, 130–134.

33   effects of bilateral hippocampal lesions in rats *

Daniel P. Kimble

1. Why is it so difficult to discover the effects of hippocampal lesions on behavior? Does a knowledge of the whole limbic system help explain this difficulty?

2. In what way are these experiments related to those of McCleary (Reading 32)?

3. Is Kimble's final conclusion unduly pessimistic?

Behavioral effects of chronic lesions involving the hippocampus in various animals and

* D. P. Kimble, "The Effects of Bilateral Hippocampal Lesions in Rats," *J. comp. physiol. Psychol.*, 56 (1963), 273–283. Reprinted with permission.

man have been reported by several investigators. Such seemingly diverse findings as "short term" memory deficits (10, 17), increases in sexual activity (4), increases (13, 15) and decreases (6) in affective responses, and slower (11) as well as faster (3) learning of an avoidance response have been noted. However, no clear-cut functional significance of the hippocampus has emerged from these studies.

The present experiments were designed to investigate the behavior of rats with bilateral hippocampal damage in a variety of behavioral situations. The experiments are reported in chronological order.

method

subjects

Thirty-three male hooded rats from the Long-Evans strain were gentled and acclimated to the laboratory environment for 2–3 weeks. Following preoperative behavioral measures, 10 Ss received bilateral damage to the hippocampus and 11 Ss received only bilateral removal of cortex overlying the hippocampal formation. Twelve Ss served as unoperated controls.

surgery

All operations were performed in one stage using clean surgical technique. The Ss were anesthetized with pentobarbital (40 mg/kg) and the lesions made while the Ss were held in a stereotaxic instrument. After suitable openings were made in the skull with trephine and rongeurs, the dura was opened and the cortex overlying the hippocampus aspirated, exposing the hippocampus in the ventral surface of the lateral ventricle. In the experimental group, the hippocampus was then removed by suction as completely as possible, both me-

dially and ventrally, care being taken to spare the underlying thalamus. After all bleeding had ceased, gelfoam was inserted in the wound, the temporal muscles replaced over the opening in the skull, and the scalp closed. In the operative control Ss the hippocampus was similarly exposed, but not damaged. The cortical lesion was enlarged before the wound was closed. The Ss received penicillin and terramycin for 3 days postoperatively.

experiment 1: open-field behavior

The hippocampal group, the cortically damaged group and the unoperated control group were compared pre- and postoperatively on open-field behavior. This experiment was designed to investigate exploratory behavior as well as "emotionality" among the three groups.

procedure

The apparatus was an open-field maze, a square wooden enclosure, 30 × 30 in., with walls 5 in. high. The floor was divided into 36 5-in. squares marked off by black paint. The maze was placed on the floor of a windowless room, directly under a fluorescent light.

Three measures were used in the open field situation. (a) The number of squares S entered in a 10 min. test period. (b) The number of fecal boluses produced by each S during this same period. (c) The number of urinations produced by each S within this time period.

Preoperatively, all Ss were run consecutively during one evening. Each S was taken from its individual living cage, carried by hand into the experimental room and placed in the center of the open field. After the 10 min. observational period, it was removed and replaced in its living cage. Between observations of Ss, all feces and urinations were removed and the floor of the maze cleaned with a damp sponge and paper toweling.

Each of the operated Ss was retested on Day 8 following its operation, using an identical procedure. The unoperated control Ss, matched for elapsed time, were retested at the same time.

results

The major result was that the hippocampal Ss entered over four times as many squares postoperatively as they had before operation. An analysis of variance (9) of the data presented in Table 1 revealed that no significant differences appeared among the three groups on the number of squares entered preoperatively. However, a significant difference was obtained on the *postoperative* data ($p < .01$).

Although both the unoperated and cortically damaged groups also increased slightly

in the number of entries postoperatively, Scheffé contrast tests (12) showed that the cortical control-unoperated control mean difference did not reach statistical significance. However, the difference between the hippocampal Ss and each of the other two groups was significant ($p < .01$).

Qualitative differences between the hippocampal Ss and the other two groups were also observed. The hippocampal Ss initially ran rapidly along the perimeter of the open field, stopping only rarely. They typically traversed the interior of the field only after 2–5 min. The most striking characteristic of their behavior was an extremely repetitive running pattern. The behavior of the other two groups differed radically from that of the hippocampal group. It consisted of "bursts" and "stops." A typical performance was to run to one wall, explore around the perimeter of the field once or twice, stop and groom, stand up on the hind legs and sniff, run out into the center of the field, explore in a seemingly random fashion, and return to a corner for more grooming and occasional crouching.

Two measures were taken to obtain gross estimates of "emotionality" in the field situation. No significant differences were obtained in the number of boluses dropped by Ss in the several groups. However, both the hippocampal and the cortically damaged groups urinated less in the maze postoperatively than did the unoperated controls ($p < .01$). No significant difference appeared between the two operated groups on this measure.

Table 1. Comparison of Preoperative and Postoperative Open-Field Behavior of Hippocampal, Cortical, and Normal Rats

Experimental Condition	Group					
	Hippocampal		Cortical		Normal	
	M	Range	M	Range	M	Range
Number of Squares Entered						
Preoperatively	118	21–218	126	35–213	144	75–224
Postoperatively	505	303–685	230	55–550	157	64–294
Number of Urinations						
Preoperatively	<1	0–1	1	0–2	<1	0–2
Postoperatively	<1	0–1	<1	0–1	1	0–2
Number of Feces						
Preoperatively	6	3–10	5	0–12	5	3–9
Postoperatively	4	0–8	3	0–6	5	0–9

experiment 2: simultaneous-successive brightness discrimination learning

Previous reports have indicated that hippocampal damage in both monkeys (16) and humans (10, 17) results in a behavioral impairment which is interpreted as one of *recall* of recent events. However, when the relevant stimuli are presented simultaneously (16) or when *recognition* of the appropriate stimulus is required (17), these Ss are less handicapped.

A behavioral test similar to that employed by Stepien et al. consists of simultaneous and successive discriminations. In a simultaneous discrimination, all the relevant stimuli are present on each trial, but the solution of a successive discrimination appears to depend upon the strengthening of an approach response to a compound stimulus, occurring across individual trials (14). If the behavioral deficit seen in animals with hippocampal damage indeed stems from their inability to perform adequately when all of the relevant stimuli are not immediately present, this deficit should appear selective on the successive discrimination problem.

procedure

The apparatus was a Y maze with removable walls and floors in the arms serving as the stimulus cues. In the simultaneous discrimination, one of the arms was always white, the other black. In the successive discrimination, both of the maze arms were either black or white on any given trial.

Seven days prior to testing (17–41 days postoperative), all Ss were placed on a 23 hr. food deprivation schedule. Water was available at all times. During this time, the Ss were handled for 10 min. each day. Each S was run five trials on the first experimental day, and 10 trials each following day until a criterion of 10 consecutive correct responses was reached. Gellerman orders were used to determine the reward pattern, and identical patterns were used for all Ss. A noncorrection procedure

was used. The reinforcement consisted of several small Purina lab pellets. The intertrial interval was *8 min.* in all cases.

The simultaneous discrimination was a black-white discrimination. Seventeen Ss were trained to approach black (5 hippocampals, 6 cortical controls and 6 normals). The remaining Ss were trained to approach the white goal arm.

In the successive discrimination both arms were the same brightness for any given trial and the pattern was consistent for a given S. The right arm contained the food reward when both arms were white and the left arm contained the reward when both arms were black, for the 17 Ss trained on black-right, white-left. The remaining 16 Ss were trained to black-left, white-right.

The order of the discriminations was balanced. Seventeen Ss (5 hippocampals, 6 cortical controls, and 6 normals) were trained first

Table 2. Trials to Criterion, Latencies, and 1-Week Retention Scores on Simultaneous and Successive Brightness Discriminations by Hippocampal, Cortical, and Normal Rats

Type of Discrimination	Group					
	Hippocampal		Cortical		Normal	
	M	Range	M	Range	M	Range
Trials to Criterion						
Simultaneous	29	10–44	33	12–57	31	10–61
Successive	120	53–164	76	37–108	55	18–105
Latency (in sec.)						
Simultaneous	4.0	1.0–6.9	4.0	1.4–10.6	5.0	0.7–18.7
Successive	3.0	1.6–7.1	4.2	1.7–15.0	4.0	1.4–7.6
1-Week Retention Test: Percentage Correct						
Simultaneous	72	50–100	74	50–100	81	50–100
Successive	70	40–100	75	50–90	72	40–100

on the successive discrimination. The other 16 Ss were trained first on the simultaneous discrimination. After reaching criterion on the first task, the S was started on the second discrimination the following day. The E recorded latencies for the elapsed time from the S's emergence from the start box until its entrance into the goal arm. Each S was tested 7 days a week continuously from the beginning of training.

Retention tests of 10 trials were made on the sixth and seventh day following completion of the two discrimination tasks. Seventeen Ss (5 hippocampals, 6 cortical controls and 6 normals) were tested on Day 6 for retention of the first discrimination they had acquired. On Day 7 they were tested for retention of the other discrimination. This sequence was reversed for the remaining 16 Ss.

results

The hippocampal Ss took significantly more trials to reach criterion on the successive discrimination, while no differences appeared on the simultaneous discrimination.

A Type I analysis of variance (9) yielded F ratios significant at $<.001$ for the between groups component, the between problems component, and the interaction ratio.

Scheffé contrast tests showed that on the successive discrimination, both the hippocampal-cortical control mean difference and the hippocampal-normal mean difference were significant at $<.01$.

No significant latency differences appeared among the groups for either problem. No differences occurred among the three groups on the retention tests given 1 week subsequently. All groups performed well, showing better than 70% correct responses on both problems during the retention trials.

experiment 3: hebb-williams maze learning

Several studies (2, 7, 8, 14) have indicated that the successive problem is more difficult for normal rats. Therefore, a possible explanation for the results of Experiment 2 could be that the hippocampal Ss are impaired on complex tasks, but relatively unimpaired on simpler discriminations. In order to investigate the behavior of hippocampal Ss on a "complexity of task" dimension, a relatively simple Maze 1 and a relatively complex Maze 6 were chosen from the 12 mazes of the Hebb-Williams series (1). The hypothesis was that if hippocampal damage causes impairment in performance as a function of complexity of task, it should be more severe on Maze 6 than on Maze 1. In this experiment, the Ss were the same as in the first two experiments, with the exception that two of the cortically damaged rats were removed because of illness.

procedure

The apparatus was a standard Hebb-Williams maze (1) painted a medium gray. The floor plans of the two mazes used in the present experiment are shown in Figure 1.

Each S received 3 days of pretraining, with food in the goal box. The Ss were placed in the maze in groups of 4–6 on the first pretrain-

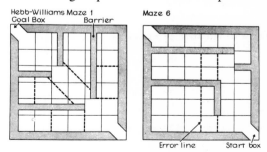

Fig. 1. Floor plans of Hebb-Williams Mazes 1 (simple) and 6 (complex).

ing day, no inserts being present. On the next 2 days the *S*s were run individually with inserts presented to form extremely simple mazes. By the third pretraining day, all *S*s were running seven complete trials in a maximum of 5 min. On Test Days 4 and 5, the *S*s were run individually. Each *S* was run until he had completed seven trials or until the maximum time limit had elapsed. This time limit was 10 min. for the "simple" maze, and 20 min. for the "complex" maze.

An *S* was considered to have made an error if its two forepaws crossed an error line (see Figure 1). Errors were recorded as the total number committed during seven complete runs to the goal box or for the maximal time of the test period if *S* did not complete seven trials. The *S*s were run in two groups. One group (4 hippocampals, 4 cortical controls and 6 normals) was tested first on the "simpler" maze (1) and then on the "more complex" Maze 6. The order was reversed for the remaining *S*s.

results

The hippocampal *S*s made significantly more errors on *both* maze problems, and were in fact *worse* on the simpler maze than on the more complex maze. The data are presented in Table 3.

A Type I analysis of variance and Scheffé

contrast tests revealed that the difference between the hippocampal group mean and each of the other group means was significant at <.01 for both maze problems. Although the cortically damaged *S*s made more errors than the unoperated *S*s on both problems, these differences did not reach statistical significance. The between-problem mean difference reached statistical significance only for the hippocampal *S*s ($p < .01$).

Two factors are relevant in describing the behavioral differences among the three groups in the maze situation.

First, the simpler maze actually has more error lines (seven) than the more complex maze (four).

Second, the hippocampal *S*s, when placed in the start box typically entered one of the two side alleys, progressed to the end and then turned and entered the other alley. These *S*s, in sharp contrast to the other two groups, then re-entered the originally chosen alley, rather than moving into the center of the maze, as the typical control *S* did. This repetitive tracing of the two side alleys by the hippocampal *S*s continued 50–75 times. Eventually, all the hippocampal *S*s reached the goal box, yet the striking repetitive behavior was only slightly diminished on subsequent trials. This behavior was quite similar to that seen in the maze when it was used as the open field in Experiment 1.

Since the simpler maze contained almost twice as many error lines as the more complex maze, the repetitive tracing resulted in approximately twice as many errors on Maze 1.

experiment 4: passive avoidance

The repetitive behavior displayed by the hippocampal *S*s in both Experiments 1 and 3

Table 3. Number of Errors on Two Hebb-Williams Mazes Made by Hippocampal, Cortical, and Normal Rats

Maze	Group					
	Hippocampal		Cortical		Normal	
	M	Range	M	Range	M	Range
Simple	148	43–247	37	3–91	6	1–13
Complex	70	10–170	29	12–54	17	10–29

suggested that these Ss may have been relatively unable to inhibit their motor responses. Kimura (5) has reported that rats with small, posterior hippocampal lesions are less able to withhold an approach response which has been subsequently punished by electric shock. Experiment 4 was designed to investigate the ability of the Ss in the present study to inhibit an approach response.

procedure

The apparatus consisted of a start box, straight runway, and goal box. The entire apparatus was 53 in. long, 4 in. wide and 4¼ in. deep. A guillotine door separated the start box from the runway. An aluminum food cup was attached to the rear wall of the goal box with a brass screw. This screw served as one of the terminals for the shock circuit. The other terminal was a copper wire soldered onto a metal plate which was fitted into the bottom of the goal box. This plate was wrapped in cloth and kept damp with dilute saline solution. The food provided was a wet mash. When S was eating the wet mash, his body completed the electrical circuit. The remainder of the circuit consisted of a variable rheostat and a telegraph key. The E controlled both the amount and timing of the shock.

The Ss were given 10 trials each day for 4 days. Each trial consisted of placing the S in the start box, lifting the guillotine door, and allowing the S to run down the runway and eat in the goal box for a period of 30 sec. It was then removed and replaced in the start box for the next trial. Latencies were recorded manually for the elapsed time from S's emergence from the start box until it began to eat in the goal box. No shock was administered until the fourth trial of Day 3. On that trial, S had approached the food cup and was eating

the wet mash when E completed the shock circuit. The voltage was approximately 22 v. The appropriate voltage had been determined previously with pilot animals. The S was removed from the goal box (or runway) and replaced in the start box for the fifth trial of that day. No more shock was given.

The latency of the S's return was then measured. Each elapsed minute was considered a trial, even if S had not returned to the goal box. Six trials were run in this manner following the shock trial. If S did return to the goal box, it was allowed the usual 30 sec. to eat before being replaced in the start box.

Table 4. Mean Latencies during Postshock Trials in a Passive Avoidance Situation by Hippocampal, Cortical, and Normal Rats

Group	Latencies (in sec.)	
	M	Range
Hippocampal	25.0	3.2–52.2
Cortical	38.7	21.1–60.0
Normal	47.8	6.7–60.0

The criterion for a "return" was a complete four-footed entry and at least 5 sec. of consecutive eating. A two-footed entry or tentative sniffing at the food was not considered as a "return." The procedure for Day 4 was identical to that for Days 1 and 2.

results

The hippocampal Ss showed the *least* postshock avoidance, and the unoperated Ss the most. The cortically damaged Ss fell between these groups, but nearer to the hippocampal Ss in their degree of avoidance. No differences had appeared among the three groups for the approach latencies of the two preshock days. An analysis of variance performed on the postshock latencies was significant for the be-

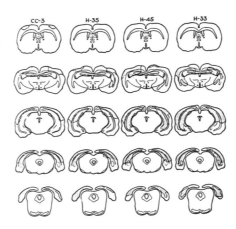

Fig. 2. Lesion reconstructions. (CC-3 = representative cortical control lesiôn; H-35 = hippocampal *S* with minimal hippocampal damage; H-45 = hippocampal *S* with average hippocampal damage; H-33 = hippocampal *S* with maximal hippocampal damage.)

tween-groups component ($p < .05$). Scheffé tests revealed that although the hippocampal-normal difference was significant ($p < .05$), the cortically damaged *S*s were not significantly different from *either* of the other two groups.

By combining the two operated groups, and comparing their group mean with the unoperated group, brain damage per se appeared as a significant factor in these results ($p < .05$) but the behavioral effects cannot be reliably accounted for by the locus of the lesion.

anatomical results

The brains of the two operated groups were fixed in 10% formalin, dehydrated, and embedded in pariffin. Sections were cut 20 μ thick. Every fifth section was mounted and stained with thionin.

An examination of the brains of the hippocampal *S*s showed that bilateral hippocampal lesions were produced in each *S* (see Figures 2

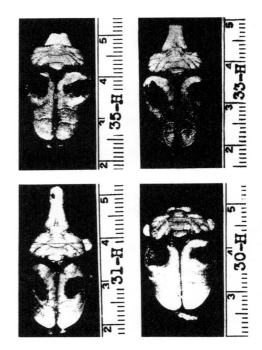

Fig. 3. Dorsal view of four brains from hippocampal group.

and 3). These lesions included destruction of the fimbria. In no case was the hippocampus completely destroyed, but a complete transection of the hippocampus was effected bilaterally in every S. The lesions varied from about 60% to over 90% destruction. The portions generally escaping damage were the dorsal and rostral portions and the ventral tip of Ammon's horn. The middle aspect of the hippocampal formation was the most damaged. The overlying cortical lesions in the hippocampal group chiefly involved the projection areas of the auditory and visual systems. Slight damage to the optic radiations and lateral geniculate bodies was present in six of the hippocampal Ss. In only two of these six was the thalamic involvement bilateral.

Damage among the cortical lesion group was largely restricted to lateral and dorsal neocortex, although very shallow surface invasion of the dorsal hippocampus did occur in some of these Ss. In two of these Ss, the lesion extended more deeply into the hippocampus. One of these two also suffered severe damage to the caudate nucleus and putamen, as well as the fornix and septal area. This lesion was presumably due to secondary bleeding subsequent to the operation. This S was the only one to show any apparent correlation between thalamic damage and subsequent behavior. While the other cortical Ss entered an average of 125 more squares in the open field postoperatively, this S entered a total of 136 *less* squares than he had upon preoperative testing. Also, this S completed no runs on Maze 1 and only one run on Maze 6.

The extent of the cortical lesion among cortical control group was consistently larger than the cortical damage incurred by the hippocampal Ss. A planimetric analysis of the sections was carried out to determine the extent of *total* neural tissue removed. The extent of brain removed in the two groups

proved not to be significantly different $(t < 1)$.

discussion

The three results that separate the hippocampal Ss from the other two groups are most likely to yield clues to hippocampal function. These results are:

1. The repetitive running behavior of the hippocampal Ss in the open field situation, which resulted in the greatly increased number of squares entered postoperatively.

2. The poorer performance of the hippocampal Ss on the successive brightness discrimination.

3. The greater number of errors committed in the Hebb-Williams mazes by the hippocampal Ss.

One current idea is that the hippocampus is primarily concerned with motivational or emotional mechanisms. Another view holds that the hippocampus mediates "short-term memory." The present series of experiments do not lend support to either of these concepts.

The emotional state of the hippocampal Ss did not appear to be changed by the operation. These Ss did not differ from either of the control groups in the amount of defecation in an open field, a standard measure of emotionality in the rat. Nor were any emotionality differences observed in handling the Ss. In the passive avoidance situation, analysis of the postshock latencies indicated that the shorter latencies observed in the operated Ss were most probably a result of brain damage per se, and not reliably related to the locus of the lesion.

Interpretation of the present results in terms of a simple short-term memory deficit is difficult because the hippocampal Ss were unimpaired in the simultaneous discrimination in which the intertrial interval was 8 min. Also, the experimental Ss showed good retention of both discrimination problems a week following acquisition.

One possible interpretation of these data is that the hippocampal Ss are "hyperactive." Hyperactivity might account for the increased square entries, and possibly for the greater number of errors in the mazes. It does not appear to explain the successive discrimination impairment. Several other facts diminish the explanatory value of the hyperactivity hypothesis. No differences appeared in the latencies in either of the discrimination problems. No latency differences occurred in the preshock trials of the avoidance situation. Also, Kim (4) has reported hippocampal rats to be only slightly more active than normals, and then only when the ambient temperature is below normal.

The hippocampal Ss in the present study might be described in a general way as demonstrating an increased degree of perseverative behavior. This description seems particularly apt when applied to the open field and maze data. In the discrimination situations, however, a "perseveration" hypothesis would need qualification since a deficit was noted only during the successive discrimination. It might be postulated, for example, that perseverative behavior varies directly with the difficulty of the discrimination.

At the present stage of our knowledge of brain function in general and hippocampal function in particular, any monolithic interpretation of the behavior of hippocampectomized animals is likely to be an oversimplification. Although the present experiments have not fully clarified the role of the hippocampus in behavior, they do indicate that neither a motivational-emotional hypothesis nor a short-term memory concept is able to account for the behavior of the hippocampal Ss.

To determine whether variability in the behavioral data among the operated Ss might be related to the extent of either hippocampal or extrahippocampal damage, tau coefficients were calculated for the various behavioral measures. The coefficients between extent of hippocampal damage and behavioral impairment were low (none exceeding .37). However, with two exceptions, these correlations were in the direction expected from the data. The highest correlations were on the number of trials to criterion for the successive discrimination (tau = .37, $p < .06$), the number of squares entered postoperatively in the open field (tau = .33, $p < .10 > .06$), and the number of errors on the simpler maze in Experiment 3 (tau = .35, $p < .10 > .06$).

On the other hand, the correlations between the total amount of extrahippocampal loss and these behavioral measures either showed a smaller coefficient than those found in the hippocampal group, or were in the opposite direction. The only coefficient which reached a probability level of less than .10 was a negative relationship between the amount of extrahippocampal tissue loss and the number of squares entered postoperatively (tau = −.33, $p < .09$).

references

1. Hebb, D. O., & Williams, K. A method of rating animal intelligence. *J. genet. Psychol.*, 1946, **34**, 59–65.
2. Heyman, M. Transfer of discrimination learning following three conditions of initial training. Unpublished doctoral dissertation, State University of Iowa, 1951.
3. Isaacson, R. L, Douglass, R. J., & Moore, R. Y. The effect of radical hippocampal ablation on acquisition of avoidance re-

sponses. *J. comp. physiol. Psychol.*, 1961, **54**, 625–628.

4. Kim, D. Nest building, general activity and salt preference of rats following hippocampal ablation. *J. comp. physiol. Psychol.*, 1960, **53**, 11–16.

5. Kimura, D. Effects of selective hippocampal damage on avoidance behavior in the rat. *Canad. J. Psychol.*, 1958, **12**, 213–218.

6. Klüver, H., & Bucy, P. C. "Psychic blindness" and other symptoms following bilateral temporal lobectomy in rhesus monkey. *Amer. J. Physiol.* 1937, **119**, 352–353.

7. Lawrence, D. H. Acquired distinctiveness of cues: I. Transfer between discriminations on the basis of familiarity with the stimulus. *J. exp. Psychol.*, 1949, **39**, 770–784.

8. Lawrence, D. H. Acquired distinctiveness of cues: II. Selective association in a constant stimulus situation. *J. exp. Psychol.*, 1950, **40**, 175–188.

9. Lindquist, E. F. *Design and analysis of experiments in psychology and education.* Boston: Houghton Mifflin, 1956.

10. Milner, B., & Penfield, W. The effect of hippocampal lesions on recent memory. *Trans. Amer. Neurol. Ass.*, 1955, **80**, 42–48.

11. Pribram, K. H., & Weiskrantz, L. A comparison of the effects of medial and lateral cerebral resections on conditioned avoidance behavior of monkeys. *J. comp. physiol. Psychol.*, 1957, **50**, 74–80.

12. Scheffé, H. *The analysis of variance.* New York: Wiley, 1959.

13. Schreiner, L., & Kling, A. Behavioral changes following rhinencephalic injury in the cat. *J. Neurophysiol.*, 1953, **16**, 643–659.

14. Spence, K. W. *Behavior theory and learning.* Englewood Cliffs, N.J.: Prentice-Hall, 1960.

15. Spiegel, E. A., Miller, H. R., & Oppenheimer, J. J. Forebrain and rage reactions. *J. Neurophysiol.*, 1940, **3**, 538–548.

16. Stepien, L. S. Cordeau, J. P., & Rasmussen, T. The effect of temporal lobe and hippocampal lesions on auditory and visual recent memory in monkeys. *Brain*, 1960, **83**, 470–489.

17. Walker, A. E., Recent memory impairment in unilateral temporal lesions. *AMA Arch. Neurol. Psychiat.*, 1957, **78**, 543–552.

glossary of selected terms

Ablation The removal of a part of an organism (usually, a part of the nervous system) by surgical means.

Acetylcholine A chemical substance known to be a transmitter substance at certain synapses (termed cholinergic synapses).

Achromatic Without color; visual sensations in black, white, and gray.

ACTH (adrenocorticotrophic hormone) A pituitary hormone that controls the secretion of hormones in the cortex (outer part) of the adrenal glands.

Adenylic acid A chemical substance that combines with a phosphate in the breakdown of carbohydrates in metabolism to produce adenosine triphosphate (ATP), which stores energy for instant release.

Adrenal glands A pair of ductless glands near the kidney.

Adrenalectomy The removal of the adrenal glands.

Adrenaline (epinephrine) A hormone secreted by the medulla (inner part) of the adrenal glands; important in the physiology of emotions, particularly fear and anger.

Agnosia Inability to recognize an object due to brain damage, although the sensory modalities involved are normal. Agnosia may be visual, auditory, or tactile.

Albumin A protein found in animal tissues; albuminuria (albumin in the urine) indicates an abnormal condition in which the serum albumin from the blood appears in the urine.

Amygdala An almond-shaped mass of gray matter in the ventral-medial tip of the temporal lobe; part of the limbic system; important in emotional behavior.

Androgen A hormone that stimulates male characteristics; produced by the gonads and adrenal glands.

Antibody Enzyme-like substance in the blood; builds immunity against foreign protein.

Archipallium "Old" brain tissue; a term used to distinguish the part of the mammalian forebrain that appears early phylogenetically (e.g., hippocampus).

Babinski reflex The extension of the big toe when the sole of the foot is stroked; in adults and older children (not infants) it is usually a sign of damage to the pyramidal tract.

Barbiturates Derivatives of barbituric acid, such as phenobarbital and amytal; habit-forming narcotics; effects range from mild sedation to deep sleep to coma and death.

Baroreceptor elements Receptors sensitive to the stretching of tissues of the body.

Basal ganglia (or corpus striatum) A mass of gray matter in the ventral and nonolfactory part of the mammalian forebrain. Includes the caudate nucleus, the putamen, and the globus pallidus.

Bioassay The estimation of the strength of a drug by quantitatively comparing its effects on living material with those of a standard substance.

Brightness The reported lightness or darkness of a stimulus; a psychological dimension correlated primarily with the physical dimension of intensity of light.

Cardiovascular Refers to the heart and blood vessels.

Catechol amines The catechol hormones including epinephrine and norepinephrine of the adrenal medulla; derived from phenylalanine.

Caudate nucleus One of the basal ganglia.

Chlorpromazine hydrochloride A tranquilizer, derived from phenothiazine. Among its effects is a partial blocking of activity in the RAS (reticular activating system) in the brain stem.

Cholinesterase A substance that breaks down acetylcholine into acetic acid and choline; important in synaptic transmission at cholinergic synapses (*see* Acetylcholine).

Chorda tympani A branch of the facial nerve; its efferent (outgoing) fibers serve glands in the mouth; its afferent (incoming) fibers serve the sense of taste.

Collateral Side by side; a side branch of an axon; an accessory nerve.

Constructional apraxia Inability to assemble parts so as to construct an object; the result of brain damage.

Corpus callosum The "great commissure" (fiber system) which crosses the midline of the brain and forms reciprocal connections between corresponding structures of the right and left cerebral hemispheres.

Corpus striatum   Synonym for basal ganglia.

Decibel (db)   A measure, obtained by means of a logarithmic scale, of the ratio of the intensity of one sound to another sound.

Demedullation   Removal of the myelin sheath of a nerve.

Deuteranomaly   A color weakness for greens; color vision otherwise normal.

Deuteranope   A person with deuteranopia (partial color blindness).

Dextro-amphetamine sulfate   A synthetic drug which has as one of its effects excitation of the central nervous system.

Dichromatism   A type of partial color blindness in which all of the colors seen by the person can be made by mixing only two colors (hues) (*see* Trichromatism).

Diencephalon (interbrain)   That part of the brain that lies between the telencephalon (endbrain) and the mesencephalon (midbrain); includes the thalamus, hypothalamus, optic tracts, retinas of the eyes, pituitary body, mammillary bodies, and the third ventricle.

Diethyl stilbestrol   A synthetic preparation with some of the same properties as the natural estrogens.

Epinephrine   Synonym for adrenaline.

Estrogen   A hormone that stimulates female characteristics; produced by the ovarian follicle and by other tissues.

Fornix   A band of fibers connecting the two cerebral hemispheres; also, an important pathway between the hippocampus, the septal area, and the hypothalamus.

Glia   Shortened form of "neuroglia"; refers to the non-neural cells found in great numbers in the nervous system; its function is not yet completely known, although it is known to be important for the metabolism of neural tissue.

Glucagon   A hormone secreted by the pancreas; it has the opposite effect of insulin in that it increases blood sugar via its effect on the liver.

Glutathione   A tripeptide of several amino acids; important as an oxygen carrier in cellular respiration.

Gonadectomy   Removal of the gonads (either male testes or female ovaries); castration.

Habenula   A narrow band of nerve fibers connecting both sides of the pineal gland with the anterior part of the fornix.

Hemidecorticate   An animal with one half of the cerebral cortex destroyed.

Hippocampus   A seahorse-shaped structure in the vertebrate brain; archipallium, or "old" cortex; part of the limbic system; its function is not yet fully understood, although it may be important in emotion, motivation, and memory.

Histamine   A substance produced by body tissues in response to injury (causes the redness of a skin burn) and in response to allergens; excessive amounts may cause surgical shock; neutralized by the antihistamine drugs.

Hue   The attribute of a color perception that determines whether it is red, blue, yellow, etc. Correlated primarily with the physical wavelength of light.

Hyperinsulinism   Excessive insulin in the blood; usually caused by disturbance of the islets of Langerhans in the pancreas or by insulin injection; symptoms include hunger, sweating, coma, and in extreme cases death.

Hyperthermia   Very high fever, occasionally used as treatment for disease (e.g., syphilis).

Hyperthyroidism   An abnormal condition caused by overactivity of the thyroid glands; symptoms include speeding up of metabolism and, in some cases, exopthalamic goiter (Grave's disease), characterized by protrusion of the eyeballs.

Hypoglycemia   Low blood sugar; may accompany hyperinsulinism.

Hypogonadism   A deficiency of internal secretion of the gonads.

Hypophysectomy   Removal of the hypophysis (pituitary gland).

Hypothyroidism   An abnormal condition caused by insufficient thyroid gland activity; symptoms include lowered metabolism, obesity, dry skin, and (in untreated young children) cretinism.

Immunoassay   The estimation of the strength of an immunological reaction.

Interstitial tissue   Tissue that lies between essential parts and tissues of an organ, e.g., fibrous or connective tissue.

Islet-cell adenoma A tumor (neoplasm) of the glandular epithelium in the islets of Langerhans in the pancreas.

Lenticular nucleus A neuroanatomical term referring to the putamen and the globus pallidus, which along with the caudate nucleus make up the basal ganglia.

Limbic system A series of neural structures involving both cortical and subcortical parts of the brain; borders the diencephalon; function not yet clearly known; involved in emotion and motivation.

Lobotomy A surgical procedure which disconnects the prefrontal cerebral cortex from the dorsal medial nucleus of the thalamus; the connecting white fibers are cut, gray matter not removed.

Local potential An electrical potential that travels with decrement in a nerve cell or cell process; contrasted with the "all-or-none" spike potential characteristic of the neuronal axon, which travels without decrement along the axon.

Mecholyl A drug that stimulates the parasympathetic division of the autonomic nervous system; used in research on physiological aspects of fear and anger.

Medial geniculate body A nucleus in the dorsal thalamus of mammals; important as a relay station to the cerebral cortex for auditory impulses from the ear.

Meprobamate A tranquilizer; reduces muscle tension and spasms. Most common trade names are Miltown and Equanil.

Mesencephalon (midbrain) Includes the superior and inferior colliculi and the aqueduct of Sylvius.

Modality In psychology, a sense organ, its stimuli, and resulting sensations.

Morphine The principal alkaloid found in opium; a narcotic used in medicine as a sedative and pain killer.

Morphology The science of structure and form.

Myelin A white fatty substance that forms sheath around the axion fibers of neurons; acts as insulation and protection; also contributes to ability of neuron to increase speed of neural transmission compared with unmyelinated fibers.

Neocortex The phylogenetically-recent outer part of the cerebral hemispheres in mammals; together with the underlying white matter, forms the neopallium.

Neopallium *see* Neocortex.

Neuroblast The embryonic cell from which a neuron develops; arises from the neural crest.

Noradrenaline (norepinephrine) One of the hormones secreted by the adrenal medulla; also, a transmitter substance at some synapses (called adrenergic); important in the physiology of emotion.

Norepinephrine *see* Noradrenaline.

Ontogenesis The beginning and development of an individual organism—in contrast with phylogenesis, the development of phyla or groups.

Ovariectomy The removal of the ovaries; castration of a female.

Paleocortex "Old" cortex; usually three-layered; appears early phylogenetically; includes some (but not all) of the limbic system.

Pallidum The globus pallidus, one of the basal ganglia.

Pentobarbital sodium One of the barbiturates. Common trade name is Nembutal.

Phenylalanine An essential amino acid. An inherited inability to metabolize phenylalanine results in phenylketonuria, marked by severe mental retardation (phenylpyruvic oligophrenia) if not corrected by proper diet early in life.

Phenylketonuria (PKU) A condition of excessive phenylpyruvic acid in the urine, caused by an enzyme lack resulting from a mutant recessive gene. If not controlled (by proper diet) leads to phenylpyruvic oligophrenia.

Phenylpyruvic acid A substance formed when a lack of liver enzyme prevents phenylalanine from being metabolized.

Photochemical absorption In the retina of the eye, chemical substances such as rhodopsin, porphyropsin, and iodopsin absorb light and react to it by chemical breakdown; this photochemical reaction produces a local, graded "generator" potential which acts as a trigger to initiate nerve impulses which are carried to the brain in the optic nerve.

Phylogenesis The growth and development of phyla or groups.

Placebo A sugar pill or other innocuous substance used in medicine and as a control measure in certain experiments.

Progesterone Hormone produced by the corpus luteum of the ovary; prepares the uterus for the implantation of the ovum.

Progynon A trade name of a preparation of the female sex hormone extracted from the placenta.

Prolactin An anterior pituitary hormone which stimulates the mammary glands to produce milk.

Protanomaly A color weakness for reds, and a confusion of certain shades of red and green.

Protanopia A partial color blindness for reds and greens; certain reds and greens are matched by the person with gray.

Psychoticism A term coined by Hans Eysenck as a name for the alleged inherited tendency toward psychosis.

Reticular activating system (RAS) Refers to much of the reticular formation of the brain; extends from the hindbrain into the midbrain; acts as a nonspecific activating mechanism for the entire cortex; important in many aspects of behavior.

Reticular formation An anatomical designation for a region in the brain stem (*see* Reticular activating system).

Reticulum A network of cells.

Reticulum cell A parent cell that in the fetus forms various blood cells (erythrocytes, monocytes, leucocytes, etc.); found in the bone marrow and lymph nodes; not active in postnatal life.

Rhinencephalon An anatomical term used to designate certain structures thought to have primarily to do with olfaction; these structures make up a system now usually referred to as the limbic system.

Ribonucleic acid (RNA) A complex protein molecule found in cells; with DNA (deoxyribonucleic acid) forms the genetic material of the cell; may be important in memory functions; there are several kinds of RNA, one kind being "messenger" RNA, which travels from cell nucleus to cytoplasm.

Ringer's solution An aqueous solution usually composed of 0.7% sodium chloride, 0.3% potassium chloride, and 0.025% calcium chloride.

Roentgen An international measure of radiation; used to quantify the amount of radiation absorbed by an organism or object exposed to radioactive substances.

Salmonella A form of bacteria that can cause intestinal and other disturbances; some types are responsible for meat poisoning.

Sarcoma A malignant tumor of the non-epithelial, connective tissue; affects bone, kidneys, bladder, liver, lungs, etc.; a form of cancer.

Saturation In chemistry, a solution that holds all of a dissolved solid possible; in psychology, the intensity of a hue as it is diluted by white.

Septal area A region of the brain lying just under the anterior portion of the corpus callosum; serves to connect limbic system structures with hypothalamic areas; contains the septal nuclei; may be important in emotional behavior.

Septum A dividing wall or partition; in the brain refers to a region along the midline, near the anterior part of the corpus callosum; usually included in septal area.

Sodium amytal A barbiturate.

Somatotropic Attracted to and influencing body cells; stimulating growth (as the somatotropic hormone of the pituitary gland).

Spermatogenesis The process of formation of the sperm cells (spermatozoa) in the testes.

Spike potential The "all-or-none" action potential that travels without decrement down the axon of a neuron; normally occurs in response to sufficient local excitation, via local potentials, which causes axon hillock region to trigger the spike potential.

Steroids A complex organic chemical group produced in the body by the adrenal cortex (corticosterone, etc.) and by the gonads (progesterone, testosterone, etc.).

Sympathectomy The removal or deactivation of the sympathetic division of the autonomic nervous system.

Sympathomimetic drugs Drugs capable of mimicking the action of the sympathetic division of the autonomic nervous system.

Tegmentum Part of the midbrain of vertebrates.

Testosterone A steroid hormone produced by

the testes; male sex hormone; influences both primary and secondary sexual characteristics.

Testosterone propionate The propionic acid ester of testosterone, a very potent form of this hormone.

Tetartanopia A form of yellow-blue color blindness in which there is a normal luminosity function with confused connections of yellow and blue receptor processes.

Thalamic nuclei Groups of cell bodies in the thalamus.

Thalamus Part of the diencephalon, a mass of tissue in the middle of the brain; functions in part as a great relay station for sensory impulses from the sense organs on their way to the cerebral cortex.

Thiopentone sodium A general anesthetic agent.

Trichromatism Normal color vision; refers to notion that for normal color vision three primary lights are necessary to match all perceived hues.

Tritanopia A form of yellow-blue color blindness in which there is a loss of luminosity in the blues.

D-tubocurarine A curare-like substance which blocks the neuromuscular synapse; used as a muscle relaxant and also in certain experimental procedures.

Vena cava The large inferior and superior veins that bring blood to the right atrium of the heart.

Vitreous humor A transparent, jellylike substance filling the eyeball.

X radiation Radiations of extremely short wavelength; X rays are emitted as a result of a sudden change in velocity of a moving charge hitting a target and causing atomic changes.

index

Ablation. *See* Surgical techniques

Achromatic interval and responses, 44, 46–53 *passim*

Acoustical equipment, 7–9

Activation theory of emotion, 145

Adolph, E. F., 190, 191

Adrenalin, 9, 143–144, 155, 169–174 *passim*

Adrian, E. D., 85

Afferent impulses. *See* Sensory systems

Aggressive behavior, 163–164, 238, 264–274 *passim*

de Ajuriaguerra, J., 316–331

Alimentary functions, 32

All-or-none impulse, 14–24 *passim*

Allport, F. H., 152

Amassian, V. E., 89, 112

Amygdala functions, 144, 153–155 *passim*, 179–181 *passim*, 210–212, 219, 231–235 *passim*, 243, 256

Anatomical procedures, 177–178

Androgens. *See* Hormones; Sex hormones

Anesthesia effects, 28, 84, 89–90

Anger, 143–144, 168–174

Anticipatory set, 292–295 *passim*, 301–302

Anxiety conditioning, 163

Aphagia, 195

Aphasia, 328

Apparatus, 3

    capillary microelectrode. *See* Microelectrode techniques

    pipets. *See* Pipet techniques

Approach behavior, 148–150 *passim*

Apraxia, 315–331, 332–347 *passim*

Arduini, A., 160, 210, 211

Arousal and inhibitory functions, 25–29 *passim*

    anticipatory set, 292–295 *passim*, 301–302

    in conditioning, 249–251, 292–293, 301–302

    and drive, 289, 192, 206–212

Arousal and inhibitory functions (continued)

    and hibernation, 287–289

    limbic system lesions and, 348–359

    in sensory activity, 147–148, 156, 157–160

    in sex functions, 243–252 *passim*, 255

Arrest reactions, 218–219

Arseni, C., 333

Ascending reticular system. *See* Reticular activating system

Attention, 83–86, 207–212 *passim*

Auditory cortex, 113, 115

Auditory functions, 7–8. *See also* Sensory systems

    anatomy and physiology, 41

    attention and, 84–85

    and conditioning, 297–303 *passim*

    discriminatory capacity, 73–80

Autonomic nervous system, 150–155 *passim*, 156–157, 168–174. *See also* Limbic system; Sensory systems; Sympathetic and parasympathetic systems

Avoidance responses, 221–230 *passim*, 296–303, 316, 348–359

Ax, Albert F., 173

Axon and axonal processes, 13, 15–24 *passim*, 114

Azide, 68–69, 70

Babinski reflex, 239

Bagshaw, M., 32

Ball, Josephine, 190

Bard, Phillip, 9, 145, 187, 190–192 *passim*, 243

Bare, J. K., 193

Bash, K. W., 190

Beach, Frank, 10, 187, 194, 237, 238–263, 273

Behavior:

    and chemical factors, 238

    drugs, mood and, 151

Behavior (continued)
  electrical activity and, 147
  food seeking. *See* Food-seeking functions
  motivation of. *See* Drive; Motivation
  and nervous system, 238, 239–240
  nest-building, 275–280
  sex activity. *See* Sex functions
  social activity, 264–274
Beidler, L. M., 118
Bell, Sir Charles, 6, 7, 8
Bellows, R. T., 190
Betz cells, 113
Bezold-Brücke hue-shift phenomenon, 44
Biochemical factors, 9–11 *passim*, 29. See also
    Chemical factors; Hormones
Birch, H. G., 264, 273
Bleaching, 51–53 *passim*
Blood pressure, 169–174 *passim*, 286
Body temperature, 281–289 *passim*
Bohm, E., 133
Bradley, P. B., 147
Brady, J. V., 37*n*, 215, 357
Brain. *See also* Central nervous system;
    Cortex
  anatomy and functions, 14, 26, 201–202
  internal stimuli and rhythms, 199
  language functions, 328–329
  non-specific mechanisms, 206–212
  research, 6, 10, 11
Brain damage, 315–368. *See also* Pathology;
    Surgical techniques
  and auditory discrimination, 77
  and coma, 27
  and intellectual functions, 146, 328–329,
    331–347 *passim*
  and learning, 291, 296–302, 303–306, 347–
    358
  and motor functions, 316–368 *passim*
  and perceptual functions, 315–347
  research, 11, 32
Bremer, F., 96
Brightness discrimination, 47–48, 52–53, 361–
    363

Broca, Paul, 10, 11, 30, 31
Brooks, C., 243
Brown, K. T., 66, 67
Brutkowski, S., 358
Bucy, P. C., 243
Bullock, Theodore, 6, 13–24
Bursten, Ben, 185, 214–220
Byzov, A. L., 67, 68

Cade, T. J., 289
Cadilhac, J., 35, 37
Cajal, S. Ramon y, 6, 15–16, 30, 33
Campbell, B. A., 199
Cannon, W. B., 9, 10, 145, 168–170, 186–187
Cannon-Bard emotion theory, 145
Capillary ultramicroelectrode, 19–20, 23. *See
    also* Microelectrode techniques; Pipet
    techniques
Carlson, A. J., 190
Carr, W. J., 193
Carreras, M., 211
Cell body, 13
Central cephalic brain stem, 207–212 *passim*
Central motive state, 188–204 *passim*
Central nervous system:
  chemical effects, 241–242
  excitatory and inhibitory functions, 157–
    160, 181–204 *passim*, 207–212
  in reflex behavior, 239–240
Central theory of drive, 184–204
Cerebrum, 309–314
Chang, H.-T., 112, 113, 114
Chemical factors. *See also* Drugs; Enzymes;
    Hormones
  behavior and, 238, 240–252 *passim*
  in learning, 291
  in neural development, 240–242
  in pathology, 242
  in sex behavior, 237–252 *passim*. *See also*
    Sex hormones
Chemical receptors, 97–99

Chemical stimulation, 33, 34, 36, 66, 69, 70, 107–108, 118–127, 191–192, 196

Cholinesterase, 309–314

Chorda tympani, 88–116 *passim*, 118–127 *passim*

Chromatic adaptation, 51–53

Chromatic responses, 46–53, 63, 64, 65. *See also* Color vision

Clark, G., 243, 264, 273

Cochlear nucleus, 84–85

Coghill, G. E., 149, 239

Cohen, M. J., 8, 87, 88–116

Cole, L. E., 292*n*

Color anomalies, 53–57

Color blindness, 44, 55–57

Color mixture, 48–49

Color vision, 7, 40–58

Coma, 27, 207

Conditioning, 290–314. *See also* Learning; Reinforcement
    to anxiety, 163
    avoidance and escape responses, 221–230 *passim*, 296–303, 316, 348–359
    discrimination of stimuli, 27
    hippocampus in, 303–306
    limbic system and, 348–359
    nervous system activity, 88–101, 106–107, 174–183, 291–296
    research, 10
    in sex behavior, 248–251
    thalamus in, 296–303
    thyroid in, 306–309

Conduction velocities of nerve fibers, 92–95, 98–99, 104, 132

Cone action potential, 63

Conflict (motive), 218, 229

Consciousness:
    body functions, 150
    reticular formation and, 27–28. *See also* Arousal and inhibitory functions; Reticular activating system
    sensory information and, 84–86

Constructional apraxia, 315–331, 332–347 *passim*

Contralateral transfer, 135–142

Corona radiata, 217–219 *passim*

Corpus callosum, 8, 135–143, 217–219 *passim*

Corpus striatum, 180

Cortex, 6–7, 26–28 *passim*, 29–39.
    in arousal functions, 26–29 *passim*, 157–158, 207–212 *passim*
    in auditory discrimination, 41, 76–80 *passim*
    in conditioning, 299
    in emotion, 160–161
    hypothalamus and, 160–161
    in hypothesis behavior, 309–314
    in motor activity, 96
    in sex functions, 237, 238, 243–245, 250, 253–263 *passim*
    in taste and touch, 88–116

Crawford, M. P., 264, 273

Critchley, M., 317–318, 332, 346

Cue stimuli, 200

Cullen, C., 112, 113, 115

Curiosity drive, 197–198

Cutaneous senses, 88, 128–134. *See also* Taste; Touch
    in temperature regulation, 281

Dartnall, H. J., 53

Darwin, Charles, 5

Decremental conduction, 17, 20, 21

Delgado, José, 9, 144, 174–183, 185, 214–220

Dendrite and dendritic processes, 13, 15–24 *passim*

Denny-Brown, D., 316, 328

Depression, 68–74 *passim*

Deuteranomaly, 54

Deuteranopes, 56

Diminution of neuron potential, 22

Discrimination of stimuli, 27. *See also* Respective senses

Dogiel's cells, 67

Dominance, 238, 264–274

Dorsal columns, 132–133
Drive, 185–204. *See also* Motivation
Drive reduction, 189, 192, 197–200 *passim,*
    229
    satiation, 231–236
Drugs:
    and arousal, 147–148, 158, 301
    and emotion, 155, 170–174 *passim*
    and feeling tone, 150–151
    and hypothalamic balance, 161, 162–163
    and sensory response, 28, 33, 34, 36, 89–90,
        99
    and thalamic depression, 301
Duensing, F., 318
Dynamic polarization, 16
Dysphasia, 327–329 *passim*

Eccles, J. C., 13
EEG findings. *See* Electrical activity; Micro-
    electrode techniques
Electrical activity, 6, 13, 16–24 *passim,* 60–71,
    147, 287. *See also* Microelectrode tech-
    niques; Spikes
Electrical stimulation, 35, 36, 39–116 *passim,*
    116–117, 129, 147, 174–182 *passim,* 196,
    214, 219, 220–230, 231. *See also* Micro-
    electrode techniques.
Electrode techniques. *See* Microelectrode
    techniques
Electrolytes, 118–127 *passim*
Electrophysiology, 14–24, 57, 74, 206–212. *See
    also* Microelectrode techniques
Electroretinogram, 61–71 *passim*
Electroshock therapy, 162, 163
Embryo development, 239, 240–241
Emotion, 8–9, 143–183
    anger, 143–144, 168–174
    and arousal and inhibition, 159
    in avoidance behavior. *See* Avoidance be-
        havior
    conditioning and, 174–183, 299–300
    depression, 68–74 *passim*

Emotion (continued)
    drive and, 203–204
    drugs and, 162–163
    fear, 143–144, 159, 168–173, 174–183, 221–
        230 *passim*
    glandular activity, 168–174
    hippocampus and, 145–146, 153, 179–180,
        360–361
    hypothalamic balance and, 162–164
    neurophysiological factors, 9, 32, 143, 162–
        164, 168–174, 174–183 *passim*
    in neurosis, 156–157, 162–164 *passim*
    and self- and species-preservation, 37
    theories of, 144–146
Endocrine glands, 240–242 *passim,* 284
Engrams, 10, 290–314 *passim*
Enzymes, 240–242 *passim,* 309–314
Ergotropic system, 149–154 *passim*
Erickson, T., 36
Escape responses, 221–230 *passim*
Estrogens. *See* Sex hormones
Ethanol, 70
Ettlinger, G., 318
Experimentation. *See* Methodology; Research
Exploratory behavior, 360–361
Exploratory drive, 197
Extracellular space, 65
Extrapolation, 3
Eysenck, H. J., 151

Fear, 143–144, 159, 168–173, 174–183, 221–230
    passim
Fechner, Gustav, 5, 8
Feedback systems, 231–235
Feeling, 148–150
Feeling tone, 150–151
Fetus development, 239, 240–241
Fixed-image technique, 45
Flight response. *See* Escape
Flourens, Pierre, 6, 10, 11
Food-seeking functions, 32–33
    limbic-system damage and, 348–357 *passim*

Food-seeking functions (continued)
  selectivity, 191, 193, 199–200, 242
  sex hormones and, 264–274
Forel, Auguste, 6
French, J. D., 9, 14, 25–29
Freud, Sigmund, 9, 29
Frings, H., 124
Fulton, J. F., 36
Funkenstein, Daniel, 9, 143, 168–174

Ganglion cells, 67, 69, 70
Ganzfeld technique, 45
Gardner, E., 133
Gaze, R. M., 8, 88, 128–134
Gellhorn, E., 9, 143, 144–164
Gerard, R. W., 19
Glia cells, 65
Gloor, P., 154
Goldberg, J. M., 77n, 78
Golgi, Camillio, 15
Gordon, G., 8, 88, 128–134
Granit, R., 57, 61, 69–70, 110
Green, J. D., 160, 210, 211
Grooming activity, 33–36 passim
Grüsser, O. J., 66
Gustatory nerve impulses, 117–127

Habituation, 210
Haddad, B., 133
Hagbarth, K.-E., 209
Hall, Marshall, 6
Harlow, H. F., 197
Harris, W., 108
Harterius, H. O., 36
Hartline, H. K., 57
Head, H., 346
Hearing. See Auditory functions
Heart rate, 285, 286, 287
Hebb, D. O., 144–145, 200, 201
Hécaen, H., 316–331, 332
Helmholtz, Hermann von, 7

Henderson, E., 256n
Hering color vision theory, 7, 40, 41, 43–44, 57, 58
Hernández-Peón, Raúl, 8, 41, 83–86, 210
Herrick, C. J., 147, 149
Hess, W. R., 36, 145, 173
Hibernation, 238, 281–289
Hines, M., 239–240
Hippocampus:
  in arousal and inhibition, 157–158, 160, 210–212
  damage effects, 316, 359–368
  in emotion, 145–146, 153, 179–180, 360–361
  in learning, 303–306, 361–368
  and somato-genital sense, 33–36
Hock, R. J., 283
Hodgkin, A. L., 13, 21
Hokfelt, Bernt, 174
Hooker, D., 239
Horenstein, S., 318, 328
Hormones:
  in body development and behavior, 239–252 passim, 276
  in emotion, 9, 143–144, 155
  in incubation behavior, 275–281
  in learning, 11, 291
  in motivation, 10, 187, 191–204 passim
  in sex behavior, 245–248, 261. See also Sex hormones
  in social behavior, 264–274
Hue, 47–48, 49–51 passim
Hull, C. L., 192
Humphrey, T., 239
Hunger and thirst, 186–187, 190–200 passim, 348–357 passim
Hurvich, Leo, 7, 40–59
Huxley, A. F., 13
Hyperphagia, 195, 200, 201
Hypothalamus:
  balance, 161–163
  cortex connections, 30, 160
  and drive, 191–193, 195–196, 201–202
  drug reactions, 150–151, 161, 162–163

Hypothalamus (continued)
  in emotion, 9, 145, 146–164 *passim*, 173,
    174–175, 181
  in learning, 221–230
  in neurosis, 156–157
  and personality, 151
  and reticular formation, 147–148
  in self-stimulation satiation, 231–236 *passim*
  in sex functions, 243
  in temperature regulation, 281
Hypothesis behavior, 309–314

Impulse spikes. *See* Electrical activity; Spikes
Incubation behavior, 275–281, 283
Ingraham, F. D., 36
Inhibitory processes. *See* Arousal and inhibitory functions
Instinct, 19, 198
Intellectual processes, 146, 328–329, 331–347
    passim

James, William, 5, 8–9
James-Lange emotion theory, 144
Jameson, Dorothea, 7, 40–59
Jasper, H., 112, 113, 115
Jaynes, J., 255–263
Jouvet, Michel, 83–86, 210
Jung, R., 37

Kaada, B. R., 181, 348
Katz, 21
Kerr, D. I. B., 209
Kim, Chul, 36, 368
Kimble, Daniel, 11, 291, 303–306, 316
Kleist, K., 317, 332
Kling, A., 33, 243
Klüver, H., 243
Knee-jerk reflex, 28–29
Kollros, J. J., 241
Kuffler, S. W., 70

Laboratory equipment, 3
Lahr, E. L., 276, 279
Landgren, S., 88–116
Lange, Carl, 9, 144
Language functions, 328–329
Lashley, K. S., 10, 187
Latency of response, 104–106 *passim*, 116–117
Lateral geniculate body, 113
Learning, 10–11, 290–314. *See also* Conditioning
  anticipatory set, 292–295 *passim*, 301–302
  avoidance and escape, 221–230 *passim*, 297–302
  vs. drive, 197–198
  habituation, 210. *See also* Reinforcement
  hippocampus in, 303–306, 361–368
  hormonal role, 291, 306–309
  neuronal basis, 19
  rewards. *See* Rewards
Learning theory, 192, 198
Lehrman, Daniel, 10, 194, 238, 275–281
Lesions. *See* Brain damage; Surgical techniques
Levine, S., 358
Levinson, G., 194
Li, C.-L., 112, 113, 115
Liberson, W. T., 37
Lilly, J. C., 37*n*
Limbic system, 6–7, 9, 11, 14, 29–39
  in conditioning, 301, 348–359
  in emotion, 9, 143–164 *passim*, 181–182
  lesion effects, 316, 348–359
  in reinforcement, 215–220
  in sex behavior, 243
Lindsley (Donald) activation theory, 145
Ling, G., 19
Linnaeus, 8
Lloyd, D. P. C., 132
Localization:
  of cortical functions, 255
  of sound, 74–80 *passim*
  of tongue receptors, 110–111
Lockhart, Walter, 36

Looney, Edmund, 174–183
Luminance, 49–51 *passim*, 52–53
Luminosity responses, 62–65 *passim*
Lundberg, A., 65
Lyman, Charles, 238, 281–289

MacLean, Paul, 6–7, 9, 14, 29–39, 146, 161, 181
MacNichol, E. F., 64
Magoun, H. W., 10, 26, 41, 115, 185, 206–212
Maher, B. A., 358
Mammal phylogeny, 30
Manipulative drive, 197
Maslow, A. H., 273
Masserman, J. H., 174
Massonnet, J., 317
Mayer-Gross, W., 332
McBride, K. E., 346
McCleary, Robert, 11, 316, 348–359
McFie, J., 11, 315–316, 317, 331–347
McIntire, R. W., 358
McIntyre, A. K., 132
Mecholyl test, 162, 168–174 *passim*
Meites, J., 279
Memory, 303–306. *See also* Conditioning;
    Learning
Mental disorders, 28, 328–329, 331–347 *passim*.
    See also Brain damage; Neuropsychiatric
    disorders
Mesencephalon, 180
Metabolism:
    in hibernation, 282–288 *passim*
    and learning, 306–307
Methodology, 3. *See also* Chemical stim-
    ulation; Microelectrode techniques;
    Pipet techniques; Surgical techniques
Meyer, A. E., 26
Meyer, J., 318, 328
Microelectrode techniques, 19–20, 23, 41, 60–
    63 *passim*, 68, 84, 90–91, 97–98, 101, 175–
    176, 207–212 *passim*, 221–223, 231–232,
    284, 286
Midbrain, 30, 221, 296–303 *passim*

Miller, N., 181, 192, 194
Milner, P., 36, 37, 184, 215
Mirsky, Allan, 238, 264–274
Montgomery, M. F., 190, 197
Mood, 149, 150–151
Morgan, Clifford, 10, 184, 185–204
Morgan, J. D., 190
Moruzzi, Giuseppe, 26
Motivation, 9–10, 184–289
    conflict, 218, 229
    drive reduction. *See* Drive reduction
    escape and avoidance, 221–230
    hibernation, 281–288
    incubation behavior, 275–281
    physiological theory of, 185–204
    reinforcement, *See* Reinforcement
    satiation effects, 231–235
    social behavior, 264–274
Motokawa, K., 69
Motor activity:
    anticipatory set, 292–295 *passim*, 301–302
    arousal and inhibition of, 28, 157, 292–295
    brain lesions and, 315–369 *passim*
    conditioning. *See* Conditioning
    contralateral transfer and, 141
    cortex stimulation and, 96
    cortical localization, 255
    and emotion, 144–145, 152–164 *passim*, 176–
        182 *passim*, 299–300
    hypothalamus and, 224
    reticular formation and, 28
Murakama, 69
Muscle tone, 28, 154, 159

Naka, K., 61
Nauta, W. J. H., 30, 181, 195, 357
Need, 187, 196–197
Need reduction and satisfaction, 197
Neff, William, 8, 41, 73–80
Nerve cells, 6
Nerve impulse, 16–24 *passim*. *See also* Spikes
Nervous system, 6, 13–39, 73–74, 239–240

Nervous system (continued)
 anticipatory set, 292–295
 arousal and inhibitory functions. *See*
   Arousal and inhibitory functions
 behavior and, 237–263 *passim*
 chemical factors. *See* Chemical factors;
   Hormones
 in drive, 185–200 *passim*, 201–202, 231–235,
   275–280 *passim*
 in emotion, 143–164 *passim*, 168–174
 extracellular space, 65
 in hibernation, 282, 286–287
 hormonal sensitization, 237–255 *passim*, *See
   also* Hormones
 in learning, 290–314
 pathology. *See* Brain damage; Surgical
   techniques
 in sex functions, 237–263 *passim*
 temperature and, 282
Neuroanatomy and neurophysiology, 6
Neuron theory, 6, 13, 14–24
Neuropsychiatric disorders, 151, 156–157,
   162–163, 170–174 *passim*. *See also*
   Brain damage; Psychotherapy
Newton, Sir Isaac, 7
Nissen, H., 250
Noradrenalin, 9, 143–144, 155, 170–174 *passim*
Nowlis, V., 264

Oder, H. E., 77*n*
Oesterreich, R. E., 78
Ogawa, T., 69
Oikawa, T., 69
Olds, James, 36, 37, 184, 195, 215, 218–219,
   231–235
Olfactory nervous system, 31*n*, 32, 33, 243
Opponent-process color vision theory, 41–58
Orrego, F., 112, 113
Owen, Richard, 31*n*

Pain, 132, 149

Painted-image technique, 45
Papez, J. W.) theory of emotion, 9, 143, 145–
   146, 181
Paranoia, 174
Parasympathetic system. *See* Sympathetic and
   parasympathetic systems
Paresis, 327–328
Parietal-lobe dysfunction, 332
Patel, M. D., 276
Paterson, A., 317
Pathology (physical). *See also* Brain damage;
   Surgical techniques and behavior, 241–
   252 *passim*, 255–263 *passim* and emotion,
   154–155
Patton, H. D., 89
Pavlov, I. P., 10
Peirce, J. T., 11, 291, 309–314
Perceptual dysfunctions, 315–368 *passim*
Periodicity theory, 7
Peripheral theory of drive, 184–204 *passim*
Personality:
   hormonal effects, 273–274
   hypothalamus and, 151
   somatic drives and, 203
Pfaffmann, Carl, 8, 88, 117–127, 193
Photochemical activity, 40–58 *passim*
Phrenology, 6
Physiological psychology, 5–12
Piano theory, 7
Piercy, Malcolm, 11, 315, 316–331
Pipet techniques, 61–62, 63, 64, 68, 91, 196
Pituitary functions, 196, 276
Place theory, 7
Pleasure principle, 37
Poetzl, O., 317
Polley, H., 112, 113
Preservation of species, 29, 33–36
Pribram, K. H., 32, 306
Procreative functions, 30, 33. *See also* Sex
   functions
Progesterone, 275–281
Prolactin, 276, 279
Protanomaly, 54

Protanopia, 56
Psychoanalytic theory, 37, 174
Psychomotor epilepsy, 32
Psychotherapy:
    physiological factors, 163–164, 170–174
        passim
    reciprocal inhibition, 143, 163–164
    shock, 162, 163
Punishment, 220–230. *See also* Conditioning;
    Reinforcement
Pyriform cortex, 243, 256

R membrane, 67–68, 69
Racine, Ronald, 11, 291, 303–306
Ranson, S. W., 148, 192
Rayleigh equation, 54
Reaction time, 104–106 *passim*, 116–117
Receptors, 8, 103, 107, 126. *See also* Sensory
    system
Reciprocal inhibition psychotherapy, 143
Reflexes, 148–150
    chemical and neural factors, 28–29, 239–
        240, 241
    in fetus and infant, 239–240
    neurosis and, 156
    reticular formation and, 28–29
Reinforcement. *See also* Conditioning
    in drive and drive satisfaction, 189, 192, 194,
        197, 200, 203, 249
    by electrical stimulation, 214–220, 220–230
    by termination of stimulus, 221–230 *passim*
"Releaser" stimuli, 198, 200
Renshaw cell, 114
Research, 3, 5–12, 40–41
Resonance theory, 7
Respiration in hibernation, 286
Reticular activating system, 9, 14, 15–24 *pas-
    sim*, 25–29, 185
    arousal and inhibitory functions, 15–24 *pas-
        sim*, 157–164 *passim*, 192–193, 195, 207–
        212 *passim*
    and conditioning, 301

Reticular activating system (continued)
    and drive, 192–193, 195, 199
    drugs and, 150
    emotion, 143–148 *passim*, 156
    sensory response, 29, 84–85, 115, 156
Retina electrical activity, 60–71
Rhinencephalon, 31, 146
Richards, W. J., 11, 291, 306–309
Richter, C. P., 193, 309
Richter, G. P., 242
Riddle, O., 276, 279
Ringer solution, 68, 103, 107
Roberts, W. W., 181, 185, 220–230
Rogers, C. M. 243
Root, W. S., 190
Rosvold, Enger, 174–183
Reusch, J., 173

S potential, 61–71 *passim*
Salivary gland, 65
Saphenous nerve, 129–134 *passim*
Sasaki, 69
Satiation effects, 231–235
Sawyer, C. H., 240–241
Scharlock, D. P., 77n
Scherrer, H., 83–86, 210
Schiff, J. M., 132
Schreiner, L., 33, 243
Scientific articles, 1–4
Secondary sources, 2
Self-preservation, 29–33 *passim*
Self-stimulation, 10, 184–185, 231–235. *See
    also* Conditioning; Reinforcement
Sensory deprivation, 198–199
Sensory drives, 197–199
Sensory systems, 7–9. *See also* respective
    senses
    arousal of, 29, 157
    arousal function of, 207–212 *passim*, 212
    attention and, 83–86, 156
    and behavior, 242
    and body feelings, 150

Sensory systems (continued)
  in conditioned response, 292–295 *passim*,
    296–302 *passim*
  cortical localization, 255
  and drive, 188–204 *passim*
  and emotion, 156, 181
  modality distribution, 88–116
  patterning hypothesis, 87–88
  reticular formation and, 29, 84–85, 115, 156
  selectivity, 84–85
  and temperature regulation, 281
Septum, 154, 219, 231–235 *passim*
Set, 292–295 *passim*, 301–302
Sex functions, 33
  chemical factors, 237–252 *passim*, 261
  cortical functions, 237, 238, 243–245, 250,
    255–263 *passim*
  experiential factors, 248–251
  hibernation and, 289
  hypersexuality, 36
  motivation, 187, 190, 191, 192, 194, 196–
    197, 237–263 *passim*
  nervous-system functions, 161, 237–263
    passim
  somato-genital sense, 33–36, 187, 190
Sex hormones, 191, 197, 245–248, 261, 264–
    274, 275–289 *passim*
Sheffield, F. D., 199
Sherrington, C., 144
Shock therapy, 162, 163
Sidman, M., 215
Sjöstrand, F. S., 65
Skin stimuli, 127–134
Sleep. *See* Arousal and inhibitory functions
Sleep-inducing drugs, 28
Smith, Elliot, 31*n*
Social behavior, 238, 264–274
Soliday, S., 358
Solomon, L. M., 198
Somatic drives, 197–199, 203
Somato-sensory system, 112–113 *passim*, 161
Somesthetic sense, 88
Sound discrimination, 73–80

Spatial agnosia, 315–330 *passim*, 331–347
Spatial hypothesis behavior, 309–314
Spatial interaction, 45, 66, 70
Sperry, Roger, 2, 8, 10–11, 88, 135–142, 240,
    290, 291–296
Spikes (discharges, potentials, and thresholds),
    13–24 *passim*, 61, 66–67, 92–94, 97, 98,
    101, 102, 105, 108, 111, 113, 114, 130
Spinal cord, 28
Spindle, 28, 158
Spontaneous neuron activity, 23–24, 111
Stamm, John, 8, 88, 135–142
Starzl, T. E., 115
Statistics, 3
Stellar, E., 193
Stereotaxis, 33, 84
Stevens, S. S., 8
Stimulant drugs, 28
Stockburger, J. C., 11, 291, 306–309
Stone, C. P., 243
Ström, L., 88–116
Strominger, N. L., 77
Strumwasser, F., 285
Strychnine, 99
Subjects, 3
Surgical techniques, 74, 76, 78–79, 90, 129–
    134 *passim*, 135–136, 177, 190, 257–258,
    295, 297, 304, 349, 350, 352–353, 360. *See
    also* Brain damage
Svaetichin, G., 61–65 *passim*
Sympathetic and parasympathetic systems,
    150–164 *passim*. *See also* Motor activity;
    Sensory systems
Synapse, 6, 13, 16–24
Synaptic delay, 94–95

Tactile response, *See* Touch
Tainter, M. L., 170
Tasaki, K., 68, 112, 113
Taste, 8, 87–88
  chorda tympani action, 117–127
  cortical action, 107–108

Taste (continued)
  and hunger, 193
Taylor, C., 115
Teitelbaum, P., 200
Telencephalon, 231–235 *passim*
Temperature, 87
  cortical action, 108
  regulation of, 281–289 *passim*
Temporal cortex, 243
Termination of stimulus effects, 221–230
    passim
Tertartanopia, 57
Thalamic process emotion theory, 145
Thalamic relay nucleus, 112, 113, 115, 146, 210
Thalamus:
  arousal and inhibitory functions, 157–158
  in conditioned response, 296–303
  cutaneous impulses, 128–135
  and emotion, 180
  and learning, 221
Thirst. *See* Hunger and thirst
Thompson, Robert, 3–4, 11, 291, 296–303
Thompson, W. R., 198
Thyroid activity, 291, 306–309
Tomita, Tsuneo, 7, 41, 60–71
Tosaka, T., 65
Touch, 8, 87–88
  contralateral transfer, 135–142
  cortical activity, 88–116 *passim*
Trembly, Bruce, 36
Trigeminal component, 88–116 *passim*
Tritanopia, 57
Trophotropic system, 149–151 *passim*
Tsang, Y. C., 190
Tullar, B. F., 170
Turner, C. W., 279

Ventrolateral columns, 132–133
Visceral brain. *See* Limbic system
Vision, 7, 40–41
  brain-damage effects, 315–347

Vision (continued)
  color theory, 41–58
  in conditioning, 297–303
  constructional apraxia, 315–330
  contralateral transfer, 60–71
  electrical activity, 60–71
  neural development, 240
  spatial agnosia, 315–330 *passim*, 331–347
Visual hypothesis behavior, 309–314
Von Bechterew, W., 36
Von Euler, U. S., 173

Waldeyer, W., 6
Wangensteen, O. H., 190
Ward, A. A., Jr., 36
Warrington, E., 318
Watanabe, K., 20, 65, 67
Wave-length factors, 47–48, 49–51, 53–54, 64–
  65
Weber, E. H., 8
Weisenburg, T. H., 346
West, G. B., 174
Wiesel, T. N., 62, 66, 67
Withdrawal behavior, 148–150 *passim. See also*
    Avoidance responses
Witkin, H. A., 310
Wolff, H. G., 170
Wolpe, J., 163
Woodworth, R. S., 9–10
Wundt, Wilhelm, 5

Yamashita, E., 69
Yerkes, R. M., 264, 273
Young, P. T., 199
Young, Thomas, 7
Young-Helmholtz vision theory, 40, 42–43

Zangwill, O. L., 11, 315–316, 317, 318, 331–347
Zitrin, A., 255–263
Zotterman, Y., 88–116